Everyday Mathematics®

The University of Chicago School Mathematics Project

Teacher's Lesson Guide
Volume 2

Grade

 **Education**

Chicago, IL • Columbus, OH • New York, NY

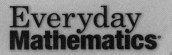

The University of Chicago School Mathematics Project (UCSMP)

Max Bell, Director, UCSMP Elementary Materials Component; Director, *Everyday Mathematics* First Edition; James McBride, Director, *Everyday Mathematics* Second Edition; Andy Isaacs, Director, *Everyday Mathematics* Third Edition; Amy Dillard, Associate Director, *Everyday Mathematics* Third Edition; Rachel Malpass McCall, Associate Director, *Everyday Mathematics* Common Core State Standards Edition

Authors
Max Bell, John Bretzlauf, Amy Dillard, Robert Hartfield, Andy Isaacs, James McBride, Kathleen Pitvorec, Denise Porter‡, Peter Saecker, Noreen Winningham*, Robert Balfanz†, William Carroll†

*Third Edition only   †First Edition only   ‡Common Core State Standards Edition only

Technical Art
Diana Barrie

Third Edition Teachers in Residence
Fran Goldenberg, Sandra Vitantonio

Mathematics and Technology Advisor
James Flanders

UCSMP Editorial
Rosina Busse, Laurie K. Thrasher, David B. Spangler

ELL Consultant
Kathryn B. Chval

Contributors
Regina Littleton (Office Manager), Kriszta Miner (Project Manager), Sandra R. Overcash, Serena Hohmann, Sally S. Johnson, Colleen M. Kelly, Kimberley Dawn Sowa, Tracy Lynn Selock, Tammy Belgrade, Diana Carry, Debra Dawson, Kevin Dorken, Laurel Hallman, Ann Hemwall, Elizabeth Homewood, Linda Klaric, Lee Kornhauser, Judy Korshak-Samuels, Deborah Arron Leslie, Joseph C. Liptak, Sharon McHugh, Janet M. Meyers, Susan Mieli, Donna Nowatzki, Sheila Sconiers, Kevin J. Smith, Theresa Sparlin, Laura Sunseri, Kim Van Haitsma, John Wilson, Mary Wilson, Carl Zmola, Theresa Zmola

 This material is based upon work supported by the National Science Foundation under Grant No. ESI-9252984. Any opinions, findings, conclusions, or recommendations expressed in this material are those of the authors and do not necessarily reflect the views of the National Science Foundation.

everyday**math**.com

 Education

Send all inquiries to:
McGraw-Hill Education
STEM Learning Solutions Center
P.O. Box 812960
Chicago, IL 60681

ISBN: 978-0-07-657691-3
MHID: 0-07-657691-4

Printed in the United States of America.

1 2 3 4 5 6 7 8 9 RMN 17 16 15 14 13 12 11

STEM

McGraw-Hill is committed to providing instructional materials in Science, Technology, Engineering, and Mathematics (STEM) that give all students a solid foundation, one that prepares them for college and careers in the 21st century.

The **McGraw·Hill** Companies

Contents

Volume 1

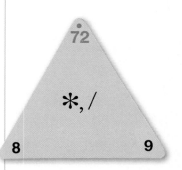

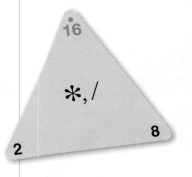

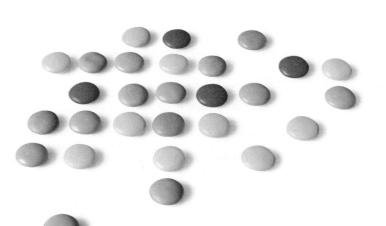

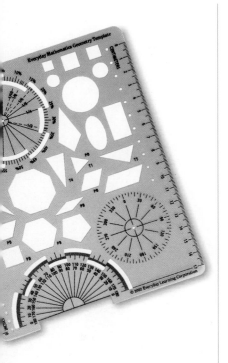

Volume 2

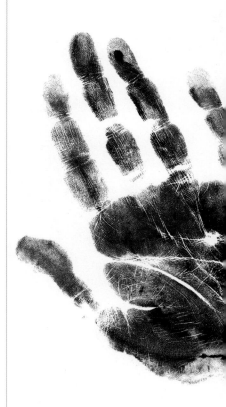

Exponents and Negative Numbers

> Overview

The main purpose of Unit 7 is to investigate prealgebra concepts and skills. Students are introduced to the notational conventions of exponents, scientific notation, and number-and-word notation. They develop rules for the addition and subtraction of positive and negative numbers and continue the American Tour, using its data to construct line graphs. Students also make and analyze line plots involving fractional units. Unit 7 has four main areas of focus:

◆ To understand the conventions associated with exponents,

◆ To avoid ambiguities in the interpretation of number sentences,

◆ To recognize the need to use negative numbers in certain situations, and

◆ To organize and analyze data using line graphs and line plots.

Linking to the Common Core State Standards

The content of Unit 7 addresses the Common Core State Standards for Mathematics in *Operations and Algebraic Thinking* and *Number and Operations in Base Ten*. The correlation of the Common Core State Standards to the *Everyday Mathematics* Grade 5 lessons begins on page CS1.

10^0

10^1

These elaborately conceived and executed panels were created by the Eames Office for *Powers of Ten.* Forty-two large square images that mark the powers of ten were used in the production of the film and later reproduced for the 1982 book, *Powers of Ten: A Book About the Relative Size of Things in the Universe and the Effect of Adding Another Zero,* written by Philip Morrison, Phylis Morrison, and the Office of Charles and Ray Eames.

Contents

10^2

10^3

Learning In Perspective

	Lesson Objectives	Links to the Past	Links to the Future
7·1	To develop concepts related to exponential notation.	In fourth grade, students extend basic multiplication facts to products of ones and tens and products of tens and tens.	In sixth grade, students develop and practice strategies for multiplying powers of 10.
7·2	To introduce number-and-word notation for large numbers and exponential notation for powers of 10.	In fourth grade, students explore the relationship between place value and exponential notation.	In sixth grade, students read and write large numbers in standard, expanded, and number-and-word notation.
7·3	To introduce scientific notation.	In fourth grade, students find equivalent names using powers of 10.	In sixth grade, students convert between scientific and standard notation.
7·4	To review the use of parentheses.	In fourth grade, students insert parentheses to make true number sentences.	In sixth grade, students review the rules for order of operations.
7·5	To introduce the rules for order of operations.	In fourth grade, students review the use of parentheses in number sentences.	In sixth grade, students evaluate number expressions using order of operations and write number sentences using order of operations.
7·6	To introduce the construction of line graphs.	In fourth grade, students display data using bar and circle graphs.	In sixth grade, students display data using broken-line, bar, circle, and step graphs, and box plots.
7·7	To review the uses, ordering, and comparing of negative numbers.	In fourth grade, students play *High-Number Toss, Addition Top-It,* and *Subtraction Top-It* to compare numbers.	In sixth grade, students play *Top-It* to compare positive and negative numbers.
7·8	To develop rules for adding positive and negative numbers.	In fourth grade, students review positive and negative numbers on the number line.	In sixth grade, students develop and apply rules for adding positive and negative numbers.
7·9	To develop a rule for subtracting positive and negative numbers.	In fourth grade, students review positive and negative numbers on a number line.	In sixth grade, students further develop and apply rules for subtracting positive and negative numbers.
7·10	To provide experience creating and interpreting line plots with fractional units.	In fourth grade, students practice making line plots with fractional units such as $\frac{1}{2}$.	In sixth grade, students use a variety of graphic methods to display and analyze data.
7·11	To facilitate exploring the use of calculators to add and subtract positive and negative numbers.	In fourth grade, students use calculators to perform operations.	In sixth grade, students add and subtract positive and negative numbers using a spreadsheet.

	Key Concepts and Skills	Grade 5 Goals*
7·1	Write numbers in standard and exponential notation.	Number and Numeration Goal 4
	Compare numbers written in exponential notation.	Number and Numeration Goal 6
	Describe the number patterns inherent to exponential notation.	Patterns, Functions, and Algebra Goal 1
7·2	Explore place value using powers of 10.	Number and Numeration Goal 1
	Write and translate numbers in and between standard and exponential notation.	Number and Numeration Goal 4
	Compare exponential notation and standard notation for positive powers of 10.	Number and Numeration Goal 4
	Describe the number patterns inherent to powers of ten.	Patterns, Functions, and Algebra Goal 1
7·3	Explore the place value of numbers written as powers of 10.	Number and Numeration Goal 1
	Translate numbers from scientific notation to standard and number-and-word notation.	Number and Numeration Goal 1
	Use number patterns to solve problems involving exponents.	Patterns, Functions, and Algebra Goal 1
7·4	Identify and write sentences that model number stories.	Patterns, Functions, and Algebra Goal 2
	Solve problems involving parentheses and nested parentheses.	Patterns, Functions, and Algebra Goal 3
	Insert parentheses in order to make true number sentences.	Patterns, Functions, and Algebra Goal 3
7·5	Write an open sentence to model a number story.	Patterns, Functions, and Algebra Goal 2
	Evaluate numerical expressions using order of operations.	Patterns, Functions, and Algebra Goal 3
	Use the precedence of multiplication and division over addition and subtraction.	Patterns, Functions, and Algebra Goal 3
7·6	Use given data to create line graphs.	Data and Chance Goal 1
	Use line graph data to answer questions.	Data and Chance Goal 2
7·7	Compare and order signed whole numbers, fractions, and decimals.	Number and Numeration Goal 6
	Plot signed numbers on a number line.	Measurement and Reference Frames Goal 4
7·8	Model sums of positive and negative numbers with manipulatives.	Operations and Computation Goal 1
	Use signed number addition patterns to describe rules for adding signed numbers.	Patterns, Functions, and Algebra Goal 1
	Recognize the additive inverse.	Patterns, Functions, and Algebra Goal 4
7·9	Model differences of positive and negative numbers with manipulatives.	Operations and Computation Goal 1
	Write and solve the equivalent addition number model for signed number subtraction problems.	Operations and Computation Goal 1
	Use signed-number subtraction patterns to describe a rule for subtracting signed numbers.	Patterns, Functions, and Algebra Goal 1
	Write number sentences that model signed-number addition and subtraction problems.	Patterns, Functions, and Algebra Goal 2
7·10	Identify equivalent fractions.	Number and Numeration Goal 5
	Identify fractions on a number line.	Number and Numeration Goal 6
	Add fractions and mixed numbers with like and unlike denominators.	Operations and Computation Goal 4
	Create a line plot.	Data and Chance Goal 1
	Analyze a data set.	Data and Chance Goal 2
7·11	Use a calculator to add and subtract signed numbers.	Operations and Computation Goal 1
	Write number sentences that model signed-number addition and subtraction problems.	Number and Numeration Goal 6

*See the Appendix for a complete list of Grade 5 Goals.

A Balanced Curriculum

Ongoing Practice

Everyday Mathematics provides numerous opportunities for ongoing practice. These activities are embedded throughout the lessons:

  Mental Math and Reflexes activities promote speed and accuracy in mental computation.

 Math Boxes offer mixed practice and are paired across lessons as shown in the brackets below. This makes them useful as assessment tools. The last one or two boxes on each page preview the next unit's content.

Mixed practice	[7♦1, 7♦3], [7♦2, 7♦4, 7♦6], [7♦5, 7♦8], [7♦7, 7♦10], [7♦9, 7♦11]
Mixed practice with writing/reasoning opportunity	7♦1, 7♦4, 7♦6, 7♦7, 7♦11

 Study Links are daily homework assignments that review the content of the lesson and often contain ongoing facts practice or computation practice.

 5-Minute Math problems are offered for additional practice in Lessons 7♦4, 7♦7, and 7♦9.

EM Facts Workshop Game provides online practice of basic facts and computation.

EXTRA PRACTICE **Extra Practice** activities are included in Lessons 7♦1, 7♦2, 7♦3, 7♦4, 7♦6, 7♦7, 7♦9, and 7♦10.

Practice through Games

Games are an essential component of practice in the *Everyday Mathematics* program. Games offer skills practice and promote strategic thinking. See the *Differentiation Handbook* for ways to adapt games to meet students' needs.

Lesson	Game	Skill Practiced
7♦1	Exponent Ball	Converting exponential notation to standard notation [NN Goal 4]
7♦2	First to 100	Solving open number sentences [PFA Goal 2]
7♦3	Scientific-Notation Toss	Writing and comparing numbers in scientific notation [NN Goals 1 and 6]
7♦4, 7♦7	Name That Number	Applying number properties, equivalent names, arithmetic operations, and basic facts [NN Goal 4 and PFA Goal 3]
7♦8	Credits/Debits Game	Adding signed numbers [OC Goal 1]
7♦8	500	Understanding addition of negative numbers [OC Goal 1]
7♦9	High-Number Toss: Decimal Version	Writing and comparing decimals [NN Goals 1 and 6]
7♦11	Top-It Games with Positive and Negative Numbers	Adding and subtracting signed numbers [NN Goal 6 and OC Goal 1]
7♦11	Broken Calculator	Adding and subtracting negative numbers [OC Goal 1]

[NN] Number and Numeration
[MRF] Measurement and Reference Frames
[OC] Operations and Computation
[GEO] Geometry
[DC] Data and Chance
[PFA] Patterns, Functions, and Algebra

Problem Solving

Experts at problem solving and mathematical modeling generally do these things:

- Identify the problem.
- Decide what information is needed to solve the problem.
- Play with and study the data to find patterns and meaning.
- Identify and use mathematical procedures to solve the problem.
- Decide whether the solution makes sense and whether it can be applied to other problems.

The table below lists some of the opportunities in this unit for students to practice these strategies.

Lesson	Activity
7•2	Use patterns to complete a place-value table.
7•4	Match number stories with expressions that represent the stories; write number stories for given expressions.
7•7	Use a number line to graph positive and negative numbers.
7•8	Use counters to add and subtract positive and negative numbers; develop rules for adding and subtracting positive and negative numbers.

Lessons that teach through problem solving, not just about problem solving

See Chapter 18: Problem Solving in the *Teacher's Reference Manual* for more information.

The Language of Mathematics

Everyday Mathematics provides lesson-specific suggestions to help all students acquire, process, and express mathematical ideas. Throughout Unit 7, there are lesson-specific language development notes that address the needs of English language learners, indicated by **ELL**.

ELL SUPPORT Activities to support English language learners are in Part 3 of Lessons 7•1, 7•3, 7•8, and 7•11.

The *English Learners Handbook* and the *Differentiation Handbook* have suggestions for promoting language development and acquisition of mathematics vocabulary. See Unit 7 in each handbook.

Literacy Connection

The King's Chessboard, by David Birch, Puffin, 1993

Anno's Mysterious Multiplying Jar, by Mitsumasa Anno and Masaichiro Anno, Putnam Juvenile, 1999

Can You Count to a Googol? by Robert E. Wells, Albert Whitman and Co., 2000

G is for Googol, by David M. Schwartz, Tricycle Press, 1998

For more literacy connections, see the *Home Connection Handbook,* Grades 4–6.

Cross-Curricular Links

Social Studies
Lesson 7•1 Students discuss the origin of Fibonacci numbers.

Science
Lesson 7•3 Students figure out how many years ago an event presented in scientific notation took place.

Unit 7 Vocabulary

- account balance
- ambiguous
- axis
- base
- change-sign key [+/−]
- debt
- expanded notation
- exponent
- exponential notation
- expression
- factor
- in the black
- in the red
- line graph
- negative number
- nested parentheses
- number-and-word notation
- opposite
- order of operations
- powers of 10
- power of a number
- scientific notation
- standard notation
- trend
- Venn diagram

Balanced Assessment

 ## Daily Assessments

◆ **Recognizing Student Achievement** – A daily assessment that is included in every lesson to evaluate students' progress toward the Grade 5 Grade-Level Goals.

◆ **Informing Instruction** – Notes that appear throughout the unit to help anticipate students' common errors and suggest appropriate problem-solving strategies.

Lesson	Recognizing Student Achievement	Informing Instruction
7◆1	Accurately identify and correct mistakes in exponential notation. [NN Goal 4]	
7◆2	Write equivalent names using powers of 10. [NN Goal 4]	Use a place-value chart to determine the exponent.
7◆3	Translate numbers from standard notation to expanded notation. [NN Goal 1]	
7◆4	Write expressions containing parentheses to represent a number story. [PFA Goal 3]	
7◆5	Correctly place relations symbols to compare decimals. [NN Goal 6]	Underline operations that should be carried out first.
7◆6	Add and subtract fractions with like and unlike denominators. [OC Goal 4]	Use the minimum from a data set to determine the vertical scale increments for a graph.
7◆7	Use the order of operations to write number sentences that demonstrate accuracy and flexibility. [PFA Goal 3]	
7◆8	Model problems by pairing positive counters with negative counters to find the answers. [OC Goal 1]	Make all possible matches of a [+] counter and a [−] counter to find the balance.
7◆9	Write and compare decimals. [NN Goals 1 and 6]	
7◆10	Add and compare fractions. [NN Goal 6 and OC Goal 4]	
7◆11	Accurately convert improper fractions to whole numbers or mixed numbers in simplest form. [NN Goal 5]	Rewrite subtraction problems as addition problems.

[NN] Number and Numeration   [OC] Operations and Computation   [DC] Data and Chance
[MRF] Measurement and Reference Frames   [GEO] Geometry   [PFA] Patterns, Functions, and Algebra

Portfolio Opportunities

The following lessons provide opportunities to gather samples of students' mathematical writings, drawings, and creations to add balance to the assessment process: Lessons 7◆1, 7◆2, 7◆3, 7◆4, 7◆6, 7◆7, 7◆11, and 7◆12.

See pages 16 and 17 in the *Assessment Handbook* for more information about portfolios and how to use them.

Unit Assessment

Progress Check 7 – A cumulative assessment of concepts and skills taught in Unit 7 and in previous units, providing information for evaluating students' progress and planning for future instruction. These assessments include oral/slate, written, and open-response activities, as shown below in the sample Progress Check lesson opener.

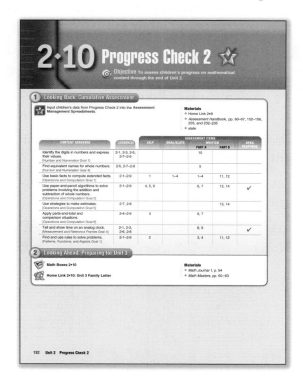

Core Assessment Resources

Assessment Handbook

- **Unit 7 Assessment Overview,** pages 102–109
- **Unit 7 Assessment Masters,** pages 185–189
- **Unit 7 Individual Profiles of Progress,** pages 270, 271, and 302
- **Unit 7 Class Checklists,** pages 272, 273, and 303
- **Math Logs,** pages 306–308
- **Exit Slip,** page 311
- **Other Student Assessment Forms,** pages 304, 305, 309, and 310

Assessment Management Spreadsheets

The Assessment Management Spreadsheets consist of the Digital Class Checklists and Individual Profile of Progress Checklists. Use them to monitor, record, and report student progress.

Addressing All Needs

Differentiated Instruction

Adjusting the Activity – suggests adaptations that target advanced learners, English language learners, or learners who need additional instructional support.

ELL SUPPORT / **ELL** – provides lesson-specific suggestions to help English language learners understand and process the mathematical content.

READINESS – accesses students' prior knowledge or previews content that prepares students to engage in the lesson's Part 1 activities.

EXTRA PRACTICE – provides additional opportunities to apply the mathematical content of the lesson.

ENRICHMENT – enables students to apply or further explore the mathematical content of the lesson.

Lesson	Adjusting the Activity	ELL Support/ ELL	Readiness	Extra Practice	Enrichment
7•1		•	•	•	•
7•2		•	•	•	•
7•3	•	•	•	•	
7•4		•	•		•
7•5		•	•		•
7•6		•	•		
7•7	•	•	•	•	•
7•8		•	•		•
7•9	•			•	•
7•10	•		•	•	•
7•11		•			•

▷ Additional Resources

Differentiation Handbook
Provides ideas and strategies for differentiating instruction.
Pages 92–98

English Learners Handbook
Contains lesson-specific comprehension strategies.
Pages 59–69

Multilingual Handbook
Previews concepts and vocabulary. It is written in six languages.
Pages 117–138

Planning Tips

Multiage Classroom

Companion Lessons from Grades 4 and 6 can help you meet instructional needs of a multiage classroom. The full Scope and Sequence can be found in the Appendix.

Grade 4			3•6, 3•7		3•10		10•6	10•6	10•6, 11•6	2•8	10•6
Grade 5	7•1	7•2	7•3	7•4	7•5	7•6	7•7	7•8	7•9	7•10	7•11
Grade 6	2•10	2•10	2•9	9•4	6•6	1•2		6•3	6•3	1•2	6•3

Pacing for Success

Pacing depends on a number of factors, such as students' individual needs and how long your school has been using *Everyday Mathematics*. At the beginning of Unit 7, you may want to use tools available at www.everydaymathonline.com to help you set your pace.

Home Support

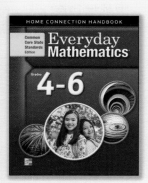

Unit 7 Family Letter (English/Spanish) provides families with an overview, Do-Anytime Activities, Building Skills through Games, a list of vocabulary, and answers to the daily homework (Study Links). Family Letters in English, Spanish, and seven other languages are also available online.

Study Links are the daily homework assignments. They consist of active projects and ongoing review problems.

▶ Home Support Resources

Home Connection Handbook
Offers ideas and reproducible masters for communicating with families. See Table of Contents for unit information.

Student Reference Book
Provides a resource for students and parents.
Pages 5, 7, 91, 92, 119–121, 124, 257, 285, 286, 301, 305, 308, 321, 325, 329, 335, 336, 365, 381

Technology Resources

Algorithms Practice

EM Facts Workshop Game™

Family Letters

Interactive Teacher's Lesson Guide

www.everydaymathonline.com

Technology Resources www.everydaymathonline.com

ePresentations

eToolkit

Algorithms Practice

EM Facts Workshop Game™

Family Letters

Assessment Management

Common Core State Standards

Curriculum Focal Points

Interactive Teacher's Lesson Guide

Lesson	Masters	Manipulative Kit	Other Items
7·1	Game Master, p. 451 Study Link Master, p. 187 Teaching Masters, pp. 188–190 *Differentiation Handbook*, p. 142	slate; 1 six-sided die	Class Data Pad; penny or other counter; overhead calculator*; calculator
7·2	Teaching Aid Master, p. 433 Transparency of Teaching Aid Master, p. 433 Study Link Master, p. 191 Game Masters, pp. 456–458 Teaching Masters, pp. 192 and 193	slate; 2 six-sided dice	Geometry Template; calculator
7·3	Study Link Master, p. 194 Teaching Masters, pp. 195 and 196 *Differentiation Handbook*, p. 149	slate; per partnership: 2 six-sided dice	Class Data Pad
7·4	Teaching Aid Master, p. 414 Study Link Master, p. 197 Teaching Masters, pp. 198 and 199	slate; per partnership: 1 complete deck of number cards	
7·5	Study Link Master, p. 200 Teaching Masters, pp. 201 and 202	slate	Class Data Pad; per partnership: 1 four-function and 1 scientific calculator*
7·6	Study Link Master, p. 203 Teaching Masters, pp. 204 and 205		newspapers and magazines
7·7	Study Link Master, p. 206 Game Master, p. 490 Teaching Master, p. 207	slate; per partnership: 1 deck of number cards	Class Data Pad*; calculator
7·8	Teaching Aid Master, p. 432 Study Link Master, p. 208 Game Master, p. 450	slate; per partnership: complete deck of number cards, 1 six-sided die	Class Data Pad; red pencil or crayon; envelope; overhead counters in two colors*; scissors; 2 different-colored counters*; Geometry Template; black, blue, and red pencils; poster paper; per partnership: 1 paper clip, pencil, 1 penny
7·9	Study Link Master, p. 209 Teaching Master, p. 210	slate; per partnership: 4 each of number cards 0–9	[+] and [−] counters from Lesson 7◆8
7·10	Teaching Masters, pp. 211 and 213 Study Link Master, p. 212	slate	calculator; Probability Meter Poster*; Fraction Cards (*Math Journal 2*, Activity Sheets 5–7)
7·11	Study Link Masters, pp. 214 and 215 Teaching Master, p. 216 *Differentiation Handbook*, p. 142	per partnership: 1 complete set of number cards	calculator
7·12	Assessment Masters, pp. 185–189 Study Link Masters, pp. 217–220	slate	

*Denotes optional materials

Mathematical Background

The discussion below highlights the major content ideas presented in Unit 7 and helps establish instructional priorities.

Exponential and Scientific Notation
(Lessons 7•1–7•3)

Lesson 7-1 extends students' knowledge of exponents, which were introduced in Unit 1. Whole-number exponents are presented as a shorthand for repeated multiplication of the same factor (5^7 instead of $5 * 5 * 5 * 5 * 5 * 5 * 5$), just as multiplication in its simplest whole-number form is often explained as a shorthand for repeated addition of the same number ($7 * 5$ instead of $5 + 5 + 5 + 5 + 5 + 5 + 5$). This notation is then exploited with powers of 10 (Lesson 7-2) and scientific notation (Lesson 7-3), both of which are important notations that have often been neglected in elementary school mathematics.

In Lesson 7-1 a new game, *Exponent Ball,* is introduced to provide continued practice with exponents and ratios.

 For additional information about exponential and scientific notation, see Section 10.1.2 of the *Teacher's Reference Manual.*

Note

Repeated addition breaks down as the basis for multiplication as soon as multiplication of fractions, decimals, or percents is needed (for instance, when solving $\frac{3}{4}$ of $\frac{2}{3}$). Likewise, repeated multiplication as the basis for exponential notation breaks down when the exponents are fractions or decimals, as will be seen in more advanced mathematics courses. Please present repeated multiplication as one interpretation of exponential notation, but not as the only interpretation.

Parentheses and Order of Operations (Lessons 7•4 and 7•5)

Numerical expressions and equations have many of the same underlying rules of structure and grammar as phrases, clauses, and sentences using words. Just as appropriate syntax and punctuation can resolve ambiguities in writing, so can proper use of parentheses ensure that number expressions and number sentences are not ambiguous. Lesson 7-4 is another in a series of lessons teaching and practicing the use of parentheses.

Because of the well-defined conventions for the order in which operations are performed, it is often unnecessary to use parentheses in expressions and number sentences. Even though students are introduced to the rules of order of operations in Lesson 7-5, they may continue to use parentheses as a way of making explicit the order in which operations are performed when evaluating number expressions.

 More information about order of operations can be found in Section 10.2.3 of the *Teacher's Reference Manual.*

Using Data (Lessons 7•6 and 7•10)

In Lesson 7-6, students continue on their American Tour. Students are asked to describe the similarities and differences among various ways to organize data. The discussion leads to the conclusion that line graphs are different from bar graphs or circle graphs in that they can be used to show trends. Students make line graphs to model and compare data.

Lesson 7-10 extends students' ability to make and use line plots by having them model a data set of measurements involving fractions of a unit. Students must locate fractions on a number line and record the frequency of each fraction in the line plot. Because the units along the scale are fractions, students practice fraction computation when they find the various data landmarks.

 More information about line graphs and line plots can be found in Section 12.2.3 of the *Teacher's Reference Manual*.

Using Negative Numbers
(Lessons 7◆6–7◆9)

Whole numbers were originally developed for counting. Eventually, fractions and decimals were invented to deal with measures that cannot be represented by whole numbers, that is, measures that fall within intervals between two consecutive whole numbers. The invention of negative numbers came later, prompted in part by a desire to make our numbering system more complete and functional. For example, it is desirable to have answers to any subtraction problem and to have number names for the points on both sides of zero on the number line.

Of even greater practical importance is the need to specify locations in reference frames in relation to a starting point (the zero-point) for naming measures that extend in both directions from the zero-point. Examples of the latter include temperatures above and below a zero-point, elevations above and below sea level, years B.C. and A.D. on historical timelines, and profits and losses in business.

Since Kindergarten, students in *Everyday Mathematics* have used positive and negative numbers with thermometers, timelines, and profits and losses; in "change" situations; and on classroom number lines that include negative numbers. The initial motivations for these "extensions" of our number system nearly always involve some practical, real-world need. In this spirit, Lesson 7-7 asks students to discuss situations in which negative numbers may occur.

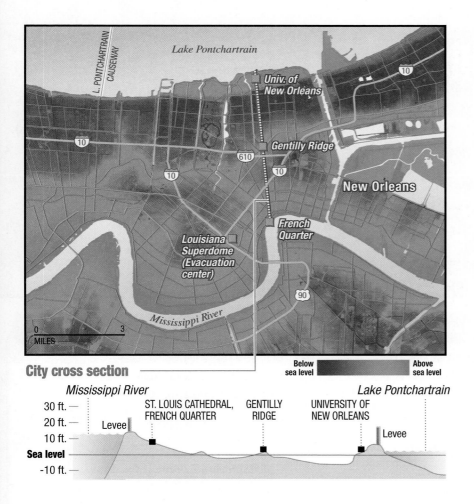

City cross section

Below sea level | Above sea level

Mississippi River   *Lake Pontchartrain*

30 ft. —
20 ft. —   ST. LOUIS CATHEDRAL, GENTILLY UNIVERSITY OF
       FRENCH QUARTER   RIDGE   NEW ORLEANS
10 ft. — Levee   Levee
Sea level
-10 ft. —

Students have also done quite a bit of informal addition and subtraction with these numbers in previous grades, mostly in start-change-end number stories (for example, "If the temperature is 15°F at noon and gets 20 degrees colder by sundown, what is the temperature at sundown?"). In Lessons 7-8 and 7-9, students continue this work in the context of business situations using red counters (debits) and black counters (credits) to model account balances before and after credit and debit transactions. They also use the number line to model addition and subtraction of signed numbers. Offering still another approach to positive and negative numbers, Lesson 7-11 reviews how to use the negative key (⊖) on calculators to enter negative numbers and to find the opposite of whatever number is shown in the calculator display. This key makes it possible to add and subtract positive and negative numbers on the calculator.

Using a variety of approaches helps students develop rules for adding and subtracting positive and negative numbers. Students may generate a variety of rules for subtraction. *Everyday Mathematics,* however, prefers the rule "To subtract a number, add the opposite of the number," since it has the most promise for later work in algebra.

 Refer to Section 9.4 of the *Teacher's Reference Manual* for additional information about using negative numbers.

> ### Note
>
> Red and white game chips can be used to act out these situations and may be easier to use than the counters cut from *Math Masters,* page 432.

7·1 Exponential Notation

Objective To develop concepts related to exponential notation.

Technology Resources www.everydaymathonline.com

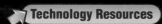

ePresentations   eToolkit   Algorithms Practice   EM Facts Workshop Game™   Family Letters   Assessment Management   Common Core State Standards   Curriculum Focal Points   Interactive Teacher's Lesson Guide

1   Teaching the Lesson

Key Concepts and Skills

- Write numbers in standard and exponential notation.
  [Number and Numeration Goal 4]

- Compare numbers written in exponential notation.
  [Number and Numeration Goal 6]

- Describe the number patterns inherent to exponential notation.
  [Patterns, Functions, and Algebra Goal 1]

Key Activities

Students express numbers written in exponential notation as repeated-factor expressions and in standard notation. They practice forming and comparing exponential values by playing *Exponent Ball*.

 Ongoing Assessment:
Recognizing Student Achievement
Use journal page 210.
[Number and Numeration Goal 4]

Key Vocabulary

standard notation ◆ exponential notation ◆ base ◆ exponent ◆ factor ◆ power of a number

Materials

Math Journal 2, pp. 209 and 210
Student Reference Book, p. 305
Math Masters, p. 451
Class Data Pad ◆ slate ◆ calculator ◆
1 six-sided die ◆ penny or other counter ◆
overhead calculator (optional)

2   Ongoing Learning & Practice

Math Boxes 7·1

Math Journal 2, p. 211
Students practice and maintain skills through Math Box problems.

Study Link 7·1

Math Masters, p. 187
Students practice and maintain skills through Study Link activities.

3   Differentiation Options

READINESS
Exploring Exponents
Math Masters, p. 188
Students identify number patterns in exponential notation.

ENRICHMENT
Exploring Exponent Patterns in Fibonacci Numbers
Math Masters, p. 189
Students use exponential notation to explore number patterns within the Fibonacci sequence.

EXTRA PRACTICE
Counting Computer Passwords
Math Masters, p. 190
Students practice and apply their understanding of exponential notation.

ELL SUPPORT
Building a Math Word Bank
Differentiation Handbook, p. 142
Students write, define, and illustrate exponential notation terms.

Advance Preparation

For Part 1, copy the table from Problem 2 on *Math Journal 2,* page 209 onto the Class Data Pad.

For a mathematics and literacy connection, obtain a copy of **G is for Googol** by David M. Schwartz.

 Teacher's Reference Manual, **Grades 4–6** pp. 94–98

Getting Started

Mental Math and Reflexes

Have students find the prime factorization.

- ●○○ 6 $2 * 3$
  - 9 $3 * 3$, or 3^2
  - 14 $2 * 7$
- ●●○ 12 $2 * 2 * 3$, or $2^2 * 3$
  - 16 $2 * 2 * 2 * 2$, or 2^4
  - 8 $2 * 2 * 2$, or 2^3
- ●●● 20 $2 * 2 * 5$, or $2^2 * 5$
  - 75 $3 * 5 * 5$, or $3 * 5^2$
  - 100 $2 * 2 * 5 * 5$, or $2^2 * 5^2$

Math Message

Complete the Math Message problem at the top of journal page 209.

① Teaching the Lesson

Math Message Follow-Up

 WHOLE-CLASS ACTIVITY

(*Math Journal 2*, p. 209)

> **Interactive whiteboard-ready ePresentations** are available at www.everydaymathonline.com to help you teach the lesson.

Ask students to share what they know about standard and exponential notation. Record their statements on the Class Data Pad for later reference. Expect answers like the following:

▷ **Standard notation** is the way numbers are usually written in everyday situations.

▷ Standard notation uses place value and the digits 0–9.

▷ Standard notation uses commas to separate the periods (groups of three digits).

▷ **Exponential notation** is a shorthand way to write repeated-factor expressions.

▷ Exponential notation has two parts: a **base** and an **exponent**. The exponent tells how many times the base is used as a **factor**. So, 10^4 is shorthand for $10 * 10 * 10 * 10$.

Have students share their answers and reasoning for Problem 1.

Ask students to find the prime factorization of 36. $2 * 2 * 3 * 3$ Write the multiplication expression on the board. Ask: *Can exponential notation be used to write this expression?* Yes, $2 * 2 * 3 * 3 = 2^2 * 3^2 = 36$. Add the exponential notation and standard notation to the multiplication expression on the board.

Ask students to complete Problem 2 on journal page 209. Have volunteers share their strategies and then record their answers in the chart on the Class Data Pad. Ask volunteers to identify any repeated factor expressions that are also prime factorizations. $5 * 5 * 5 * 5$ and $2 * 2 * 2 * 2 * 2$ Have students find the prime factorizations for the remaining expressions and add these to the Class Data Pad. $6^4 = 6 * 6 * 6 * 6 = 2 * 2 * 2 * 2 * 3 * 3 * 3 * 3 = 2^4 * 3^4$ and $9^2 = 9 * 9 = 3 * 3 * 3 * 3 = 3^4$. Remind students that the number 1 is neither prime nor composite.

Student Page

Date _____ Time _____

LESSON 7·1 **Exponents**

Math Message

1. Which is true: $4^3 = 12$, or $4^3 = 64$? Explain your answer.
   4³ = 64 because 4³ = 4 * 4 * 4, which is equal to 64.

Exponential Notation

In exponential notation, the **exponent** tells how many times the **base** is used as a factor. For example, $4^3 = 4 * 4 * 4 = 64$. The base is 4, and the exponent is 3. The product, 64, is written in **standard notation**.

2. Complete the table.

Exponential Notation	Base	Exponent	Repeated Factors	Standard Notation
5^4	5	4	$5 * 5 * 5 * 5$	625
6^4	6	4	$6 * 6 * 6 * 6$	1,296
9^2	9	2	$9 * 9$	81
1^7	1	7	$1 * 1 * 1 * 1 * 1 * 1 * 1$	1
2^5	2	5	$2 * 2 * 2 * 2 * 2$	32

Exponents on a Calculator

3. Use your calculator to find the standard notation for the bases and exponents shown in the table. Record your keystrokes in the third column. Record the calculator display in the fourth column.
Sample answers:

Base	Exponent	Keystrokes	Resulting Calculator Display
4	3	4 ∧ 3 Enter	64
2	4	2 ∧ 4 Enter	16
3	2	3 ∧ 2 Enter	9
1	10	1 ∧ 1 0 Enter	1

Math Journal 2, p. 209

▶ Working with Exponents on a Calculator

PARTNER ACTIVITY

(*Math Journal 2,* pp. 209 and 210)

The **power of a number** is the product of factors that are all the same. Exponential notation can be read in reference to the power. 5^3 is read *5 to the third power,* or *the third power of 5.* All scientific calculators have a key to find powers. Some label the key $\boxed{y^x}$ (read *y to the x*). Others label it $\boxed{x^y}$ (read *x to the y*). Still others use a caret $\boxed{\wedge}$. Ask students to complete Problem 3 on journal page 209 using the powers key on their calculators. If your students' calculators do not have a powers key, have them complete the table using repeated multiplication, ignore the keystroke question, and go on to journal page 210.

✓ **Ongoing Assessment:**
Recognizing Student Achievement

Journal Page 210 ★
Problems 4–6

Use **journal page 210, Problems 4–6** to assess students' understanding of exponential notation and the meaning of exponents. Students are making adequate progress if they accurately identify the mistakes and write the correct solutions.

[Number and Numeration Goal 4]

▶ Playing *Exponent Ball*

PARTNER ACTIVITY

(*Student Reference Book,* p. 305; *Math Masters,* p. 451)

Have partners read the game rules on page 305 in the *Student Reference Book.* Lead the class through a demonstration game. Ask volunteers to suggest each step. When choosing whether to run or kick, call students' attention to the columns in the tables on the gameboard that compare the odds of certain plays occurring. Have students compare the chances of moving the ball at least 20 yards on the ground versus kicking it at least 20 yards.

② Ongoing Learning & Practice

▶ Math Boxes 7·1

INDEPENDENT ACTIVITY

(*Math Journal 2,* p. 211)

Mixed Practice Math Boxes in this lesson are paired with Math Boxes in Lesson 7-3. The skills in Problems 2 and 6 preview Unit 8 content.

![Portfolio Ideas]

Writing/Reasoning Have students write a response to the following: *Explain how to use division to find equivalent fractions.* Sample answer: You can use division to find an equivalent fraction by dividing the numerator and denominator of a fraction by the same number.

Study Link 7·1

(*Math Masters*, p. 187)

👤 **INDEPENDENT ACTIVITY**

Home Connection Students use given bases and exponents to convert between repeated factor expressions and exponential notation. They identify errors in problems and convert between exponential notation and standard notation.

③ Differentiation Options

READINESS

Exploring Exponents

(*Math Masters*, p. 188)

👤 **INDEPENDENT ACTIVITY**

🕐 **5–15 Min**

To explore the meaning of exponents, have students look for patterns in numbers written in exponential notation. When students have completed the problems on the *Math Masters* page, have them share their explanations of how to write numbers in exponential notation.

ENRICHMENT

Exploring Exponent Patterns in Fibonacci Numbers

(*Math Masters*, p. 189)

👥 **PARTNER ACTIVITY**

🕐 **15–30 Min**

To explore number patterns that involve exponents and Fibonacci numbers, have students complete *Math Masters*, page 189. Consider having students make posters to display their patterns and explanations from Problems 2 and 3.

⭕ **Social Studies Link** Fibonacci numbers were named after Leonardo da Pisa (better known as Fibonacci), a brilliant mathematician and problem solver, who lived from about 1175 to about 1230. In 1225, the Holy Roman Emperor Frederick II brought mathematicians to test Fibonacci's talents. Fibonacci passed with flying colors.

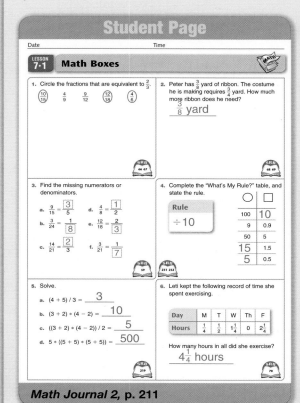

Student Page

Date _____ Time _____

LESSON 7·1 **Math Boxes**

1. Circle the fractions that are equivalent to $\frac{2}{3}$.
$\frac{10}{15}$ $\frac{4}{9}$ $\frac{9}{12}$ $\frac{12}{18}$ $\frac{4}{6}$

2. Peter has $\frac{3}{8}$ yard of ribbon. The costume he is making requires $\frac{3}{4}$ yard. How much more ribbon does he need?

$\frac{3}{8}$ yard

3. Find the missing numerators or denominators.

a. $\frac{9}{15} = \frac{3}{5}$ d. $\frac{4}{8} = \frac{1}{2}$

b. $\frac{3}{24} = \frac{1}{8}$ e. $\frac{12}{18} = \frac{2}{3}$

c. $\frac{14}{21} = \frac{2}{3}$ f. $\frac{3}{21} = \frac{1}{7}$

4. Complete the "What's My Rule?" table, and state the rule.

Rule ÷10	⭕	☐
	100	10
	9	0.9
	50	5
	15	1.5
	5	0.5

5. Solve.

a. $(4 + 5) / 3 =$ __3__

b. $(3 + 2) * (4 - 2) =$ __10__

c. $((3 + 2) * (4 - 2)) / 2 =$ __5__

d. $5 * ((5 + 5) * (5 + 5)) =$ __500__

6. Leti kept the following record of time she spent exercising.

Day	M	T	W	Th	F
Hours	$\frac{1}{4}$	$\frac{1}{2}$	$1\frac{1}{4}$	0	$2\frac{1}{4}$

How many hours in all did she exercise?

$4\frac{1}{4}$ hours

Math Journal 2, p. 211

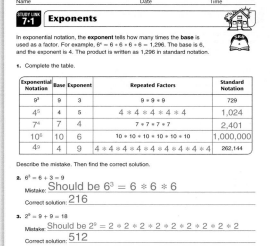

Study Link Master

Name _____ Date _____ Time _____

STUDY LINK 7·1 **Exponents**

In exponential notation, the **exponent** tells how many times the **base** is used as a factor. For example, $6^4 = 6 * 6 * 6 * 6 = 1,296$. The base is 6, and the exponent is 4. The product is written as 1,296 in standard notation.

1. Complete the table.

Exponential Notation	Base	Exponent	Repeated Factors	Standard Notation
9^3	9	3	$9 * 9 * 9$	729
4^5	4	5	$4 * 4 * 4 * 4 * 4$	1,024
7^4	7	4	$7 * 7 * 7 * 7$	2,401
10^6	10	6	$10 * 10 * 10 * 10 * 10 * 10$	1,000,000
4^9	4	9	$4 * 4 * 4 * 4 * 4 * 4 * 4 * 4 * 4$	262,144

Describe the mistake. Then find the correct solution.

2. $6^3 = 6 + 3 = 9$

Mistake: Should be $6^3 = 6 * 6 * 6$

Correct solution: 216

3. $2^9 = 9 + 9 = 18$

Mistake: Should be $2^9 = 2 * 2 * 2 * 2 * 2 * 2 * 2 * 2 * 2$

Correct solution: 512

4. $4^7 = 4 * 7 = 28$

Mistake: Should be $4^7 = 4 * 4 * 4 * 4 * 4 * 4 * 4$

Correct solution: 16,384

Practice

5. $351.82 + n = 366.52$ 6. $100 - r = 99.52$ 7. $\frac{4}{7} + u = \frac{19}{7}$

$n =$ __14.7__ $r =$ __0.48__ $u = \frac{15}{7}$, or $2\frac{1}{7}$

Math Masters, p. 187

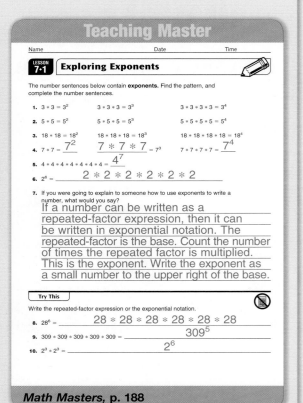

Teaching Master

Name _____ Date _____ Time _____

LESSON 7·1 Exploring Exponents

The number sentences below contain **exponents**. Find the pattern, and complete the number sentences.

1. $3 * 3 = 3^2$ $3 * 3 * 3 = 3^3$ $3 * 3 * 3 * 3 = 3^4$

2. $5 * 5 = 5^2$ $5 * 5 * 5 = 5^3$ $5 * 5 * 5 * 5 = 5^4$

3. $18 * 18 = 18^2$ $18 * 18 * 18 = 18^3$ $18 * 18 * 18 * 18 = 18^4$

4. $7 * 7 = \underline{7^2}$ $\underline{7 * 7 * 7} = 7^3$ $7 * 7 * 7 * 7 = \underline{7^4}$

5. $4 * 4 * 4 * 4 * 4 * 4 * 4 = \underline{4^7}$

6. $2^6 = \underline{2 * 2 * 2 * 2 * 2 * 2}$

7. If you were going to explain to someone how to use exponents to write a number, what would you say?
If a number can be written as a repeated-factor expression, then it can be written in exponential notation. The repeated-factor is the base. Count the number of times the repeated factor is multiplied. This is the exponent. Write the exponent as a small number to the upper right of the base.

Try This

Write the repeated-factor expression or the exponential notation.

8. $28^6 = \underline{28 * 28 * 28 * 28 * 28 * 28}$

9. $309 * 309 * 309 * 309 * 309 = \underline{309^5}$

10. $2^3 * 2^3 = \underline{2^6}$

Math Masters, p. 188

EXTRA PRACTICE

INDEPENDENT ACTIVITY 15–30 Min

▶ Counting Computer Passwords

(*Math Masters*, p. 190)

Students practice and apply their understanding of exponential notation to calculate the number of possible computer passwords consisting of 4 characters and express that total using exponents.

Ask students what would change about the exponential notation for Problem 2 if the number of characters for each password was changed. In exponential notation the number of possible characters is the base and the number of characters for a password is the exponent, so the exponent would change. Have them write the exponential notation to represent the number of possible different passwords if there were 7, 10, or 20 characters in each password. 62^7, 62^{10}, 62^{20}

ELL SUPPORT

SMALL-GROUP ACTIVITY 15–30 Min

▶ Building a Math Word Bank

(*Differentiation Handbook*, p. 142)

To provide language support for exponents, have students use the Word Bank Template found on *Differentiation Handbook*, page 142. Ask students to write the terms *prime factorization, base, exponent,* and *power;* draw pictures to represent each term; and write other related words. See the *Differentiation Handbook* for more information.

Teaching Master

Name _____ Date _____ Time _____

LESSON 7·1 Patterns with Fibonacci Numbers

1. The sequence of numbers 1, 1, 2, 3, 5, 8, 13, ... is called the **Fibonacci sequence**. In the Fibonacci sequence, every number, starting with the third number, is equal to the sum of the two numbers that come before it.

Examples:

Third number: $1 + 1 = 2$ Fourth number: $1 + 2 = 3$

Fill in the next three Fibonacci numbers. 1, 1, 2, 3, 5, 8, 13, $\underline{21}$ $\underline{34}$ $\underline{55}$

2. Study the following pattern: $1^2 + 1^2 = 1 * 2$
$1^2 + 1^2 + 2^2 = 2 * 3$
$1^2 + 1^2 + 2^2 + 3^2 = 3 * 5$
$1^2 + 1^2 + 2^2 + 3^2 + 5^2 = 5 * 8$

a. Write the next two number sentences in the pattern.
$1^2 + 1^2 + 2^2 + 3^2 + 5^2 + 8^2 = 8 * 13$ and
$1^2 + 1^2 + 2^2 + 3^2 + 5^2 + 8^2 + 13^2 = 13 * 21$

b. Describe the pattern in words.
Sample answer: Add the squares of Fibonacci numbers. The sum is equal to the product of the last number in the sequence times the next number in the sequence.

3. a. Solve the following problems: $2^2 - (1 * 3) = \underline{1}$ $3^2 - (2 * 5) = \underline{-1}$
$5^2 - (3 * 8) = \underline{1}$ $8^2 - (5 * 13) = \underline{-1}$

b. Write the next two number sentences in the pattern.
$13^2 - (8 * 21) = 1$ and $21^2 - (13 * 34) = -1$

c. Describe the pattern in words.
The square of a Fibonacci number minus the product of the number before and the number after it in the sequence equals positive or negative 1.

Math Masters, p. 189

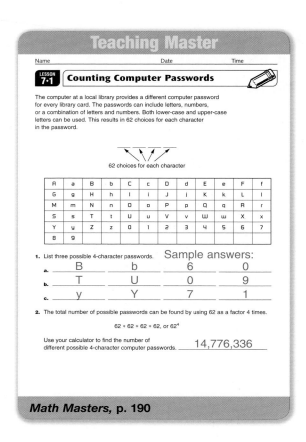

Teaching Master

Name _____ Date _____ Time _____

LESSON 7·1 Counting Computer Passwords

The computer at a local library provides a different computer password for every library card. The passwords can include letters, numbers, or a combination of letters and numbers. Both lower-case and upper-case letters can be used. This results in 62 choices for each character in the password.

62 choices for each character

A	a	B	b	C	c	D	d	E	e	F	f
G	g	H	h	I	i	J	j	K	k	L	l
M	m	N	n	O	o	P	p	Q	q	R	r
S	s	T	t	U	u	V	v	W	w	X	x
Y	y	Z	z	0	1	2	3	4	5	6	7
8	9										

1. List three possible 4-character passwords. Sample answers:
a. $\underline{B}$ $\underline{b}$ $\underline{6}$ $\underline{0}$
b. $\underline{T}$ $\underline{U}$ $\underline{0}$ $\underline{9}$
c. $\underline{y}$ $\underline{Y}$ $\underline{7}$ $\underline{1}$

2. The total number of possible passwords can be found by using 62 as a factor 4 times.
$62 * 62 * 62 * 62$, or 62^4

Use your calculator to find the number of different possible 4-character computer passwords. $\underline{14,776,336}$

Math Masters, p. 190

7·2 Exponential Notation for Powers of 10

 Objective To introduce number-and-word notation for large numbers and exponential notation for powers of 10.

Technology Resources www.everydaymathonline.com

| ePresentations | eToolkit | Algorithms Practice | EM Facts Workshop Game™ | Family Letters | Assessment Management | Common Core State Standards | Curriculum Focal Points | Interactive Teacher's Lesson Guide |

1 Teaching the Lesson

Key Concepts and Skills

• Explore place value using powers of 10.
[Number and Numeration Goal 1]

• Write and translate numbers in and between standard and exponential notation.
[Number and Numeration Goal 4]

• Compare exponential notation and standard notation for positive powers of 10.
[Number and Numeration Goal 4]

• Describe the number patterns inherent to powers of ten.
[Patterns, Functions, and Algebra Goal 1]

Key Activities

Students use standard notation, number-and-word notation, and exponential notation to represent large numbers.

 Ongoing Assessment:
Recognizing Student Achievement
Use the Math Message.
[Number and Numeration Goal 4]

 Ongoing Assessment:
Informing Instruction See page 549.

Key Vocabulary

number-and-word notation ◆ powers of 10

Materials

Math Journal 2, p. 212
Student Reference Book, p. 5
Study Link 7◆1
Math Masters, p. 433
transparency of *Math Masters,* p. 433 ◆ slate

2 Ongoing Learning & Practice

 Playing *First to 100*
Student Reference Book, p. 308
Math Masters, pp. 456–458
per partnership: 2 six-sided dice, calculator
Students practice solving open number sentences.

 Math Boxes 7·2
Math Journal 2, p. 213
Geometry Template
Students practice and maintain skills through Math Box problems.

 Study Link 7·2
Math Masters, p. 191
Students practice and maintain skills through Study Link activities.

3 Differentiation Options

READINESS
Finding Patterns in Powers of 10
Math Masters, p. 192
Students complete a powers-of-10 table and describe patterns they see in the table.

ENRICHMENT
Introducing Negative Exponents and Powers of 0.1
Student Reference Book, p. 7
Math Masters, p. 193
Students explore patterns and notation of negative exponents.

EXTRA PRACTICE
Multiplying Decimals by Powers of 10
Students solve problems involving the multiplication of decimals by powers of 10.

Advance Preparation

For Part 1, copy the place-value chart from the top of journal page 212 on the board. If possible, use semipermanent chalk, or make a transparency of *Math Masters,* page 433. Make copies of it available to students. It will also be used in Lesson 7-3. For Part 3, extend the display to include negative powers of 10.

For the Math Message, draw 3 name-collection boxes on the board and label 100, 1,000, and 1,000,000. For a mathematics and literacy connection, obtain a copy of ***Can You Count to a Googol?*** by Robert E. Wells.

 Teacher's Reference Manual, Grades 4–6 pp. 94–98

Getting Started

Mental Math and Reflexes

Use slates. Dictate numbers and have students identify digits in given places.

● ○ ○ 6③0,726. Circle the 10-thousands digit. Underline the hundred-thousands digit.

● ● ○ 2⑥3,0̲14,613. Circle the 10-millions digit. Underline the ten-thousands digit.

● ● ● ④3,269,432.8̲9. Circle the 10-millions digit. Underline the tenths digit.

Math Message ★

On a half-sheet of paper, make name-collection boxes for 100; 1,000; and 1,000,000. Write three different names in each box. Use exponential notation at least once.

Study Link 7·1 Follow-Up

Have partners share answers and resolve any differences.

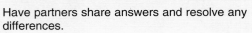

1 Teaching the Lesson

▶ Math Message Follow-Up

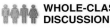 WHOLE-CLASS DISCUSSION

Have students share their answers. Write the different names in name-collection boxes on the board. Answers should include the following:

▷ 100: $10 * 10$; $\frac{1,000}{10}$; 1 hundred; 10^2

▷ 1,000: $10 * 10 * 10$; $\frac{10,000}{10}$; 1 thousand; 10^3

▷ 1,000,000: $10 * 10 * 10 * 10 * 10 * 10$; $\frac{5,000,000}{5}$; 1 million; 10^6

Ask students to describe the kinds of notation that are included on the board. Examples of **powers of 10** written in exponential notation are 10^2, 10^3, and 10^6. Examples of powers of 10 written in **number-and-word notation** are 1 hundred, 1 thousand, and 1 million.

Explain that number-and-word notation is often used to express large numbers using a few numerals and one or two words (for example, 25 billion, 5 hundred thousand), because long strings of zeros can be hard to read. Write *number-and-word notation* along with the example 25 billion on the board or transparency. Write *standard notation* along with the example 25,000,000,000. Ask students to compare the two ways of expressing the same number.

Discuss how to translate from number-and-word notation to standard notation.

▷ One way: 25 billion = $25 * 1,000,000,000 = 25,000,000,000$

---

548   **Unit 7   Exponents and Negative Numbers**

▷ Another way: Use a place-value chart to position the leading digits. Then add zeros to complete the number.

Have volunteers write number-and-word notations for the class to write in standard notation.

Introducing Exponential Notation for Powers of 10

 **WHOLE-CLASS DISCUSSION**

(*Student Reference Book*, p. 5)

Refer students to page 5 of the *Student Reference Book*. As a class, discuss the presented definition of powers of 10 — whole numbers that can be written using only 10s as factors. For example, $1,000 = 10 * 10 * 10 = 10^3$.

Ask students to look at the Powers of 10 Chart on the page and share their ideas about what patterns might help them figure out standard notation for powers of 10. Guide them to observe that the number of zeros in a power of 10, written in standard notation, is equal to the exponent of that number, written in exponential notation. For example, 1,000,000 has 6 zeros, so the exponent of the power of 10 is 6; $1,000,000 = 10^6$.

The next three periods to the left of billions are trillions, then quadrillions, then quintillions.

- How many zeros are needed to write 1 trillion in standard notation? 12 zeros

- How many times will 10 appear in the repeated factor expression? 12 times

- How many periods are to the right of trillions? 4 periods

- What is the relationship between the number of periods to the right of trillions and the exponent when 1 trillion is written in exponential notation? Each period has 3 digits, so 1 trillion would have 3 digits * 4 periods, or 12 zeros.

Record a few examples on the board, and ask students to write these numbers in exponential or standard notation. *Suggestions:*

▷ 10,000 10^4; 100,000 10^5; 10 10^1; 10,000,000 10^7

▷ 10^3 1,000; 10^2 100; 10^5 100,000; 10^{10} 10,000,000,000

Using Guides for Powers of 10

PARTNER ACTIVITY

(*Math Journal 2*, p. 212; *Student Reference Book*, p. 5; *Math Masters*, p. 433)

Have students read the introductory paragraphs on journal page 212. Use the example to discuss how to use the place-value chart and the table of prefixes to work with powers of 10. Mention that these guides are also found on the inside front cover of their journals. Assign the problems on the rest of the page.

Ongoing Assessment: Informing Instruction

Watch for students who have difficulty identifying the exponents for Problems 3 and 4. Suggest that they use the place-value chart on the journal page to first write the number in standard notation and then count the 0s to determine the exponent. Alternatively, use a transparency of *Math Masters*, page 433 and have students use copies of the page to practice writing in standard notation.

Student Page

Date _____ Time _____

LESSON 7·2 Math Boxes

1. Measure the length and width of each of the following objects to the nearest half inch.

   Answers vary.

   a. piece of paper   b. dictionary

   length _____ in. width _____ in.   length _____ in. width _____ in.

   c. palm of your hand   d. _____ (your choice)

   length _____ in. width _____ in.   length _____ in. width _____ in.

2. Amanda collects dobsonflies. Below are the lengths, in millimeters, for the flies in her collection.

   95, 107, 119, 103, 102, 91, 115, 120, 111, 114, 115, 107, 110, 98, 112

   a. Circle the stem-and-leaf plot below that represents this data.

Stems (100s and 10s)	Leaves (1s)	Stems (100s and 10s)	Leaves (1s)	Stems (100s and 10s)	Leaves (1s)
9	1 5 8	9	1 5 8	9	1 5 8 8 8
10	2 3 7 7	10	2 3 7	10	2 3 7 7 7
11	0 1 2 4 5 5 9	11	0 1 2 4 5 9	11	0 1 2 4 5 5 5
12	0	12	0	12	0

   b. Find the following landmarks for the data.

   Median: __110__ Minimum: __91__ Range: __29__ Mode(s): __107, 115__

3. Measure ∠P to the nearest degree.

   ∠P measures about __19°__

4. Calculate the sale price.

Regular Price	Discount	Sale Price
$12.00	25%	$9.00
$7.99	25%	$5.99
$80.00	40%	$48.00
$19.99	25%	$14.99

Math Journal 2, p. 213

2 Ongoing Learning & Practice

▶ Playing *First to 100*

(*Student Reference Book*, p. 308; *Math Masters*, pp. 456–458)

PARTNER ACTIVITY

COMPUTATION PRACTICE

Algebraic Thinking Students practice solving open number sentences by playing *First to 100*. This game was introduced in Lesson 4-7. For detailed instructions, see *Student Reference Book*, page 308.

▶ Math Boxes 7·2

(*Math Journal 2*, p. 213)

INDEPENDENT ACTIVITY

Mixed Practice Math Boxes in this lesson are paired with Math Boxes in Lessons 7-4 and 7-6. The skill in Problem 4 previews Unit 8 content.

▶ Study Link 7·2

(*Math Masters*, p. 191)

INDEPENDENT ACTIVITY

Home Connection Students are asked to memorize the Guides for Powers of 10 and answer questions about them.

3 Differentiation Options

READINESS

▶ Finding Patterns in Powers of 10

(*Math Masters*, p. 192)

PARTNER ACTIVITY

15–30 Min

PROBLEM SOLVING

To investigate patterns in powers of 10, have students complete the table on the *Math Masters* page and describe the patterns they identify in the table.

ENRICHMENT

▶ Introducing Negative Exponents and Powers of 0.1

(*Student Reference Book*, p. 7; *Math Masters*, p. 193)

PARTNER ACTIVITY

15–30 Min

To apply students' understanding of exponents, have them explore the patterns and notation of negative exponents. Read and discuss *Student Reference Book*,

---

Study Link Master

Name _____ Date _____ Time _____

STUDY LINK 7·2 Guides for Powers of 10

There are prefixes that name powers of 10. You know some of them from the metric system. For example, *kilo-* in kilometer (1,000 meters). It's helpful to memorize the prefixes for every third power of 10 through one trillion.

Memorize the table below. Have a friend quiz you. Then cover the table, and try to complete the statements below.

Standard Notation	Number-and-Word Notation	Exponential Notation	Prefix
1,000	1 thousand	10^3	kilo-
1,000,000	1 million	10^6	mega-
1,000,000,000	1 billion	10^9	giga-
1,000,000,000,000	1 trillion	10^{12}	tera-

1. More than 10^9, or one __billion__ people live in China.

2. One thousand, or $10^{\boxed{3}}$, feet is a little less than $\frac{1}{5}$ of a mile.

3. Astronomers estimate that there are more than 10^{12}, or one __trillion__ stars in the universe.

4. More than one million, or $10^{\boxed{6}}$, copies of *The New York Times* are sold every day.

5. A kiloton equals one __thousand__, or $10^{\boxed{3}}$, metric tons.

6. A megaton equals one __million__, or $10^{\boxed{6}}$, metric tons.

Practice

Find the prime factorization of each number, and write it using exponents.

7. 48 = __$2^4 * 3$__   8. 60 = __$2^2 * 3 * 5$__

Write each number in expanded notation.

9. 3,264 = __3,000 + 200 + 60 + 4__

10. 675,511 = __600,000 + 70,000 + 5,000 + 500 + 10 + 1__

Math Masters, p. 191

page 7. Emphasize that negative exponents are another way to represent numbers that are less than 1.

Use examples to discuss converting between exponential notation with negative exponents and fractions.

Suggestions:

$$5^{-2} = \frac{1}{5^2} = \frac{1}{5 * 5} = \frac{1}{25}$$

$$4^{-3} = \frac{1}{4^3} = \frac{1}{4 * 4 * 4} = \frac{1}{64}$$

$$2^{-4} = \frac{1}{2^4} = \frac{1}{2 * 2 * 2 * 2} = \frac{1}{16}$$

Negative exponents can be used to express negative powers of 10.

$$10^{-3} = \frac{1}{10^3} = \frac{1}{10 * 10 * 10} = \frac{1}{1,000}$$

This equation also shows that negative powers of 10 are also positive powers of 0.1.

$$10^{-3} = \frac{1}{10} * \frac{1}{10} * \frac{1}{10} = 0.1 * 0.1 * 0.1 = 0.1^3 = 0.001$$

Discuss the table on *Math Masters,* page 193. Students work with their partners, using the table to answer the questions that follow. Briefly go over the answers.

 Links to the Future

Negative exponents and powers of 0.1 will be investigated further in *Sixth Grade Everyday Mathematics.* The Enrichment activity is provided for exposure only.

EXTRA PRACTICE

Multiplying Decimals by Powers of 10

 **WHOLE-CLASS DISCUSSION**

5–15 Min

To offer students more practice multiplying decimals by powers of 10, pose problems like those below. For each problem, have students write the original problem, rewrite the problem with the power of 10 written in standard notation, and then solve the problem.

- $2.3 * 10^1$ $2.3 * 10; 23$
- $35.1 * 10^3$ $35.1 * 1,000; 35,100$
- $40.7 * 10^4$ $40.7 * 10,000; 407,000$
- $0.52 * 10^5$ $0.52 * 100,000; 52,000$

Have students explain the relationship between multiplying by a power of 10 and the placement of the decimal point in the product.

Math Masters, p. 192

Math Masters, p. 193

7·3 Scientific Notation

Objective To introduce scientific notation.

Technology Resources www.everydaymathonline.com

| ePresentations | eToolkit | Algorithms Practice | EM Facts Workshop Game™ | Family Letters | Assessment Management | Common Core State Standards | Curriculum Focal Points | Interactive Teacher's Lesson Guide |

---

1 Teaching the Lesson

Key Concepts and Skills

- Explore the place value of numbers written as powers of 10.
  [Number and Numeration Goal 1]

- Translate numbers from scientific notation to standard and number-and-word notation.
  [Number and Numeration Goal 1]

- Use number patterns to solve problems involving exponents.
  [Patterns, Functions, and Algebra Goal 1]

Key Activities

Students use powers of 10 to write numbers in expanded notation. They solve multiplication expressions containing exponents and translate numbers written in scientific notation into standard and number-and-word notation. Students practice writing and comparing numbers written in scientific notation by playing *Scientific Notation Toss*.

 Ongoing Assessment:
Recognizing Student Achievement
Use journal page 217.
[Number and Numeration Goal 1]

Key Vocabulary

expanded notation ◆ scientific notation

Materials

Math Journal 2, pp. 214–217
Student Reference Book, p. 329
Study Link 7·2
Class Data Pad ◆ slate ◆ per partnership:
2 six-sided dice

2 Ongoing Learning & Practice

 Math Boxes 7·3
Math Journal 2, p. 218
Students practice and maintain skills through Math Box problems.

 Study Link 7·3
Math Masters, p. 194
Students practice and maintain skills through Study Link activities.

3 Differentiation Options

READINESS
Using Place Value to Rename Numbers
Math Masters, p. 195
Students rename numbers using place value and number-and-word notation.

EXTRA PRACTICE
Writing Numbers in Expanded Notation
Math Masters, p. 196
Students write whole numbers in expanded notation as addition and multiplication expressions.

ELL SUPPORT
Comparing Notations for Numbers
Differentiation Handbook, p. 149
Students compare and contrast the terms *standard notation* and *exponential notation*.

Advance Preparation

🍎 *Teacher's Reference Manual, Grades 4–6* pp. 94–98

Getting Started

Mental Math and Reflexes

Use your slate procedures for problems such as the following:

○●○○ $3.4 * 10 = 34$
$3.4 * 10^2 = 340$
$3.4 * 10^3 = 3,400$

○●●○ $2.41 * 10^2 = 241$
$2.41 * 10^3 = 2,410$
$0.241 * 10^2 = 24.1$

●●● $54 * 10^3 = 54,000$
$5,400 \div 10^3 = 5.4$
$5,400 \div 10^4 = 0.54$

Math Message

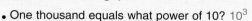

Complete Problems 1–10 on page 214 in your journal. Reminder: *Calculations with exponents are done before other factors are multiplied.*

Study Link 7·2 Follow-Up

Partners share their solutions. Then have students answer the following questions on their slates:

- One thousand equals what power of 10? 10^3
- Which prefix means *thousand*? kilo-
- What is another name for 10^6? 1 million
- Which prefix means *million*? mega-
- What does the prefix *tera-* mean? trillion
- 1 trillion equals what power of 10? 10^{12}

---

1 Teaching the Lesson

▶ Math Message Follow-Up

WHOLE-CLASS ACTIVITY

(*Math Journal 2*, p. 214)

Ask students to share their solutions for Problems 1–10. Ask a volunteer to write 236 on the Class Data Pad using **expanded notation.** $236 = 200 + 30 + 6$ Show the use of powers of 10 to write numbers in expanded notation. Write $236 = (2 * 10^2) + (3 * 10^1) + (6 * 10^0)$ on the Class Data Pad. Ask another volunteer to evaluate the expressions in parentheses. $236 = (2 * 10 * 10) + (3 * 10) + (6 * 1) = (2 * 100) + (3 * 10) + (6 * 1) = 200 + 30 + 6$ Ask students what observations or connections they notice between the number sentences. Point out that the expanded notation expressions contain powers of 10 written in standard notation, as products of 10s, and in exponential notation.

As a class, read the introduction to **scientific notation** on the journal page. Problems 6–14 are given in scientific notation.

Do Problems 11–14 as a class. Ask volunteers to rename the power of 10 as a product of 10s. Then carry out the multiplication.

Example: $5 * 10^3 = 5 * (10 * 10 * 10) = 5 * 1,000 = 5,000$

▶ Translating Scientific Notation

PARTNER ACTIVITY

(*Math Journal 2*, pp. 215 and 216)

⬤ **Science Link** Ask a student to select an event from journal page 215 and read, in scientific notation, how many years ago the event took place. Demonstrate how to use the place-value chart on page 216 to write the number in standard notation.

Student Page

Date _____ Time _____

LESSON 7·3 Scientific Notation

Complete the following pattern.

1. $10^2 = 10 * 10 = 100$

2. $10^3 = 10 * 10 * 10 = $ __1,000__

3. $10^4 = $ __$10 * 10 * 10 * 10$__ $= $ __10,000__

4. $10^5 = $ __$10 * 10 * 10 * 10 * 10$__ $= $ __100,000__

5. $10^6 = $ __$10 * 10 * 10 * 10 * 10 * 10$__ $= $ __1,000,000__

Use the answers to Problems 1–5 to help you complete the following.

6. $2 * 10^2 = 2 * 100 = 200$

7. $3 * 10^3 = 3 * $ __1,000__ $= $ __3,000__

8. $4 * 10^4 = $ __4__ $* $ __10,000__ $= $ __40,000__

9. $6 * 10^5 = $ __6__ $* $ __100,000__ $= $ __600,000__

10. $8 * 10^6 = $ __8__ $* $ __1,000,000__ $= $ __8,000,000__

When you write a number as the product of a number and a power of 10, you are using **scientific notation.** Scientific notation is a useful way to write large or small numbers. Many calculators display numbers one billion or larger with scientific notation.

Example: In scientific notation, 4,000 is written as $4 * 10^3$. It is read as four times ten to the third power.

Write each of the following in standard notation and number-and-word notation.

	Standard Notation	Number-and-Word Notation
11. $5 * 10^3 = $	5,000	5 thousand
12. $7 * 10^2 = $	700	7 hundred
13. $2 * 10^4 = $	20,000	20 thousand
14. $5 * 10^6 = $	5,000,000	5 million

Math Journal 2, p. 214

Date _____ Time _____

LESSON 7·3 History of Earth *continued*

	Billion 10⁹	100 M 10⁸	10 M 10⁷	Million 10⁶	100 Th 10⁵	10 Th 10⁴	Thousand 10³	100 10²	10 10¹	One 10⁰
1	5	0	0	0	0	0	0	0	0	0
2		4	0	0	0	0	0	0	0	0
3			4	0	0	0	0	0	0	0
4			3	0	0	0	0	0	0	0
5			2	5	0	0	0	0	0	0
6			1	0	0	0	0	0	0	0
7				6	5	0	0	0	0	0
8				6	0	0	0	0	0	0
9					8	0	0	0	0	0
10						2	0	0	0	0

Work with a partner to answer the questions. Write your answers in standard notation.

11. According to the estimates by scientists, about how many years passed from the formation of Earth until the first signs of life?

About 1,000,000 years

12. About how many years passed between the appearance of the first fish and the appearance of forests and swamps?

About 100,000,000 years

13. According to the geological record, about how long did dinosaurs roam on Earth?

About 185,000,000 years

Math Journal 2, p. 216

Date _____ Time _____

LESSON 7·3 Expanded Notation

Each digit in a number has a value depending on its place in the numeral.

Example: 2,784

— 4 ones   or 4 * 1   or 4
— 8 tens   or 8 * 10   or 80
— 7 hundreds   or 7 * 100   or 700
— 2 thousands   or 2 * 1,000   or 2,000

Numbers written in expanded notation are written as addition expressions showing the value of the digits.

1. a. Write 2,784 in expanded notation as an addition expression.
$2{,}784 = 2{,}000 + 700 + 80 + 4$

 b. Write 2,784 in expanded notation as the sum of multiplication expressions.
$2{,}784 = (2 * 1{,}000) + (7 * 100) + (8 * 10) + (4 * 1)$

 c. Write 2,784 in expanded notation as the sum of multiplication expressions using powers of 10.
$2{,}784 = (2 * 10^3) + (7 * 10^2) + (8 * 10^1) + (4 * 10^0)$

2. Write 987 in expanded notation as an addition expression.
$987 = 900 + 80 + 7$

3. Write 8,945 in expanded notation as the sum of multiplication expressions.
$8{,}945 = (8 * 1{,}000) + (9 * 100) + (4 * 10) + (5 * 1)$

4. Write 4,768 in expanded notation as the sum of multiplication expressions using powers of 10.
$4{,}768 = (4 * 10^3) + (7 * 10^2) + (6 * 10^1) + (8 * 10^0)$

5. a. Write 6,125 in expanded notation as an addition expression.
$6{,}125 = 6{,}000 + 100 + 20 + 5$

 b. Write 6,125 in expanded notation as the sum of multiplication expressions.
$6{,}125 = (6 * 1{,}000) + (1 * 100) + (2 * 10) + (5 * 1)$

 c. Write 6,125 in expanded notation as the sum of multiplication expressions using powers of 10.
$6{,}125 = (6 * 10^3) + (1 * 10^2) + (2 * 10^1) + (5 * 10^0)$

Math Journal 2, p. 217

Example: The first fish appeared about $4 * 10^8$ years ago. To express this number of years in standard notation, find 10^8 on the place-value chart and write 4 beneath it, followed by the appropriate number of zeros in the cells to the right. From the chart, $4 * 10^8$ can easily be read as *four hundred million.*

Ask partners to complete Problems 1–8 on the chart. Circulate and assist.

The scientific notations for Problems 5 and 7 contain decimals. Discuss the meanings of decimals in scientific notation. For example, to convert $6.5 * 10^7$ to standard notation, think of number-and-word notation. The 6 represents 6 ten millions, or 60 million. The 0.5 represents half of 1 ten million, or 5 million. So $6.5 * 10^7 = 65$ million. Write the 6 in the 10^7 column, the 5 in the 10^6 column, and complete the row with 0s. This shows that $6.5 * 10^7 = 65{,}000{,}000$.

List the following numbers on the Class Data Pad, and ask volunteers to rename the numbers using decimals.

▷ 15 hundred 1.5 thousand

▷ 35 thousand 3.5 ten thousand

▷ 230 million 2.3 hundred million

Ask students to explain how they would write these answers in scientific notation. Thousands is 10^3, so 1.5 thousand $= 1.5 * 10^3$; ten thousands is 10^4, so 3.5 ten thousand $= 3.5 * 10^4$; hundred millions is 10^8, so 2.3 hundred million $= 2.3 * 10^8$. Add students' responses to the Class Data Pad.

Ask partners to complete the journal page. Circulate and assist.

Ongoing Assessment: Recognizing Student Achievement   Journal Page 217 Problems 1–5

Use **journal page 217, Problems 1–5** to assess students' understanding of place value and their ability to translate numbers written in standard notation to expanded notation. Students are making adequate progress if they have accurately converted the numbers to expanded notation. Some students may be able to write in expanded notation using powers of 10.

[Number and Numeration Goal 1]

▶ **Reviewing Expanded Notation**   INDEPENDENT ACTIVITY

(*Math Journal 2*, p. 217)

Portfolio Ideas

Ask volunteers to identify the value of each digit in 2,784. Ask other volunteers to write the solutions for Problem 1 on the board. Discuss how the number sentences are related. Expect students to reference ideas from the Math Message discussion. Then have students complete the page.

Playing *Scientific-Notation Toss*

PARTNER ACTIVITY

(*Student Reference Book,* p. 329)

Have students read the directions on page 329 in the *Student Reference Book*. Ask a volunteer to demonstrate how the game is played.

---

2 Ongoing Learning & Practice

Math Boxes 7·3

INDEPENDENT ACTIVITY

(*Math Journal 2,* p. 218)

Mixed Practice Math Boxes in this lesson are paired with Math Boxes in Lesson 7-1. The skills in Problems 2 and 6 preview Unit 8 content.

Study Link 7·3

INDEPENDENT ACTIVITY

(*Math Masters,* p. 194)

Home Connection Students practice reading and interpreting numbers written in scientific notation. Then they write the numbers in number-and-word notation.

---

3 Differentiation Options

READINESS

PARTNER ACTIVITY

🕐 15–30 Min

Using Place Value to Rename Numbers

(*Math Masters,* p. 195)

To explore the use of place value and number-and-word notation to rename numbers, have partners complete name-collection boxes. Refer students to the place-value chart on *Math Masters,* page 195.

Pose the following questions:

- What is $\frac{1}{10}$ of 10? 1
- What is $\frac{1}{10}$ of 100? 10
- What is $\frac{1}{10}$ of 1,000? 100
- What is $\frac{1}{10}$ of 10,000? 1,000

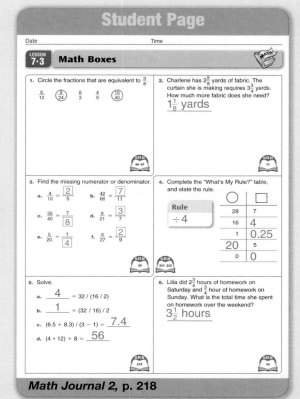

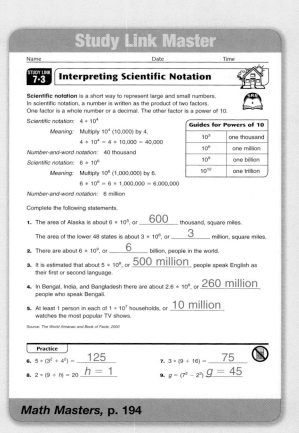

Explain that just as we think of the place-value of each column as 10 times that of the column to its right, we can also think of the place-value of each column as $\frac{1}{10}$ of the column to its left.

We can use these relationships to rename numbers. In the example on the *Math Masters* page, we can think *how many hundreds in 1,300?* and rename it as 13 hundred. If we think *how many thousands in 1,300,* we can rename it as 1.3 thousand. Since 100 is $\frac{1}{10}$ of 1,000, then 300 is $\frac{3}{10}$ of 1,000.

Ask students to first write the numbers from the name-collection box tags in the place-value chart and then follow the pattern in the example to complete the name-collection boxes for these numbers.

Have students share their answers. Consider making posters to display the completed name-collection boxes.

EXTRA PRACTICE

INDEPENDENT ACTIVITY

15–30 Min

▶ Writing Numbers in Expanded Notation

(*Math Masters*, p. 196)

Students practice writing whole numbers in expanded notation as addition expressions and multiplication expressions.

Adjusting the Activity

Have students write expanded notation as multiplication expressions for decimals. *Suggestions:* 9.56, 87.125, 392.394

AUDITORY ◆ KINESTHETIC ◆ TACTILE ◆ VISUAL

ELL SUPPORT

SMALL-GROUP ACTIVITY

15–30 Min

▶ Comparing Notations for Numbers

(*Differentiation Handbook*, p. 149)

To provide language support for number notations, ask students to compare and contrast the terms *standard notation* and *exponential notation*. Have students use the Venn diagram found on *Differentiation Handbook*, page 149. See the *Differentiation Handbook* for more information.

7·4 Parentheses in Number Sentences

Objective To review the use of parentheses.

Technology Resources www.everydaymathonline.com

 ePresentations   eToolkit   Algorithms Practice   EM Facts Workshop Game™   Family Letters   Assessment Management   Common Core State Standards    Curriculum Focal Points   Interactive Teacher's Lesson Guide

1 Teaching the Lesson

Key Concepts and Skills

- Identify and write sentences that model number stories.
  [Patterns, Functions, and Algebra Goal 2]
- Solve problems involving parentheses and nested parentheses.
  [Patterns, Functions, and Algebra Goal 3]
- Insert parentheses in order to make true number sentences.
  [Patterns, Functions, and Algebra Goal 3]

Key Activities

Students use parentheses in number sentences involving more than one operation. They translate number stories into number sentences, inserting parentheses in the proper places, and determine whether number sentences containing parentheses are true or false.

 Ongoing Assessment:
Recognizing Student Achievement
Use an Exit Slip (*Math Masters*, page 414).
[Patterns, Functions, and Algebra Goal 3]

Key Vocabulary

expression ◆ ambiguous ◆ nested parentheses

Materials

Math Journal 2, pp. 219 and 220
Study Link 7·3
Math Masters, p. 414
slate

2 Ongoing Learning & Practice

 Playing *Name That Number*
Student Reference Book, p. 325
per partnership: 1 complete deck of number cards (from the Everything Math Deck, if available)
Students apply number properties, equivalent names, arithmetic operations, and basic facts.

 Math Boxes 7·4
Math Journal 2, p. 221
Students practice and maintain skills through Math Box problems.

Study Link 7·4
Math Masters, p. 197
Students practice and maintain skills through Study Link activities.

3 Differentiation Options

READINESS
Reviewing Parentheses in Number Sentences
Math Masters, p. 198
Students insert parentheses to make number sentences true.

ENRICHMENT
Describing Dot Patterns with Number Models
Math Masters, p. 199
Students partition dot grids and use the patterns to write number models.

EXTRA PRACTICE
5-Minute Math
5-Minute Math™, pp. 77 and 78
Students practice using grouping symbols.

Advance Preparation

 Teacher's Reference Manual, Grades 4–6 pp. 98, 99, 102, 103, 288, 289

Getting Started

Mental Math and Reflexes

Use your slate procedures for problems such as the following:

● ○ ○ $47 * 10^4 = 470{,}000$
       $4.7 * 10^3 = 4{,}700$
       $0.47 * 10^2 = 47$
       $0.047 * 10 = 0.47$

● ● ○ $356 * 10^3 = 356{,}000$
       $42.6 * 10^2 = 4{,}260$
       $0.862 * 10^2 = 86.2$
       $0.009 * 10^3 = 9$

● ● ● $0.109 * 10^3 = 109$
       $7.08 * 10^4 = 70{,}800$
       $0.084 * 10^2 = 8.4$
       $79.04 * 10^3 = 79{,}040$

Math Message

Complete Problems 1 and 2 at the top of journal page 219.

Study Link 7·3 Follow-Up

Have partners compare answers and resolve differences.

---

1 Teaching the Lesson

▶ ## Math Message Follow-Up

WHOLE-CLASS ACTIVITY

(*Math Journal 2*, p. 219)

Algebraic Thinking Discuss students' answers. Ask: *What do parentheses mean in number sentences?* Operations inside parentheses are done first.

Write the statements from Problem 1 on the board with their correct expressions, but without parentheses. Guide students to see that without the mathematical punctuation of parentheses, number expressions can take on different values depending on the order in which the operations are performed. Without parentheses, the **expression** is said to be **ambiguous** because it has more than one possible meaning.

NOTE An expression is a group of mathematical symbols (numbers, operation signs, variables, grouping symbols) that represents a number—or can represent a number if values are assigned to any variables it contains. A number sentence is made up of at least two numbers or expressions separated by a relation symbol such as $=$, $>$, or $<$.

Example: The number sentence $6 * 4 - 2 / 2 = n$ includes the expression $6 * 4 - 2 / 2$, the variable n, and the equal symbol $=$.

Ask volunteers to share their answers to Problem 2 and explain the steps they used to solve the problem. As the students explain the steps, list them on the board. *For example:*

Steps	Numerical Expression
Multiply 6 times 4.	$6 * 4$
Subtract 2 from the result.	$(6 * 4) - 2$
Divide that result by 2.	$((6 * 4) - 2) / 2$

Student Page

Date _____ Time _____

LESSON 7·4 Parentheses and Number Stories

Math Message

1. Write each statement as an expression.

  a. Add 8 and 3, and then multiply by 5. $(8 + 3) * 5$

  b. Add 8 to the product of 3 and 5. $8 + (3 * 5)$

  c. 10 times the difference of 7 subtracted from 8. $10 * (8 - 7)$

  d. The product of 10 and 8, minus 7. $(10 * 8) - 7$

2. Insert parentheses to rewrite the following problem to make four different true sentences.

  $6 * 4 - 2 / 2 = ?$ Sample answers:

    $((6 * 4)) - 2) / 2 = 11$
    $6 * (4 - 2) / 2 = 6$
    $(6 * 4) - (2 / 2) = 23$
    $6 * (4 - (2 / 2)) = 18$

Draw a line to match each number story with the expression that fits it.

3. **Story 1**   **Tom's Total Number of Bottles of Juice**

  Tom had 4 bottles of juice.
  He went shopping and bought
  3 six-packs of bottles of juice. $(4 + 3) * 6$

  Story 2

  Tom had 4 six-packs of bottles of juice.
  He went shopping and bought 3 more
  six-packs of bottles of juice. $4 + (3 * 6)$

Math Journal 2, p. 219

Point out that when two or more sets of parentheses are used in the same expression, the operation inside the inner parentheses is done first. In $((6 * 4) - 2) / 2$, 6 times 4 is the operation in the inner parentheses. The operation in the outer parentheses is done next, followed by all the remaining operations. Parentheses inside parentheses are referred to as **nested parentheses.**

 Links to the Future

This lesson stresses the use of parentheses to create unambiguous expressions. Lesson 7-5 will introduce the conventional order of operations, which often reduces or eliminates the need for grouping symbols in many number sentences.

▶ Matching Number Stories to Appropriate Expressions

 PARTNER ACTIVITY

PROBLEM SOLVING

(*Math Journal 2,* pp. 219 and 220)

Ask students to read the two number stories in Problem 3 on journal page 219 and match each story with an expression. Ask volunteers to explain their choices. Story 1 goes with the second expression since 3 must be multiplied by 6 to find the total number of cans in 3 six-packs. Story 2 goes with the first expression since 4 + 3 stands for the total number of six-packs.

Assign journal page 220. When most students are done, bring the class together and go over the answers. Have students explain their reasons for matching a given number story with a particular expression.

 Ongoing Assessment: Recognizing Student Achievement

Exit Slip ★

Use an **Exit Slip** (*Math Masters,* page 414) to assess students' facility with writing expressions containing parentheses to represent a number story. Have students explain how they used parentheses in Problem 6 on journal page 220 to write the expression for the total number of undamaged cans. Students are making adequate progress if they refer to the use of nested parentheses to identify the total number of undamaged cans.

[Patterns, Functions, and Algebra Goal 3]

2 Ongoing Learning & Practice

▶ Playing *Name That Number*

 PARTNER ACTIVITY

(*Student Reference Book,* p. 325)

Students practice applying number properties, equivalent names, arithmetic operations, and basic facts by playing *Name That*

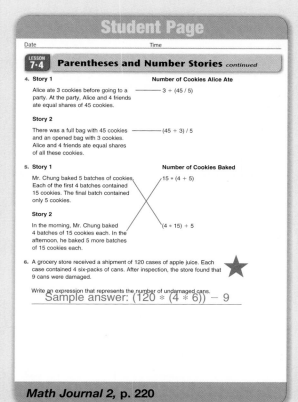

Student Page

Date _____ Time _____

LESSON 7·4 **Parentheses and Number Stories** *continued*

4. Story 1
Alice ate 3 cookies before going to a party. At the party, Alice and 4 friends ate equal shares of 45 cookies.

Number of Cookies Alice Ate

3 + (45 / 5)

Story 2
There was a full bag with 45 cookies and an opened bag with 3 cookies. Alice and 4 friends ate equal shares of all these cookies.

(45 + 3) / 5

5. Story 1
Mr. Chung baked 5 batches of cookies. Each of the first 4 batches contained 15 cookies. The final batch contained only 5 cookies.

Number of Cookies Baked

15 * (4 + 5)

Story 2
In the morning, Mr. Chung baked 4 batches of 15 cookies each. In the afternoon, he baked 5 more batches of 15 cookies each.

(4 * 15) + 5

6. A grocery store received a shipment of 120 cases of apple juice. Each case contained 4 six-packs of cans. After inspection, the store found that 9 cans were damaged.

Write an expression that represents the number of undamaged cans.
Sample answer: $(120 * (4 * 6)) - 9$

Math Journal 2, p. 220

Student Page

Games

Name That Number

Materials ☐ 1 complete deck of number cards
Players 2 or 3
Skill Naming numbers with expressions
Object of the game To collect the most cards.
Directions
1. Shuffle the deck and deal 5 cards to each player. Place the remaining cards number-side down on the table between the players. Turn over the top card and place it beside the deck. This is the **target number** for the round.
2. Players try to match the target number by adding, subtracting, multiplying, or dividing the numbers on as many of their cards as possible. A card may only be used once.
3. Players write their solutions on a sheet of paper. When players have written their best solutions:
   ♦ Each player sets aside the cards they used to match the target number.
   ♦ Each player replaces the cards they set aside by drawing new cards from the top of the deck.
   ♦ The old target number is placed on the bottom of the deck.
   ♦ A new target number is turned over, and another round is played.
4. Play continues until there are not enough cards left to replace all of the players' cards. The player who has set aside the most cards wins the game.

Example | Target number: 16

Player 1's cards: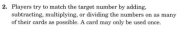

Some possible solutions:
$10 + 8 - 2 = 16$ (3 cards used)
$7 * 2 + 10 - 8 = 16$ (4 cards used)
$8 / 2 + 10 + 7 - 5 = 16$ (all 5 cards used)
The player sets aside the cards used to make a solution and draws the same number of cards from the top of the deck.

Student Reference Book, p. 325

Student Page

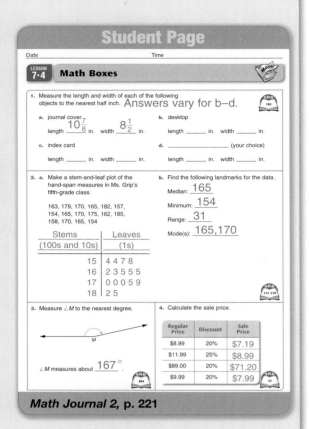

Date _____ Time _____

LESSON 7·4 Math Boxes

1. Measure the length and width of each of the following objects to the nearest half inch. **Answers vary for b–d.**

   a. journal cover
   length __10 7/8__ in. width __8 1/2__ in.

   b. desktop
   length _____ in. width _____ in.

   c. index card
   length _____ in. width _____ in.

   d. _____ (your choice)
   length _____ in. width _____ in.

2. a. Make a stem-and-leaf plot of the hand-span measures in Ms. Grip's fifth-grade class.

   163, 179, 170, 165, 182, 157, 154, 165, 170, 175, 162, 185, 158, 170, 165, 154

Stems (100s and 10s)	Leaves (1s)
15	4 4 7 8
16	2 3 5 5 5
17	0 0 0 5 9
18	2 5

   b. Find the following landmarks for the data.
   Median: __165__
   Minimum: __154__
   Range: __31__
   Mode(s): __165,170__

3. Measure ∠M to the nearest degree.

   M

   ∠M measures about __167__°

4. Calculate the sale price.

Regular Price	Discount	Sale Price
$8.99	20%	$7.19
$11.99	25%	$8.99
$89.00	20%	$71.20
$9.99	20%	$7.99

Math Journal 2, p. 221

Study Link Master

Name _____ Date _____ Time _____

STUDY LINK 7·4 Using Parentheses

Make each sentence true by inserting parentheses.

1. 2 = (3 * 2) − (4 / 1)   2. 3 = (4 + 3 − 1) / 2

3. 4 = (3 − 1) + (4 / 2)

Sample answers for Problems 1–6:

4. Write seven names for 8. Use only numbers less than 10, and use at least three different operations in each name. Use parentheses. Follow the directions in Problem 7 to fill in the last two rows.

8
(9 × 1) − (1 / 1)
(9 − 5) + (2 × 2)
(0.5 / 1) + (2.5 × 3)
(6.3 + 9.7) / (6 − 4)
(6.2 / 2) + (7 − 2.1)
(1/2 × 8) + (9 − 5)
(7² − 9) ÷ 5
(4² − (3 * 3)) + 1
((2 + 1)⁴ ÷ 9) − 1

Make each sentence true by inserting parentheses.

Reminder: When you have a pair of parentheses inside another pair, the parentheses are called **nested parentheses.**

Example: 8 = ((5 * 6) + 2) / 4

5. 1 = (4 + 1 − 3) / 2   6. 7 = (4 * 3 / 2) + 1

7. Add two names to your name-collection box in Problem 4. Use nested parentheses.

Practice

Find the number that each variable represents.

8. 2 5/12 = (1 1/12 + a) __a = 1 4/12, or 1 1/3__
9. (1 1/2 + p) * 2² = 12 __p = 1 1/2__
10. 6 5/8 + d = 7 15/8 __d = 2 2/8, or 2 1/4__
11. 6.4 − y = 6 2/5 __y = 0__

Math Masters, p. 197

560 Unit 7 Exponents and Negative Numbers

Number. Encourage students to extend the game by using the cards in their hands to form exponents and/or fractions.

▶ Math Boxes 7·4

 INDEPENDENT ACTIVITY

(Math Journal 2, p. 221)

 **Mixed Practice** Math Boxes in this lesson are paired with Math Boxes in Lessons 7-2 and 7-6. The skill in Problem 4 previews Unit 8 content.

Writing/Reasoning Have students write a response to the following: *Use your solution for Problem 2 to explain how to read a stem-and-leaf plot.* Sample answer: In this problem, the stems are the hundreds and tens digits for each number, and the leaves are the ones digits. The first number on this stem-and-leaf plot has 1 in the hundreds place, 5 in the tens place, and 4 in the ones place. It is read *one hundred fifty-four.*

▶ Study Link 7·4

INDEPENDENT ACTIVITY

(Math Masters, p. 197)

Home Connection Students insert parentheses to make number sentences true. In several cases, students will need to insert nested parentheses.

---

③ Differentiation Options

READINESS

PARTNER ACTIVITY

 15–30 Min

▶ Reviewing Parentheses in Number Sentences

(Math Masters, p. 198)

To explore the use of parentheses in number sentences, have students insert parentheses to make true sentences. Students compare the use of commas in text sentences to the use of parentheses in number sentences. When students have finished the page, have them share why they think parentheses are important.

ENRICHMENT

Describing Dot Patterns with Number Models

(Math Masters, p. 199)

Portfolio Ideas

To apply students' understanding of parentheses, have them write number sentences to describe dot patterns. Students partition a dot grid and write number sentences to model the indicated number patterns.

EXTRA PRACTICE

5-Minute Math

To offer students more experience with grouping symbols, see *5-Minute Math,* pages 77 and 78.

Planning Ahead

In Lesson 7-6, you will need newspapers and magazines that contain line graphs.

Name   Date   Time

LESSON 7·4 | **Reviewing Parentheses**

1. Read the following sentence. Mary Grace the lizard ate three crickets.

This sentence could have multiple meanings.

1. The speaker is telling someone named Mary Grace that the lizard ate three crickets.

2. The lizard, named Mary Grace, ate three crickets.

3. The speaker is telling someone named Mary that the lizard, named Grace, ate three crickets.

Without commas, it's hard to tell which meaning was intended. Write the number of the meaning next to each sentence below.

a. __2__ Mary Grace, the lizard, ate three crickets.

b. __1__ Mary Grace the lizard ate three crickets.

c. __3__ Mary, Grace the lizard, ate three crickets.

By adding commas, the meaning of a sentence becomes clear. In number sentences, parentheses are used to indicate what to calculate first.

2. Insert parentheses in each sentence to make the sentence true.

a. $3 * 4 + 7 = 33$ $3 * (4 + 7) = 33$

b. $6 + 9 * 5 = 51$ $6 + (9 * 5) = 51$

c. $27 / 4 + 5 + 6 = 9$ $27 / (4 + 5) + 6 = 9$

3. Insert parentheses in the expressions below, and find their solutions.

a. $7 * 5 - 4 =$ $(7 * 5) - 4 = 31; 7 * (5 - 4) = 7$

b. $6 + 9 \div 3 =$ $(6 + 9) \div 3 = 5; 6 + (9 \div 3) = 9$

Math Masters, p. 198

Name   Date   Time

LESSON 7·4 | **Describing Dot Patterns**

The total dots in this dot array can be found by using patterns.

Here is one way to find the total:

$((3 * 3) + (4 * 3) + 4)$

Use shape outlines or colors to identify a pattern on this dot array. Write a number model for your pattern. Then write a number story that matches your number model.

Sample answers:

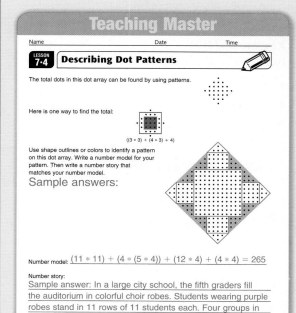

Number model: $(11 * 11) + (4 * (5 * 4)) + (12 * 4) + (4 * 4) = 265$

Number story:
Sample answer: In a large city school, the fifth graders fill the auditorium in colorful choir robes. Students wearing purple robes stand in 11 rows of 11 students each. Four groups in gold robes stand in 4 rows of 5 students each. There are 4 groups of 12 students in black robes and 4 groups of 4 students in green robes. How many students are in the auditorium?

Math Masters, p. 199

7·5 Order of Operations

 Objective To introduce the rules for order of operations.

Technology Resources www.everydaymathonline.com

 ePresentations

 eToolkit

 Algorithms Practice

 EM Facts Workshop Game™

 Family Letters

 Assessment Management

 Common Core State Standards

 Curriculum Focal Points

 Interactive Teacher's Lesson Guide

1 Teaching the Lesson	**2 Ongoing Learning & Practice**	**3 Differentiation Options**

1 Teaching the Lesson

Key Concepts and Skills

- Write an open sentence to model a number story.
  [Patterns, Functions, and Algebra Goal 2]
- Evaluate numerical expressions using order of operations.
  [Patterns, Functions, and Algebra Goal 3]
- Use the precedence of multiplication and division over addition and subtraction.
  [Patterns, Functions, and Algebra Goal 3]

Key Activities

Students are introduced to the rules that govern the order in which operations are performed in an expression.

 Ongoing Assessment: Informing Instruction See page 564.

Key Vocabulary

order of operations

Materials

Math Journal 2, pp. 222 and 223
Study Link 7·4
Class Data Pad ◆ slate

2 Ongoing Learning & Practice

Practicing Renaming Fractions

Math Journal 2, p. 224
Students practice finding equivalent fractions in simplest form.

 Math Boxes 7·5

Math Journal 2, p. 225
Students practice and maintain skills through Math Box problems.

 Ongoing Assessment: Recognizing Student Achievement
Use Math Boxes, Problem 5.
[Number and Numeration Goal 6]

 Study Link 7·5

Math Masters, p. 200
Students practice and maintain skills through Study Link activities.

3 Differentiation Options

READINESS

Evaluating Expressions

Math Masters, p. 201
per partnership: 1 four-function calculator and 1 scientific calculator (optional)
Students explore the need to use rules for the order of operations.

ENRICHMENT

Discovering Exponent Patterns

Math Masters, p. 202
Students apply their understanding of order of operations by solving problems that involve exponents and operations.

Advance Preparation

For Part 1, copy the list of abbreviated rules for order of operations on *Teacher's Lesson Guide,* page 564 onto the Class Data Pad.

 Teacher's Reference Manual, **Grades 4–6** p. 102

Getting Started

Mental Math and Reflexes

Have students write each expression in standard notation on their slates. *Suggestions:*

○●○ 5^2 25   ○●○ 1^2 1   ●●● 2^4 16
　 5^1 5   　 1^{10} 1   　 3^4 81
　 2^3 8   　 10^4 10,000 10^5 100,000

Math Message

Solve the Math Message problems at the top of journal page 222.

Study Link 7·4 Follow-Up

Survey students for their answers to Problem 4. Record the number sentences on the board or Class Data Pad.

1 Teaching the Lesson

▶ Math Message Follow-Up

👥👥 **WHOLE-CLASS DISCUSSION**

(Math Journal 2, p. 222)

Discuss the story with the class. The discussion should include the following points:

▷ Robin asked her friends to solve $4 + 5 * 8$.

▷ Some of her friends solved $(4 + 5) * 8$ and got 72.

▷ The other friends solved $4 + (5 * 8)$ and got 44.

▷ When Robin explained what she wanted, her friends knew that the number model $4 + (5 * 8) = 44$ was right because it fit the situation.

▷ The expression $4 + 5 * 8$ caused confusion because it is ambiguous.

▶ Introducing the Rules for Order of Operations

👥👥 **WHOLE-CLASS ACTIVITY**

Ask: *How do parentheses help clarify ambiguous expressions?* Because operations inside parentheses are done first, the order for computation in an expression can be shown with the parentheses.

Explain that the use of parentheses is only one part of a set of rules that define in what order to do the computation when evaluating an expression. Refer students to the list of rules you prepared on the Class Data Pad.

Student Page

Date _____ Time _____

LESSON 7·5 Order of Operations

Math Message

Robin asked her friends to help figure out how much money she needed to go to the movies. She asked her friends, "How much is 4 plus 5 times 8?" Frances and Zac said, "72." Anne and Rick said, "44."

1. How did Frances and Zac get 72? $(4 + 5) * 8 = 72$

2. How did Anne and Rick get 44? $4 + (5 * 8) = 44$

Robin's friends could not agree on who was right. Finally, Robin said, "I need to buy one under-12 ticket for $4, and 5 adult tickets for $8." Then Robin's friends knew who was right.

3. Who do you think was right? Explain your answer. Anne and Rick.
   The five adult tickets cost $5 * 8$ dollars. The one
   under-12 ticket costs 4 dollars. The sum is $4 + (5 * 8)$.

Use the rules for order of operations to complete these number sentences.

4. $100 + 500 / 2 =$ ___350___   5. $24 / 6 + 3 * 2 =$ ___10___

6. $2 * 4^2 =$ ___32___   7. $25 - 10 + 5 * 2 + 100 / 20 =$ ___30___

8. $24 / 6 / 2 + 12 - 3 * 2 =$ ___8___

Insert parentheses in each of the following problems to get as many different answers as you can. The first one is done as an example.

9. $5 + 4 * 9 =$ ___$(5 + 4) * 9 = 81; 5 + (4 * 9) = 41$___

10. $4 * 3 + 10 =$ ___$(4 * 3) + 10 = 22; 4 * (3 + 10) = 52$___

11. $6 * 4 / 2 =$ ___$(6 * 4) / 2 = 12; 6 * (4 / 2) = 12$___

12. $10 - 6 - 4 =$ ___$(10 - 6) - 4 = 0; 10 - (6 - 4) = 8$___

Math Journal 2, p. 222

Rules for Order of Operations

1. **P**arentheses
2. **E**xponents
3. **M**ultiplication and **D**ivision
4. **A**ddition and **S**ubtraction

NOTE Even though this lesson introduces the conventional order of operations, which reduces the need for parentheses, *Everyday Mathematics* encourages you to continue to use parentheses generously when you write number sentences for students. *Everyday Mathematics* believes that students benefit from more explicit mathematical notation, such as inserting parentheses, even when they are not strictly required.

The **order of operations** eliminates ambiguity in number expressions by providing the steps used to evaluate them.

1. Do any operations inside **P**arentheses first. If there are nested parentheses, start with the innermost set of parentheses. To determine the order of operations inside parentheses, use Steps 2–4.

2. Calculate **E**xponents in order from left to right.

3. **M**ultiply and **D**ivide. Neither multiplication nor division has priority over the other; simply work from left to right.

4. **A**dd and **S**ubtract. Neither addition nor subtraction has priority over the other; simply work from left to right.

NOTE The mnemonic device **P**lease **E**xcuse **M**y **D**ear **A**unt **S**ally helps many students remember the order of operations. Present this device by showing its correspondence to the abbreviated rules on the Class Data Pad and the steps for the order of operations.

 Ongoing Assessment: Informing Instruction

Watch for students who have difficulty following the list of rules as they evaluate expressions. Have them underline the operations that should be carried out first. Students then carry out those operations and recopy the expression, substituting the answer for the underlined portion. Repeat in this fashion to evaluate each operation in a problem following the rules for order of operations.

Pose problems for students to solve on their slates using the rules for order of operations.

Suggestions:

Problem: $4 + 5 * 6 = ?$

There aren't any parentheses or exponents.

Start with Step 3. $4 + \underline{5 * 6} =$

Do Step 4 next. $4 + 30 = 34$

                        $4 + 5 * 6 = 34$

Problem: $3 * 10 / 5 + 18 / 3 = ?$

There aren't any parentheses or exponents.

Start with Step 3. $\underline{3 * 10} / 5 + 18 / 3 =$

                        $\underline{30 / 5} + 18 / 3 =$

                        $6 + \underline{18 / 3} =$

Do Step 4 next. $6 + 6 = 12$

                        $3 * 10 / 5 + 18 / 3 = 12$

Problem: $(4 + 5) * (2 + 3) - (10 * 2) = ?$

Start with Step 1. $(\underline{4 + 5}) * (\underline{2 + 3}) - (\underline{10 * 2}) =$

Do Step 3 next. $\underline{9 * 5} - 20 =$

Do Step 4 next. $45 - 20 = 25$

                        $(4 + 5) * (2 + 3) - (10 * 2) = 25$

Problem: $(5 + 5)^2 = ?$

Start with Step 1. $(\underline{5 + 5})^2 =$

Do Step 2 next. $10^2 = 100$

                        $(5 + 5)^2 = 100$

Problem: $5^2 * 3^2 = ?$

Start with Step 2. $\underline{5^2} * \underline{3^2} =$

Do Step 3 next. $25 * 9 = 225$

                        $5^2 * 3^2 = 225$

Problem: $10^2 + (3 * 8) - 14 * 2 = ?$

Start with Step 1. $10^2 + (\underline{3 * 8}) - 14 * 2 =$

Do Step 2 next. $\underline{10^2} + 24 - 14 * 2 =$

Do Step 3 next. $100 + 24 - \underline{14 * 2} =$

Do Step 4 next. $\underline{100 + 24} - 28 =$

                        $124 - 28 = 96$

                        $10^2 + (3 * 8) - 14 * 2 = 96$

Date   Time

LESSON 7·5   **Story Problems**

1. Draw a line to match each story with the expression that fits that story.

Story 1   **Number of Pencils in All**

Marlene and her friend Kadeem each have $(2 * 8) + 4$
eight pencils. They buy four more pencils.

Story 2

Marlene buys 2 eight-packs of pencils. $2 * (8 + 4)$
Four free pencils come with each pack.

Write an open number sentence using parentheses to show the order of operations. Then solve.

2. LaWanda and two classmates decide to do research on horses. They find four books in the classroom and five books at the library that will help them. They divide the books equally so they can take the books home to read. How many books does each student take home?

Open number sentence: $(4 + 5) \div 3 = b$

Solution: $b = 3$

3. Coach Ewing has 32 snack bars. She divides them equally among the 16 members of the debate team. The team members share half of their snack bars with the opposing team. How many snack bars does each team member end up eating?

Open number sentence: $32 / 16 / 2 = s$

Solution: $s = 1$

4. $\underline{55} = 15 + 10 * 4$

5. $10 - 4 / 2 * 3 = \underline{4}$

6. $\underline{13} = 14 - 7 + 5 + 1$

7. $\underline{28} = (18 - 11) * 3 + 7$

8. $9.5 * 2 / 0.5 + 45 / 5 = \underline{47}$

Math Journal 2, p. 223

Date   Time

LESSON 7·5   **Fractions in Simplest Form**

A fraction is in **simplest form** if no other equivalent fraction can be found by dividing the numerator and the denominator by a whole number that is greater than 1. Another way to say this is that if the numerator and denominator do not have a common whole number factor greater than 1, then the fraction is in simplest form.

Every fraction is either in simplest form or is equivalent to a fraction in simplest form. A mixed number is in simplest form if its fractional part is in simplest form.

Example: $\frac{63}{108} = \frac{21}{36} = \frac{7}{12}$

The numerator 7 and the denominator 12 do not have a common whole number factor greater than 1, so $\frac{7}{12}$ is in simplest form.

1. a. Name the fraction for the shaded part of each circle.

 $\frac{1}{2}$ $\frac{3}{6}$ $\frac{4}{8}$

   b. Which fraction is in simplest form? $\frac{1}{2}$

Name each fraction in simplest form.

2. $\frac{20}{30}$ $\frac{2}{3}$ 3. $\frac{7}{28}$ $\frac{1}{4}$ 4. $\frac{76}{8}$ $\frac{19}{2}$

Write each mixed number as a fraction.

5. $4\frac{2}{5}$ $\frac{22}{5}$ 6. $9\frac{3}{8}$ $\frac{75}{8}$ 7. $20\frac{2}{3}$ $\frac{62}{3}$

Write each fraction as a mixed number.

8. $\frac{16}{7}$ $2\frac{2}{7}$ 9. $\frac{17}{3}$ $5\frac{2}{3}$ 10. $\frac{29}{4}$ $7\frac{1}{4}$

Name each mixed number in simplest form.

11. $7\frac{10}{12}$ $7\frac{5}{6}$ 12. $3\frac{8}{32}$ $3\frac{1}{4}$ 13. $1\frac{9}{5}$ $2\frac{4}{5}$

Math Journal 2, p. 224

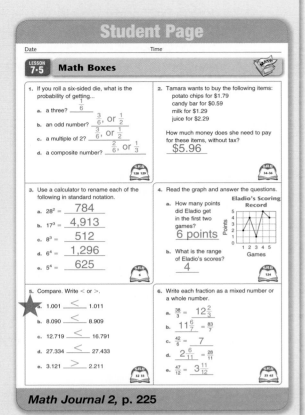

Math Journal 2, p. 225

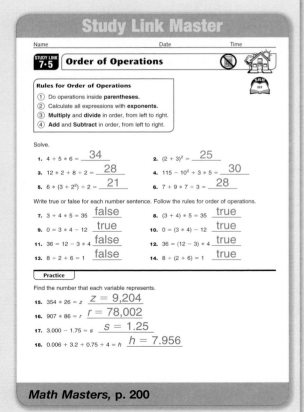

Math Masters, p. 200

▶ **Evaluating Expressions by Applying the Rules for Order of Operations** **PARTNER ACTIVITY**

(Math Journal 2, pp. 222 and 223)

Algebraic Thinking Assign journal pages 222 and 223. Circulate and assist.

When most students have finished the pages, discuss their solution strategies. Include questions like the following:

● Which operations did you do first for Problems 4–8 on journal page 222?

● How did you choose which expression matched the number stories in Problem 1 on journal page 223?

● Which operations did you do last for Problems 6 and 8 on journal page 223?

2 Ongoing Learning & Practice

▶ **Practicing Renaming Fractions**  **INDEPENDENT ACTIVITY**

(Math Journal 2, p. 224)

Students practice finding equivalent fractions in simplest form. They practice naming mixed numbers as fractions and fractions as mixed numbers.

▶ **Math Boxes 7·5**  **INDEPENDENT ACTIVITY**

(Math Journal 2, p. 225)

 Mixed Practice Math Boxes in this lesson are paired with Math Boxes in Lesson 7-8. The skill in Problem 6 previews Unit 8 content.

 Ongoing Assessment: Recognizing Student Achievement **Math Boxes Problem 5**

Use **Math Boxes, Problem 5** to assess students' ability to compare decimals. Students are making adequate progress if they choose the correct relation symbol for each number sentence.

[Number and Numeration Goal 6]

▶ **Study Link 7·5**  **INDEPENDENT ACTIVITY**

(Math Masters, p. 200)

 Home Connection Students use the rules for order of operations to solve number sentences.

③ Differentiation Options

READINESS

▶ **Evaluating Expressions**

(*Math Masters,* p. 201)

SMALL-GROUP ACTIVITY

15–30 Min

To explore order of operations rules, have students compare how four-function and scientific calculators evaluate expressions. If both types of calculators are available to your class, have students enter the key sequences and use the displays on their calculators for Problem 3.

ENRICHMENT

▶ **Discovering Exponent Patterns**

(*Math Masters,* p. 202)

PARTNER ACTIVITY

15–30 Min

To apply students' understanding of order of operations, have them solve problems that involve exponents and operations. They evaluate the patterns in multiplication and division problems. When students have completed the page, have them compare and discuss their answers.

Teaching Master

Name   Date   Time

LESSON 7·5   Evaluating Expressions

Janet and Alisha are using their calculators to evaluate expressions. Janet has a four-function calculator, and Alisha has a scientific calculator. They both enter the same key sequence, but their calculator displays are different.

1. Study the key sequence and calculator displays below.

Key Sequence	Janet's Display	Alisha's Display
③ ➕ ⑤ ✕ ② ➖	16	13

2. Decide the order that each calculator used to perform the operations. Use parentheses to write a number sentence that models each order.

   a. Number model for Janet's calculator: $(3 + 5) * 2 = 16$

   b. Number model for Alisha's calculator: $3 + (5 * 2) = 13$

3. Use your number models in Problem 2 to evaluate the following key sequence. Then complete the table for each calculator.

Key Sequence	Janet's Display	Alisha's Display
⑤ ✕ ③ ➕ ⑦ ➖ ⑧ ➗ ② ➖	7	18

Try This

4. Write number models that show what each calculator did in Problem 3.

   a. Number model for Janet's calculator: $(5 * 3 + 7 - 8) \div 2 = 7$

   b. Number model for Alisha's calculator: $(5 * 3) + 7 - (8 \div 2) = 18$

Math Masters, p. 201

Teaching Master

Name   Date   Time

LESSON 7·5   Discovering Exponent Patterns

Look for a pattern in the number sentences below. Then use the pattern to solve Problems 1–3.

$$7^2 * 7^3 = 7^5$$
$$12^7 * 12^3 = 12^{10}$$
$$34^6 * 34^6 = 34^{12}$$

1. $2^2 * 2^3 =$ 2^5

   Explain how you can prove your answer to Problem 1 is correct.
   I can write the numbers in standard notation and multiply the expression. If the product is the same as my answer in standard notation, then my answer in exponential notation is correct.

2. $5^5 * 5^7 =$ 5^{12} 3. $94^8 * 94^2 =$ 94^{10}

   Describe the pattern you are using to solve the problems.
   I am adding the exponents and leaving the base the same.

4. Circle the problem below for which the pattern does *not* work.

   $(28^5 * 5^3)$ $14^8 * 14^9$ $22^5 * 22^2$

Try This

5. What do you think happens when two numbers with the same base are divided?
   Sample answer: Multiplication and addition are related operations; so are division and subtraction. If you're dividing numbers with the same base, then you subtract the exponents.

6. Solve this problem to check your prediction.
   $2^5 / 2^3 =$ 2^2

Math Masters, p. 202

7·6 American Tour: Line Graphs

 Objective To introduce the construction of line graphs.

Technology Resources www.everydaymathonline.com

| ePresentations | eToolkit | Algorithms Practice | EM Facts Workshop Game™ | Family Letters | Assessment Management | Common Core State Standards | Curriculum Focal Points | Interactive Teacher's Lesson Guide |

1 Teaching the Lesson

Key Concepts and Skills

• Use given data to create line graphs.
[Data and Chance Goal 1]

• Use line graph data to answer questions.
[Data and Chance Goal 2]

Key Activities

Students compare data in the American Tour by constructing and analyzing a line graph.

Ongoing Assessment: Recognizing Student Achievement Use Mental Math and Reflexes.
[Operations and Computation Goal 4]

Ongoing Assessment: Informing Instruction See page 570.

Key Vocabulary

axis ◆ Venn diagram ◆ line graph ◆ trend

Materials

Math Journal 2, pp. 226 and 227
Student Reference Book, pp. 124 and 365
Study Link 7·5

2 Ongoing Learning & Practice

Math Boxes 7·6
Math Journal 2, p. 228
Students practice and maintain skills through Math Box problems.

Study Link 7·6
Math Masters, p. 203
Students practice and maintain skills through Study Link activities.

3 Differentiation Options

READINESS

Collecting Line Graphs

Math Masters, p. 204
newspapers and magazines
Students analyze line graphs from newspapers or magazines.

EXTRA PRACTICE

Graphing Sets of Data on a Line Graph

Math Masters, p. 205
Students make a line graph using data sets of high and low average temperatures.

Advance Preparation

For the optional Readiness activity in Part 3, you will need newspapers and magazines that contain line graphs.

 Teacher's Reference Manual, **Grades 4–6** pp. 161–169

Getting Started

Mental Math and Reflexes

Students write and solve dictated fraction addition and subtraction problems.
Encourage students to write their solutions in simplest form. *Suggestions:*

●○○ $\frac{3}{12} + \frac{3}{12} = \frac{6}{12}$, or $\frac{1}{2}$ ●●○ $\frac{6}{5} - \frac{4}{40} = \frac{44}{40}$, or $1\frac{1}{10}$ ●●● $\frac{14}{8} + \frac{1}{2} - \frac{3}{4} = \frac{6}{4}$, or $1\frac{1}{2}$

$\frac{36}{9} - \frac{18}{9} = \frac{18}{9}$, or 2 $\frac{12}{3} + \frac{3}{9} = \frac{13}{3}$, or $4\frac{1}{3}$ $9\frac{2}{7} - 4\frac{6}{14} = 4\frac{12}{14}$, or $4\frac{6}{7}$

$\frac{14}{4} + \frac{6}{4} + \frac{5}{4} = \frac{25}{4}$, or $6\frac{1}{2}$ $\frac{3}{2} - \frac{3}{12} = \frac{5}{4}$, or $1\frac{1}{2}$ $1\frac{6}{8} + 3\frac{7}{5} = 4\frac{86}{40}$, or $4\frac{43}{20}$, or $6\frac{3}{20}$

Math Message

List two methods that
can be used to organize
collected data.

Study Link 7·5 Follow-Up

Students compare answers
and resolve differences. Ask
volunteers to write the number
sentences they identified as
false on the board and insert
parentheses to make the sentences
true. $(3 + 4) * 5 = 35$; $36 = (12 - 3) * 4$; and $8 \div (2 + 6) = 1$

 Ongoing Assessment:
Recognizing Student Achievement

Mental Math and Reflexes ★

Use the **Mental Math and Reflexes problems** to assess students' ability to
add and subtract fractions with like and unlike denominators. Students are
making adequate progress if they correctly answer the ●○○ and ●●○
problems.

[Operations and Computation Goal 4]

---

1 Teaching the Lesson

▶ Math Message Follow-Up

Ask students to describe the methods they listed for organizing
collected data. Most students will identify line plots, tally charts,
stem-and-leaf plots, and/or tables as ways to organize data. Ask:
What is the advantage to organizing data? Organizing data makes
the data easier to understand.

Explain that once data has been collected and organized, it can be
displayed in ways that show comparisons between the data. Ask
volunteers to name ways that organized data can be displayed.
Bar graphs, circle graphs, and line graphs Then ask students to
describe the similarities and differences between bar graphs and
circle graphs. Expect responses such as the following:

Bar graphs and circle graphs

▷ are used to display data   ▷ show individual values

▷ have titles and data labels   ▷ show comparisons

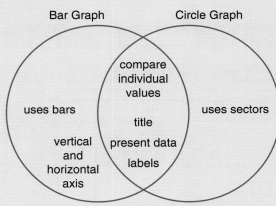

Venn diagram to compare graphs

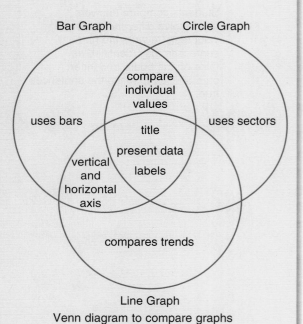

Bar Graph   Circle Graph

compare individual values

uses bars   title   uses sectors

present data

vertical and horizontal axis   labels

compares trends

Line Graph
Venn diagram to compare graphs

Bar graphs

▷ use bars to show data values

▷ use a vertical and horizontal **axis** to display data

Circle graphs

▷ use sectors to show data values

Draw a **Venn diagram** on the Class Data Pad to summarize the comparisons. (*See margin on page 569.*) Remind students that the information within the overlapping circles represents elements that are similar, while the separate areas represent elements that refer only to an individual graph.

▶ **Comparing Graphs** 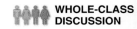 WHOLE-CLASS DISCUSSION

(*Student Reference Book*, p. 124)

Refer students to page 124 in the *Student Reference Book*. Ask students to use the information from the page to identify and discuss the similarities and differences between bar graphs, circle graphs, and **line graphs.** Point out that bar graphs, circle graphs, and line graphs all display information in a way that makes it easy to show comparisons. However, line graphs are different because they can show trends. A **trend** is how something has changed over a period of time.

Add a third circle to the Venn diagram on the Class Data Pad to show the line graph elements, and use the diagram to summarize the discussion. (*See margin.*)

▶ **Making Line Graphs**  INDEPENDENT ACTIVITY

(*Math Journal 2*, p. 226)

Read the introduction and discuss the example on journal page 226 as a class. Have students complete journal page 226. Circulate and assist.

When most students have completed the page, discuss how they chose the labels and scales for their graphs. Point out that although the graph does show the change in the number of books borrowed for the five days, this is not enough data to identify the change as a trend.

 Ongoing Assessment: Informing Instruction

Watch for students who do not use equal intervals on the vertical scale. Show them how they might use the minimum from the data set to decide on the scale increments. For example, if the minimum is 10, count by 10, or a factor of 10 to establish the scale and label the axis accordingly.

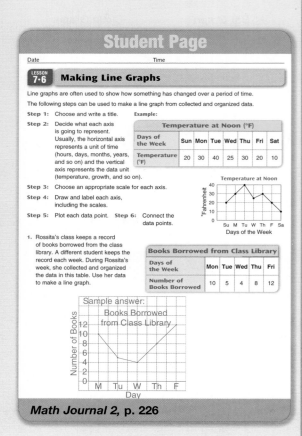

Student Page

Date   Time

LESSON 7·6   **Making Line Graphs**

Line graphs are often used to show how something has changed over a period of time.

The following steps can be used to make a line graph from collected and organized data.

Step 1: Choose and write a title.

Step 2: Decide what each axis is going to represent. Usually, the horizontal axis represents a unit of time (hours, days, months, years, and so on) and the vertical axis represents the data unit (temperature, growth, and so on).

Step 3: Choose an appropriate scale for each axis.

Step 4: Draw and label each axis, including the scales.

Step 5: Plot each data point. Step 6: Connect the data points.

Example:

Temperature at Noon (°F)

Days of the Week	Sun	Mon	Tue	Wed	Thu	Fri	Sat
Temperature (°F)	20	30	40	25	30	20	10

1. Rossita's class keeps a record of books borrowed from the class library. A different student keeps the record each week. During Rossita's week, she collected and organized the data in this table. Use her data to make a line graph.

Books Borrowed from Class Library

Days of the Week	Mon	Tue	Wed	Thu	Fri
Number of Books Borrowed	10	5	4	8	12

Sample answer:

Math Journal 2, p. 226

American Tour: Comparing Data on Line Graphs

(Math Journal 2, p. 227; Student Reference Book, p. 365)

PARTNER ACTIVITY

Line graphs can also be used to compare two or more sets of data. Refer students to the graph on *Student Reference Book,* page 365, and discuss Problems 1–5 on the journal page. Then have students complete the page.

2 Ongoing Learning & Practice

Math Boxes 7·6

(Math Journal 2, p. 228)

Mixed Practice Math Boxes in this lesson are paired with Math Boxes in Lessons 7-2 and 7-4. The skill in Problem 4 previews Unit 8 content.

Writing/Reasoning Have students write a response to the following: *Explain how to use your Geometry Template to draw the angle in Problem 3.* First, draw a straight line. Align the center of the protractor with the end of the line, keeping the line flush with the bottom of the protractor. Then tick the 170° mark, and connect the end of the line to the tick mark.

Study Link 7·6

INDEPENDENT ACTIVITY

(Math Masters, p. 203)

Home Connection Students make a line graph for the estimated percent of households with television sets from 1940 to 2000. They compare this data with a line graph of movie ticket sales over the same period.

3 Differentiation Options

READINESS

PARTNER ACTIVITY

Collecting Line Graphs

30+ Min

(Math Masters, p. 204)

To provide experience with line graphs, have students locate line graphs in the newspapers or magazines you collected. They analyze the graphs to complete *Math Masters,* page 204.

Student Page

Date   Time

LESSON 7·6   **Investigating Data in the American Tour**

Line graphs can be used to make comparisons of two or more sets of data. Use the graph on page 365 of the *Student Reference Book* to answer the following questions.

1. What is the title of the graph?
   Years of Life Expected at Birth 1900–2010

2. What information is given on the horizontal axis?
   Year the data was collected

3. What information is given on the vertical axis?
   Years of Life Expected at Birth

4. What two sets of data are being compared on the graph?
   The changes in the years of life expected at birth for females compared to males over the last 100 years

5. What was the life expectancy of a female born in 1940?
   About 66 years

6. Use the information in the graph to write two true statements about life expectancy.
   Sample answer: Life expectancy for males and females has increased during the last century. Females continue to live longer than males.

7. True or false? A man born in 1950 will live until the year 2015, when he will be 65 years old. Explain.
   Sample answer: The graph presents averages, meaning that some men will die younger and that some will live longer than the average of 65 years. Therefore, it is impossible to tell exactly how long an individual will live.

Math Journal 2, p. 227

NOTE Remind students that a double bar graph is another display that can be used to compare two or more sets of data.

Student Page

Date   Time

LESSON 7·6   **Math Boxes**

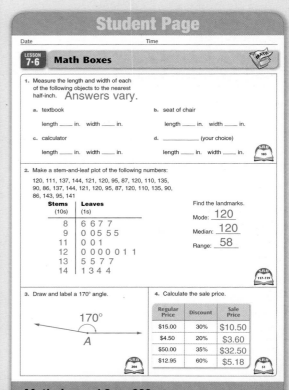

1. Measure the length and width of each of the following objects to the nearest half-inch. **Answers vary.**

   a. textbook   b. seat of chair
   length ____ in. width ____ in.   length ____ in. width ____ in.

   c. calculator   d. _____ (your choice)
   length ____ in. width ____ in.   length ____ in. width ____ in.

2. Make a stem-and-leaf plot of the following numbers:
   120, 111, 137, 144, 121, 120, 95, 87, 120, 110, 135, 90, 86, 137, 144, 121, 120, 95, 87, 120, 110, 135, 90, 86, 143, 95, 141

Stems (10s)	Leaves (1s)
8	6 6 7 7
9	0 0 5 5 5
11	0 0 1
12	0 0 0 0 1 1
13	5 5 7 7
14	1 3 4 4

   Find the landmarks.
   Mode: 120
   Median: 120
   Range: 58

3. Draw and label a 170° angle.

   170°
   A

4. Calculate the sale price.

Regular Price	Discount	Sale Price
$15.00	30%	$10.50
$4.50	20%	$3.60
$50.00	35%	$32.50
$12.95	60%	$5.18

Math Journal 2, p. 228

Name _____ Date _____ Time _____

STUDY LINK 7·6 | **Making Line Graphs**

Bar graphs, circle graphs, and line graphs display information in a way that makes it easy to show comparisons, but line graphs can also show trends.

1. Use the information in the line graph to write two true statements about movie ticket sales.

   Sales were at their highest in 1930. Sales dropped by 60 million from 1940 to 1970.

Average Number of Movie Tickets Sold per Week (in Millions), 1922–2000

Total Population	
1930	123 million
1960	151 million
2000	281 million

2. The table data lists the estimated percent of households with television sets from 1940 to 2000. Plot the data on the line graph below.

Estimated Percent of Households with Television Sets, 1940–2000

Year	1940	1950	1960	1970	1980	1990	2000
Percentage	0%	12%	88%	96%	98%	98%	98%

Estimated Percent of Households with Television Sets, 1940–2000

3. Compare the information in the line graphs from Problems 1 and 2. What relationships do you see?

   Before TV sets were common, more people went to the movies.

Math Masters, p. 203

Have partners answer and discuss each other's written questions for the graphs. Add the graphs and completed *Math Masters* pages to the American Tour section of your classroom.

EXTRA PRACTICE

PARTNER ACTIVITY

5–15 Min

▶ Graphing Sets of Data on a Line Graph

(*Math Masters,* p. 205)

Students make a line graph using data sets of high and low average temperatures. Consider having students make a display version of their graphs for the American Tour section of your classroom.

Name _____ Date _____ Time _____

LESSON 7·6 | **Looking at Line Graphs**

Look closely at the graph you have. List each of the following features for your graph. If any of the features are missing from your graph, make up one that is appropriate. **Answers vary.**

1. Title of the graph: _____

2. Label for the horizontal axis: _____

3. Label for the vertical axis: _____

4. Range of the data: _____

5. Write three questions that can be answered by looking at your graph.

   _____
   _____
   _____
   _____

6. Line graphs are often used to show trends—how things change over time. If your graph shows a trend, describe what it shows. If not, explain what you think the graph tells you.

   _____
   _____
   _____
   _____
   _____
   _____

Math Masters, p. 204

Name _____ Date _____ Time _____

LESSON 7·6 | **Graphing Sets of Data on a Line Graph**

The following table shows the average high and low temperatures (°F) of a city in the Midwest United States.

Average Temperatures (°F)

Month	Jan	Feb	Mar	Apr	May	Jun	Jul	Aug	Sep	Oct	Nov	Dec
High	33	36	46	59	72	80	85	82	75	62	49	38
Low	20	22	29	39	51	60	65	64	56	45	36	25

Make a line graph for this data using the grid below. Use a different colored pencil to connect the points for each data set.

1. Choose and write a title for the graph.

2. Label each axis.

3. Plot all the points for the high temperatures. Connect the data points. Write the words *High Temperature* above the line formed.

4. Plot all the points for the low temperatures. Connect the data points. Write the words *Low Temperature* under the line formed.

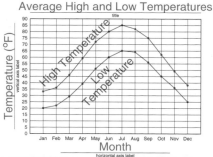

Average High and Low Temperatures

Math Masters, p. 205

7·7 Using Negative Numbers

Objective To review the uses, ordering, and comparing of negative numbers.

Technology Resources www.everydaymathonline.com

| ePresentations | eToolkit | Algorithms Practice | EM Facts Workshop Game™ | Family Letters | Assessment Management | Common Core State Standards | Curriculum Focal Points | Interactive Teacher's Lesson Guide |

① Teaching the Lesson

Key Concepts and Skills

- Compare and order signed whole numbers, fractions, and decimals.
  [Number and Numeration Goal 6]
- Plot signed numbers on a number line.
  [Measurement and Reference Frames Goal 4]

Key Activities

Students review situations in which negative numbers may occur. They use a number line to graph, compare, and order positive and negative numbers.

Key Vocabulary

negative number

Materials

Math Journal 2, pp. 229 and 230
Student Reference Book, p. 91
Study Link 7·6
Class Data Pad (optional) ◆ slate

② Ongoing Learning & Practice

Playing *Name That Number*

Student Reference Book, p. 325
Math Masters, p. 490
per partnership: 1 complete deck of number cards (from the Everything Math Deck, if available)
Students practice applying number properties, equivalent names, arithmetic operations, and basic facts.

Ongoing Assessment:
Recognizing Student Achievement
Use the Record Sheet (*Math Masters,* page 490).
[Patterns, Functions, and Algebra Goal 3]

Math Boxes 7·7

Math Journal 2, p. 231
Students practice and maintain skills through Math Box problems.

Study Link 7·7

Math Masters, p. 206
Students practice and maintain skills through Study Link activities.

③ Differentiation Options

READINESS

Skip-Counting with Negative Numbers

Student Reference Book, pp. 285 and 286
calculator
Students skip-count backward on a calculator to review negative numbers.

ENRICHMENT

Exploring Positive and Negative Numbers in Price Changes

Math Masters, p. 207
Students apply their understanding of negative numbers to fraction-of problems.

EXTRA PRACTICE

5-Minute Math

5-Minute Math™, p. 175
Students practice using negative numbers.

Advance Preparation

For Part 1, draw a number line from −8 to 8 on the board or Class Data Pad. Students will also use your classroom number line. For Part 2, copy and cut apart *Math Masters,* page 490. Allow one half-sheet of paper per student.

 ***Teacher's Reference Manual,* Grades 4–6** pp. 71–74, 85–87, 246–248

Getting Started

Mental Math and Reflexes

Have students convert scientific notation to standard notation. Then ask students to explain the patterns they observe in the number of zeros as well as the placement of the decimal point in the product when multiplying numbers by powers of 10. *Suggestions:*

●○○ $4 * 10^2$ 400
$7 * 10^2$ 700
$8 * 10^2$ 800

●●○ $5 * 10^4$ 50,000
$9 * 10^6$ 9,000,000
$7 * 10^5$ 700,000

●●● $3.2 * 10^3$ 3,200
$6.4 * 10^6$ 6,400,000
$1.02 * 10^8$ 102,000,000

Math Message

Complete Problem 1 on journal page 229.

Study Link 7·6 Follow-Up

Discuss students' answers for Problems 2 and 3.

NOTE Avoid using the term *minus* when referring to negative numbers. Reading −10 as "minus ten" may cause students to confuse a number (−10) with an operation (subtracting 10). When naming a negative number, such as −10, say "negative ten" or "the opposite of ten."

Student Page

Date _____ Time _____

LESSON 7·7 Positive and Negative Numbers on a Number Line

Math Message

1. Plot each of the following bicycle race events on the number line below. Label each event with its letter. (*Hint:* Zero on the number line stands for the starting time of the race.)

A Check in 5 minutes before the race starts.
B Change gears 30 seconds after the race starts.
C Get on the bicycle 30 seconds before the race starts.
D The winner finishes at 6 minutes, 45 seconds.
E Complete the first lap 3 minutes, 15 seconds after the race starts.
F Check the tires 7 minutes before the race starts.

F   A   C B   E   D
−8 −7 −6 −5 −4 −3 −2 −1 0 1 2 3 4 5 6 7 8
                    minutes

2. Mr. Pima's class planned a raffle. Five students were asked to sell raffle tickets. The goal for each student was $50 in ticket sales. The table below shows how well each of the five students did. Complete the table. Then plot the amounts from the last column on the number line below the table. Label each amount with that student's letter.

Student	Ticket Sales	Amount That Ticket Sales Were Above or Below Goal
A	$5.50 short of goal	−$5.50
B	Met goal exactly	$0
C	Exceeded goal by $1.75	+$1.75
D	Sold $41.75	−$8.25
E	Sold $53.25	+$3.25

   D   A   B C E
−10 −9 −8 −7 −6 −5 −4 −3 −2 −1 0 1 2 3 4 5 6 7 8 9 10
              $ sales above or below goal

Math Journal 2, p. 229

---

1 Teaching the Lesson

▶ Math Message Follow-Up

WHOLE-CLASS DISCUSSION

(*Math Journal 2,* p. 229; *Student Reference Book,* p. 91)

Ask volunteers to plot and label the events from Problem 1 on your prepared number line. Ask: *What is the unit for the plotted points?* minutes Write *minutes* under the number line. Verify that students understand that 0 represents the race's start time. Discuss the meaning of the positive and **negative number** for each event. Ask students why *minutes* might be shown as negative or positive. Negative numbers refer to times before the race begins, and positive numbers refer to times after the race begins.

As a class, discuss the examples of real-world situations that have 0 as a starting point on page 91 in the *Student Reference Book.* Ask volunteers to describe experiences from their own lives that use negative-, positive-, or zero-number vocabulary. Highlight the following points:

▷ The common meaning of the word *negative*, that is, *disagreeable*, does not apply to negative numbers.

▷ The meanings of *negative, positive,* and *zero* depend on the given situation or context. In some cases, these numbers describe situations in relation to a reference point, like the instant of a rocket blast-off, a temperature of zero degrees, or sea level. Positive and negative numbers can be used to measure seconds before and after blast-off, degrees above and below zero, and elevations above and below sea level. Positive and negative numbers may also describe increases and decreases, such as a win or loss in a football game, or a gain or loss in weight.

▶ Graphing Positive and Negative Numbers on a Number Line

PARTNER ACTIVITY

PROBLEM SOLVING

(*Math Journal 2*, p. 229)

Ask students to complete journal page 229.

In the remaining problem, students will calculate the amount by which sales differed from the goal. Then they graph amounts above or below $50, using positive numbers for sales exceeding the goal and negative numbers for sales below the goal.

▶ Comparing and Ordering Positive and Negative Numbers

PARTNER ACTIVITY

(*Math Journal 2*, p. 230)

Before students begin to work on journal page 230, remind them how to use a number line to compare numbers. For any two numbers on a number line, the number on the right (or farther up if the number line is vertical) is the greater of the two numbers. Briefly review the *greater than* (>) and *less than* (<) symbols.

⬆⬇ Adjusting the Activity   ELL

To help students remember the meaning of the < and > symbols, you might draw two dots by the greater number and one dot by the lesser one; then connect the dots.
Example: 6 < 8

AUDITORY ◆ KINESTHETIC ◆ TACTILE ◆ VISUAL

---

② Ongoing Learning & Practice

▶ Playing *Name That Number*

PARTNER ACTIVITY

(*Student Reference Book*, p. 325; *Math Masters*, p. 490)

Students practice applying number properties, writing equivalent names, choosing arithmetic operations, and computing basic facts by playing *Name That Number.*

✓ Ongoing Assessment: Recognizing Student Achievement

Math Masters
Page 490 ★

Portfolio Ideas

Use the **Record Sheet** for *Name That Number* (*Math Masters,* page 490) to assess students' facility with problem-solving skills and their understanding of order of operations. Students are making adequate progress if their number sentences demonstrate accuracy and flexibility.

[Patterns, Functions, and Algebra Goal 3]

Date _____ Time _____

LESSON 7·7   Comparing and Ordering Numbers

For any pair of numbers on the number line, the number to the left is less than the number to the right.

–10 is less than –5 because –10 is to the left of –5.
We use the < (less than) symbol to write –10 < –5.

+10 is greater than +5 because +10 is to the right of +5.
We use the > (greater than) symbol to write +10 > +5.

Reminder: When writing the > or < symbol, be sure the arrow tip points to the smaller number.

Write < or >.

1. –5 $<$ 5   2. 10 $>$ –10   3. –10 $<$ 0

4. 14 $>$ 7   5. –14 $<$ –7   6. 0 $>$ $-6\frac{1}{2}$

Answer the following.

7. What is the value of π to two decimal places? __3.14__

8. –π = __–3.14__

List the numbers in order from least to greatest.

9. –10, 14, –100, $\frac{8}{2}$, –17, 0 __–100, –17, –10, 0, $\frac{8}{2}$, 14__

10. –0.5, 0, –4, –π, –4.5 __–4.5, –4, –π, –0.5, 0__

Answer the following. Sample answers:

11. Name four positive numbers less than π. __1, 0.2, 2, 0.5__

12. Name four negative numbers greater than –π. __–1, –0.2, –2, –1.5__

Math Journal 2, p. 230

NOTE You may want to pose questions about the *Associative Property of Addition or Multiplication,* such as: *When three numbers are added together to name the target number, does it make a difference in which order you add them?* no *Does the order make a difference if you are multiplying?* no Ask students to give examples to defend their thinking.

Name _____ Date _____ Time _____

Name That Number Record Sheet

Round 1

Target number: _____ My cards: ____ ____ ____ ____ ____

My best solution (number model): _____

Number of cards used: _____

Round 2

Target number: _____ My cards: ____ ____ ____ ____ ____

My best solution (number model): _____

Number of cards used: _____

Math Masters, page 490

Student Page

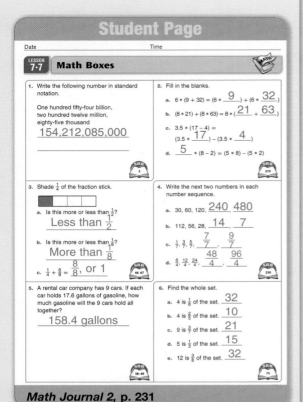

Math Journal 2, p. 231

Study Link Master

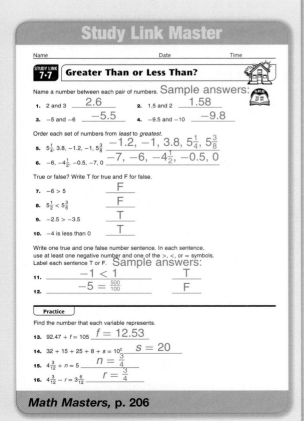

Math Masters, p. 206

▶ **Math Boxes 7·7** INDEPENDENT ACTIVITY

(*Math Journal 2*, p. 231)

Mixed Practice Math Boxes in this lesson are paired with Math Boxes in Lesson 7-10. The skill in Problem 6 previews Unit 8 content.

Writing/Reasoning Have students write a response to the following: *Explain how you identified the missing numbers in Problem 4a.* Sample answer: Each of the first 3 numbers in the sequence is double the previous number, so I applied the rule of ∗ 2 to find the remaining numbers.

▶ **Study Link 7·7** INDEPENDENT ACTIVITY

(*Math Masters*, p. 206)

Home Connection Students practice comparing and ordering positive and negative numbers.

③ Differentiation Options

READINESS SMALL-GROUP ACTIVITY
5–15 Min

▶ **Skip-Counting with Negative Numbers**

(*Student Reference Book*, pp. 285 and 286)

To provide experience with negative numbers using a concrete model, have students use a calculator to skip-count back from a positive whole number into the negative numbers. Have students record each display during the count on a half-sheet of paper. *Suggestions:*

▷ Start at 12. Count back by 2s to −12.

▷ Start at 20. Count back by 4s to −20.

▷ Start at 25. Count back by 5s to −25.

▷ Start at 27. Count back by 3s to −27.

When students have performed several counts, have them discuss any patterns that they notice. Sample answer: For each positive number you land on, you will also land on its opposite (when the number you count back by is a factor of the start number).

ENRICHMENT

Exploring Positive and Negative Numbers in Price Changes

(*Math Masters*, p. 207)

PARTNER ACTIVITY
15–30 Min

To apply students' understanding of negative numbers to fraction-of problems, have them complete *Math Masters*, page 207. Students calculate the dollar amounts for increases or decreases in the price of goods and the resulting new prices.

EXTRA PRACTICE

5-Minute Math

SMALL-GROUP ACTIVITY
5–15 Min

To offer students more experience using negative numbers, see *5-Minute Math*, page 175.

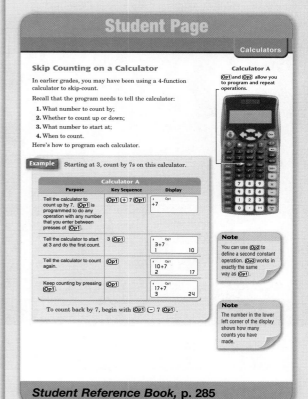

Skip Counting on a Calculator

In earlier grades, you may have been using a 4-function calculator to skip-count.

Recall that the program needs to tell the calculator:
1. What number to count by;
2. Whether to count up or down;
3. What number to start at;
4. When to count.

Here's how to program each calculator.

Calculator A
[Op1] and [Op2] allow you to program and repeat operations.

Example Starting at 3, count by 7s on this calculator.

Purpose	Key Sequence	Display
Tell the calculator to count up by 7. [Op1] is programmed to do any operation with any number that you enter between presses of [Op1].	[Op1] [+] 7 [Op1]	Op1 +7
Tell the calculator to start at 3 and do the first count.	3 [Op1]	Op1 3+7 1 10
Tell the calculator to count again.	[Op1]	Op1 10+7 2 17
Keep counting by pressing [Op1].	[Op1]	Op1 17+7 3 24

To count back by 7, begin with [Op1] [−] 7 [Op1].

Note
You can use [Op2] to define a second constant operation. [Op2] works in exactly the same way as [Op1].

Note
The number in the lower left corner of the display shows how many counts you have made.

Student Reference Book, p. 285

Name   Date   Time

LESSON 7·7   Change in Price

A local store is changing the price of some popular items. Listed below are the items with the new changes. Complete the table.

Item	Original Price	Change in Price (Fraction)	Change in Price (Dollars)	Price After Change
Gloves	$5.00	$-\frac{1}{5}$	−$1.00	$4.00
Hats	$7.50	$-\frac{1}{10}$	−$0.75	$6.75
Belts	$10.00	$+\frac{1}{4}$	+$2.50	$12.50
Socks	$1.50	$+\frac{1}{2}$	+$0.75	$2.25
Pants	$12.00	$-\frac{1}{20}$	−$0.60	$11.40
Shirts	$8.50	$+\frac{3}{10}$	+$2.55	$11.05

1. Which item has the largest price increase? __shirts__

2. Which item has the largest price decrease? __gloves__

3. Which item has a 20% change? __gloves__

4. If you were to purchase a hat and belt after the price change, would you pay more or less than the original price? __more__

   How much more or less? __$1.75__

5. If you purchased one each of the items before the price changes and one of each item after the price changes, what would be the total change in cost? State your answer as a positive or negative number. Explain your solution.

   The total change in cost would be +$3.45. The total of the original prices was $44.50. After the price change, the total cost was $47.95. $47.95 is greater than $44.50, so the total cost increased, making the change a positive number.

Math Masters, p. 207

7·8 Addition of Positive and Negative Numbers

 **Objective** To develop rules for adding positive and negative numbers.

Technology Resources www.everydaymathonline.com

 ePresentations
 eToolkit
 Algorithms Practice
 EM Facts Workshop Game™
 Family Letters
 Assessment Management
 Common Core State Standards
 Curriculum Focal Points
 Interactive Teacher's Lesson Guide

---

1 Teaching the Lesson

Key Concepts and Skills

- Model sums of positive and negative numbers with manipulatives.
  [Operations and Computation Goal 1]

- Use signed number addition patterns to describe rules for adding signed numbers.
  [Patterns, Functions, and Algebra Goal 1]

- Recognize the additive inverse.
  [Patterns, Functions, and Algebra Goal 4]

Key Activities

Students use counters to explore addition of positive and negative numbers. They describe a rule for adding such numbers and practice applying that rule.

 Ongoing Assessment: Informing Instruction See page 580.

 Ongoing Assessment: Recognizing Student Achievement Use journal page 233.
[Operations and Computation Goal 1]

Key Vocabulary

account balance ◆ debt ◆ in the black ◆ in the red

Materials

Math Journal 2, pp. 232 and 233
Study Link 7·7
Math Masters, p. 432
Class Data Pad ◆ slate ◆ red pencil or crayon ◆ envelope ◆ overhead counters in two colors (optional) ◆ scissors ◆ 2 different-colored counters (optional)

2 Ongoing Learning & Practice

Measuring and Drawing Line Segments

Math Journal 2, p. 234
Geometry Template
Students practice measuring to the nearest $\frac{1}{16}$ in. on a ruler and finding equivalent fractions.

 Math Boxes 7·8

Math Journal 2, p. 236
Students practice and maintain skills through Math Box problems.

 Study Link 7·8

Math Masters, p. 208
Students practice and maintain skills through Study Link activities.

3 Differentiation Options

READINESS

Playing the *Credits/Debits Game* (Advanced Version)

Student Reference Book, p. 301
Math Masters, p. 450
per partnership: 1 complete deck of number cards (the Everything Math Deck, if available), 1 penny
Students explore addition and subtraction of positive and negative numbers.

ENRICHMENT

Playing *500*

Math Journal 2, p. 235
per partnership: 1 six-sided die, 1 paper clip, pencil
Students apply their understanding of the addition of negative numbers.

ELL SUPPORT

Making a Visual Aid

black, blue, and red pencils ◆ poster paper
Students create a visual aid for accounting terms.

Advance Preparation

For the Math Message, make one copy of *Math Masters,* page 432 for each student. For Part 1, you might want to use a set of red and black counters on the overhead to model problems. Students will need to store their cash and debt cards for use in Part 3 and Lesson 7-9. Draw the function machine and table from *Teacher's Lesson Guide,* page 582 on the Class Data Pad.

 Teacher's Reference Manual, Grades 4–6 pp. 100–102

Getting Started

Mental Math and Reflexes

Have students use >, <, and = to compare dictated number pairs. *Suggestions:*

● ○ ○ −5 and −7 −5 > −7 or −7 < −5

● ● ○ $\frac{3}{8}$ and −1 $\frac{3}{8}$ > −1 or −1 < $\frac{3}{8}$

● ● ● −$\frac{8}{4}$ and −2 −$\frac{8}{4}$ = −2

Math Message

Lightly shade the cash cards with a regular pencil and the debt cards with a red pencil. Cut out the cards.

Study Link 7·7 Follow-Up

Have partners compare answers and resolve differences. Ask volunteers to share their true and false number sentences.

---

1 Teaching the Lesson

▶ Math Message Follow-Up

WHOLE-CLASS DISCUSSION

(*Math Masters,* p. 432)

Ask students to use the cash and debt cards as positive and negative counters, and model the numbers as specified. *Suggestions:*

▷ Show +5 with 9 counters. 7 +counters and 2 −counters

▷ Show −4 with 8 counters. 6 −counters and 2 +counters

▷ Show −3 with 9 counters. 6 −counters and 3 +counters

▶ Using ⊞ and ⊟ Counters to Calculate Account Balances

WHOLE-CLASS ACTIVITY

ELL

PROBLEM SOLVING

Explain that in this lesson students will add positive and negative numbers. Modeling problems with ⊞ and ⊟ counters can help them understand operations with negative numbers.

Ask students to pretend that they are accountants, keeping track of Jane Doe's account balance. To support English language learners, write the following ideas on the board as you discuss them. The **account balance** is simply the current total value of an account. Explain that each ⊞ counter represents $1 of cash in Jane's account, and each ⊟ counter represents $1 of **debt**, or money that Jane owes to someone else.

NOTE Use two-color counters as an alternative to the cash and debt cards. Chips that are red on one side and black on the other are an effective substitute, but any two-color counters will work. Each student needs 20 counters.

An account balance is said to be **in the black** when there is more cash in an account than there are debts, that is, when there are more black ⊞ counters than red ⊟ counters. A balance is **in the**

Teaching Aid Master

Name	Date	Time

Cash and Debt Cards

+	+	−	−
$1 Cash	$1 Cash	$1 Debt	$1 Debt
+	+	−	−
$1 Cash	$1 Cash	$1 Debt	$1 Debt
+	+	−	−
$1 Cash	$1 Cash	$1 Debt	$1 Debt
+	+	−	−
$1 Cash	$1 Cash	$1 Debt	$1 Debt
+	+	−	−
$1 Cash	$1 Cash	$1 Debt	$1 Debt

Math Masters, p. 432

red when there are more debts than there is cash in the account, that is, when there are more red ⊟ counters than black ⊞ counters.

Describe various situations, and ask students to model each one using their counters. *Suggestions:*

● Take 5 black ⊞ and 3 red ⊟ counters. What does this show? $5 in cash and $3 in debts What is Jane's account balance? It shows a balance of +$2. Jane Doe's account balance is in the black.

● Take 8 red ⊟ counters and 3 black ⊞ counters. What is Jane's account balance? Jane has $8 in debt and $3 in cash for a balance of −$5. Jane's balance is in the red.

Ask: *What will happen if the same number of ⊞ and ⊟ counters are added to or removed from Jane's account?* The account balance, or current value of the account, will remain the same. Model this situation using counters on an overhead projector. Show 7 ⊞ and 2 ⊟ counters. Ask: *What is the account balance?* +5 Add 5 ⊞ counters and 5 ⊟ counters to the display. Ask: *What is the balance now?* +5 Explain that when there is the same number of positive and negative counters, they offset each other, so there is no effect on the balance. Another way to say this is that the net effect on the balance is 0.

▶ Finding Account Balances

PARTNER ACTIVITY

(*Math Journal 2*, p. 232)

Assign the problems on journal page 232. Circulate and assist.

> ### ✔ Ongoing Assessment: Informing Instruction
>
> Watch for students who are confused about how to find the account balances. Have them make as many matches of a ⊞ counter with a ⊟ counter as possible. The remaining unmatched counters represent the account balance. For example, given 5 ⊞ and 3 ⊟ counters, students can match 3 ⊞ with 3 ⊟ counters, leaving 2 ⊞ counters. So the account balance is +2.

When most students have finished, bring the class together to share solutions. Students should use counters to model their answers. (The answers below assume each student has 10 ⊞ and 10 ⊟ counters. With more counters, other answers are possible.)

▷ For Problem 2, there are six possible combinations: 5 ⊞ and 0 ⊟, 6 ⊞ and 1 ⊟, 7 ⊞ and 2 ⊟, and so on.

▷ For Problem 3, there are three possible combinations: 0 ⊞ and 8 ⊟, 1 ⊞ and 9 ⊟, and 2 ⊞ and 10 ⊟.

▷ For Problem 4, there are 11 possible combinations: 0 ⊞ and 0 ⊟ (no transactions), 1 ⊞ and 1 ⊟, 2 ⊞ and 2 ⊟, 3 ⊞ and 3 ⊟, and so on.

Finding Sums of Positive and Negative Numbers

 PARTNER ACTIVITY

COMPUTATION PRACTICE

(*Math Journal 2*, p. 233)

Before assigning journal page 233, describe several possible transactions that will change Jane Doe's account balance. Ask students how they would model each transaction using counters. Then write a number model for each transaction on the board or a transparency. *Suggestions:*

▷ Jane has $4 in cash and no debts. Show this situation with counters. 4 black ⊞ counters Suppose that Jane earns $3 and adds this to her account. Use counters to show this. Add 3 more black ⊞ counters. What is Jane's account balance? She has a total of +$7, or simply $7. Write the number models on the board or a transparency: +4 + (+3) = +7 and 4 + 3 = 7.

▷ Jane has $8 in cash and no debts. Show this situation with counters. 8 black ⊞ counters Suppose Jane borrows $5. Use counters to show this. Add 5 red ⊟ counters. What is the account balance? She has 3 black ⊞ counters or +$3. Write the number models on the board: +8 + (−5) = +3 and 8 + (−5) = 3.

Write several number models on the board or a transparency. Ask students to use their counters to model and solve the problems. Have students interpret each situation as an account balance transaction. Use examples like the following:

▷ 9 + (−6) = ? Add 6 red ⊟ to 9 black ⊞ counters for a balance of 3 black ⊞ counters.

▷ −6 + 5 = ? Add 5 black ⊞ to 6 red ⊟ counters for a balance of 1 red ⊟ counter.

▷ −3 + (−3) = ? Add 3 red ⊟ counters to 3 red ⊟ counters for a balance of 6 red ⊟ counters.

Assign journal page 233. Point out that parentheses on the journal page are used to separate signed numbers from the addition sign. Allow students to use their color counters to represent and solve Problems 1–3. They will not have enough counters to model the rest of the problems, but they can still think about these problems as account balance transactions—combining cash and debt amounts to find totals.

Ongoing Assessment:
Recognizing Student Achievement

Journal Page 233 Problems 1–3 ★

Use **journal page 233, Problems 1–3** to assess students' understanding of how to model problems with positive and negative counters. Students are making adequate progress if they pair positive counters with negative counters to find their answers.

[Operations and Computation Goal 1]

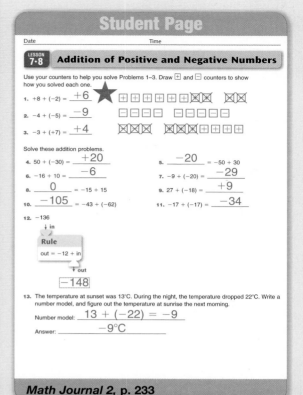

Date   Time

LESSON 7·8   Addition of Positive and Negative Numbers

Use your counters to help you solve Problems 1–3. Draw ⊞ and ⊟ counters to show how you solved each one.

1. +8 + (−2) = **+6** ★

2. −4 + (−5) = **−9**

3. −3 + (+7) = **+4**

Solve these addition problems.

4. 50 + (−30) = **+20**

5. **−20** = −50 + 30

6. −16 + 10 = **−6**

7. −9 + (−20) = **−29**

8. **0** = −15 + 15

9. 27 + (−18) = **+9**

10. **−105** = −43 + (−62)

11. −17 + (−17) = **−34**

12. −136

↓ in

Rule

out = −12 + in

↓ out

−148

13. The temperature at sunset was 13°C. During the night, the temperature dropped 22°C. Write a number model, and figure out the temperature at sunrise the next morning.

Number model: **13 + (−22) = −9**

Answer: **−9°C**

Math Journal 2, p. 233

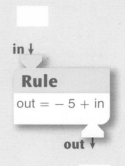

in	out
15	10
10	5
5	0
0	-5
-5	-10
-10	-15

in ↓

Rule

out = − 5 + in

out ↓

NOTE For more practice using rules to describe numeric patterns, see www.everydaymathonline.com.

Date _____ Time _____

LESSON
7·8 **Ruler Fractions**

1. Mark each of these lengths on the ruler shown below. Write the letter above your mark. Point A has been done for you.

A: $2\frac{1}{16}$ in.   B: $4\frac{3}{8}$ in.   C: $3\frac{3}{4}$ in.   D: $1\frac{7}{16}$ in.   E: $2\frac{4}{8}$ in.

D ⬇   A ⬇   E ⬇   C ⬇   B ⬇

0 1 2 3 4 5 6
inches

2. Measure the following line segments to the nearest $\frac{1}{16}$ of an inch.

a. _____   b. _____
$3\frac{4}{16}$, or $3\frac{1}{4}$ in. $\frac{9}{16}$ in.

c. _____
$5\frac{1}{16}$ in.

d. _____
$2\frac{10}{16}$, or $2\frac{5}{8}$ in.

3. Draw a line segment that is $4\frac{3}{16}$ inches long.
_____

4. Draw a line segment that is $3\frac{1}{2}$ inches long.
_____

5. Complete these ruler puzzles.

Example: $\frac{1}{4}$ in. = $\frac{x}{8}$ in. = $\frac{y}{16}$ in.   x = __2__   y = __4__

a. $\frac{6}{8}$ in. = $\frac{x}{16}$ in. = $\frac{3}{y}$ in.   x = __12__   y = __4__

b. $3\frac{2}{8}$ in. = $3\frac{m}{4}$ in. = $3\frac{4}{n}$ in.   m = __1__   n = __16__

c. $\frac{6}{7}$ in. = $\frac{12}{8}$ in. = $\frac{t}{4}$ in. Sample answer: r = __8__   s = __16__   t = __3__

Math Journal 2, p. 234

► **Developing Rules for Adding Positive and Negative Numbers**  WHOLE-CLASS DISCUSSION PROBLEM SOLVING

(*Math Journal 2,* p. 233)

Display the prepared function table and machine on the Class Data Pad. Ask volunteers to identify the rule for this table. out = (−5) + in Expect students to express the rule in terms of subtraction. Tell them that the rule for this table is actually addition of a negative number.

Ask students to think about the function table values only as positive and negative numbers and follow along with you. Point to each number in the table and read it as positive or negative. For the top row, negative + positive in = positive out; for the bottom row negative + negative in = negative out. Ask: *How could we use the addition problems on journal page 233 to help us make a set of rules for adding positive and negative numbers?* Expect answers like the following:

▷ If both addends have the same sign (both + or both −), add the number parts, and write the sign of the addends in front of the sum.

Example 1: $-6 + (-3) = ?$

1. Add the number parts: $6 + 3 = 9$.

2. Write the sign of the addends in front of the sum: $-6 + (-3) = --9$.

▷ If the addends have unlike signs (one + and one −), subtract the smaller from the larger number part, and write the sign of the addend with the larger number part in front of the answer.

Example 2: $-8 + 6 = ?$

1. Subtract the smaller from the larger number part: $8 - 6 = 2$.

2. Write the sign with the larger number part in front of the answer: $-8 + 6 = -2$.

2 **Ongoing Learning & Practice**

► **Measuring and Drawing Line Segments**   INDEPENDENT ACTIVITY

(*Math Journal 2,* p. 234)

Students practice reading fractions on a ruler, measuring to the nearest $\frac{1}{16}$ inch, and finding equivalent fractions.

▶ Math Boxes 7·8

(*Math Journal 2*, p. 236)

INDEPENDENT ACTIVITY

Mixed Practice Math Boxes in this lesson are paired with Math Boxes in Lesson 7-5. The skill in Problem 6 previews Unit 8 content.

▶ Study Link 7·8

(*Math Masters*, p. 208)

INDEPENDENT ACTIVITY

Home Connection Students practice solving inequalities and adding positive and negative numbers.

---

③ Differentiation Options

READINESS

▶ Playing the *Credits/Debits Game* (Advanced Version)

(*Student Reference Book*, p. 301; *Math Masters*, p. 450)

PARTNER ACTIVITY

15–30 Min

COMPUTATION PRACTICE

To explore adding signed numbers, have students play the *Credits/Debits Game* (Advanced Version). When they have played a round, have them describe how they find the balance when they add a debit.

ENRICHMENT

▶ Playing *500*

(*Math Journal 2*, p. 235)

PARTNER ACTIVITY

15–30 Min

To apply students' understanding of the addition of negative numbers in a different context, have students play a game of *500* and record their scores.

ELL SUPPORT

▶ Making a Visual Aid

SMALL-GROUP ACTIVITY

5–15 Min

To support language development for credits and debits, make a visual aid that includes words and color-coded representations for the terms *account balance, in the black, in the red, debt,* and *cash.*

$24 + $2 = $26 **CASH** The <u>account balance</u> is **IN THE BLACK.**	$2 − $24 = −$22 **DEBT** The <u>account balance</u> is **IN THE RED.**

Student Page

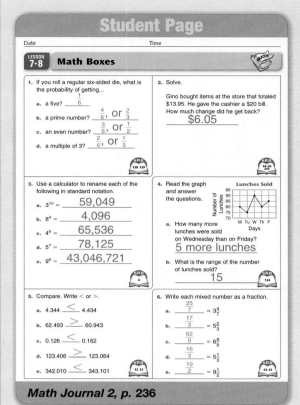

Math Journal 2, p. 236

Study Link Master

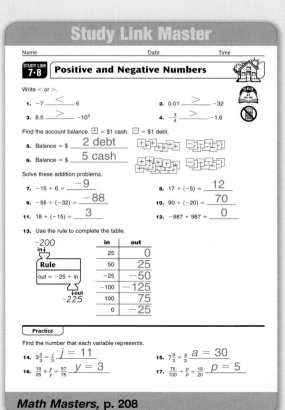

Math Masters, p. 208

Lesson 7·8 583

7·9 Subtraction of Positive and Negative Numbers

Objective To develop a rule for subtracting positive and negative numbers.

Technology Resources www.everydaymathonline.com

 ePresentations
 eToolkit
 Algorithms Practice
 EM Facts Workshop Game™
 Family Letters
 Assessment Management
 Common Core State Standards
 Curriculum Focal Points
 Interactive Teacher's Lesson Guide

---

1 Teaching the Lesson

Key Concepts and Skills

- Model differences of positive and negative numbers with manipulatives.
  [Operations and Computation Goal 1]

- Write and solve the equivalent addition number model for signed number subtraction problems.
  [Operations and Computation Goal 1]

- Use signed number subtraction patterns to describe a rule for subtracting signed numbers.
  [Patterns, Functions, and Algebra Goal 1]

- Write number sentences that model signed-number addition and subtraction problems.
  [Patterns, Functions, and Algebra Goal 2]

Key Activities

Students use their ⊞ and ⊟ counters to explore and describe a rule for subtracting positive and negative numbers. They practice applying the rule.

Materials

Math Journal 2, pp. 237–240
Study Link 7·8
⊞ and ⊟ counters from Lesson 7·8 ◆ slate

2 Ongoing Learning & Practice

 Playing *High-Number Toss: Decimal Version*
Student Reference Book, p. 321
Math Masters, p. 511
per partnership: 4 each of number cards 0–9 (from the Everything Math Deck, if available)
Students compare decimals and practice writing decimals in scientific notation.

 Ongoing Assessment:
Recognizing Student Achievement
Use *High-Number Toss* Record Sheet.
[Number and Numeration Goals 1 and 6]

 Math Boxes 7·9
Math Journal 2, p. 241
Students practice and maintain skills through Math Box problems.

Study Link 7·9
Math Masters, p. 209
Students practice and maintain skills through Study Link activities.

3 Differentiation Options

ENRICHMENT
Comparing Elevations
Student Reference Book, p. 381
Math Masters, p. 210
Students use addition and subtraction to compare elevations of various places in the world.

EXTRA PRACTICE
5-Minute Math
5-Minute Math™, pp. 153 and 234
Students find a rule for in/out patterns with negative numbers.

Advance Preparation

 Teacher's Reference Manual, Grades 4–6 pp. 100–102

Getting Started

Mental Math and Reflexes

Add positive and negative numbers. Students may use ⊞ and ⊟ counters.
Suggestions:

●○○ 9 + (−3) 6
●●○ −32 + 17 −15
●●● −18 + (−18) −36

Math Message

Use your ⊞ and ⊟ cash cards to help you complete page 237 in your journal.

Study Link 7·8 Follow-Up

Partners compare answers and resolve differences.

1 Teaching the Lesson

▶ Math Message Follow-Up

WHOLE-CLASS DISCUSSION

(*Math Journal 2*, p. 237)

Algebraic Thinking Ask students to show how they used their ⊞ and ⊟ counters to obtain their answers.

Use Problem 3 to remind students that if the same number of ⊞ and ⊟ counters are added to a balance, the balance will remain the same. For Problem 5, 4 ⊞ and 4 ⊟ counters must be added to the balance before the required counters can be taken away. Then use change diagrams and number models to summarize Problems 1–5.

Problem 1:

Number model: 5 + (−5) = 0

Problem 2:

Number model: 5 + (−7) = −2

Student Page

Date _____ Time _____

LESSON 7·9 Finding Balances

Math Message

Use your ⊞ and ⊟ cash card counters to model the following problems. Draw a picture of the ⊞ and ⊟ counters to show how you found each balance.

Example:

You have 3 ⊟ counters. Add 6 ⊞ counters.
Balance = 3 ⊞ counters

1. You have 5 ⊞ counters. Add 5 ⊟ counters.
   Balance = __0__ counters

2. You have 5 ⊞ counters. Add 7 ⊟ counters.
   Balance = __2 ⊟__ counters

3. Show a balance of −7 using 15 of your ⊞ and ⊟ counters.

4. You have 7 ⊟ counters. Take away 4 ⊟ counters.
   Balance = __3 ⊟__ counters

5. You have 7 ⊞ counters. Take away 4 ⊟ counters.
   Balance = __11 ⊞__ counters

Math Journal 2, p. 237

Student Page

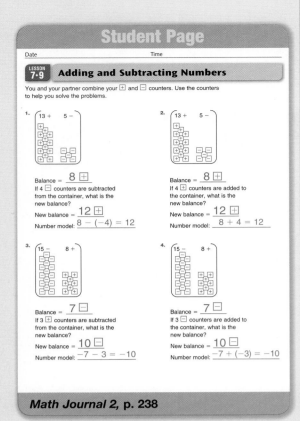

Math Journal 2, p. 238

Problem 3:

Number model: $(-11) + 4 = -7$

Problem 4:

Number model: $(-7) - (-4) = -3$

Problem 5:

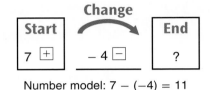

Number model: $7 - (-4) = 11$

▶ ## Developing a Rule for Subtracting Positive and Negative Numbers

PARTNER ACTIVITY

(*Math Journal 2*, pp. 238 and 239)

Ask partners to pool their counters so they have 20 positive and 20 negative counters to use as they work through problems. Have them complete problems 1–8 on journal pages 238 and 239.

When most students have finished, bring the class together to go over the answers. For each problem, ask volunteers to draw a change diagram and write a number model on the board. The number models should be displayed in pairs, as follows:

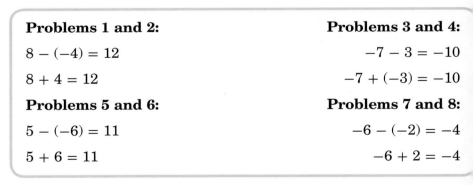

Problems 1 and 2:	**Problems 3 and 4:**
$8 - (-4) = 12$	$-7 - 3 = -10$
$8 + 4 = 12$	$-7 + (-3) = -10$
Problems 5 and 6:	**Problems 7 and 8:**
$5 - (-6) = 11$	$-6 - (-2) = -4$
$5 + 6 = 11$	$-6 + 2 = -4$

Ask the class to look for similarities and differences between the problems and number models for each of these pairs. Ask students to write about what they notice. As you discuss their written responses, include the following:

Similarities

▷ Where containers start with the same combination of ⊞ and ⊟ counters, the starting balances are the same, and the first numbers in the number models are the same.

Student Page

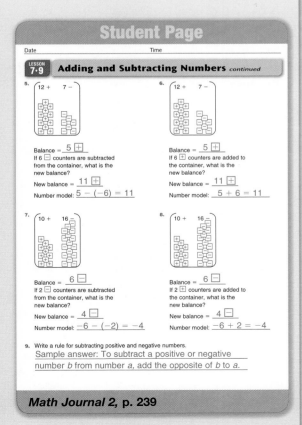

Math Journal 2, p. 239

▷ Where the same number of counters is added to or taken out of the containers, the second numbers in the number models are the same.

▷ Where the new balances after the transactions are the same, the results of the number model operations are the same.

Differences

▷ Where the transactions for a pair of counters are opposites of each other, the operations in the number models are opposites of each other. One is subtraction, and the other is addition.

▷ Where the counters that are subtracted or added have opposite signs, the second numbers in the number models are opposites.

Refer students to Problem 1. Subtracting −4 from 8 has the same effect as adding 4 to 8. In Problem 3, subtracting 3 has the same effect as adding −3.

Help students describe a rule for subtracting positive and negative numbers. Ask them to record the rule in their own words in Problem 9 on journal page 239.

Have students use slates to practice subtracting positive and negative numbers. Ask students to write the equivalent addition number model. *Suggestions:*

- 6 minus 9 $6 + (−9) = −3$
- 6 minus −9 $6 + 9 = 15$
- −6 minus 9 $−6 + (−9) = −15$
- −6 minus −9 $−6 + 9 = 3$

Adjusting the Activity

Have students use larger numbers. Remind students of their rule for subtracting positive and negative numbers. *Suggestions:*

- 52 minus (−25) 77
- −47 minus 22 −69
- −36 minus (−24) −12

A U D I T O R Y ◆ K I N E S T H E T I C ◆ T A C T I L E ◆ V I S U A L

Subtracting Positive and Negative Numbers

PARTNER ACTIVITY

(*Math Journal 2*, p. 240)

Ask students to complete journal page 240 independently, then compare answers with a partner and resolve differences. Circulate and assist.

Date   Time

LESSON 7·9 Math Boxes

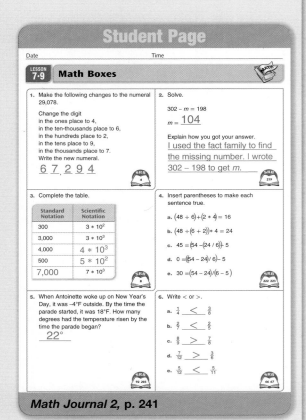

1. Make the following changes to the numeral 29,078.

Change the digit
in the ones place to 4,
in the ten-thousands place to 6,
in the hundreds place to 2,
in the tens place to 9,
in the thousands place to 7.
Write the new numeral.

6 7, 2 9 4

2. Solve.

$302 - m = 198$

$m = 104$

Explain how you got your answer.

I used the fact family to find
the missing number. I wrote
$302 - 198$ to get m.

3. Complete the table.

Standard Notation	Scientific Notation
300	$3 * 10^2$
3,000	$3 * 10^3$
4,000	$4 * 10^3$
500	$5 * 10^2$
7,000	$7 * 10^3$

4. Insert parentheses to make each sentence true.

a. $(48 \div 6) + (2 * 4) = 16$

b. $(48 \div (6 + 2)) * 4 = 24$

c. $45 = (54 - (24 / 6)) \cdot 5$

d. $0 = (54 - 24) / 6) - 5$

e. $30 = (54 - 24) / (6 - 5)$

5. When Antoinette woke up on New Year's Day, it was −4°F outside. By the time the parade started, it was 18°F. How many degrees had the temperature risen by the time the parade began?

22°

6. Write < or >.

a. $\frac{1}{4} < \frac{3}{8}$

b. $\frac{2}{7} < \frac{2}{5}$

c. $\frac{8}{9} > \frac{7}{8}$

d. $\frac{7}{12} > \frac{3}{6}$

e. $\frac{5}{12} < \frac{5}{11}$

Math Journal 2, p. 241

Name   Date   Time

STUDY LINK 7·9 Addition and Subtraction Problems

Solve each problem. Be careful. Some problems involve addition, and some involve subtraction.

Reminder:
To subtract a number, you can add the opposite of that number.

1. $-25 + (-16) = -41$

2. $0 - (-43) = 43$

3. $-4 - (-4) = 0$

4. $-4 - 4 = -8$

5. $29 - (-11) = 40$

6. $9 - (-11) = 20$

7. $-100 + 15 = -85$

8. $10 - 10.5 = -0.5$

9. $4\frac{1}{2} + (-2\frac{1}{2}) = 2$

10. $10 - (-10) = 20$

11. For each temperature change in the table, two number models are shown in the Temperature after Change column. Only one of the number models is correct. Cross out the incorrect number model. Then complete the correct number model.

Temperature before Change	Temperature Change	Temperature after Change	
40°	up 7°	$40 + 7 = 47°$	$40 + (-7) =$
10°	down 8°	$10 - (-8) =$	$10 - 8 = 2°$
−15° (15° below zero)	up 10°	$-15 + 10 = -5°$	$15 + 10 =$
−20° (20° below zero)	down 10°	$-20 - 10 = -30°$	$20 - (-10) =$

Practice

Find the number that each variable represents.

12. $684 * 96 = u$ $u = 65,664$

13. $69 \div e = 23$ $e = 3$

14. $32.486 - 1.645 = w$ $w = 30.841$

15. $9.45 - m = 3.99$ $m = 5.46$

Math Masters, p. 209

---

2 Ongoing Learning & Practice

▶ Playing *High-Number Toss: Decimal Version*

PARTNER ACTIVITY

(*Student Reference Book*, p. 321; *Math Masters*, p. 511)

High-Number Toss was introduced in Lesson 2-5. Have students play the decimal version of the game as indicated on *Student Reference Book*, page 321 and record their rounds on the Record Sheet (*Math Masters*, page 511).

Ongoing Assessment: Recognizing Student Achievement

High Number Toss Record Sheet ★

Use the **Record Sheet** (*Math Masters*, page 511) for *High Number Toss: Decimal Version* to assess students' ability to write and compare decimals. Students are making adequate progress if they have written and compared the decimals correctly through thousandths. Some students may be able to find the difference between the two decimals.

[Number and Numeration Goals 1 and 6]

▶ Math Boxes 7·9

INDEPENDENT ACTIVITY

(*Math Journal 2*, p. 241)

Mixed Practice Math Boxes in this lesson are paired with Math Boxes in Lesson 7-11. The skill in Problem 6 previews Unit 8 content.

▶ Study Link 7·9

INDEPENDENT ACTIVITY

(*Math Masters*, p. 209)

Home Connection Students solve problems involving addition and subtraction of positive and negative numbers.

3 Differentiation Options

ENRICHMENT

INDEPENDENT ACTIVITY

15–30 Min

▶ Comparing Elevations

(*Student Reference Book*, p. 381; *Math Masters*, p. 210)

To apply students' understanding of adding and subtracting signed numbers, have them compare the elevations of U.S. locations that are above and below sea level. When they have finished the page, consider having them identify these locations on the landform map of the United States on *Student Reference Book*, page 381 and compare this information with the chart of elevation along the 39th parallel on the *Student Reference Book* page.

EXTRA PRACTICE

SMALL-GROUP ACTIVITY

5–15 Min

5-Minute Math

Algebraic Thinking To offer students more experience solving "What's My Rule?" problems involving negative numbers, see *5-Minute Math,* pages 153 and 234.

Teaching Master

Name Date Time

LESSON 7•9 **Comparing Elevations**

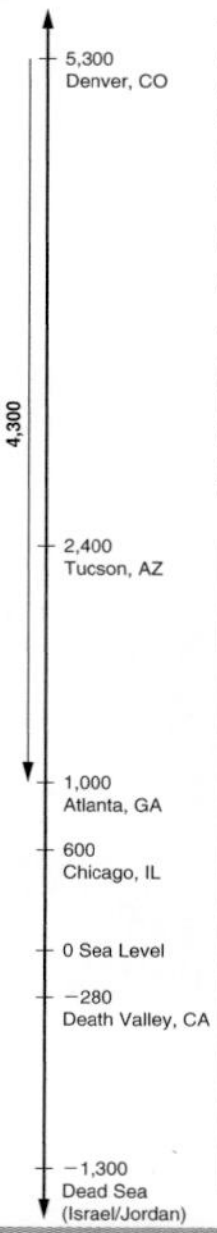

5,300
Denver, CO
4,300
2,400
Tucson, AZ
1,000
Atlanta, GA
600
Chicago, IL
0 Sea Level
−280
Death Valley, CA
−1,300
Dead Sea
(Israel/Jordan)

This number line shows the elevation of several places. Elevation measures how far above or below sea level a location is. For example, an elevation of 5,300 for Denver means that Denver is 5,300 feet above sea level. An elevation of −280 for Death Valley means that some point in Death Valley is 280 feet below sea level.

Fill in the table below. Use the example as a guide.

Example:

If you start at Denver and travel to Atlanta, what is your change in elevation?

Solution:

Draw an arrow next to the number line. Start it at the elevation for Denver (5,300 feet). End it at the elevation for Atlanta (1,000 feet). Use the number line to find the length of the arrow (4,300 feet). Your final elevation is lower, so report the change in elevation as *4,300 feet down.* Write a number model for the problem: 5,300 − 1,000 = 4,300.

Start at	Travel to	Change in Elevation
		Number Model
Denver	Atlanta	4300 feet down
		5300 − 1000 = 4300
Chicago	Tucson	1,800 feet up
		600 + 1,800 = 2,400
Death Valley	Dead Sea	1,020 feet down
		−280 + (−1,020) = −1,300
Dead Sea	Death Valley	1,020 feet up
		−1,300 + 1,020 = −280
Tucson	Death Valley	2,680 feet down
		2,400 + (−2,680) = −280
Dead Sea	Atlanta	2,300 feet up
		−1,300 + 2,300 = 1,000

Math Masters, p. 210

Student Page

American Tour

Geography

Landform Map of the United States

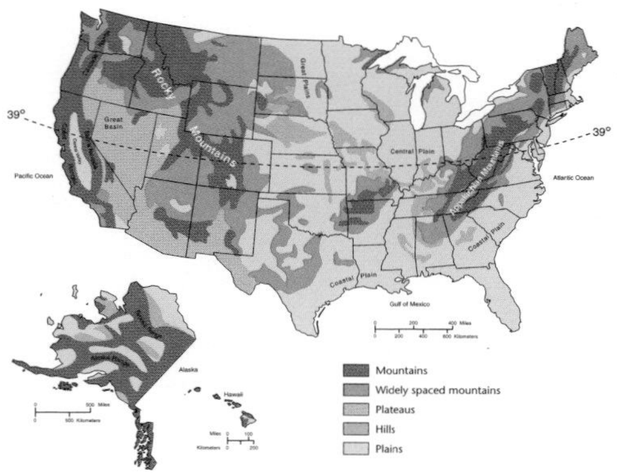

39°
39°
Mountains
Widely spaced mountains
Plateaus
Hills
Plains

Elevation along the 39th Parallel

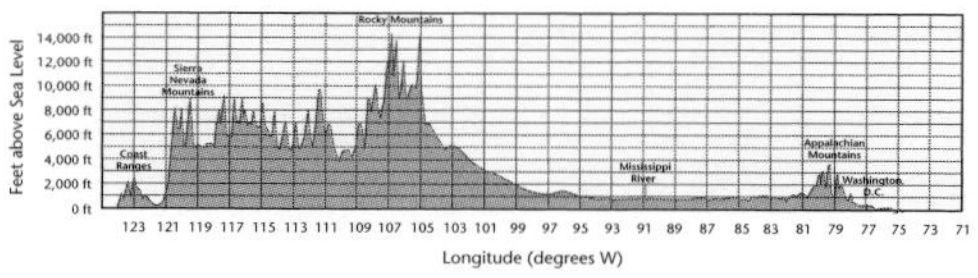

Feet above Sea Level
Rocky Mountains
Appalachian Mountains
Mississippi River
Longitude (degrees W)

Student Reference Book, p. 381

Student Page

Games

High-Number Toss: Decimal Version

Materials □ number cards 0–9 (4 of each)
□ scorecard for each player

Players 2

Skill Decimal place value, subtraction, and addition

Object of the game To make the largest decimal numbers possible.

Directions

1. Each player makes a scorecard like the one at the right. Players fill out their own scorecards at each turn.
2. Shuffle the cards and place them number-side down on the table.
3. In each round:
   - Player 1 draws the top card from the deck and writes the number on any of the 3 blanks on the scorecard. It need not be the first blank—it can be any of them.
   - Player 2 draws the next card from the deck and writes the number on one of his or her blanks.
   - Players take turns doing this 2 more times. The player with the larger number wins the round.
4. The winner's score for a round is the difference between the two players' numbers. (Subtract the smaller number from the larger number.) The loser scores 0 points for the round.

Scorecard

Game 1	
Round 1	Score
0. ___ ___ ___	______
Round 2	
0. ___ ___ ___	______
Round 3	
0. ___ ___ ___	______
Round 4	
0. ___ ___ ___	______
Total:	______

Example Player 1: 0 . 6 5 4
Player 2: 0 . 7 5 3
Player 2 has the larger number and wins the round.
Since 0.753 − 0.654 = 0.099, Player 2 scores 0.099 point for the round.
Player 1 scores 0 points.

5. Players take turns starting a round. At the end of 4 rounds, they find their total scores. The player with the larger total score wins the game.

Student Reference Book, p. 321

7·10 Line Plots

Objective To provide experience creating and interpreting line plots with fractional units.

Technology Resources www.everydaymathonline.com

 ePresentations

 eToolkit

 Algorithms Practice

 EM Facts Workshop Game™

 Family Letters

 Assessment Management

 Common Core State Standards

 Curriculum Focal Points

iTLG Interactive Teacher's Lesson Guide

---

1 Teaching the Lesson

Key Concepts and Skills

- Identify equivalent fractions.
  [Number and Numeration Goal 5]

- Identify fractions on a number line.
  [Number and Numeration Goal 6]

- Add fractions and mixed numbers with like and unlike denominators.
  [Operations and Computation Goal 4]

- Create a line plot.
  [Data and Chance Goal 1]

- Analyze a data set.
  [Data and Chance Goal 2]

Key Activities

Students make a line plot to display and analyze a data set of measurements in fractions of a unit. Students use equivalent fractions and operations of fractions including addition and subtraction to solve problems involving information presented in line plots.

Materials

Math Journal 2, pp. 242 and 242A
Fraction Cards *(Math Journal 2,* Activity Sheets 5–7)
Student Reference Book, pp. 119–121 (optional)
calculator ◆ Probability Meter Poster (optional)

2 Ongoing Learning & Practice

Operations with Multidigit Whole Numbers and Decimals

Math Journal 2, p. 242B
Students practice solving problems involving operations with multidigit whole numbers and decimals.

 Math Boxes 7·10

Math Journal 2, p. 243
Students practice and maintain skills through Math Box problems.

 Ongoing Assessment: Recognizing Student Achievement
Use Math Boxes, Problem 3.
[Number and Numeration Goal 6 and Operations and Computation Goal 4]

 Study Link 7·10

Math Masters, p. 212
Students practice and maintain skills through Study Link activities.

3 Differentiation Options

READINESS

Identifying Fractions on a Number Line

Math Masters, p. 211
Students label fractions on number lines.

EXTRA PRACTICE

Plotting Rain Gauge Data

Math Master, p. 213
Students read measures from pictures of rain gauges, plot the data on a line plot, and then answer questions about data landmarks.

Advance Preparation

For Part 1, students need Fraction Cards *(Math Journal 2,* Activity Sheets 5–7), which were cut out and used in Lesson 5-1.

Getting Started

Mental Math and Reflexes

Have students rename fractions as decimals and as percents. *Suggestions:*

●○○ $\frac{3}{10}$ 0.3; 30% ●●○ $\frac{1}{3}$ $0.\overline{3}$; $33.\overline{3}$% ●●● $\frac{3}{8}$ 0.375; 37.5%

$\frac{4}{8}$ 0.50; 50% $\frac{2}{5}$ 0.40; 40% $\frac{2}{3}$ $0.\overline{6}$; $66.\overline{6}$%

$\frac{3}{4}$ 0.75; 75% $\frac{1}{8}$ 0.125; 12.5% $\frac{4}{4}$ 1.00; 100%

Math Message

Sort the Fraction Cards to find the cards equivalent to 0, $\frac{1}{4}$, $\frac{1}{2}$, $\frac{3}{4}$, and 1. Use your slate to record the number of cards in each group. Be ready to justify your choices.

Study Link 7·9 Follow-Up

Have partners compare answers and resolve differences.

---

1 Teaching the Lesson

▶ **Math Message Follow-Up** WHOLE-CLASS ACTIVITY

(*Math Journal 2,* Activity Sheets 5–7)

Draw a number line on the Class Data Pad, and label the benchmarks 0, $\frac{1}{4}$, $\frac{1}{2}$, $\frac{3}{4}$, and 1. Label the line plot Sorting Fraction Cards, the *x*-axis Fractions, and the *y*-axis Number of Cards. Place the title, Sorting Fraction Cards, above the number line, allowing enough room for data to be added for a line plot.

Tell students that the number line will be used to create a line plot displaying the results of the equivalent-fraction card sorting activity.

Ask students to share the results of their card sorting and justify their choices as you record the results on the Class Data Pad.

Possible questions to ask include the following:

● How many cards show a fraction equivalent to 1? eight: $\frac{2}{2}$, $\frac{3}{3}$, $\frac{4}{4}$, $\frac{5}{5}$, $\frac{6}{6}$, $\frac{8}{8}$, $\frac{10}{10}$, $\frac{16}{16}$

● How do you know these fractions are all equivalent to 1? Sample answers: The front of each of these cards is fully colored. The numerator is equal to the denominator in each fraction.

● How many cards show a fraction equivalent to $\frac{1}{2}$? seven: $\frac{1}{2}$, $\frac{2}{4}$, $\frac{3}{6}$, $\frac{4}{8}$, $\frac{5}{10}$, $\frac{6}{12}$, $\frac{8}{16}$

● How do you know these fractions are all equivalent to $\frac{1}{2}$? Sample answers: The denominator in each of these fractions is twice the numerator. The number of spaces shaded blue on each of these cards is equal to the number of spaces that are white.

● How many cards show a fraction equivalent to $\frac{1}{4}$? three: $\frac{1}{4}$, $\frac{2}{8}$, $\frac{3}{12}$

● How many cards show a fraction equivalent to $\frac{3}{4}$? three: $\frac{3}{4}$, $\frac{6}{8}$, $\frac{9}{12}$

● How many cards show a fraction equivalent to 0? three: $\frac{0}{5}$, $\frac{0}{10}$, $\frac{0}{16}$

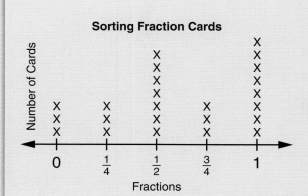

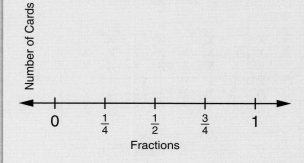

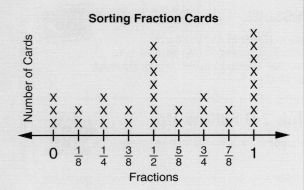

Sorting Fraction Cards

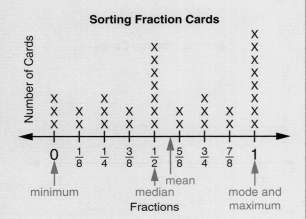

Sorting Fraction Cards

Ask volunteers to label the fractions $\frac{1}{8}$, $\frac{3}{8}$, $\frac{5}{8}$, and $\frac{7}{8}$ on the line plot. Ask students to explain their reasoning for the placement of each fraction as it is recorded.

Have students continue to sort the Fraction Cards to find those that are equivalent to the fractions for eighths that were just added to the number line. Continue discussing students' findings as you complete the line plot. Ask:

● How many cards did you find for each new fraction we marked on the number line? There are 2 cards for each: $\frac{1}{8}$ is equal to $\frac{2}{16}$, $\frac{3}{8}$ is equal to $\frac{6}{16}$, $\frac{5}{8}$ is equal to $\frac{10}{16}$, and $\frac{7}{8}$ is equal to $\frac{14}{16}$.

● How can you use the line plot to find the total number of cards sorted? Count all the Xs in the line plot.

▶ Using a Line Plot to Analyze Data

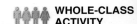 **WHOLE-CLASS ACTIVITY**

(*Student Reference Book,* pp.119–121)

Refer students to *Student Reference Book,* pages 119–121 to review data landmarks, if necessary.

Have students use slates to record information about the data on the Sorting Fraction Cards line plot. Ask students to share their thinking as they analyze the data. As they determine the various landmarks, label them on the line plot on the Class Data Pad.

● Which number on the line plot has the most equivalent fractions? 1 whole, or 1 What do we call the landmark for the value or values that occur with the greatest frequency in a set of data? mode

● What is the maximum value in the set of data? 1 What is the minimum value in the set of data? 0

● What is the range of data displayed on the line plot? 1 How did you find the range? I subtracted the minimum from the maximum: $1 - 0 = 1$.

● What is the median? $\frac{1}{2}$ How did you find the median? I started at each end and then worked toward the center until I found the middle number.

● How many cards do we have in our data set? 32

● If the blue shading on the cards represents blue liquid in a beaker, for how many beakers do we have data? 32

● What landmark would tell us how much liquid each beaker would have if the liquid were distributed equally among all the beakers? mean

● If you actually had these beakers of liquid, what would you do to distribute the liquid equally among all beakers? Sample answer: I'd pour liquid from the beakers with more liquid into the beakers with less liquid until the liquid levels in all of the beakers were equal.

● How do you find the mean for a set of data? Sample answer: Add all of the data values, and then divide the sum by the number of data values.

Finding the Mean

PARTNER ACTIVITY

Ask students to work with a partner to find the sum of the data values using various strategies. $18\frac{1}{2}$ Ask students to share their strategy for finding the sum.

Adjusting the Activity

Students who need a visual model to find the sum of the fractions may benefit from using the Fraction Cards. Have students match cards that together add to a sum of 1 whole. For example, $\frac{7}{8}$ and $\frac{1}{8}$ add to 1 whole. Using this method, all cards except for one of the $\frac{1}{2}$ cards has a "match" to make 1 whole.

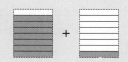

AUDITORY ◆ KINESTHETIC ◆ TACTILE ◆ VISUAL

Students then use a calculator to find the mean of the set of data. Students may convert $18\frac{1}{2}$ to a decimal and then use the calculator to divide the sum by 32 to find the mean. Ask students to round the quotient in the calculator display to the nearest hundredth. 18.5 / 32 = 0.578125, or about 0.58 **Ask:**

- Between which two fractions on your line plot does 0.58 fall? Between $\frac{1}{2}$ and $\frac{5}{8}$

- Which fraction on your line plot is 0.58 closest to? How do you know? Sample answer: 0.58 is closest to $\frac{5}{8}$ because $\frac{5}{8} = 0.625$, and $0.625 - 0.58 = 0.045$. This is less than the distance between 0.58 and 0.5, which is 0.08.

Students then use estimation to determine an approximate placement on the line plot for the mean of the set of data.

Adjusting the Activity

Students who need a visual model to estimate the placement of the mean on the line plot may benefit from referring to the Probability Meter Poster. After determining the approximate location of the decimal on the decimal side of the probability meter, students look on the opposite side of the meter to determine the fraction that is closest to the one found on the line plot. Students should notice that 0.58 is greater than 0.5 and less than 0.625, and that it is closer to 0.625.

AUDITORY ◆ KINESTHETIC ◆ TACTILE ◆ VISUAL

Displaying and Analyzing Data on a Line Plot

PARTNER ACTIVITY

(*Math Journal 2*, pp. 242 and 242A)

Students work with a partner. Have students solve the problems on journal pages 242 and 242A involving plotting data points on a line plot with fractional units and analyzing the data with landmarks. Circulate and assist.

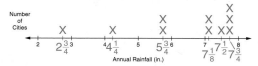

Student Page

Date _____ Time _____

LESSON 7·10 Line Plots and Data in Fractional Units

Use the data in the table below to create a line plot.

Rainfall in the Driest U.S. Cities			
City and State	Annual Rainfall (in.)	City and State	Annual Rainfall (in.)
Yuma, Arizona	$2\frac{3}{4}$	Alamosa, Colorado	$7\frac{1}{8}$
Las Vegas, Nevada	$4\frac{1}{4}$	Reno, Nevada	$7\frac{1}{2}$
Bishop, California	$5\frac{3}{4}$	Winslow, Arizona	$7\frac{1}{2}$
Bakersfield, California	$5\frac{3}{4}$	El Paso, Texas	$7\frac{3}{4}$
Phoenix, Arizona	$7\frac{1}{8}$	Winnemucca, Nevada	$7\frac{3}{4}$

Source: National Climatic Data Center

1. Place an X on the line plot below to represent the annual rainfall in each of the 10 driest cities in the United States. Label the line plot with the mixed numbers for the data.

Rainfall in the Driest U.S. Cities

Now analyze the data from the table and line plot to answer the questions about the annual rainfall in the 10 driest U.S. cities.

2. What is the minimum amount of annual rainfall? $2\frac{3}{4}$ in.

3. What is the range of annual rainfall? 5 in.

4. What is the mode of annual rainfall? $7\frac{3}{4}$ in.

5. What is the median annual rainfall? $7\frac{1}{8}$ in.

6. What is the combined annual rainfall for the 10 driest cities? $63\frac{1}{2}$ in.

7. What is the mean annual rainfall for the 10 driest cities? 6.35 in.

Math Journal 2, p. 242

Student Page

Date _____ Time _____

LESSON 7·10 Line Plots and Data in Fractional Units *cont.*

The table below shows rainfall for 10 days in one of the driest cities. Organize the data in a line plot. Then analyze the data to answer questions about the plotted rainfall.

Rainfall Data										
Day	1	2	3	4	5	6	7	8	9	10
Rainfall (in.)	$\frac{3}{8}$	$\frac{1}{2}$	0	0	$\frac{1}{8}$	$\frac{5}{8}$	$\frac{3}{4}$	0	0	0

8. Label the approximate locations on the line plot for $\frac{1}{8}$, $\frac{2}{8}$, $\frac{3}{8}$, $\frac{4}{8}$, $\frac{5}{8}$, $\frac{6}{8}$, and $\frac{7}{8}$.

9. Plot the rainfall data from the table.

Rainfall Data

10. Identify the following landmarks for the rainfall data:

a. mode: 0 in.

b. range: $\frac{6}{8}$ or $\frac{3}{4}$ in.

c. median: $\frac{1}{16}$ in.

d. mean (as a decimal, rounded to the nearest hundredth inch): 0.24 in.

Math Journal 2, p. 242A

Student Page

Date _____ Time _____

LESSON 7·10 — Operations with Multidigit Whole Numbers and Decimals

1. Use the standard algorithm to complete the multiplication problem shown at right.

```
      2 0 7
    *   5 4
    ─────────
      8 2 8   ← 4 * 207
  + 1 0 3 5 0 ← 50 * 207
  ──────────
  1 1 1 7 8
```

2. $7,550 is shared equally among 25 people.

   a. Write an open number sentence to show how much money each person gets.

   $7,550 \div 25 = m$

   b. Will a reasonable estimate for the quotient be in the tens, hundreds, or thousands?

   In the hundreds

   c. Each person gets $ __302__

3. In a store, Denny picks out jeans for $34.98 and a shirt for $16.49. He has $50 with him.

   a. Does he have enough money to buy the jeans and shirt? __no__

   b. If not, how much more money does he need? __$1.47__

4. a. The correct digits for the product are given. Write the decimal point in the product without actually multiplying.

   $0.98 * 39.39 = 3\,8.6\,0\,2\,2$

   b. Explain how you decided where to place the decimal point.
   Sample answer: 0.98 is almost 1, so I knew that the product would be close to 39.

5. a. Explain how you could use the shading in the grid to find the quotient $0.65 \div 0.05$.
   Sample answer: The shading shows 13 groups of 0.05 in 0.65.

   b. What whole number division problem has the same quotient?
   Sample answer: $65 \div 5$

Math Journal 2, p. 242B

---

2 Ongoing Learning & Practice

▶ Operations with Multidigit Whole Numbers and Decimals

 **INDEPENDENT ACTIVITY**

(*Math Journal 2*, p. 242B)

Students practice solving problems involving operations with multidigit whole numbers and decimals.

▶ Math Boxes 7·10

INDEPENDENT ACTIVITY

(*Math Journal 2*, p. 243)

Mixed Practice Math Boxes in this lesson are paired with Math Boxes in Lesson 7-7. The skills in Problem 6 previews Unit 8.

✓ Ongoing Assessment Recognizing Student Achievement

 Math Boxes Problem 3

Use **Math Boxes, Problem 3** to assess students' ability to add fractions with unlike denominators and to use benchmarks to compare fractions. Students are making adequate progress if they can compare the fraction $\frac{3}{8}$ to $\frac{1}{2}$ and find the sum of the two fractions. Some students may be able to compare the fraction to $\frac{1}{4}$.

[Number and Numeration Goal 6 and Operations and Computation Goal 4]

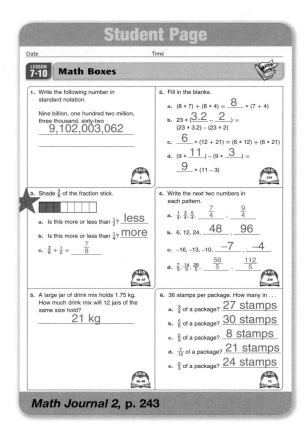

Math Journal 2, p. 243

Study Link 7·10

(*Math Masters*, p. 212)

INDEPENDENT ACTIVITY 👤

Home Connection Students practice making line plots with fractional increments using insect data.

---

③ Differentiation Options

READINESS

SMALL-GROUP ACTIVITY 👥👥
🕐 5–15 Min

▶ Identifying Fractions on a Number Line

(*Math Masters*, p. 211)

Students label fractions on number lines.

EXTRA PRACTICE

SMALL-GROUP ACTIVITY 👥👥
🕐 5–15 Min

▶ Plotting Rain Gauge Data

(*Math Masters*, p. 213)

Students use rain gauge data to practice creating a line plot with fractional increments and then answer questions about the landmarks of the data set.

Study Link Master

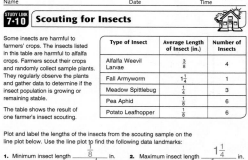

STUDY LINK 7·10 Scouting for Insects

Some insects are harmful to farmers' crops. The insects listed in this table are harmful to alfalfa crops. Farmers scout their crops and randomly collect sample plants. They regularly observe the plants and gather data to determine if the insect population is growing or remaining stable.

The table shows the result of one farmer's insect scouting.

Type of Insect	Average Length of Insect (in.)	Number of Insects
Alfalfa Weevil Larvae	$\frac{3}{8}$	4
Fall Armyworm	$1\frac{1}{4}$	1
Meadow Spittlebug	$\frac{1}{4}$	3
Pea Aphid	$\frac{1}{8}$	6
Potato Leafhopper	$\frac{1}{8}$	6

Plot and label the lengths of the insects from the scouting sample on the line plot below. Use the line plot to find the following data landmarks:

1. Minimum insect length $\frac{1}{8}$ in.
2. Maximum insect length $1\frac{1}{4}$ in.
3. Range of insect lengths $1\frac{1}{8}$ in.
4. Median insect length $\frac{1}{8}$ in.
5. Mean insect length $\frac{1}{4}$ in.

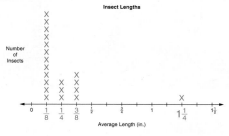

Insect Lengths

Math Masters, p. 212

Teaching Master

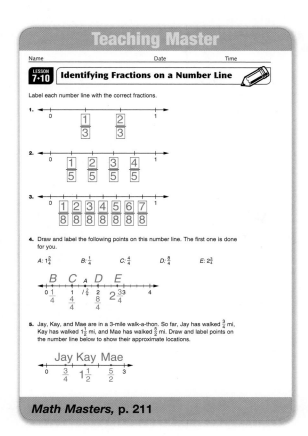

LESSON 7·10 Identifying Fractions on a Number Line

Label each number line with the correct fractions.

1. $\boxed{\frac{1}{3}}$ $\boxed{\frac{2}{3}}$

2. $\boxed{\frac{1}{5}}$ $\boxed{\frac{2}{5}}$ $\boxed{\frac{3}{5}}$ $\boxed{\frac{4}{5}}$

3. $\boxed{\frac{1}{8}}$ $\boxed{\frac{2}{8}}$ $\boxed{\frac{3}{8}}$ $\boxed{\frac{4}{8}}$ $\boxed{\frac{5}{8}}$ $\boxed{\frac{6}{8}}$ $\boxed{\frac{7}{8}}$

4. Draw and label the following points on this number line. The first one is done for you.

A: $1\frac{2}{4}$ B: $\frac{1}{4}$ C: $\frac{4}{4}$ D: $\frac{8}{4}$ E: $2\frac{3}{4}$

5. Jay, Kay, and Mae are in a 3-mile walk-a-thon. So far, Jay has walked $\frac{3}{4}$ mi, Kay has walked $1\frac{1}{2}$ mi, and Mae has walked $\frac{5}{2}$ mi. Draw and label points on the number line below to show their approximate locations.

Math Masters, p. 211

Teaching Master

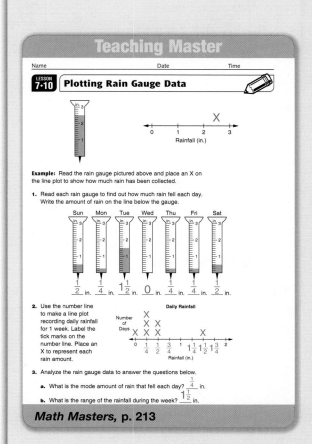

LESSON 7·10 Plotting Rain Gauge Data

Example: Read the rain gauge pictured above and place an X on the line plot to show how much rain has been collected.

1. Read each rain gauge to find out how much rain fell each day. Write the amount of rain on the line below the gauge.

Sun $\frac{1}{2}$ in. Mon $\frac{1}{4}$ in. Tue $1\frac{1}{2}$ in. Wed 0 in. Thu $\frac{1}{4}$ in. Fri $\frac{1}{4}$ in. Sat $\frac{1}{2}$ in.

2. Use the number line to make a line plot recording daily rainfall for 1 week. Label the tick marks on the number line. Place an X to represent each rain amount.

Daily Rainfall

3. Analyze the rain gauge data to answer the questions below.

a. What is the mode amount of rain that fell each day? $\frac{1}{4}$ in.

b. What is the range of the rainfall during the week? $1\frac{1}{2}$ in.

Math Masters, p. 213

Lesson 7·10 595

7·11 Calculator Practice: Working with Negative Numbers

 Objective To facilitate exploring the use of calculators to add and subtract positive and negative numbers.

Technology Resources www.everydaymathonline.com

 ePresentations

 eToolkit

 Algorithms Practice

 EM Facts Workshop Game™

 Family Letters

 Assessment Management

 Common Core State Standards

 Curriculum Focal Points

 Interactive Teacher's Lesson Guide

---

1 Teaching the Lesson

Key Concepts and Skills

• Use a calculator to add and subtract signed numbers.
[Operations and Computation Goal 1]

• Write number sentences that model signed-number addition and subtraction problems.
[Patterns, Functions, and Algebra Goal 2]

Key Activities

Students explore how to enter parentheses and negative numbers in their calculators. They add and subtract positive and negative numbers using a calculator.

 Ongoing Assessment: Recognizing Student Achievement Use Mental Math and Reflexes.
[Number and Numeration Goal 5]

 Ongoing Assessment: Informing Instruction See page 598.

Key Vocabulary

negative number ◆ opposite ◆ change-sign key ⊖ or ⁺⁄₋

Materials

Math Journal 2, pp. 244 and 245
Student Reference Book, p. 257
Study Link 7·10
calculator

2 Ongoing Learning & Practice

 Playing *Top-It Games with Positive and Negative Numbers*
Student Reference Book,
pp. 335 and 336
per partnership: 1 complete set of number cards (the Everything Math Deck, if available), calculator (optional)
Students practice addition and subtraction of signed numbers.

 Math Boxes 7·11
Math Journal 2, p. 246
Students practice and maintain skills through Math Box problems.

 Study Link 7·11
Math Masters, pp. 214 and 215
Students practice and maintain skills through Study Link activities.

3 Differentiation Options

ENRICHMENT
Playing *Broken Calculator*
Math Masters, p. 216
calculator
Students practice addition and subtraction of negative numbers only.

ELL SUPPORT
Building a Math Word Bank
Differentiation Handbook, p. 142
Students write, illustrate, and identify other words related to the term *negative numbers.*

Advance Preparation

 Teacher's Reference Manual, Grades 4–6 pp. 29–35, 71–74, 100–102

Getting Started

Mental Math and Reflexes

Have students convert fractions to whole or mixed numbers. *Suggestions:*

●○○ $\frac{12}{3}$ 4   ●●○ $\frac{27}{8}$ $3\frac{3}{8}$ ●●● $\frac{728}{9}$ $80\frac{8}{9}$

$\frac{20}{9}$ $2\frac{2}{9}$ $\frac{51}{4}$ $12\frac{3}{4}$ $\frac{365}{4}$ $91\frac{1}{4}$

Math Message

Complete Problem 1 on journal page 244.

Study Link 7·10 Follow-Up

Have partners compare their line plots. Ask volunteers to share their solutions for Problems 1–5.

Ongoing Assessment: Recognizing Student Achievement

Mental Math and Reflexes ★

Use the **Mental Math and Reflexes problems** to assess students' ability to convert fractions to whole numbers or mixed numbers in simplest form. Students are making adequate progress if they correctly answer the problems.

[Number and Numeration Goal 5]

---

① Teaching the Lesson

▶ Math Message Follow-Up

 WHOLE-CLASS DISCUSSION

(*Math Journal 2*, p. 244; *Student Reference Book*, p. 257)

Ask volunteers to write the key sequence they used to display a negative number. Expect that some students will have used the minus key. Explain that the minus key represents subtraction and that subtraction is different from negative numbers. **Negative numbers** are numbers that are less than zero, to the left of zero on a horizontal number line, or below zero on a vertical number line. Another way to think of a negative number is as the **opposite** of a positive number.

A number's sign tells whether it is negative or positive. The change-sign key on a scientific calculator changes a number's sign from a positive number to negative or a negative number to positive. Refer students to *Student Reference Book,* page 257, and work through the examples.

Summarize this exploration with the following points:

- The ⊖ or ⊬⁻ key is usually called a **change-sign key** in calculator manuals. It can also be called the OPP key, where OPP is short for opposite. The change-sign key allows you to enter a negative number, or it converts a number to its opposite.

- Calculators always display a − sign in a negative number, but rarely display a + sign in a positive number. Unless a − sign appears, the number displayed is positive or zero.

Student Page

Date   Time

LESSON 7·11   **Entering Negative Numbers on a Calculator**

Math Message

1. Write the key sequence to display −4 on your calculator.
 <u>Sample answers: ⊖ 4 , or 4 ⊬⁻</u>

2. What does the change-of-sign or change-sign key do?
 <u>It changes the number key to its opposite, from positive to negative and back again.</u>

Addition and Subtraction Using a Calculator

Use a calculator to solve each problem. Record the key sequence you used.

Sample answers:

Example:	Calculator Entry
12 + (−17) = <u>−5</u>	12 ⊕ ⊖ 17 **Enter**
3. −10 − 17 = <u>−27</u>	⊖ 10 ⊖ 17 **Enter**
4. −10 + (−17) = <u>−27</u>	⊖ 10 ⊕ ⊖ 17 **Enter**
5. −27 + 220 = <u>193</u>	⊖ 27 ⊕ 220 **Enter**
6. 19 − 43 = <u>−24</u>	19 ⊖ 43 **Enter**
7. −35 − (−35) = <u>0</u>	⊖ 35 ⊖ ⊖ 35 **Enter**
8. 72 + (−47) = <u>25</u>	72 ⊕ ⊖ 47 **Enter**
9. −35 − (−35) = <u>0</u>	⊖ 35 ⊖ ⊖ 35 **Enter**
10. 72 + (−47) = <u>25</u>	72 ⊕ ⊖ 47 **Enter**

Math Journal 2, p. 244

Student Page

Date _____ Time _____

LESSON 7·11 Entering Negative Numbers on a Calculator *cont.*

Solve. Use your calculator.

11. $3.65 - 2.02 = $ __1.63__

12. $10 - (-5) = $ __15__

13. $-901 - 199 = $ __−1,100__

14. $-7.1 + 18.6 = $ __11.5__

15. $-2 + (-13) + 7 = $ __−8__

16. $2 - 7 - (-15) = $ __10__

17. $41 / 328 = $ __0.125__

18. $3 * 3.14 = $ __9.42__

19. $-41 / 328 = $ __−0.125__

20. $-(3 * 3.14) = $ __−9.42__

21. $41 * (7 + 2) = $ __369__

22. $41 * (7 + (-2)) = $ __205__

Number Stories

23. A salesperson is often assigned a quota. A quota is the dollar value of the goods the salesperson is expected to sell. Suppose a salesperson is $3,500 below quota and then makes a sale of $4,700.

Did the salesperson exceed or fall short of his or her quota? __exceed__

Write a number model to figure out by how much the salesperson exceeded or fell short. Use negative and positive numbers. Think about a number line with the quota at 0.

Number model: __$-3,500 + 4,700 = 1,200$__

Solution: __$1,200 above the quota__

24. Stock prices change every day. Suppose on the first day a stock's price went up $\frac{1}{4}$ dollar per share. The next day it went down $\frac{1}{2}$ dollar. The third day it went up $\frac{5}{8}$ dollar.

Did the value increase or decrease from the beginning of Day 1 to the end of Day 3? __increase__

Write a number model to figure out by how much the stock increased or decreased over the 3-day period. Use negative and positive numbers. Think about a number line with the Day 1 starting price at 0.

Number model: __$\frac{1}{4} - \frac{1}{2} + \frac{5}{8} = \frac{3}{8}$__

Solution: __$\frac{3}{8}$ dollar increase__

Math Journal 2, p. 245

NOTE Different calculators may use different symbols to represent functions, and key sequences may differ, but the change-sign key performs the same function on all calculators.

Student Page

Date _____ Time _____

LESSON 7·11 Math Boxes

1. Make the following changes to the numeral 34,709.

Change the digit
in the ones place to 6,
in the tens place to 5,
in the thousands place to 0,
in the ten-thousands place to 9,
in the hundreds place to 3.
Write the new numeral.

__90,356__

2. Solve.

a. $m + 2,532 = 5,094$

$m = $ __2,562__

b. $489.16 - n = 243.04$

$n = $ __246.12__

3. Complete the table.

Standard Notation	Scientific Notation
60,000	$6 * 10^4$
500,000	$5 * 10^5$
400,000	$4 * 10^5$
700,000	$7 * 10^5$

4. Insert parentheses to make each sentence true.

a. $22 + (3 / 3) - 2 = 21$

b. $(22 + 3) / (3 - 2) = 25$

c. $(18 / 6) + (3 * 5) = 18$

d. $18 / (6 + 3) * 5 = 10$

e. $((5 + 7) * 3) / 9 = 4$

5. The temperature in Chicago at 5 P.M. was 35°F. By midnight, the temperature had dropped 48 degrees. What was the temperature at midnight?

__−13°F__

6. Write > or <.

a. $\frac{3}{8}$ __<__ $\frac{3}{4}$

b. $\frac{9}{10}$ __>__ $\frac{9}{16}$

c. $\frac{6}{7}$ __>__ $\frac{5}{7}$

d. $\frac{10}{12}$ __>__ $\frac{4}{6}$

e. $\frac{8}{9}$ __>__ $\frac{6}{7}$

Math Journal 2, p. 246

598   Unit 7   Exponents and Negative Numbers

▶ **Introducing Operations with Signed Numbers on a Calculator**

 WHOLE-CLASS ACTIVITY

Write $6 + (-4) = ?$ on the board or a transparency, and ask students to solve it on their calculators. Ask volunteers to share their answers and the key sequences they used. 2

If a volunteer did not get the correct answer, ask the class to figure out why the key sequence was wrong.

Repeat the process for the following problems:

● $6 - (-2) = ?$ 8   ● $-6 - (-2) = ?$ −4

Pose several other simple addition and subtraction problems. Verify that students are using the change-sign key ⊖ or ⁺∕₋ and the appropriate key sequence for a sign-change problem.

▶ **Practicing Addition and Subtraction Using the Calculator**

 PARTNER ACTIVITY

(*Math Journal 2,* pp. 244 and 245)

Have students complete journal pages 244 and 245 on their own and then compare answers with a partner.

★ Ongoing Assessment: Informing Instruction

Watch for students who have difficulty entering the subtraction problems on their calculators. Have them rewrite the subtraction problems as addition problems and then enter the key sequences.

---

2 Ongoing Learning & Practice

▶ **Playing *Top-It Games with Positive and Negative Numbers***

 PARTNER ACTIVITY

(*Student Reference Book,* pp. 335 and 336)

Students are familiar with *Top-It* games. This version practices addition and subtraction with signed numbers.

▶ **Math Boxes 7·11**

 **INDEPENDENT ACTIVITY**

(*Math Journal 2,* p. 246)

 Mixed Practice Math Boxes in this lesson are paired with Math Boxes in Lesson 7-9. The skill in Problem 6 previews Unit 8 content.

Writing/Reasoning Have students write a response to the following: *Explain your strategy for solving the open number sentence in Problem 2a.* Sample answer: I found out what I needed to add to 2,532 to get 5,094. To do that, I subtracted 2,532 from 5,094 and got 2,562.

▶ Study Link 7·11

(*Math Masters*, pp. 214 and 215)

INDEPENDENT ACTIVITY

Home Connection This Study Link reviews skills and concepts taught in this unit.

③ Differentiation Options

ENRICHMENT

PARTNER ACTIVITY

▶ Playing *Broken Calculator*

15–30 Min

(*Math Masters*, p. 216)

To apply students' understanding of operations with signed numbers, have them play *Broken Calculator*. They solve problems involving negative numbers without using a designated calculator key. They make problems of their own for their partners to solve.

ELL SUPPORT

SMALL-GROUP ACTIVITY

▶ Building a Math Word Bank

5–15 Min

(*Differentiation Handbook*, p. 142)

To provide language support for number properties, have students use the Word Bank Template found on *Differentiation Handbook*, page 142. Ask students to write the term *negative numbers*, draw a picture relating to that term, and write other related words. See the *Differentiation Handbook* for more information.

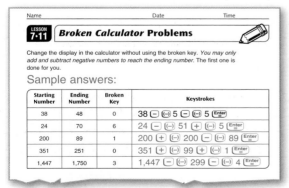

Math Masters, page 216

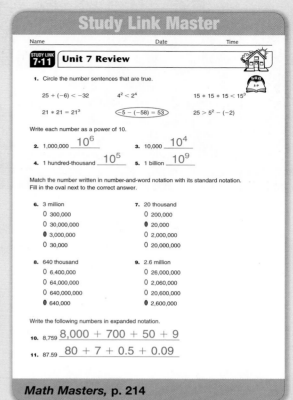

Math Masters, p. 214

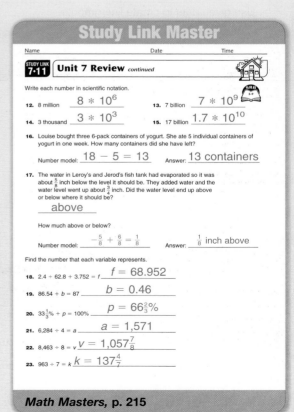

Math Masters, p. 215

7·12 Progress Check 7

Objective To assess students' progress on mathematical content through the end of Unit 7.

---

1   Looking Back: Cumulative Assessment

 Input student data from Progress Check 7 into the **Assessment Management Spreadsheets**.

Materials
- Study Link 7◆11
- *Assessment Handbook,* pp. 102–109, 185–189, 222, and 270–273
- slate

CONTENT ASSESSED	LESSON(S)	SELF	ORAL/SLATE	WRITTEN PART A	WRITTEN PART B	OPEN RESPONSE
Understand and apply scientific notation. [Number and Numeration Goal 1]	7·3	1	4		34	
Understand and apply powers of 10. [Number and Numeration Goal 4]	7·2, 7·3	2	2		34	
Understand and apply exponential notation. [Number and Numeration Goal 4]	7·1, 7·2	3		4, 6, 10, 17		
Add and subtract positive and negative numbers. [Operations and Computation Goal 1]	7·8–7·11	7	3	7–10, 18–26	27–33	
Use mental math and paper-and-pencil algorithms to solve problems. [Operations and Computation Goals 1 and 3]						✔
Order and compare positive and negative numbers. [Operations and Computation Goal 6]	7·7	4	1	1–9		
Use given data to create line graph. [Data and Chance Goal 1]	7·6				36	
Interpret line graphs. [Data and Chance Goal 2]	7·6				35	
Identify number sentences. Tell whether a number sentence is true or false. [Patterns, Functions, and Algebra Goal 2]	7·4, 7·9, 7·11	5		10		
Understand and apply the use of parentheses in number sentences and use them to make true number sentences. [Patterns, Functions, and Algebra Goal 3]	7·4–7·5	6		11–17		✔
Understand and apply order of operations to evaluate expressions and solve number sentences. [Patterns, Functions, and Algebra Goal 3]	7·5	8		11–17		✔

---

2   Looking Ahead: Preparing for Unit 8

Math Boxes 7◆12

 Study Link 7◆12: Unit 8 Family Letter

Materials
- *Math Journal 2,* p. 247
- *Math Masters,* pp. 217–220

Getting Started

Math Message • Self Assessment
Complete the Self Assessment (Assessment Handbook, page 185).

Study Link 7·11 Follow-Up
Briefly review students' answers.

1 Looking Back: Cumulative Assessment

▶ Math Message Follow-Up

INDEPENDENT ACTIVITY

(Self Assessment, *Assessment Handbook*, p. 185)

 The Self Assessment offers students the opportunity to reflect upon their progress.

▶ Oral and Slate Assessments

WHOLE-CLASS ACTIVITY

Problems 1 and 2 provide summative information and can be used for grading purposes. Problems 3 and 4 provide formative information that can be useful in planning future instruction.

Oral Assessment

1. Use >, <, or = to compare numbers.

- -7 and 7 $-7 < 7$ or $7 > -7$
- 0 and $-\frac{3}{4}$ $0 > -\frac{3}{4}$ or $-\frac{3}{4} < 0$
- $-\frac{5}{10}$ and $-\frac{9}{18}$ $-\frac{5}{10} = -\frac{9}{18}$
- -4 and -10 $-4 > -10$ or $-10 < -4$
- $-\frac{3}{8}$ and $-\frac{3}{8}$ $-\frac{3}{8} = -\frac{3}{8}$
- -35 and 34 $-35 < 34$ or $34 > -35$

2. Which power of 10 do these numbers express?

- 1 billion 10^9
- 1 thousand 10^3
- 10 million 10^7
- 100 million 10^8
- 100 thousand 10^5
- 10 billion 10^{10}

Slate Assessment

3. Solve.

- $-15 + (-15)$ -30
- $-50 + 20$ -30
- $-5 + (-7)$ -12
- $-5 - (-7)$ 2
- $-5 - 7$ -12
- $0 - (-8)$ 8

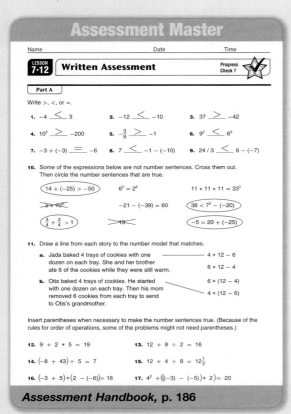

Assessment Handbook, p. 186

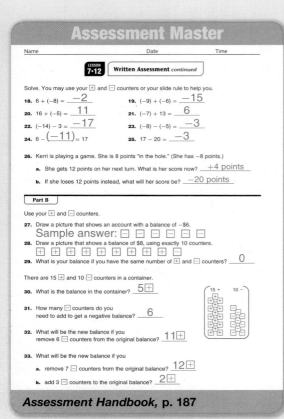

Assessment Handbook, p. 187

4. Write numbers given in scientific notation in number-and-word notation.

- $5 * 10^6$ 5 million
- $4 * 10^9$ 4 billion
- $1 * 10^8$ 100 million
- $7 * 10^3$ 7 thousand
- $6 * 10^5$ 600 thousand
- $3.2 * 10^9$ 3.2 billion, or 3 billion 200 million

▶ # Written Assessment

INDEPENDENT ACTIVITY

(*Assessment Handbook*, pp. 186–188)

Part A Recognizing Student Achievement

Problems 1–26 provide summative information and may be used for grading purposes.

Problem(s)	Description
1–9	Order and compare positive and negative numbers.
7–10, 18–26	Add and subtract positive and negative numbers.
10	Identify number sentences and tell whether they are true or false.
11–17	Understand and apply order of operations to evaluate expressions and solve number sentences.
11–17	Understand and apply the use of parentheses in number sentences.

Part B Informing Instruction

Problems 27–36 provide formative information that can be useful in planning future instruction.

Problem(s)	Description
27–33	Add and subtract positive and negative numbers.
34	Understand and apply scientific notation, powers of 10, and exponential notation.
35, 36	Create and use line graphs.

 Use the checklists on pages 271 and 273 of the *Assessment Handbook* to record results. Then input the data into the **Assessment Management Spreadsheets** to keep an ongoing record of students' progress toward Grade-Level Goals.

Open Response

(*Assessment Handbook*, p. 189)

Operations in the Klasies Caves

The open-response item requires students to apply skills and concepts from Unit 7 to solve a multistep problem. See *Assessment Handbook*, pages 105–109 for rubrics and students work samples for this problem.

INDEPENDENT ACTIVITY

---

(2) Looking Ahead: Preparing for Unit 8

Math Boxes 7·12

INDEPENDENT ACTIVITY

(*Math Journal 2*, p. 247)

Mixed Practice This Math Boxes page previews Unit 8 content.

Study Link 7·12: Unit 8 Family Letter

INDEPENDENT ACTIVITY

(*Math Masters*, pp. 217–220)

Home Connection The Unit 8 Family Letter provides parents and guardians with information and activities related to Unit 8 topics.

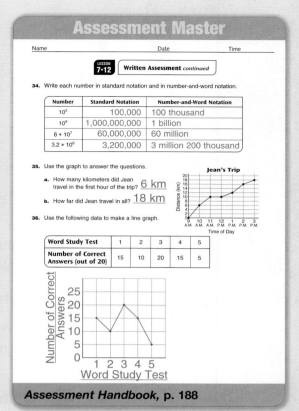

Assessment Handbook, p. 188

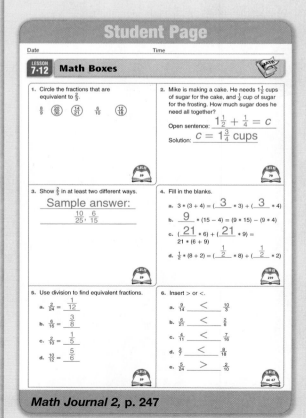

Math Journal 2, p. 247

Fractions and Ratios

▶ Overview

In Unit 8, students will review the concept of renaming fractions as equivalent fractions. They will also be introduced to algorithms for the multiplication of fractions and mixed numbers, and they will practice estimating and calculating a percent of a number. Unit 8 has four main areas of focus:

◆ To rename fractions as equivalent fractions,

◆ To use equivalent names for fractions and mixed numbers to perform operations,

◆ To introduce algorithms for the multiplication of fractions and mixed numbers,

◆ To practice estimating and calculating a percent of a number, and

◆ To introduce division of fractions with visual models.

CCSS Linking to the Common Core State Standards

The content of Unit 8 addresses the Common Core State Standards for Mathematics in *Number and Operations–Fractions*. The correlation of the Common Core State Standards to the *Everyday Mathematics* Grade 5 lessons begins on page CS1.

30% off

Contents

Unit 8 Organizer

Learning In Perspective

	Lesson Objectives	Links to the Past	Links to the Future
8·1	To review the use of equivalent fractions in comparisons.	In fourth grade, students practice identifying equivalent fractions.	In sixth grade, students find equivalents for any fraction, decimal, or percent.
8·2	To develop addition concepts related to mixed numbers.	In fourth grade, students add fractions.	In sixth grade, students add mixed numbers with like denominators.
8·3	To develop subtraction concepts related to mixed numbers.	In fourth grade, students subtract fractions.	In sixth grade, students subtract mixed numbers with like denominators.
8·4	To provide practice adding fractions with unlike denominators and using a calculator to solve fraction problems.	In fourth grade, students add and subtract fractions with like denominators.	In sixth grade, students add and subtract mixed numbers with unlike denominators.
8·5	To introduce finding a fraction of a fraction.	In fourth grade, students solve "fraction-of" number stories.	In sixth grade, students use an algorithm to find products of fractions.
8·6	To develop a fraction multiplication algorithm.	In fourth grade, students review and practice whole number multiplication algorithms.	In sixth grade, students represent the fraction multiplication algorithm as a general pattern.
8·7	To provide experience finding the product of a whole number and a fraction.	In fourth grade, students solve "fraction-of" and "percent-of" number stories.	In sixth grade, students multiply mixed numbers.
8·8	To introduce multiplication with mixed numbers.	In fourth grade, students solve "fraction-of" and "percent-of" number stories.	In sixth grade, students multiply mixed numbers.
8·9	To broaden students' understanding of calculating percents to include discounts.	In fourth grade, students use a calculator to rename fractions as decimals and as percents.	In sixth grade, students solve percent problems by writing and solving proportions.
8·10	To provide practice finding the whole, given a fraction or a percent of the whole.	In fourth grade, students find the whole, or the ONE, for given fractions.	In sixth grade, students review finding a percent of a number.
8·11	To provide experience with locating information on maps and charts and using percents to make estimates.	In fourth grade, students find latitude and longitude of places on a map and identify places given latitude and longitude.	In sixth grade, students analyze real-world situations by constructing and using data tables and graphs.
8·12	To introduce division of fractions and relate the operation of division to multiplication.	In fourth grade, students explore the relationship between multiplication and division and the relationship between fractions and division.	In sixth grade, students find reciprocals and are introduced to an algorithm for the division of fractions.

	Key Concepts and Skills	**Grade 5 Goals***
8·1	Find equivalent fractions.	Number and Numeration Goal 5
	Compare and order fractions.	Number and Numeration Goal 6
	Add fractions with common denominators.	Operations and Computation Goal 4
8·2	Find equivalent fractions in simplest form.	Number and Numeration Goal 5
	Convert between and simplify fractions and mixed numbers.	Number and Numeration Goal 5
	Add fractions and mixed numbers.	Operations and Computation Goal 4
	Use benchmarks to estimate sums.	Operations and Computation Goal 6
8·3	Find equivalent names for mixed numbers.	Number and Numeration Goal 5
	Convert between fractions and mixed numbers.	Number and Numeration Goal 5
	Subtract mixed numbers.	Operations and Computation Goal 4
	Use benchmarks to estimate differences.	Operations and Computation Goal 6
8·4	Convert between fractions and mixed numbers.	Number and Numeration Goal 5
	Express fractions and mixed numbers in simplest form.	Number and Numeration Goal 5
	Compare and order fractions.	Number and Numeration Goal 6
	Use mental arithmetic, paper-and-pencil algorithms, and calculators to solve fraction and mixed-number addition problems.	Operations and Computation Goal 4
	Use benchmarks to estimate sums.	Operations and Computation Goal 6
8·5	Use unit fractions to find a fraction of a number and to find the whole.	Operations and Computation Goal 5
	Use an area model to find fractions of fractions.	Operations and Computation Goal 5
8·6	Use an area model to find fractions of fractions.	Operations and Computation Goal 5
	Write number models for fraction multiplication problems shown with an area model.	Operations and Computation Goal 7
	Describe the patterns in the area model for fraction multiplication.	Patterns, Functions, and Algebra Goal 1
	Recognize the patterns in products when a number is multiplied by a fraction that is less than or equal to 1.	Patterns, Functions, and Algebra Goal 1
8·7	Find fractions of a set.	Number and Numeration Goal 2
	Use given denominators to rename numbers as fractions.	Number and Numeration Goal 5
	Use an area model and a fraction multiplication algorithm to find fraction-by-whole-number products.	Operations and Computation Goal 5
8·8	Convert between fractions and mixed numbers.	Number and Numeration Goal 5
	Multiply mixed numbers.	Operations and Computation Goal 5
	Use the partial-products algorithm to multiply whole numbers, fractions, and mixed numbers.	Operations and Computation Goal 5
	Recognize the patterns in products when a number is multiplied by a fraction that is less than 1, equal to 1, or greater than 1.	Patterns, Functions, and Algebra Goal 1
8·9	Calculate percents and discounts, and describe strategies used.	Number and Numeration Goal 2
	Convert between fractions, decimals, and percents.	Number and Numeration Goal 5
	Use ratios expressed as percents to solve problems.	Operations and Computation Goal 7
8·10	Use unit fractions and unit percents to find the whole.	Number and Numeration Goal 2
	Use unit fractions to solve fraction-of problems and unit percents to solve percent-of problems.	Number and Numeration Goal 2
	Find the unit fraction or percent of a given whole.	Number and Numeration Goal 2
	Convert between fractions and percents.	Number and Numeration Goal 5
8·11	Use unit fractions to solve fraction-of problems and unit percents to solve percent-of problems.	Number and Numeration Goal 2
	Find the unit fraction or unit percent of a given whole.	Number and Numeration Goal 2
	Collect and organize data from maps and charts.	Data and Chance Goal 1
8·12	Find common denominators for pairs of fractions.	Number and Numeration Goal 5
	Use diagrams and visual models for division of fractions problems.	Operations and Computation Goal 5
	Solve number stories involving division of a fraction by a whole number, division of a whole number by a fraction, and division of a fraction by a fraction.	Operations and Computation Goal 5
	Write equations to model number stories.	Patterns, Functions, and Algebra Goal 2

*See the Appendix for a complete list of Grade 5 Goals.

A Balanced Curriculum

Ongoing Practice

Everyday Mathematics provides numerous opportunities for ongoing practice. These activities are embedded throughout the lessons:

 Mental Math and Reflexes activities promote speed and accuracy in mental computation.

 Math Boxes offer mixed practice and are paired across lessons as shown in the brackets below. This makes them useful as assessment tools. The last one or two boxes on each page preview the next unit's content.

Mixed practice   [8•1, 8•3], [8•2, 8•4], [8•5, 8•7], [8•6, 8•8], [8•9, 8•11], [8•10, 8•12]

Mixed practice with writing/reasoning opportunity   8•2, 8•3, 8•4, 8•5, 8•8, 8•9

 Study Links are daily homework assignments that review the content of the lesson and often contain ongoing facts practice or computation practice.

 5-Minute Math problems are offered for additional practice in Lessons 8•3, 8•4, and 8•7.

 EM Facts Workshop Game provides online practice of basic facts and computation.

EXTRA PRACTICE **Extra Practice** activities are included in Lessons 8•2, 8•3, 8•4, 8•6, 8•7, 8•8, and 8•12.

Practice through Games

Games are an essential component of practice in the *Everyday Mathematics* program. Games offer skills practice and promote strategic thinking. See the *Differentiation Handbook* for ways to adapt games to meet students' needs.

Lesson	Game	Skill Practiced
8•1, 8•12	*Build-It*	Putting fractions in order from smallest to largest [NN Goal 6]
8•2, 8•11	*Fraction Capture*	Comparing fractions and finding equivalent fractions [NN Goal 5 and OC Goal 4]
8•3	*Mixed-Number Spin*	Estimating sums and differences of mixed numbers [OC Goals 4 and 6]
8•4	*Fraction Action, Fraction Friction*	Estimating sums of fractions using benchmarks [OC Goals 4 and 6]
8•5	*Fraction Spin*	Estimating sums and differences of fractions [OC Goals 4 and 6]
8•7	*Name That Number*	Writing number sentences using order of operations [NN Goal 4 and PFA Goal 3]
8•8	*Frac-Tac-Toe*	Converting between fractions, decimals, and percents [NN Goal 5]
8•10	*Factor Captor*	Practicing multiplication and division facts and factorization skills [NN Goal 3 and OC Goal 2]

[NN] Number and Numeration   [OC] Operations and Computation   [DC] Data and Chance
[MRF] Measurement and Reference Frames   [GEO] Geometry   [PFA] Patterns, Functions, and Algebra

Problem Solving

Experts at problem solving and mathematical modeling generally do these things:

- Identify the problem.
- Decide what information is needed to solve the problem.
- Play with and study the data to find patterns and meaning.

- Identify and use mathematical procedures to solve the problem.
- Decide whether the solution makes sense and whether it can be applied to other problems.

The table below lists some of the opportunities in this unit for students to practice these strategies.

Lesson	Activity
8◆3	Use a pattern to add and subtract unit fractions.
8◆4	Create equivalent fractions.
8◆5	Fold paper to solve fraction-of problems.
8◆6	Use an area model for fraction multiplication to solve problems.
8◆8	Use the partial products method to multiply mixed numbers.
8◆9	Calculate discount when given the percent of discount.
8◆10	Use a unit fraction or unit percent to solve number stories involving percents.
8◆11	Estimate rural and urban population in the United States in 1790, 1850, 1900, and 2000.
8◆12	Solve number stories involving division of fractions.

Lessons that teach through problem solving, not just about problem solving

See Chapter 18: Problem Solving in the *Teacher's Reference Manual* for more information.

The Language of Mathematics

Everyday Mathematics provides lesson-specific suggestions to help all students acquire, process, and express mathematical ideas. Throughout Unit 8, there are lesson-specific language development notes that address the needs of English language learners, indicated by **ELL**.

ELL SUPPORT Activities to support English language learners are in Part 3 of Lessons 8◆1 and 8◆5.

The *English Learners Handbook* and the *Differentiation Handbook* have suggestions for promoting language development and acquisition of mathematics vocabulary. See Unit 8 in each handbook.

> ## Unit 8 Vocabulary
> area model
> discount
> horizontal
> Quick Common
>   Denominator (QCD)
> unit fraction
> unit percent
> vertical

Literacy Connection

Fraction Action, by Loreen Leedy, Holiday House, 1996

Only One, by Marc Harshman, Dutton Children's, 1993

For more literacy connections, see the *Home Connection Handbook,* Grades 4–6.

Cross-Curricular Links

Science
Lesson 8◆4 Students study friction.

Social Studies
Lesson 8◆11 Students examine information about the United States in 1790, 1850, 1900, and 2000.

Balanced Assessment

 Daily Assessments

◆ **Recognizing Student Achievement** – A daily assessment that evaluates students' progress toward the Grade 5 Grade-Level Goals.

◆ **Informing Instruction** – Notes that help anticipate students' common errors and suggest appropriate problem-solving strategies.

Lesson	Recognizing Student Achievement	Informing Instruction
8◆1	Compare fractions and indicate whether a fraction is closest to 0, $\frac{1}{2}$, 1, $1\frac{1}{2}$, or 2. [NN Goal 6]	Use a straightedge to find the equivalent decimal for each fraction on the decimal number line.
8◆2	Rename fractions to have common denominators and to be in simplest form. [NN Goal 5 and OC Goal 4]	Discuss the meanings of *numerator* and *denominator,* and rename the fractional parts in the mixed numbers.
8◆3	Add, subtract, and compare mixed numbers. [OC Goals 4 and 6]	Practice renaming mixed numbers for subtraction.
8◆4	Identify the least, middle, and greatest fractions and place one or more fractions in proximity to each of these three. [NN Goal 6]	
8◆5	Demonstrate an understanding of fractional parts on a number line. [OC Goal 5]	
8◆6	Use and accurately sketch the area model for fraction multiplication. [OC Goal 5]	Use the folded-paper method to help sketch an area model.
8◆7	Convert fractions to decimals and percents and demonstrate an understanding of the role of the numerator and the denominator. [NN Goal 5]	
8◆8	Multiply mixed numbers and accurately describe the method used. [OC Goal 5]	Use a diagram to help write partial products in a column.
8◆9	Convert between fractions, decimals, and percents and express fractions in simplest form. [NN Goal 5]	
8◆10	Use unit fractions and unit percents to solve problems correctly. [NN Goal 2]	
8◆11	Use equivalent fractions to find pairs of fractions with sums greater than $\frac{1}{2}$. [NN Goal 5 and OC Goal 4]	
8◆12	Use a visual model to divide a whole number by a unit fraction. [OC Goal 5]	

[NN] Number and Numeration
[MRF] Measurement and Reference Frames

[OC] Operations and Computation
[GEO] Geometry

[DC] Data and Chance
[PFA] Patterns, Functions, and Algebra

Portfolio Opportunities

The following lessons provide opportunities to gather samples of students' mathematical writings, drawings, and creations: Lessons 8◆2, 8◆3, 8◆4, 8◆5, 8◆8, 8◆9, 8◆11, 8◆12, and 8◆13. See pages 16 and 17 in the *Assessment Handbook* for more information.

Unit Assessment

Progress Check 8 – A cumulative assessment of concepts and skills taught in Unit 8 and in previous units, providing information for evaluating students' progress and planning for future instruction. These assessments include oral/slate, written, and open-response activities, as shown below in the sample Progress Check lesson opener.

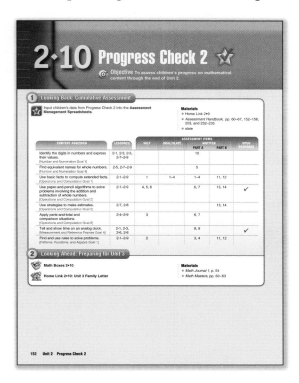

Core Assessment Resources

Assessment Handbook

- **Unit 8 Assessment Overview,** pages 110–117
- **Unit 8 Assessment Masters,** pages 190–193
- **Unit 8 Individual Profiles of Progress,** pages 274, 275, and 302
- **Unit 8 Class Checklists,** pages 276, 277, and 303
- **Math Logs,** pages 306–308
- **Exit Slip,** page 311
- **Other Student Assessment Forms,** pages 304, 305, 309, and 310

Assessment Management Spreadsheets

The Assessment Management Spreadsheets consist of the Digital Class Checklists and Individual Profile of Progress Checklists. Use them to monitor, record, and report student progress.

Addressing All Needs

Differentiated Instruction

 Adjusting the Activity – suggests adaptations that target advanced learners, English language learners, or learners who need additional instructional support.

ELL SUPPORT / **ELL** – provides lesson-specific suggestions to help English language learners understand and process the mathematical content.

READINESS – accesses students' prior knowledge or previews content that prepares students to engage in the lesson's Part 1 activities.

EXTRA PRACTICE – provides additional opportunities to apply the mathematical content of the lesson.

ENRICHMENT – enables students to apply or further explore the mathematical content of the lesson.

Lesson	Adjusting the Activity	ELL Support/ ELL	Readiness	Extra Practice	Enrichment
8·1	•	•	•		•
8·2			•	•	
8·3			•	•	•
8·4	•		•	•	•
8·5	•	•	•		•
8·6			•	•	
8·7			•	•	•
8·8			•	•	
8·9			•		•
8·10	•		•		•
8·11	•	•	•		•
8·12			•	•	•

▷ Additional Resources

Differentiation Handbook
Provides ideas and strategies for differentiating instruction.
Pages 99–105

English Learners Handbook
Contains lesson-specific comprehension strategies.
Pages 70–81

Multilingual Handbook
Previews concepts and vocabulary. It is written in six languages.
Pages 139–162

Planning Tips

Multiage Classroom

Companion Lessons from Grades 4 and 6 can help you meet instructional needs of a multiage classroom. The full Scope and Sequence can be found in the Appendix.

Grade 4	7•6, 7•7, 7•9				7•5		3•5	3•5		7•10		3•5
Grade 5	8•1	8•2	8•3	8•4	8•5	8•6	8•7	8•8	8•9	8•10	8•11	8•12
Grade 6	4•2	4•3	4•4			4•6		4•7, 6•1	4•8, 4•9, 4•11			6•2

Pacing for Success

Pacing depends on a number of factors, such as students' individual needs and how long your school has been using *Everyday Mathematics*. At the beginning of Unit 3, you may want to use tools available at www.everydaymathonline.com to help you set your pace.

Home Support

Unit 8 Family Letter (English/Spanish) provides families with an overview, Do-Anytime Activities, Building Skills through Games, a list of vocabulary, and answers to the daily homework (Study Links). Family Letters in English, Spanish, and seven other languages are also available online.

Study Links are the daily homework assignments. They consist of active projects and ongoing review problems.

▷ Home Support Resources

Home Connection Handbook
Offers ideas and reproducible masters for communicating with families. See Table of Contents for unit information.

Student Reference Book
Provides a resource for students and parents.
Pages 50, 52, 53, 74–78B, 80A, 80B, 260–265, 300, 306, 309–312, 325, 350, 351, 363, 376, 399, 401

Technology Resources

Algorithms Practice

EM Facts Workshop Game™

Family Letters

Interactive Teacher's Lesson Guide

www.everydaymathonline.com

Unit 8 Organizer

Materials

Technology Resources www.everydaymathonline.com

ePresentations

eToolkit

Algorithms Practice

EM Facts Workshop Game™

Family Letters

Assessment Management

Common Core State Standards

Curriculum Focal Points

Interactive Teacher's Lesson Guide

Lesson	Masters	Manipulative Kit	Other Items
8·1	Game Masters, pp. 446 and 447 Transparencies of *Math Masters*, pp. 446* and 447* Study Link Master, p. 221 Teaching Master, p. 222 *Differentiation Handbook*, p. 142		Geometry Template; 3" by 5" index cards cut in half*; red and blue colored pencils or markers; heavy string or rope 8'–10' long; 3" by 5" index cards; thick marker; paper clips; scissors; straightedge; calculator
8·2	Teaching Aid Master, p. 414 Study Link Master, p. 223 Game Master, p. 460 Teaching Master, p. 253A	slate; per partnership: 2 six-sided dice	Class Data Pad*
8·3	Teaching Aid Master, p. 414 Study Link Master, p. 224 Game Masters, pp. 488 and 489 Teaching Master, p. 225	slate	Geometry Template; per partnership: 1 large paper clip
8·4	Game Master, p. 459 Study Link Master, p. 226 Teaching Masters, pp. 227 and 228 Transparency of *Math Masters*, p. 227	slate	scissors; per partnership: eight 3" by 5" cards cut in half*; overhead calculator*; calculator
8·5	Teaching Aid Master, p. 414 Transparency of Teaching Aid Master, p. 434* Study Link Master, p. 229 Game Master, p. 471 Teaching Master, p. 230 *Differentiation Handbook*, p. 142	slate	5 sheets of $8\frac{1}{2}$" by 11" paper; scissors; posterboard; Class Data Pad*; per partnership: large paper clip, 3" by 5" index cards (15)*; calculator
8·6	Transparency of *Math Masters*, p. 231* Study Link Master, p. 232 Teaching Masters, pp. 233 and 234	slate	Geometry Template
8·7	Study Link Master, p. 235 Teaching Master, p. 236	slate; per partnership: 4 each of number cards 0–9	Class Data Pad*; calculator*
8·8	Teaching Aid Master, p. 414 Study Link Master, p. 237 Game Masters, pp. 472–484	slate; per partnership: 4 each of number cards 0–10	per partnership: counters; calculator*
8·9	Study Link Master, p. 238 Teaching Masters, pp. 239 and 240	slate	overhead calculator*; calculator
8·10	Transparency of *Math Masters*, p. 435 Study Link Master, p. 241 Game Masters, pp. 454 and 455 Teaching Masters, pp. 242 and 243	slate	Class Data Pad; ruler; paper and pencil; per partnership: 70 counters; calculator
8·11	Transparency of *Math Masters*, p. 244 Study Link Master, p. 245 Game Masters, pp. 460 and 461 Teaching Masters, pp. 246 and 247	slate; per partnership: 2 six-sided dice	2 different-colored pencils; calculator
8·12	Transparency of Teaching Aid Master, p. 440B* Study Link Master, p. 248 Teaching Master, p. 249 Game Masters, pp. 446 and 447	slate; per partnership: 1 six-sided die	Class Data Pad; calculator; ruler
8·13	Assessment Masters, pp. 190–193 Study Link Masters, pp. 250–253	slate	ruler; calculator

*Denotes optional materials

Mathematical Background

The discussion below highlights the major content ideas presented in Unit 8 and helps establish instructional priorities.

Comparing, Adding, Subtracting, and Dividing Fractions and Mixed Numbers (Lessons 8•1–8•4 and 8•12)

The procedures used in *Everyday Mathematics* to compare, add, subtract, and divide fractions are based on renaming the fractions as equivalent fractions with common denominators. If two fractions have the same denominator:

- The fraction with the larger numerator is greater than the fraction with the smaller numerator.

- The sum (or difference) of the fractions is obtained by adding (or subtracting) the numerators and dividing this result by the common denominator.

- The quotient of the fractions is obtained by dividing the numerators.

Mixed numbers may be added or subtracted by operating on the whole-number part and the fraction part of the mixed numbers separately. In some addition problems, this may require renaming the sum so that the fraction part is a proper fraction. In some subtraction problems, this may require renaming the minuend, if the fraction part of the minuend is less than the fraction part of the subtrahend.

For easy fractions, which are the only fractions that most people need, it is not difficult to find common denominators once one understands what mathematical procedures to use. Students should do this first by simply scanning lists of equivalent names, perhaps finding not merely one, but several possibilities. For easy fractions, many people do a mental scan when they need common denominators.

Anticipating Algebra: Quick Common Denominators

In adding, subtracting, dividing, or comparing fractions, any common denominator works as well as any other, and finding a "quick common denominator" (QCD) as the product of two denominators is very useful. For example, a common denominator for $\frac{5}{6}$ and $\frac{3}{8}$ can be found by multiplying $6 * 8 = 48$.

Hence, finding QCDs is suggested as the preferred method whenever the fractions are complex enough that the least common denominator or other common denominators are not obvious. Furthermore, QCDs are nearly always used for fraction problems in the algebra courses your students will soon be taking. This is because algebra models for solving problems usually involve variables, and without knowing actual numbers, finding the LCD is impossible. For example, for an expression like $\frac{a}{b} + \frac{c}{d}$, the product $b * d$ is the only logical choice for the common denominator. Therefore, the algebra rule for adding fractions becomes:

$$\frac{a}{b} + \frac{c}{d} = \frac{(a * d) + (c * b)}{b * d}$$

Regarding Simplest Form, Mixed Numbers, and Fractions Greater than 1

It is important to know how to exploit the fact that there are many equivalent names for any fraction. It is useful to know that among the names, there is a fraction in "simplest form"—that is, its numerator and denominator have no common factors—and that the simplest form is a convenient label for the entire collection of equivalent fractions.

It is also useful to know that if the numerator is larger than the denominator, there are equivalent names that are "mixed numbers," some with the numerator still larger than the denominator, some with the fraction part in simplest form, and some with the fraction part not in simplest form.

 You can find more about working with mixed numbers and fractions in Section 11.3 of the *Teacher's Reference Manual.*

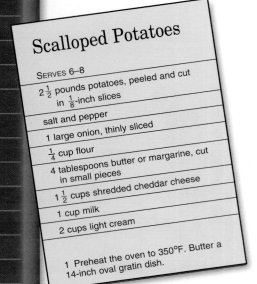

Scalloped Potatoes

SERVES 6–8

$2\frac{1}{2}$ pounds potatoes, peeled and cut in $\frac{1}{8}$-inch slices

salt and pepper

1 large onion, thinly sliced

$\frac{1}{4}$ cup flour

4 tablespoons butter or margarine, cut in small pieces

$1\frac{1}{2}$ cups shredded cheddar cheese

1 cup milk

2 cups light cream

1 Preheat the oven to 350°F. Butter a 14-inch oval gratin dish.

"Many of" and "Part of" as Indicators of Multiplication

(Lessons 8•5–8•10)

Verbal cues are generally an inadequate guide in deciding which number model to use in solving a problem. For example, "more" does not necessarily signal "add." But "many of" and "part of" do seem to be closely tied to multiplication. A student is more likely to succeed when responding to $\frac{1}{2} * 12$ as "one-half of 12," rather than as "one-half times 12." This is even more true if a student responds to "$\frac{1}{2} * \frac{1}{2}$" or "$\frac{1}{2} * \frac{2}{3}$" as "one-half of one-half" or "one-half of two-thirds," rather than as "one-half times one-half" or "one-half times two-thirds."

 For more about indicators of multiplication, refer to Section 10.3.2 of the *Teacher's Reference Manual.*

The Algorithm for Multiplication of Numbers Expressed as Fractions and Mixed Numbers

(Lessons 8•5–8•8)

These lessons provide the first introduction in *Everyday Mathematics* to the symbolic algorithm for multiplication of fractions. The algorithm for multiplication of fractions is not difficult, but without considerable informal experience, children and adults alike find the algorithm meaningless.

The paper-folding exercises of Lesson 8-5 give concrete meaning to finding a fractional part of a fractional part. These exercises show that the denominator of the product (the total number of sections in a folded sheet of paper) is the product of the two denominators, and the numerator of the product (the number of sections in the "part of a part") is the product of the numerators.

In other words, the paper-folding exercise is the exact counterpart of the algorithm. In Lesson 8-6 through 8-8 an area-model diagram is introduced that is much like a picture of the paper-folding results. It is easier and faster than paper folding, and it is also the exact counterpart of the algorithm.

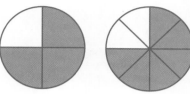

$\frac{3}{4}$ and $\frac{6}{8}$ name the same amount.
So, $\frac{3}{4}$ and $\frac{6}{8}$ are equivalent.
$$\frac{3}{4} = \frac{6}{8}$$

Lessons 8-7 and 8-8 show that multiplication of fractions and whole numbers or mixed numbers can be done by using equivalent fraction names for the whole or mixed numbers.

$$\frac{2}{3} * 4 = \frac{2}{3} * \frac{4}{1} = \frac{2*4}{3*1} = \frac{8}{3}, \text{ or } 2\frac{2}{3}$$
$$\frac{4}{5} * 3\frac{1}{2} = \frac{4}{5} * \frac{7}{2} = \frac{4*7}{5*2} = \frac{28}{10}, \text{ or } 2\frac{8}{10}$$

 **PROFESSIONAL DEVELOPMENT** More on multiplication of numbers expressed as fractions and mixed numbers can be found in Section 11.3.4 of the *Teacher's Reference Manual*.

Unit Rate, Unit Fraction, and Unit Percent Strategies (Lessons 8•9 and 8•10)

The need to use ratios, rates, and proportional thinking is very common in the everyday world. There is probably no better indication of good "number sense" and "measure sense" than ease and skill in those uses. The key to understanding ratios and rates is to have many experiences with them, and that has been one of the main goals in *Everyday Mathematics*.

One of the most powerful tools in using fractions and percents is the unit fraction (or unit percent) strategy. This strategy can be used to find a whole amount when a fractional part is known. For example:

If 10 counters are $\frac{2}{5}$ of the whole set, then 5 counters are $\frac{1}{5}$, and the whole is 5 fifths, or 25.

If the 8% sales tax on the price of an item is $3.20, then 1% of the price is $0.40, and the whole price is 100 * $0.40, or $40.

This strategy is one of those that are "better caught than taught," so the lesson consists mainly of problems to be done, with solution strategies to be discussed.

 **PROFESSIONAL DEVELOPMENT** For more unit strategies, see Section 9.3 of the *Teacher's Reference Manual*.

8·1 Review: Comparing Fractions

Objectives To review the use of equivalent fractions in comparisons.

Technology Resources www.everydaymathonline.com

 ePresentations

 eToolkit

 Algorithms Practice

 EM Facts Workshop Game™

 Family Letters

 Assessment Management

 Common Core State Standards

 Curriculum Focal Points

iTLG Interactive Teacher's Lesson Guide

1 Teaching the Lesson

Key Concepts and Skills

- Find equivalent fractions.
  [Number and Numeration Goal 5]
- Compare and order fractions.
  [Number and Numeration Goal 6]
- Add fractions with common denominators.
  [Operations and Computation Goal 4]

Key Activities

Students rename fractions as equivalent fractions. They compare fractions by renaming them as equivalent fractions with a common denominator. They play *Build-It* to practice comparing and ordering fractions.

 Ongoing Assessment: Recognizing Student Achievement Use Mental Math and Reflexes.
[Number and Numeration Goal 6]

 Ongoing Assessment: Informing Instruction See page 620.

Key Vocabulary

Quick Common Denominator (QCD)

Materials

Math Journal 2, pp. 248 and 249
Student Reference Book, pp. 300, 399, and 401
Math Masters, pp. 446 and 447
transparencies of *Math Masters,* pp. 446 and 447 (optional) ◆ 3" by 5" index cards cut in half (optional) ◆ red and blue colored pencils or markers ◆ scissors ◆ straightedge ◆ calculator

2 Ongoing Learning & Practice

 Math Boxes 8·1
Math Journal 2, p. 250
Geometry Template
Students practice and maintain skills through Math Box problems.

 Study Link 8·1
Math Masters, p. 221
Students practice and maintain skills through Study Link activities.

3 Differentiation Options

READINESS

Ordering Fractions on a Rope
rope or heavy string 8'–10' long ◆ 3" by 5" index cards ◆ thick marker ◆ paper clips
Students make and order fractions on a number line.

ENRICHMENT

Exploring Least Common Multiples
Math Masters, p. 222
Students explore methods for finding least common multiples.

ELL SUPPORT

Building a Math Word Bank
Differentiation Handbook, p. 142
Students define and illustrate the term *quick common denominator* and identify related words.

Advance Preparation

For Part 1, have students cut out the 16 fraction cards on *Math Masters,* page 446 before the lesson. They will also need to cut *Math Masters,* page 447 into halves. You can make a transparency of these *Math Masters* pages to play the game on the overhead. For the optional Readiness activity in Part 3, hang the string or rope where it will be visible to all students and within their reach during the activity.

 Teacher's Reference Manual, Grades 4–6 pp. 62, 63, 141, 142

Getting Started

Mental Math and Reflexes

State each fraction and ask students to indicate whether it is closest to the benchmark of 0, $\frac{1}{2}$, 1, $1\frac{1}{2}$, or 2. Have students use thumbs up to indicate their choices. *Suggestions:*

●○○ $\frac{2}{10}$ 0 ●●○ $\frac{3}{10}$ $\frac{1}{2}$ ●●● $\frac{5}{3}$ $1\frac{1}{2}$

    $\frac{6}{10}$ $\frac{1}{2}$ $\frac{9}{8}$ 1 $\frac{9}{5}$ 2

    $\frac{8}{10}$ 1 $\frac{15}{8}$ 2 $\frac{8}{5}$ $1\frac{1}{2}$

Math Message

Complete Problems 1–4 at the top of journal page 248.

✔ Ongoing Assessment: Recognizing Student Achievement

Mental Math and Reflexes ★

Use the **Mental Math and Reflexes** problems to assess students' ability to compare fractions. Students are making adequate progress if they indicate the correct benchmark for the ●○○ and ●●○ fractions.

[Number and Numeration Goal 6]

---

1   Teaching the Lesson

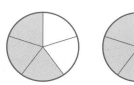

▶ Math Message Follow-Up   WHOLE-CLASS ACTIVITY

(*Math Journal 2*, p. 248; *Student Reference Book,* p. 399)

Ask students to compare their answers for the Math Message problems and share how they decided which fraction in each pair is greater. Ask volunteers to share their strategies.

▷ **Problem 1** Since the denominators are the same, the wholes are divided into the same number of parts. This means the parts are the same size, so it is easy to compare the number of shaded parts and decide which fraction is greater.

▷ **Problem 2** The numerators are the same, but the denominators are not. This means that there are the same number of shaded parts, but the parts are different sizes. The fewer the number of parts that the whole is divided into, the larger each part is. Therefore, the fraction with the smaller denominator is the greater fraction.

Interactive whiteboard-ready ePresentations are available at www.everydaymathonline.com to help you teach the lesson.

Student Page

Date _____   Time _____

LESSON 8·1

Comparing Fractions

Math Message

Write < or >. Be prepared to explain how you decided on each answer.

1. $\frac{3}{5}$ $<$ $\frac{4}{5}$ 2. $\frac{4}{5}$ $>$ $\frac{4}{7}$

3. $\frac{5}{9}$ $>$ $\frac{3}{7}$ 4. $\frac{7}{8}$ $>$ $\frac{6}{7}$

   < means *is less than.*
   > means *is more than.*

Equivalent Fractions

Cross out the fraction in each list that is not equivalent to the other fractions.

5. $\frac{2}{3}$, $\frac{4}{6}$, $\frac{12}{24}$, $\frac{20}{30}$ 6. $\frac{1}{4}$, $\frac{2}{8}$, $\frac{6}{24}$, $\frac{8}{32}$ 7. $\frac{3}{5}$, $\frac{6}{10}$, $\frac{9}{20}$, $\frac{15}{25}$

Write = or ≠ in each box.

8. $\frac{3}{5}$ $\neq$ $\frac{10}{15}$ 9. $\frac{6}{8}$ $\neq$ $\frac{16}{24}$

10. $\frac{15}{24}$ $=$ $\frac{5}{8}$ 11. $\frac{6}{14}$ $\neq$ $\frac{2}{7}$

   ≠ means *is not equal to.*

Give three equivalent fractions for each fraction. Sample answers:

12. $\frac{6}{18}$, $\frac{12}{70}$ $\frac{18}{35}$ $\frac{60}{700}$ 13. $\frac{50}{100}$, $\frac{1}{2}$ $\frac{2}{4}$ $\frac{25}{50}$ $\frac{30}{}$ $\frac{60}{}$ $\frac{5}{}$

14. $\frac{7}{10}$, $\frac{70}{100}$ $\frac{50}{}$ $\frac{1,000}{}$ 15. $\frac{15}{18}$, $\frac{30}{36}$ $\frac{60}{72}$ $\frac{5}{6}$

Fill in the missing number.

16. $\frac{3}{4} = \frac{27}{36}$ 17. $\frac{3}{5} = \frac{12}{20}$ 18. $5 = \frac{10}{2}$

19. $\frac{12}{9} = \frac{24}{18}$ 20. $\frac{9}{12} = \frac{3}{4}$ 21. $\frac{16}{20} = \frac{8}{10}$

22. $\frac{2}{5} = \frac{6}{15}$ 23. $\frac{15}{25} = \frac{3}{5}$ 24. $\frac{4}{9} = \frac{16}{36}$

Write < or >.

25. $\frac{2}{5}$ $<$ $\frac{5}{10}$ 26. $\frac{3}{4}$ $<$ $\frac{5}{6}$ 27. $\frac{3}{8}$ $>$ $\frac{2}{7}$ 28. $\frac{3}{5}$ $>$ $\frac{4}{7}$

Math Journal 2, p. 248

Tables and Charts

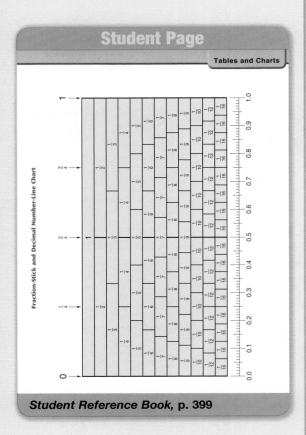

Fraction-Stick and Decimal Number-Line Chart

Student Reference Book, p. 399

▷ **Problem 3** Neither the numerators nor the denominators are the same. Use a reference number to compare the fractions. One fraction is greater than $\frac{1}{2}$ and the other fraction is less than $\frac{1}{2}$.

▷ **Problem 4** Each of the fractions is one fractional part less than a whole. The larger the part is, the smaller the denominator is, and the further away the fraction is from one whole. Therefore, the fraction with the smaller denominator is the lesser fraction.

Ask volunteers how they would determine whether $\frac{3}{5}$ or $\frac{5}{8}$ is greater. The methods outlined above don't work in this case. A method that does work is to use the Fraction-Stick and Decimal Number-Line Chart on *Student Reference Book,* page 399.

Ask a volunteer to explain how to use the chart to determine which fraction is greater. Locate $\frac{3}{5}$ and $\frac{5}{8}$ on the chart. Since the line for $\frac{5}{8}$ is to the right of the line for $\frac{3}{5}$, we know that $\frac{5}{8} > \frac{3}{5}$.

Pose several problems for students to solve with the Fraction-Stick Chart. *Suggestions:*

Which is greater?

- $\frac{5}{7}$ or $\frac{7}{10}$ $\frac{5}{7}$
- $\frac{4}{5}$ or $\frac{13}{16}$ $\frac{13}{16}$
- $\frac{2}{7}$ or $\frac{1}{4}$ $\frac{2}{7}$

 Ongoing Assessment: Informing Instruction

Watch for students who have trouble isolating the relevant rows when making comparisons on the Fraction-Stick Chart. Have them use a vertical straightedge to find the equivalent decimal for each fraction on the decimal number line. Then compare the decimals or their relative positions. For example, $\frac{3}{5}$ aligns with 0.6 and $\frac{5}{8}$ aligns with 0.63; 0.63 is to the right of 0.6, so 0.63 > 0.60, and $\frac{5}{8} > \frac{3}{5}$.

▶ **Renaming Fractions as Equivalent Fractions**

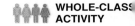 **WHOLE-CLASS ACTIVITY**

(*Student Reference Book,* pp. 399 and 401)

Ask volunteers to guide the class in the steps for using the Fraction-Stick and Decimal Number-Line Chart on page 399 to find equivalent fractions for $\frac{1}{4}$ and $\frac{2}{3}$.

Then ask students to explain how they would find equivalent fractions without using this chart. The discussion should include the following methods:

▷ Use a multiplication table.

▷ Look up fractions in the table of Equivalent Fractions, Decimals, and Percents (*Student Reference Book,* page 401). Point out that the first fraction in each row is in simplest form.

▷ Use the multiplication rule. Multiplying the numerator and denominator of a fraction by the same (nonzero) number yields an equivalent fraction.

Example: $\frac{2}{3} = \frac{2*3}{3*3} = \frac{6}{9}$

Tables and Charts

Equivalent Fractions, Decimals, and Percents

Note: The decimals for sevenths have been rounded to the nearest thousandth.

Student Reference Book, p. 401

▷ Use the division rule. Dividing the numerator and denominator of a fraction by the same (nonzero) number yields an equivalent fraction.

Example: $\frac{12}{15} = \frac{12 \div 3}{15 \div 3} = \frac{4}{5}$

NOTE The multiplication method for finding equivalent fractions can be expressed as $\frac{a}{b} = \frac{n * a}{n * b}$, where $b \neq 0$ and $n \neq 0$. This does not change the value of the original fraction because multiplying by $\frac{n}{n}$ is equivalent to multiplying by 1.

▶ Comparing Fractions Using Common Denominators

WHOLE-CLASS ACTIVITY

Ask students to compare the fractions $\frac{2}{3}$ and $\frac{3}{5}$ and share solution strategies. If the idea is not mentioned, remind students that if two fractions have the same denominator, they only have to compare numerators to tell which is greater. Another approach for comparing fractions is to rename them as equivalent fractions with a common denominator.

Review finding a common denominator and renaming fractions using the **Quick Common Denominator (QCD)** and the multiplication rule, introduced in Lesson 6-10. The QCD is the product of the denominators you are renaming.

To use this method to compare $\frac{2}{3}$ and $\frac{3}{5}$:

1. Find the QCD. $3 * 5 = 15$.
2. Rename $\frac{2}{3}$: $\frac{2}{3} = \frac{2 * 5}{3 * 5} = \frac{10}{15}$
3. Rename $\frac{3}{5}$: $\frac{3}{5} = \frac{3 * 3}{5 * 3} = \frac{9}{15}$

Because $10 > 9$, $\frac{10}{15} > \frac{9}{15}$, and $\frac{2}{3} > \frac{3}{5}$.

Write a few comparison-of-fractions problems on the board or a transparency. Ask students to solve them by renaming the fractions so they have a common denominator. *Suggestions:*

- $\frac{3}{4} \underline{\ >\ } \frac{5}{8}$
- $\frac{5}{6} \underline{\ >\ } \frac{3}{4}$
- $\frac{1}{6} \underline{\ <\ } \frac{2}{9}$
- $\frac{6}{9} \underline{\ <\ } \frac{5}{6}$

Ask volunteers to explain their solutions. The QCD can be used for all of the problems, but emphasize that depending on the fractions involved, it might not be the most efficient method for finding a common denominator.

In the first problem, only one of the fractions, $\frac{3}{4}$, needs to be renamed because 4 is a factor of 8: $\frac{3}{4} = \frac{3 * 2}{4 * 2} = \frac{6}{8}$. For the last problem, $\frac{6}{9}$ can be renamed as $\frac{2}{3}$, and 3 is a factor of 6, so $\frac{2}{3} = \frac{2 * 2}{3 * 2} = \frac{4}{6}$. Since $\frac{6}{9} = \frac{4}{6}$, then $\frac{6}{9} < \frac{5}{6}$.

▶ Finding Equivalent Fractions

PARTNER ACTIVITY

(*Math Journal 2*, pp. 248 and 249)

Ask students to complete journal pages 248 and 249. Circulate and assist.

Student Page

Date _____ Time _____

LESSON 8·1 Fraction Review

1. a. Shade $\frac{1}{4}$ of the fraction stick.
   b. Use the fraction stick to find equivalent fractions: $\frac{1}{4} = \frac{\boxed{2}}{8} = \frac{\boxed{4}}{16}$
   c. $\frac{1}{4} + \frac{1}{4} = \underline{\frac{2}{4}, \text{ or } \frac{1}{2}}$

2. a. Shade $\frac{3}{8}$ of the fraction stick.
   b. Is this more or less than $\frac{1}{2}$? Less than $\frac{1}{2}$
   c. Is this more or less than $\frac{1}{4}$? More than $\frac{1}{4}$
   d. $\frac{3}{8} + \frac{1}{8} = \underline{\frac{4}{8}, \text{ or } \frac{1}{2}}$

3. Joe had 2 granola bars. He ate $1\frac{1}{2}$ bars.
   a. Shade the part that he ate.
   b. Write the part he ate as a decimal. ____1.5____

4. Circle the decimal that is equivalent to each fraction. Use your calculator to help you.
   a. $\frac{1}{4} =$ 0.5   0.14   (0.25)   1.4
   b. $\frac{1}{10} =$ 1.10   (0.1)   0.010   0.50
   c. $\frac{2}{5} =$ (0.4)   0.25   2.5   0.2

5. Lucy had 16 beads. Half the beads were red. One fourth were blue. The rest were white.
   a. Color $\frac{1}{2}$ of the beads red and $\frac{1}{4}$ blue.
   b. What fraction of the beads are white? $\underline{\frac{4}{16}, \text{ or } \frac{1}{4}}$
   c. Lucy put away all the white beads. What fraction of the remaining beads are red? $\underline{\frac{8}{12}, \text{ or } \frac{2}{3}}$

Math Journal 2, p. 249

Student Page

Games

Build-It

Materials □ 1 *Build-It* Card Deck (*Math Masters*, p. 446)
□ 1 *Build-It* Gameboard for each player (*Math Masters*, p. 447)

Players 2

Skill Comparing and ordering fractions

Object of the game To be the first player to arrange 5 fraction cards in order from smallest to largest.

Directions

1. Shuffle the fraction cards. Deal 1 card number-side down on each of the 5 spaces on the 2 *Build-It* gameboards.

2. Put the remaining cards number-side down for a **draw pile.** Turn the top card over and place it number-side up in a **discard pile.**

3. Players turn over the 5 cards on their gameboards. Do not change the order of the cards at any time during the game.

4. Players take turns. When it is your turn:
   ◆ Take either the top card from the draw pile or the top card from the discard pile.
   ◆ Decide whether to keep this card or put it on the discard pile.
   ◆ If you keep the card, it must replace 1 of the 5 cards on your *Build-It* gameboard. Put the replaced card on the discard pile.

5. If all the cards in the draw pile are used, shuffle the discard pile. Place them number-side down in a draw pile. Turn over the top card to start a new discard pile.

6. The winner is the first player to have all 5 cards on his or her gameboard in order from the smallest fraction to the largest.

Build-It Card Deck

$\frac{5}{9}$	$\frac{1}{3}$	$\frac{11}{12}$	$\frac{1}{12}$
$\frac{7}{12}$	$\frac{3}{8}$	$\frac{1}{4}$	$\frac{1}{5}$
$\frac{2}{3}$	$\frac{3}{7}$	$\frac{4}{7}$	$\frac{3}{4}$
$\frac{3}{5}$	$\frac{4}{5}$	$\frac{7}{9}$	$\frac{5}{6}$

Build-It Gameboard

Closest to 0   Closest to 1

Student Reference Book, p. 300

Adjusting the Activity

Have students make their own set of *Build-It* cards on 3 in. by 5 in. cards that have been cut in half.

AUDITORY ◆ KINESTHETIC ◆ TACTILE ◆ VISUAL

Student Page

Date   Time

LESSON 8·1   Math Boxes

1. Make a circle graph of the survey results.

Favorite After-School Activity

Activity	Students
Eat Snack	18%
Visit Friends	35%
Watch TV	22%
Read	10%
Play Outside	15%

Favorite After-School Activity
title

18% 15% 10% 22% 35%

SRB 126 127

2. Write each numeral in number-and-word notation.

   a. 43,000,000 43 million

   b. 607,000 607 thousand

   c. 3,000,000,000 3 billion

   d. 72,000 72 thousand

SRB 4

3. True or False? Write T or F.

   a. A square is also a rectangle. T

   b. Some trapezoids are rectangles. F

   c. All kites are quadrangles. T

   d. A rhombus is not a parallelogram. F

SRB 146

4. Complete the "What's My Rule?" table and state the rule.

Rule
out = 5 * in

in	out
3	15
8	40
$\frac{1}{2}$	$2\frac{1}{2}$
10	50
4	20

SRB 231 232

5. Find the area of the rectangle.

Area = b * h

14 cm
8 cm

Area: 112 cm² (unit)

SRB 189

Math Journal 2, p. 250

▶ **Playing *Build-It***   PARTNER ACTIVITY

(*Student Reference Book,* pp. 300, 399; *Math Masters,* pp. 446, 447)

Students cut out the 16 fraction cards from *Math Masters,* page 446. They cut *Math Masters,* page 447 in half to create 2 gameboards. Only one set of cards per partnership is needed to play the game, but a gameboard is required for each student.

Go over the rules on *Student Reference Book,* page 300, and play a practice round with the class. Remind students to use the benchmarks $\frac{1}{2}$ and 1 as they consider the placement of fractions and make comparisons with the other fractions on their gameboard. Then have partners play several rounds on their own. Remind students that they cannot change the order of their 5 cards. They replace cards until the fractions are in order from smallest to largest. After students have played *Build-It* several times, suggest that they play without the game-board. Have students store their fraction cards for future use.

2 Ongoing Learning & Practice

▶ **Math Boxes 8·1**   INDEPENDENT ACTIVITY

(*Math Journal 2,* p. 250)

Mixed Practice Math Boxes in this lesson are paired with Math Boxes in Lesson 8-3. The skill in Problem 5 previews Unit 9 content.

▶ **Study Link 8·1**   INDEPENDENT ACTIVITY

(*Math Masters,* p. 221)

Home Connection Students practice comparing fractions. Remind students that they can decide which fraction is greater by using the strategies discussed in the lesson such as comparing each fraction to $\frac{1}{2}$ or finding the Quick Common Denominator. Students also find decimal equivalents for fractions.

3 Differentiation Options

READINESS   SMALL-GROUP ACTIVITY

▶ **Ordering Fractions on a Rope**   5–15 Min

To provide experience with ordering fractions, have students order fractions on a number line. Ask each student to write a fraction greater than 0 and less than 1 on a 3 in. by 5 in. card. Consider assigning denominators to small groups and having them compare their numerators in the groups to avoid duplications.

Students link two paper clips together and attach their card to it. They go to the number line string one (or a few) at a time to hang their fractions in order, between 0 and 1. Do not worry about spacing. It is more important that the fraction cards be placed in the correct order. The task will become more difficult as additional fractions are added to the string. If two fractions are equivalent, clip the fraction cards together as illustrated.

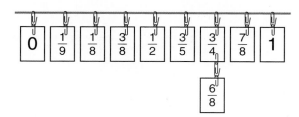

PARTNER ACTIVITY

15–30 Min

Exploring Least Common Multiples

(*Math Masters*, p. 222)

To apply students' understanding of equivalent fractions, have them explore finding the least common multiple of two or more numbers. Students find the least common multiple by making lists and using the prime factorization of numbers. When students have completed the page, have them solve the following problems:

- $\frac{4}{9} + \frac{5}{6} + \frac{1}{4}$ $\frac{55}{36}$, or $1\frac{19}{36}$
- $\frac{8}{20} + \frac{88}{90}$ $\frac{248}{180}$, $1\frac{68}{180}$, or $1\frac{17}{45}$
- $\frac{11}{15} + \frac{22}{49}$ $\frac{869}{735}$, or $1\frac{134}{735}$

In the third problem, the least common multiple and the quick common denominator are the same. Ask volunteers to share how they decide on a method to find common denominators. Sample answer: Choose the most efficient method depending on the numbers. With smaller numbers or by first using prime factorizations, you can do the computations faster, because you can do much of it mentally.

SMALL-GROUP ACTIVITY

15–30 Min

Building a Math Word Bank

(*Differentiation Handbook*, p. 142)

To provide language support for fraction concepts, have students use the Word Bank Template found on *Differentiation Handbook*, page 142. Ask students to write the term *quick common denominator*, draw pictures relating to the term, and write other related words. See the *Differentiation Handbook* for more information.

8·2 Adding Mixed Numbers

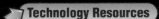

Objectives To develop addition concepts related to mixed numbers.

Technology Resources www.everydaymathonline.com

 ePresentations

 eToolkit

 Algorithms Practice

 EM Facts Workshop Game™

 Family Letters

 Assessment Management

 Common Core State Standards

 Curriculum Focal Points

 NCTM Curriculum Focal Points

 Interactive Teacher's Lesson Guide

1 Teaching the Lesson

Key Concepts and Skills

- Find equivalent fractions in simplest form.
  [Number and Numeration Goal 5]

- Convert between and simplify fractions and mixed numbers.
  [Number and Numeration Goal 5]

- Add fractions and mixed numbers.
  [Operations and Computation Goal 4]

- Use benchmarks to estimate sums.
  [Operations and Computation Goal 6]

Key Activities

Students review fraction addition. They add mixed numbers in which the fractional parts have like or unlike denominators and rename the sums in simplest form. Students use benchmarks to estimate sums.

 Ongoing Assessment:
Informing Instruction See page 626.

 Ongoing Assessment:
Recognizing Student Achievement
Use an Exit Slip (*Math Masters*, page 414).
[Number and Numeration Goal 5; Operations and Computation Goal 4]

Materials

Math Journal 2, pp. 251 and 252
Study Link 8·1
Math Masters, p. 414
slate ◆ Class Data Pad (optional)

2 Ongoing Learning & Practice

Math Boxes 8·2
Math Journal 2, p. 253
Students practice and maintain skills through Math Box problems.

Study Link 8·2
Math Masters, p. 223
Students practice and maintain skills through Study Link activities.

3 Differentiation Options

READINESS
Adding Mixed Numbers
Math Journal 2, p. 252
Students explore an alternate method for adding mixed numbers.

EXTRA PRACTICE
Playing *Fraction Capture*
Math Journal 1, p. 198
Math Masters, p. 460
per partnership: 2 six-sided dice
Students practice comparing fractions and finding equivalent fractions.

EXTRA PRACTICE
Solving Mixed-Number Addition Problems
Math Masters, p. 253A
Students practice adding mixed numbers with like and unlike denominators.

Advance Preparation

 Teacher's Reference Manual, **Grades 4–6** pp. 142, 143

Getting Started

Mental Math and Reflexes

Have students rename each fraction as a whole number or mixed number and each mixed number as an improper fraction.

●○○ $\frac{3}{3}$ 1

$2\frac{1}{2}$ $\frac{5}{2}$

$\frac{3}{2}$ $1\frac{1}{2}$

●●○ $\frac{13}{8}$ $1\frac{5}{8}$

$4\frac{1}{8}$ $\frac{33}{8}$

$\frac{17}{5}$ $3\frac{2}{5}$

●●● $\frac{37}{5}$ $7\frac{2}{5}$

$\frac{62}{5}$ $12\frac{2}{5}$

$11\frac{1}{4}$ $\frac{45}{4}$

Math Message

Solve Problems 1–9 at the top of journal page 251. Use benchmarks to estimate the sums and to check the reasonableness of your solutions.

Study Link 8·1 Follow-Up

Have partners compare answers and resolve differences. Ask volunteers to share their explanations for Problems 7, 14, and 21.

1 Teaching the Lesson

▶ Math Message Follow-Up

(*Math Journal 2*, p. 251)

 **WHOLE-CLASS ACTIVITY**

ELL

Ask students to share their strategies for estimating the sums for Problems 1–6. Make sure students make reference to the benchmarks when estimating their sums.

Ask volunteers to share their strategies for renaming the sums in Problems 3–6 to a whole or mixed number. Encourage students to use their understanding of multiplication facts to recognize when the simplest form will be a whole number. If the sum is an improper fraction and the numerator is not a multiple of the denominator, the simplest form will be a mixed number. If the numerator is a multiple of the denominator, the simplest form will be a whole number. Ask volunteers to explain how to recognize an improper fraction. If the numerator is greater than or equal to the denominator, the fraction is an improper fraction. To support English language learners, write and label examples of improper fractions on the board or Class Data Pad.

Ask students to share their estimating strategies for Problem 7 using benchmarks. Sample answer: $\frac{1}{6}$ is less than $\frac{1}{2}$, and $\frac{2}{3}$ is greater than $\frac{1}{2}$. I estimated my answer to be about 1. Survey students for what methods they used to find the common denominators for Problems 7–9. Expect a mixture of the methods discussed in Lesson 8-1. Summarize the methods on the board or Class Data Pad for student reference throughout the lesson.

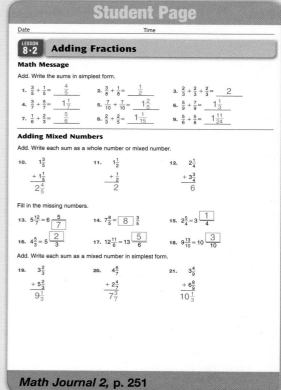

Student Page

Date _____ Time _____

LESSON 8·2 Adding Fractions

Math Message

Add. Write the sums in simplest form.

1. $\frac{3}{5} + \frac{1}{5} = \frac{4}{5}$ 2. $\frac{3}{8} + \frac{1}{8} = \frac{1}{2}$ 3. $\frac{2}{3} + \frac{2}{3} + \frac{2}{3} = 2$

4. $\frac{3}{7} + \frac{5}{7} = 1\frac{1}{7}$ 5. $\frac{7}{10} + \frac{7}{10} = 1\frac{2}{5}$ 6. $\frac{5}{9} + \frac{7}{9} = 1\frac{1}{3}$

7. $\frac{1}{6} + \frac{2}{3} = \frac{5}{6}$ 8. $\frac{2}{3} + \frac{2}{5} = 1\frac{1}{15}$ 9. $\frac{5}{6} + \frac{5}{8} = 1\frac{11}{24}$

Adding Mixed Numbers

Add. Write each sum as a whole number or mixed number.

10. $1\frac{3}{5}$ $+ 1\frac{1}{5}$ $2\frac{4}{5}$ 11. $1\frac{1}{2}$ $+ \frac{1}{2}$ 2 12. $2\frac{1}{4}$ $+ 3\frac{3}{4}$ 6

Fill in the missing numbers.

13. $5\frac{12}{7} = 6\frac{5}{7}$ 14. $7\frac{8}{5} = 8\frac{3}{5}$ 15. $2\frac{5}{4} = 3\frac{1}{4}$

16. $4\frac{5}{3} = 5\frac{2}{3}$ 17. $12\frac{11}{6} = 13\frac{5}{6}$ 18. $9\frac{13}{10} = 10\frac{3}{10}$

Add. Write each sum as a mixed number in simplest form.

19. $3\frac{2}{3}$ $+ 5\frac{2}{3}$ $9\frac{1}{3}$ 20. $4\frac{6}{7}$ $+ 2\frac{4}{7}$ $7\frac{3}{7}$ 21. $3\frac{4}{9}$ $+ 6\frac{8}{9}$ $10\frac{1}{3}$

Math Journal 2, p. 251

▶ Adding Mixed Numbers with Fractions Having Like Denominators

Explain that one way to find the sum of mixed numbers is to treat the fraction and whole number parts separately. Write the problem below on the board or a transparency:

$$3\frac{1}{8}$$
$$+\ 5\frac{3}{8}$$
$$\overline{8\frac{4}{8}\ \text{or}\ 8\frac{1}{2}}$$

Add the whole-number parts. ⌐
Then add the fraction parts. ⌐

Ask students to solve
the following problem:

$$2\frac{7}{8}$$
$$+\ 3\frac{5}{8}$$

Discuss students' solution strategies. Make sure the following strategy is presented:

1. Add the whole-number parts.
2. Add the fraction parts.

$$2\frac{7}{8}$$
$$+\ 3\frac{5}{8}$$
$$\overline{5\frac{12}{8}}$$

3. Rename $5\frac{12}{8}$ in simplest form.

$$\frac{12}{8} = \frac{8}{8} + \frac{4}{8} = 1 + \frac{4}{8} = 1\frac{4}{8}$$

Since $\frac{12}{8} = 1\frac{4}{8}$, then $5\frac{12}{8} = 5 + 1 + \frac{4}{8} = 6\frac{4}{8}$, or $6\frac{1}{2}$.

Model renaming $\frac{12}{8}$ with a picture.

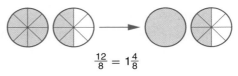

$$\frac{12}{8} = 1\frac{4}{8}$$

Pose a few more addition problems in which the addends are mixed numbers with like denominators. *Suggestions:*

- $3\frac{4}{7} + 4\frac{3}{7}$ 8
- $1\frac{3}{4} + 2\frac{3}{4}$ $4\frac{2}{4}$, or $4\frac{1}{2}$
- $6\frac{2}{3} + 2\frac{1}{3}$ 9
- $8\frac{7}{10} + 5\frac{9}{10}$ $14\frac{3}{5}$

- Madeleine purchased $3\frac{5}{8}$ yards of red ribbon and $4\frac{7}{8}$ yards of purple ribbon. How much ribbon did Madeleine purchase? $8\frac{4}{8}$, or $8\frac{1}{2}$ yards

- Mr. Marcus's class ate $6\frac{3}{4}$ pizzas and Mr. Samuel's class ate $4\frac{2}{4}$ pizzas. How many pizzas did the two classes eat? $11\frac{1}{4}$ pizzas

---

✔ Ongoing Assessment: Informing Instruction

Watch for students who have difficulty renaming mixed-number sums such as $5\frac{12}{8}$. Discuss the meanings of numerator and denominator, and have students rename the fractional parts in the mixed numbers.
Suggestions:

$4\frac{7}{5}$ $\frac{7}{5} = \frac{5}{5} + \frac{2}{5} = 1 + \frac{2}{5}$

$8\frac{4}{3}$ $\frac{4}{3} = \frac{3}{3} + \frac{1}{3} = 1 + \frac{1}{3}$

$2\frac{7}{4}$ $\frac{7}{4} = \frac{4}{4} + \frac{3}{4} = 1 + \frac{3}{4}$

Adding Mixed Numbers with Fractions Having Unlike Denominators

 **WHOLE-CLASS ACTIVITY**

Write the following problem on the board, and ask students to find the sum:

$$3\frac{3}{4}$$
$$+\,2\frac{7}{8}$$

After a few minutes, ask students to share solution strategies. Make sure the following method is discussed:

1. Find a common denominator for $\frac{3}{4}$ and $\frac{7}{8}$ 8, 16, 24, 32, ...

2. Rename the fraction parts of the mixed numbers so they have the same denominator. In this case, the least common denominator, 8, is the easiest to use.

$$3\frac{3}{4} \longrightarrow \quad 3\frac{6}{8}$$
$$+\,2\frac{7}{8} \longrightarrow +\,2\frac{7}{8}$$

3. Add. $\qquad\qquad\qquad 5\frac{13}{8}$

4. Rename the sum. $\qquad 5\frac{13}{8} = 5 + \frac{8}{8} + \frac{5}{8} = 5 + 1 + \frac{5}{8} = 6\frac{5}{8}$

Pose a few more problems that involve finding common denominators to add mixed numbers. *Suggestions:*

- $2\frac{1}{2} + 4\frac{3}{8}$ $6\frac{7}{8}$
- $6\frac{5}{6} + 3\frac{3}{5}$ $10\frac{13}{30}$
- $5\frac{2}{3} + 1\frac{5}{6}$ $7\frac{3}{6}$, or $7\frac{1}{2}$
- $1\frac{7}{8} + 8\frac{1}{6}$ $10\frac{1}{24}$
- $3\frac{4}{5} + 2\frac{1}{4}$ $6\frac{1}{20}$

- Juanita needs $1\frac{7}{8}$ yards of fabric for a dress and $5\frac{1}{6}$ yards for a jacket. How many total yards does she need? $7\frac{1}{24}$ yards

- The costumes for the lead roles in the school musical require $4\frac{5}{8}$ yards of one type of fabric and $2\frac{1}{3}$ yards of another type of fabric. How much fabric needs to be purchased? $6\frac{23}{24}$ yards

---

▶ # Adding Mixed Numbers

 PARTNER ACTIVITY

COMPUTATION PRACTICE

(*Math Journal 2*, pp. 251 and 252)

Have students complete journal pages 251 and 252. Circulate and assist.

 ## Ongoing Assessment: Recognizing Student Achievement

Exit Slip ★

Use an **Exit Slip** (*Math Masters*, page 414) to assess students' facility with adding mixed numbers. Have students explain how they found the answer to Problem 4 on journal page 252. Students are making adequate progress if their responses demonstrate an understanding of renaming fractions to have common denominators and to be in simplest form.

[Number and Numeration Goal 5; Operations and Computation Goal 4]

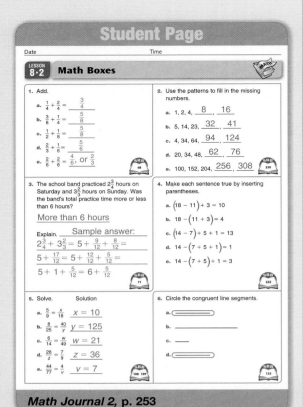

Date ____ Time ____

LESSON 8·2 Math Boxes

1. Add.

a. $\frac{1}{4} + \frac{2}{4} = \frac{3}{4}$

b. $\frac{3}{8} + \frac{1}{4} = \frac{5}{8}$

c. $\frac{1}{2} + \frac{1}{8} = \frac{5}{8}$

d. $\frac{2}{3} + \frac{1}{6} = \frac{5}{6}$

e. $\frac{2}{6} + \frac{2}{6} = \frac{4}{6}$, or $\frac{2}{3}$

2. Use the patterns to fill in the missing numbers.

a. 1, 2, 4, __8__, __16__

b. 5, 14, 23, __32__, __41__

c. 4, 34, 64, __94__, __124__

d. 20, 34, 48, __62__, __76__

e. 100, 152, 204, __256__, __308__

3. The school band practiced $2\frac{3}{4}$ hours on Saturday and $3\frac{2}{3}$ hours on Sunday. Was the band's total practice time more or less than 6 hours?

More than 6 hours

Explain.   Sample answer:

$2\frac{3}{4} + 3\frac{2}{3} = 5 + \frac{9}{12} + \frac{8}{12} =$

$5 + \frac{17}{12} = 5 + \frac{12}{12} + \frac{5}{12} =$

$5 + 1 + \frac{5}{12} = 6 + \frac{5}{12}$

4. Make each sentence true by inserting parentheses.

a. $(18 - 11) + 3 = 10$

b. $18 - (11 + 3) = 4$

c. $(14 - 7) + 5 + 1 = 13$

d. $14 - (7 + 5 + 1) = 1$

e. $14 - (7 + 5) + 1 = 3$

5. Solve.   Solution

a. $\frac{5}{9} = \frac{x}{18}$ $x = 10$

b. $\frac{8}{25} = \frac{40}{y}$ $y = 125$

c. $\frac{6}{14} = \frac{w}{49}$ $w = 21$

d. $\frac{28}{z} = \frac{7}{9}$ $z = 36$

e. $\frac{44}{77} = \frac{4}{v}$ $v = 7$

6. Circle the congruent line segments.

a. ⊂======⊃

b. _____

c. ___

d. ⊂====⊃

Math Journal 2, p. 253

---

2 Ongoing Learning & Practice

▶ **Math Boxes 8·2**

(Math Journal 2, p. 253)

👤 INDEPENDENT ACTIVITY

Mixed Practice Math Boxes in this lesson are paired with Math Boxes in Lesson 8-4. The skill in Problem 6 previews Unit 9 content.

Writing/Reasoning Have students write a response to the following: *Explain your strategy for finding the values of the variables in Problem 5.* Sample answer: I looked for the common factor of the numerators or denominators that were complete. Then I used the multiplication rule or the division rule to multiply or divide to find the values for the variables.

NOTE Alternately, students may use a table or chart to find an equivalent fraction with the given denominator or numerator.

▶ **Study Link 8·2**

(Math Masters, p. 223)

👤 INDEPENDENT ACTIVITY

Home Connection Students practice adding mixed numbers and renaming improper fractions as mixed numbers in simplest form.

---

3 Differentiation Options

Name ____ Date ____ Time ____

STUDY LINK 8·2 Adding Mixed Numbers

Rename each mixed number in simplest form.

1. $3\frac{6}{8} = 4\frac{1}{4}$

2. $\frac{16}{8} = 2$

3. $9\frac{5}{3} = 10\frac{2}{3}$

4. $1\frac{7}{5} = 2\frac{2}{5}$

5. $4\frac{6}{4} = 5\frac{1}{2}$

6. $5\frac{10}{6} = 6\frac{2}{3}$

Add. Write each sum as a whole number or mixed number in simplest form.

7. $3\frac{1}{4} + 2\frac{3}{4} = 6$

8. $4\frac{1}{5} + 3\frac{4}{5} = 8$

9. $9\frac{1}{3} + 4\frac{2}{3} = 14$

10. $3\frac{5}{7} + 8\frac{6}{7} = 12\frac{4}{7}$

11. $\frac{15}{8} + 3\frac{3}{8} = 5\frac{1}{4}$

12. $4\frac{2}{9} + 5\frac{5}{9} = 9\frac{7}{9}$

Add.

13. $2\frac{5}{8}$
    $+ 6\frac{3}{4}$
    $9\frac{3}{8}$

14. $7\frac{1}{2}$
    $+ 3\frac{2}{3}$
    $11\frac{1}{6}$

15. $4\frac{6}{8}$
    $+ 3\frac{7}{12}$
    $8\frac{1}{4}$

16. $5\frac{3}{4}$
    $+ 2\frac{4}{5}$
    $8\frac{11}{20}$

Practice

17. $3,540 \div 6 = 590$

18. $1,770 \div 3 = 590$

19. $7,080 / 12 = 590$

20. $(590 * 5) \div 2 = 1,475$

Math Masters, p. 223

READINESS

🙍🙍🙍 SMALL-GROUP ACTIVITY

▶ **Adding Mixed Numbers**

(Math Journal 2, p. 252)

◐ 15–30 Min

To explore mixed-number addition, have students use an opposite-change algorithm. Have students change one of the addends to a whole number. Pose the following problem:

$$1\frac{2}{3} + 7\frac{5}{6}$$

1. Change $1\frac{2}{3}$ to a whole number by adding $\frac{1}{3}$: $1\frac{2}{3} + \frac{1}{3} = 2$.

2. Subtract $\frac{1}{3}$ from $7\frac{5}{6}$: $\frac{1}{3} = \frac{2}{6}$; $7\frac{5}{6} - \frac{2}{6} = 7\frac{3}{6}$.

3. Add the new addends: $2 + 7\frac{3}{6} = 9\frac{3}{6}$, or $9\frac{1}{2}$.

This strategy is most efficient when the sum of the fraction parts is greater than 1. Discuss how to recognize that the fraction parts are greater than 1. Have students use this method to solve the following problems:

- $3\frac{1}{2} + 7\frac{8}{10}$ $11\frac{3}{10}$
- $2\frac{3}{4} + 6\frac{9}{12}$ $9\frac{6}{12}$, or $9\frac{1}{2}$
- $5\frac{8}{9} + 7\frac{1}{3}$ $13\frac{2}{9}$
- $4\frac{8}{10} + 3\frac{5}{6}$ $8\frac{19}{30}$

Before students begin journal page 252, have them identify problems for which this algorithm might apply. Problems 4–6

EXTRA PRACTICE

PARTNER ACTIVITY

Playing *Fraction Capture*

15–30 Min

(*Math Journal 1*, p. 198; *Math Masters*, p. 460)

Students practice comparing fractions and finding equivalent fractions by playing *Fraction Capture*. Players roll dice, form fractions, and claim corresponding sections of squares. The rules are on *Math Journal 1*, page 198, and the gameboard is on *Math Masters*, page 460.

EXTRA PRACTICE

PARTNER ACTIVITY

Solving Mixed-Number Addition Problems

15–30 Min

(*Math Masters*, p. 253A)

Students practice adding mixed numbers with like and unlike denominators and use reasoning skills to compare sums of mixed numbers with whole numbers.

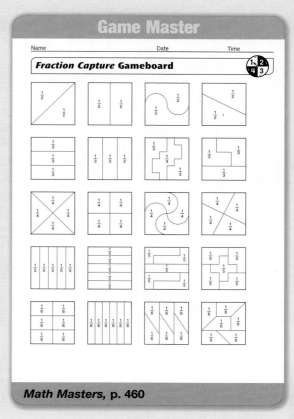

Math Masters, p. 460

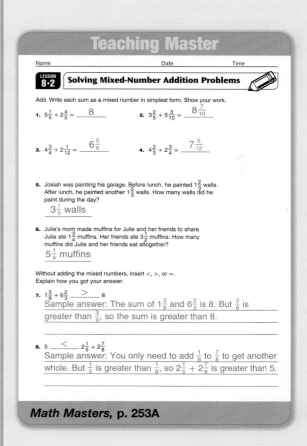

Math Masters, p. 253A

8·3 Subtracting Mixed Numbers

Objective To develop subtraction concepts related to mixed numbers.

Technology Resources www.everydaymathonline.com

 ePresentations
 eToolkit
 Algorithms Practice
 EM Facts Workshop Game™
 Family Letters
 Assessment Management
 Common Core State Standards
 Curriculum Focal Points
 Interactive Teacher's Lesson Guide

1 Teaching the Lesson

Key Concepts and Skills

- Find equivalent names for mixed numbers.
  [Number and Numeration Goal 5]
- Convert between fractions and mixed numbers.
  [Number and Numeration Goal 5]
- Subtract mixed numbers.
  [Operations and Computation Goal 4]
- Use benchmarks to estimate differences.
  [Operations and Computation Goal 6]

Key Activities

Students subtract mixed numbers with like denominators by renaming the minuend. Students use benchmarks to estimate differences.

 Ongoing Assessment:
Informing Instruction See page 632.

Materials

Math Journal 2, p. 254
Math Masters, p. 414
Study Link 8·2
slate

2 Ongoing Learning & Practice

 Playing *Mixed-Number Spin*
Math Journal 2, p. 255
Math Masters, pp. 488 and 489
per partnership: large paper clip
Students practice adding and subtracting fractions and mixed numbers with like and unlike denominators.

 Ongoing Assessment:
Recognizing Student Achievement
Use journal page 255.
[Operations and Computation Goals 4 and 6]

 Math Boxes 8·3
Math Journal 2, p. 256
Geometry Template
Students practice and maintain skills through Math Box problems.

 Study Link 8·3
Math Masters, p. 224
Students practice and maintain skills through Study Link activities.

3 Differentiation Options

READINESS
Subtracting Mixed Numbers
Students use a counting-up algorithm to explore mixed-number subtraction.

ENRICHMENT
Exploring a Pattern for Fraction Addition and Subtraction
Math Masters, p. 225
Students explore patterns that result from adding and subtracting unit fractions.

EXTRA PRACTICE
5-Minute Math
5-Minute Math™, pp. 184 and 185
Students add mixed numbers.

Advance Preparation

 Teacher's Reference Manual, **Grades 4–6** pp. 142, 143

Getting Started

Math Message

Solve Problems 1–3 at the top of journal page 254. Use benchmarks to estimate the differences and to check the reasonableness of your solutions.

Study Link 8·2 Follow-Up

Have partners compare answers and resolve differences. Ask volunteers how they know their answers are in simplest form. A fraction is in simplest form if the numerator and denominator have no common factors except 1.

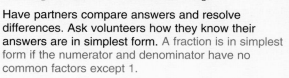

1 Teaching the Lesson

▶ Math Message Follow-Up

WHOLE-CLASS DISCUSSION

(*Math Journal 2*, p. 254)

Ask students to share their estimating strategies for Problem 2 using benchmarks. Sample answer: I know that $4\frac{4}{5}$ is close to 5 and $5 - 2 = 3$. I estimated my answer to be about 3.

Ask volunteers to write their solutions on the board and explain their strategies. Expect that most students will have subtracted the whole-number and fraction parts separately and renamed the differences in Problems 1 and 3 in simplest form.

▶ Subtracting Mixed Numbers with Renaming

WHOLE-CLASS ACTIVITY

Write this problem on the board.

$$3\frac{1}{3}$$
$$-\,1\frac{2}{3}$$

Ask: *How does this problem differ from the Math Message problems?* The fraction being subtracted from, $\frac{1}{3}$, is smaller than the fraction that is being subtracted, $\frac{2}{3}$. Ask volunteers to suggest solution strategies. Sample answer: Rename $3\frac{1}{3}$ to make the fraction part larger. $2\frac{4}{3} - 1\frac{2}{3} = 1\frac{2}{3}$

Remind students that when they add mixed numbers, some sums might have to be renamed to write them in simplest form. For example, a sum of $4\frac{7}{4}$ could be renamed: $4\frac{7}{4} = 4 + \frac{4}{4} + \frac{3}{4}$, or $4 + 1 + \frac{3}{4} = 5\frac{3}{4}$. Emphasize that the two mixed numbers are equivalent; $4\frac{7}{4}$ is another name for $5\frac{3}{4}$.

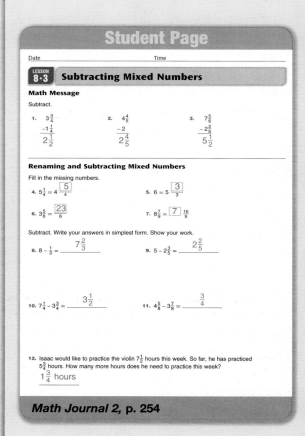

Student Page

Date _____ Time _____

LESSON 8·3 **Subtracting Mixed Numbers**

Math Message

Subtract.

1. $3\frac{3}{4}$
$-1\frac{1}{4}$
$2\frac{1}{2}$

2. $4\frac{4}{5}$
-2
$2\frac{4}{5}$

3. $7\frac{5}{6}$
$-2\frac{6}{8}$
$5\frac{1}{2}$

Renaming and Subtracting Mixed Numbers

Fill in the missing numbers.

4. $5\frac{1}{4} = 4\frac{\boxed{5}}{4}$

5. $6 = 5\frac{\boxed{3}}{3}$

6. $3\frac{5}{6} = \frac{\boxed{23}}{6}$

7. $8\frac{7}{9} = \boxed{7}\frac{16}{9}$

Subtract. Write your answers in simplest form. Show your work.

8. $8 - \frac{1}{3} = \underline{\quad 7\frac{2}{3} \quad}$

9. $5 - 2\frac{3}{5} = \underline{\quad 2\frac{2}{5} \quad}$

10. $7\frac{1}{4} - 3\frac{3}{4} = \underline{\quad 3\frac{1}{2} \quad}$

11. $4\frac{5}{8} - 3\frac{7}{8} = \underline{\quad \frac{3}{4} \quad}$

12. Isaac would like to practice the violin $7\frac{1}{2}$ hours this week. So far, he has practiced $5\frac{3}{4}$ hours. How many more hours does he need to practice this week?

$1\frac{3}{4}$ hours

Math Journal 2, p. 254

Have students rename $3\frac{1}{3}$ to an equivalent mixed number with a larger fraction part. $1\frac{7}{3}$, or $2\frac{4}{3}$ Write their responses on the board or a transparency, and illustrate the mixed numbers with pictures.

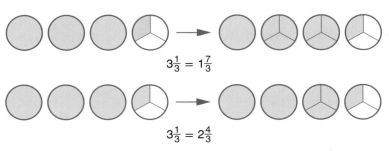

$$3\frac{1}{3} = 1\frac{7}{3}$$

$$3\frac{1}{3} = 2\frac{4}{3}$$

Ask students to use each of the responses to solve the problem. Circulate and assist. When most students have finished, have volunteers explain which mixed-number name was more efficient for solving the subtraction problem. $2\frac{4}{3}$, because with $1\frac{7}{3}$ you need to rename the fraction again in order to express the difference as a mixed number. Explain that deciding how to rename a fraction depends on the problem. Sometimes it might be more efficient to work with mixed numbers, other times it might be more efficient to work with improper fractions. In this case, the more efficient mixed-number name is a matter of personal preference.

Pose several problems. Encourage students to estimate each difference using what they know about benchmarks with fractions. They should use their estimates to check the reasonableness of their solutions. In each case, ask students first how they would rename the minuend and then how they would solve the problem. *Suggestions:*

- $8 - 3\frac{2}{3}$ $8 = 7\frac{3}{3}$; solution: $4\frac{1}{3}$
- $6 - \frac{1}{4}$ $6 = 5\frac{4}{4}$; solution: $5\frac{3}{4}$
- $4\frac{3}{5} - 1\frac{4}{5}$ $4\frac{3}{5} = 3\frac{8}{5}$; solution: $2\frac{4}{5}$
- $5\frac{1}{6} - 2\frac{5}{6}$ $5\frac{1}{6} = 4\frac{7}{6}$; solution: $2\frac{1}{3}$
- $6\frac{5}{12} - 3\frac{11}{12}$ $6\frac{5}{12} = 5\frac{17}{12}$; solution: $2\frac{1}{2}$
- Carlie purchased 10 feet of ribbon to make bows. She used $2\frac{7}{8}$ feet to make one bow. How much ribbon remains to make additional bows? $7\frac{1}{8}$ feet
- Sammy needs $3\frac{1}{4}$ cups of sugar to make sugar cookies. He only has $1\frac{3}{4}$ cups of sugar. How much more sugar does he need for the recipe? $1\frac{1}{2}$ cups

Ongoing Assessment: Informing Instruction

Watch for students who have difficulty renaming mixed numbers for subtraction. Have students practice the following steps:

1. Write the whole-number part of the mixed number as an equivalent addition expression that adds 1.

$$5\frac{2}{5} = 4 + 1 + \frac{2}{5}$$

2. Use the denominator to rename the 1 as a fraction.

$$5\frac{2}{5} = 4 + \frac{5}{5} + \frac{2}{5}$$

3. Combine the fraction parts.

$$5\frac{2}{5} = 4 + \frac{7}{5}$$

Write this problem on the board.

$$3\frac{1}{3}$$
$$-\ 1\frac{1}{2}$$

Ask: *How would you solve this problem?* Expect that students will likely recognize $\frac{1}{3}$ is smaller than $\frac{1}{2}$ and might suggest renaming the fraction parts with common denominators. Ask volunteers to model their strategies on the board. Sample answer: Use 6 as a common denominator. Rename the mixed numbers. $3\frac{2}{6} - 1\frac{3}{6}$ Rename the minuend. $3\frac{2}{6} = 2\frac{8}{6}$. Subtract. $2\frac{8}{6} - 1\frac{3}{6} = \frac{5}{6}$.

Pose a few mixed-number subtraction number stories. *Suggestions:*

- Daniel has a DVD set that provides $4\frac{1}{2}$ hours of viewing. So far, he has watched $\frac{5}{6}$ of an hour. How many more hours of the DVD set does he still have to watch? $3\frac{4}{6}$, or $3\frac{2}{3}$ hours

- Serena measured out $5\frac{2}{3}$ feet of rope to make a jump rope. Her friends told her that it needed to be $6\frac{1}{2}$ feet long. How much more rope did she need to measure out? $\frac{5}{6}$ ft more

Subtracting Mixed Numbers

PARTNER ACTIVITY

COMPUTATION PRACTICE

(*Math Journal 2*, p. 254; *Math Masters*, p. 414)

Ask students to complete the journal page. Remind them to use benchmarks to estimate the difference. Ask students to use an Exit Slip (*Math Masters*, page 414) to explain their strategy for solving Problem 10 on *Math Journal 2*, page 254.

② Ongoing Learning & Practice

Playing *Mixed-Number Spin*

PARTNER ACTIVITY

COMPUTATION PRACTICE

(*Math Journal 2*, p. 255; *Math Masters*, pp. 488 and 489)

Algebraic Thinking Students practice estimating sums and differences of mixed numbers with like and unlike denominators by playing *Mixed-Number Spin*. Players use benchmarks to estimate sums and differences as they record number expressions that fit the parameters given on the *Mixed-Number Spin* record sheet, *Math Journal 2*, page 255. Each partnership makes a spinner using a large paper clip anchored by a pencil point to the center of the spinner on *Math Masters*, page 488. They use the numbers they spin to complete the number sentences on the record sheet.

Ask students to save their spinners for future use. Copy *Math Masters*, page 489 to provide additional record sheets.

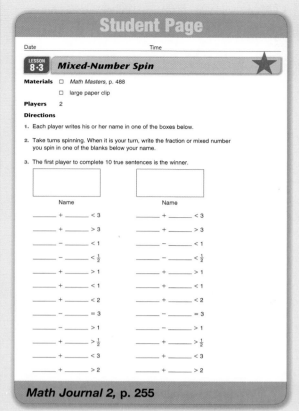

🔗 Links to the Future

Subtraction of mixed numbers with unlike denominators continues in *Sixth Grade Everyday Mathematics*.

✔ Ongoing Assessment: Recognizing Student Achievement

Journal Page 255 ★

Use the *Mixed-Number Spin* record sheet on **journal page 255** to assess students' ability to make estimates for adding and subtracting mixed numbers. Students are making adequate progress if they correctly complete number sentences using the benchmarks $\frac{1}{2}$ and 1. Some students may be able to make the estimates and comparisons using 2 and 3 as benchmarks.

[*Operations and Computation Goals 4 and 6*]

Student Page

Date   Time

LESSON 8·3   Math Boxes

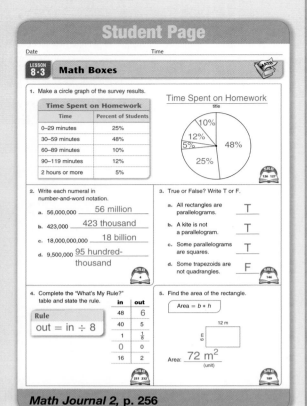

1. Make a circle graph of the survey results.

Time Spent on Homework

Time	Percent of Students
0–29 minutes	25%
30–59 minutes	48%
60–89 minutes	10%
90–119 minutes	12%
2 hours or more	5%

Time Spent on Homework
title

10%
12%
5%
48%
25%

SRB
126 127

2. Write each numeral in number-and-word notation.

a. 56,000,000 __56 million__

b. 423,000 __423 thousand__

c. 18,000,000,000 __18 billion__

d. 9,500,000 __95 hundred-thousand__

SRB
4

3. True or False? Write T or F.

a. All rectangles are parallelograms. __T__

b. A kite is not a parallelogram. __T__

c. Some parallelograms are squares. __T__

d. Some trapezoids are not quadrangles. __F__

SRB
146

4. Complete the "What's My Rule?" table and state the rule.

Rule
out = in ÷ 8

in	out
48	6
40	5
1	$\frac{1}{8}$
0	0
16	2

SRB
231 232

5. Find the area of the rectangle.

Area = b * h

12 m

6 m

Area: __72 m²__
(unit)

SRB
189

Math Journal 2, p. 256

Study Link Master

Name   Date   Time

STUDY LINK 8·3   Subtracting Mixed Numbers

Fill in the missing numbers.

1. $3\frac{3}{8} = 2\frac{\boxed{11}}{8}$

2. $4\frac{5}{6} = 3\frac{\boxed{11}}{6}$

3. $2\frac{1}{9} = 1\frac{\boxed{10}}{9}$

4. $6\frac{3}{7} = \boxed{5}\frac{10}{7}$

5. $4\frac{3}{5} = 3\frac{\boxed{8}}{5}$

6. $7\frac{2}{3} = \boxed{6}\frac{5}{3}$

Subtract. Write your answers in simplest form.

7. $5\frac{3}{4}$
    $-3\frac{1}{4}$
    $2\frac{1}{2}$

8. $6\frac{2}{3}$
    $-4\frac{1}{3}$
    $2\frac{1}{3}$

9. $5\frac{4}{5}$
    $-3\frac{3}{5}$
    $2\frac{1}{5}$

10. $4 - \frac{3}{8} = $ __$3\frac{5}{8}$__

11. $6 - \frac{5}{9} = $ __$5\frac{4}{9}$__

12. $5 - 2\frac{3}{10} = $ __$2\frac{7}{10}$__

13. $7 - 4\frac{3}{4} = $ __$2\frac{1}{4}$__

14. $3\frac{2}{5} - 1\frac{3}{5} = $ __$1\frac{4}{5}$__

15. $4\frac{3}{8} - 3\frac{7}{8} = $ __$\frac{1}{2}$__

Practice

16. $654 * 205 = $ __134,070__

17. $654 * 502 = $ __328,308__

18. $654 * 250 = $ __163,500__

19. $654 * 520 = $ __340,080__

Math Masters, p. 224

▶ **Math Boxes 8·3**

(*Math Journal 2*, p. 256)

 Mixed Practice Math Boxes in this lesson are paired with Math Boxes in Lesson 8-1. The skill in Problem 5 previews Unit 9 content.

 Writing/Reasoning Have students write a response to the following: *Explain one advantage and one disadvantage to using number and word notation in Problem 2.* Sample answer: One advantage is that the number is written the same way that it is said aloud. One disadvantage is that you cannot perform operations on them as easily.

Writing/Reasoning Have students write a response to the following: *Explain how you determined your answer to Problem 3c.* Sample answer: The answer is true because a parallelogram has two pairs of parallel sides with opposite sides congruent. When all sides of a parallelogram are the same length and form right angles, the parallelogram is also a square.

▶ **Study Link 8·3**

(*Math Masters*, p. 224)

 Home Connection Students practice renaming and subtracting mixed numbers.

3 Differentiation Options

▶ **Subtracting Mixed Numbers**

 15–30 Min

To explore mixed-number subtraction, have students use a counting-up algorithm. Remind students that another way to subtract is to count up. With whole numbers, they could solve $5 - 3$ by thinking *3 plus what equals 5?* Discuss how they would count up to solve this problem: $5\frac{2}{5} - 3\frac{4}{5}$. Expect that students will suggest "$3\frac{4}{5}$ plus what equals $5\frac{2}{5}$?" Explain that counting up is one way to answer *plus what?*

Demonstrate how to count up from $3\frac{4}{5}$ to $5\frac{2}{5}$.

1. Count up, keeping track of the amounts used.

   Count up $\frac{1}{5}$: $3\frac{4}{5} + \frac{1}{5} = 4$ $\frac{1}{5}$

   Count up 1: $4 + 1 = 5$ 1

   Count up $\frac{2}{5}$: $5 + \frac{2}{5} = 5\frac{2}{5}$ $\frac{2}{5}$

2. Add. $\frac{1}{5} + 1 + \frac{2}{5} = 1\frac{3}{5}$

So the difference between $5\frac{2}{5}$ and $3\frac{4}{5}$ is $1\frac{3}{5}$.

Pose problems for students to solve by counting up. *Suggestions:*

- $4\frac{2}{8} - 1\frac{7}{8}$ $2\frac{3}{8}$
- $3\frac{3}{5} - 1\frac{4}{5}$ $1\frac{4}{5}$
- $7 - 2\frac{8}{10}$ $4\frac{1}{5}$
- $5\frac{1}{4} - 2\frac{3}{4}$ $2\frac{1}{2}$

ENRICHMENT

Exploring a Pattern for Fraction Addition and Subtraction

PARTNER ACTIVITY

15–30 Min

(*Math Masters*, p. 225)

Algebraic Thinking To apply students' understanding of addition and subtraction of fractions, have them find patterns in unit fraction addition and subtraction problems. When most students have completed the problems, discuss the pattern in Problem 1. In each problem, the answer is the sum of the denominators over the product of the denominators.

Problem 4 asks whether this pattern works for the sum of any two unit fractions $\frac{1}{a} + \frac{1}{b}$. It does. Add $\frac{1}{a}$ and $\frac{1}{b}$ using the QCD method:

$$\frac{1}{a} + \frac{1}{b} = \frac{1*b}{a*b} + \frac{1*a}{b*a} = \frac{b}{a*b} + \frac{a}{b*a} = \frac{b+a}{a*b}$$

Have students verify that this pattern holds true for other unit fractions, for example: $\frac{1}{3} + \frac{1}{5}$.

The pattern for Problem 5 is similar. The denominator of the result is the product of the denominators of the unit fractions being subtracted. The numerator is always 1.

Problems 5a–5e involve the subtraction of two unit fractions where the difference between the denominators is 1. The pattern described in Problem 5f reflects that type of problem. You may want to extend the *Math Master* activity by having students find the results of the following subtraction problems (where the difference between the denominators of the unit fractions is greater than 1):

$\frac{1}{2} - \frac{1}{5}$ $\frac{3}{10}$ $\frac{1}{3} - \frac{1}{8}$ $\frac{5}{24}$ $\frac{1}{5} - \frac{1}{12}$ $\frac{7}{60}$

Ask students to describe a pattern for subtracting any two unit fractions. Sample answer: The numerator of the result is found by subtracting the denominator of the first fraction from the denominator of the second fraction. The denominator of the result is the product of the denominators of the two unit fractions.

EXTRA PRACTICE

5-Minute Math

SMALL-GROUP ACTIVITY

5–15 Min

To offer students more experience with adding mixed numbers, see *5-Minute Math*, pages 184 and 185.

8·4 Calculator Practice: Computation with Fractions

 Objectives To provide practice adding fractions with unlike denominators and using a calculator to solve fraction problems.

Technology Resources www.everydaymathonline.com

 ePresentations

 eToolkit

 Algorithms Practice

 EM Facts Workshop Game™

 Family Letters

 Assessment Management

 Common Core State Standards

 Curriculum Focal Points

 Interactive Teacher's Lesson Guide

---

1 Teaching the Lesson

Key Concepts and Skills

- Convert between fractions and mixed numbers. [Number and Numeration Goal 5]

- Express fractions and mixed numbers in simplest form. [Number and Numeration Goal 5]

- Compare and order fractions. [Number and Numeration Goal 6]

- Use mental arithmetic, paper-and-pencil algorithms, and calculators to solve fraction and mixed-number addition problems. [Operations and Computation Goal 4]

- Use benchmarks to estimate sums. [Operations and Computation Goal 6]

Key Activities

Students add fractions with unlike denominators using estimation and paper-and-pencil computation by playing *Fraction Action, Fraction Friction.* They use calculators to perform operations with fractions and mixed numbers.

 Ongoing Assessment:
Recognizing Student Achievement
Use the Math Message.
[Number and Numeration Goal 6]

Materials

Math Journal 2, p. 257
Student Reference Book, pp. 260–263 and 312
Study Link 8·3; *Math Masters,* p. 459
slate ◆ scissors ◆ per partnership: eight 3" by 5" index cards cut in half (optional) ◆ calculator ◆ overhead calculator for demonstration purposes (optional)

2 Ongoing Learning & Practice

 Math Boxes 8·4

Math Journal 2, p. 258
Students practice and maintain skills through Math Box problems.

Study Link 8·4

Math Masters, p. 226
Students practice and maintain skills through Study Link activities.

3 Differentiation Options

READINESS

Charting Common Denominators

Math Masters, p. 227
transparency of *Math Masters,* p. 227
Students use a flowchart to find common denominators.

ENRICHMENT

Exploring Equivalent Fractions

Math Masters, p. 228
calculator
Students use calculators to explore fraction-to-decimal conversions.

EXTRA PRACTICE

5-Minute Math

5-Minute Math™, pp. 26, 98, 99, and 113
calculator
Students use calculators to add fractions.

Advance Preparation

For the optional Readiness activity in Part 3, make a transparency of *Math Masters,* page 227.

Background Information This lesson presents example key sequences for the TI-15 and Casio *fx*-55 calculators. If other calculators are used, edit the key sequences as needed.

 Teacher's Reference Manual, Grades 4–6 pp. 29–35, 149–152

Getting Started

Mental Math and Reflexes

Have students decide if each expression is $> \frac{1}{2}$, $< \frac{1}{2}$, or $= \frac{1}{2}$.

$\bullet\circ\circ$ $\quad \frac{1}{4} + \frac{4}{8} > \frac{1}{2}$

$\frac{1}{3} + \frac{1}{16} < \frac{1}{2}$

$\frac{2}{8} + \frac{1}{4} = \frac{1}{2}$

$\bullet\bullet\circ$ $\quad \frac{1}{8} + \frac{1}{6} < \frac{1}{2}$

$\frac{2}{5} + \frac{1}{10} = \frac{1}{2}$

$\frac{3}{8} + \frac{1}{4} > \frac{1}{2}$

$\bullet\bullet\bullet$ $\quad \frac{3}{4} - \frac{1}{5} > \frac{1}{2}$

$\frac{8}{8} - \frac{3}{6} = \frac{1}{2}$

$\frac{7}{8} - \frac{2}{9} > \frac{1}{2}$

Math Message ★

Work with a partner. Take one copy of Math Masters, *page 459. Cut out the cards. Put them in order from least to greatest. Which fraction is the greatest?* $\frac{11}{12}$ *Which is the least?* $\frac{1}{12}$

Study Link 8·3 Follow-Up

Have partners compare answers and resolve differences.

---

1 Teaching the Lesson

✓ Ongoing Assessment: Recognizing Student Achievement

Math Message ★

Use the **Math Message** to assess students' ability to order fractions. Watch students as they order the cards. Students are making adequate progress if they identify the least, the middle (the benchmark of $\frac{1}{2}$), and the greatest fractions and correctly place one or two fractions in proximity to these three fractions. Some students may be able to place all of the fractions in order from least to greatest.

[Number and Numeration Goal 6]

▶ Math Message Follow-Up

WHOLE-CLASS DISCUSSION

Write $\frac{1}{2}$ on the board. Ask: *How can you use the fraction $\frac{1}{2}$ to help you place the other fractions in order?* Sample answer: I can use the benchmark $\frac{1}{2}$ to place the other fractions as either greater than $\frac{1}{2}$ or less than $\frac{1}{2}$. Ask a volunteer to write another fraction from the cards on the board, placing it in order as if on a number line. If the fraction is less than $\frac{1}{2}$, place it to the left of the fraction. If it is greater than $\frac{1}{2}$, place it to the right of the fraction. For example, a student might choose $\frac{2}{3}$ and write it to the right of $\frac{1}{2}$.

$$\frac{1}{2} \qquad\qquad \frac{2}{3}$$

Continue having volunteers add fractions to the ordered list one by one. When the list is complete, ask students to rename the fractions so they have a common denominator of 12. Have volunteers write the equivalent names above the original fractions. Ask: *Is the order correct? How do you know?* The order is correct if the numerators for the twelfths are in order from least to greatest.

The complete order not counting repeats:

$\frac{2}{12}$	$\frac{3}{12}$	$\frac{4}{12}$		$\frac{6}{12}$		$\frac{8}{12}$	$\frac{9}{12}$	$\frac{10}{12}$	
$\frac{1}{12}$	$\frac{1}{6}$	$\frac{1}{4}$	$\frac{1}{3}$	$\frac{5}{12}$	$\frac{1}{2}$	$\frac{7}{12}$	$\frac{2}{3}$	$\frac{3}{4}$	$\frac{5}{6}$	$\frac{11}{12}$

Games

Fraction Action, Fraction Friction

Materials ☐ 1 *Fraction Action, Fraction Friction* Card Deck (*Math Masters*, p. 459)
☐ 1 or more calculators

Players 2 or 3

Skill Estimating sums of fractions

Object of the game To collect a set of fraction cards with a sum as close as possible to 2, without going over 2.

Directions

1. Shuffle the deck and place it number-side down on the table between the players.

2. Players take turns.
   ◆ On each player's first turn, he or she takes a card from the top of the pile and places it number-side up on the table.
   ◆ On each of the player's following turns, he or she announces one of the following:

   "Action" This means that the player wants an additional card. The player believes that the sum of the fraction cards he or she already has is *not* close enough to 2 to win the hand. The player thinks that another card will bring the sum of the fractions closer to 2, without going over 2.

   "Friction" This means that the player does not want an additional card. The player believes that the sum of the fraction cards he or she already has *is* close enough to 2 to win the hand. The player thinks there is a good chance that taking another card will make the sum of the fractions greater than 2.

   Once a player says "Friction," he or she cannot say "Action" on any turn after that.

3. Play continues until all players have announced "Friction" or have a set of cards whose sum is greater than 2. The player whose sum is closest to 2 without going over 2 is the winner of that round. Players may check each other's sums on their calculators.

4. Reshuffle the cards and begin again. The winner of the game is the first player to win 5 rounds.

Fraction Action, Fraction Friction Card Deck

$\frac{1}{2}$	$\frac{1}{3}$	$\frac{2}{3}$	$\frac{1}{4}$
$\frac{3}{4}$	$\frac{1}{6}$	$\frac{1}{6}$	$\frac{5}{6}$
$\frac{1}{12}$	$\frac{1}{12}$	$\frac{5}{12}$	$\frac{5}{12}$
$\frac{7}{12}$	$\frac{7}{12}$	$\frac{11}{12}$	$\frac{11}{12}$

Student Reference Book, p. 312

Adjusting the Activity

Have students make their own set of *Fraction Action, Fraction Friction* cards. They should make up two fractions for each of the following denominators: 3, 4, 5, 6, 8, 9, 10, and 12. Each fraction should be less than $\frac{1}{2}$, when possible. (With thirds and fourths, this will not be possible.) Using the 3 in. by 5 in. cards, they will have a total of 16 cards, each with a different fraction. Encourage students to make estimates of their sums as they play.

AUDITORY ◆ KINESTHETIC ◆ TACTILE ◆ VISUAL

▶ Introducing *Fraction Action, Fraction Friction*

WHOLE-CLASS ACTIVITY

COMPUTATION PRACTICE

(*Student Reference Book,* p. 312;
Math Masters, p. 459)

Refer students to the fraction cards from the Math Message or the display on the board, and ask the following questions:

● What common denominator might you use to find the sum of all the fourths and all the sixths? 12, 24, and so on . . .

● What common denominator might you use to find the sum of all the thirds and all the sixths? 6, 12, and so on . . .

● What common denominator might you use to find the sum of all the thirds, fourths, and sixths? 12, 24, and so on . . .

● What is the least common denominator for all the fractions on the cards? 12

Go over the rules for *Fraction Action, Fraction Friction* on *Student Reference Book,* page 312 with the class. Play a few practice rounds against the class before partners play the game on their own. Remind students to compare the fractions with benchmarks to help them estimate the sums.

Science Link In physics, friction is a force that resists relative motion. Compare pulling a heavy box across a rough concrete floor versus pulling it across smooth ice. The greater resistance to motion on the concrete is due to greater friction.

In the game, a player might call *Friction!* to ask for resistance to motion if the player does not wish to move any further toward 2. By calling *Action!* the player asks to resume moving toward 2.

Students play *Fraction Action, Fraction Friction*. Circulate and assist.

▶ Exploring Fraction-Operation Keys on a Calculator

WHOLE-CLASS ACTIVITY

(*Student Reference Book,* pp. 260–263)

Students can use scientific calculators to perform operations with fractions and mixed numbers. Students explored these calculator operations in Lessons 5-4 and 5-5.

If you have a calculator for the overhead, have volunteers use it to demonstrate how to enter the following fractions and mixed numbers: Sample answers for TI-15 and Casio *fx-55*:

● $\frac{5}{8}$ 5 ⏹ⁿ 8 ⏹ᵈ, or 5 ⏹ᵇ/ᶜ 8

● $73\frac{2}{5}$ 73 ⏹Unit 2 ⏹ⁿ 5 ⏹ᵈ, or 73 ⏹ᵃ 2 ⏹ᵇ/ᶜ 5

● $\frac{45}{7}$ 45 ⏹ⁿ 7 ⏹ᵈ, or 45 ⏹ᵇ/ᶜ 7

Use these same numbers to have other volunteers demonstrate how to convert between fractions and mixed numbers:
Sample answers for TI-15 and Casio *fx*-55: , or

Write the following problems on the board or a transparency for students to solve using their calculators:
Sample answers for TI-15 and Casio *fx*-55:

- $2\frac{1}{2} + \frac{5}{8}$ $3\frac{1}{8}$, or $2\frac{9}{8}$
- $73\frac{2}{5} - \frac{45}{7}$ $66\frac{34}{35}$
- $\frac{4}{12} + \frac{14}{3}$ 5, or $\frac{60}{12}$

Have the class mirror the volunteers as they explain the key sequences used for their solutions. Discuss any difficulties or interesting occurrences students encountered.

Ask: *What are some of the important steps to remember when working with a calculator?* Expect these types of responses:

▷ Clear between operations.

▷ Check that the fix function is off or set appropriately.

▷ Pay attention to the display as you press keys.

Ask students to locate the $\boxed{\text{Simp}}$ or $\boxed{\text{SIMP}}$ key on their calculators. Have them explore how to use this key and what it does. Then ask them to report what they found. Refer students to *Student Reference Book,* pages 260–263. As a class, read the section on simplifying fractions, and do the examples together.

▶ Entering Fractions on a Calculator 🧑‍🤝‍🧑 PARTNER ACTIVITY

(*Math Journal 2,* p. 257)

Have students complete the journal page. Circulate and assist.

② Ongoing Learning & Practice

▶ Math Boxes 8·4 🧍 INDEPENDENT ACTIVITY

(*Math Journal 2,* p. 258)

Mixed Practice Math Boxes in this lesson are paired with Math Boxes in Lesson 8-2. The skill in Problem 6 previews Unit 9 content.

Writing/Reasoning Have students write a response to the following: *Explain how you found the answer to Problem 1b. Include the strategies and the reasoning that you used.* Answers vary.

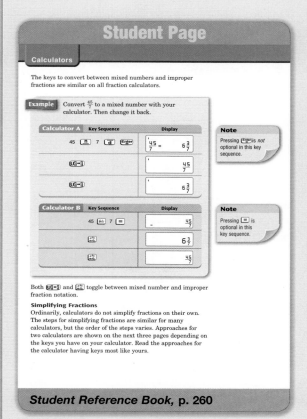

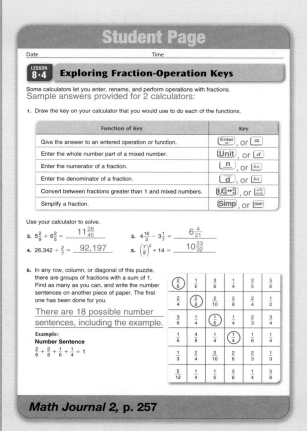

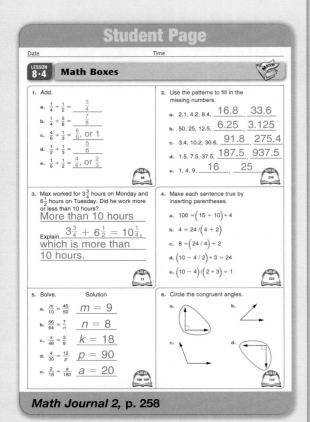

Math Journal 2, p. 258

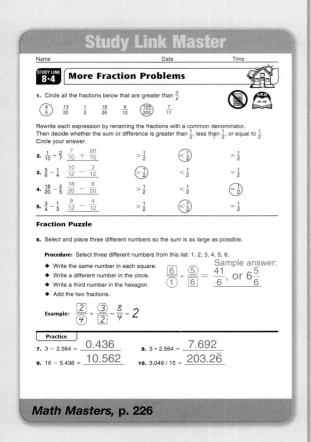

Math Masters, p. 226

▶ **Study Link 8·4**

(Math Masters, p. 226)

Home Connection Students compare fractions to $\frac{1}{2}$ and solve a fraction addition puzzle.

3 Differentiation Options

READINESS

SMALL-GROUP
ACTIVITY

▶ **Charting Common Denominators**

  15–30 Min

(Math Masters, p. 227)

Portfolio Ideas

To explore fraction addition using a common-denominator strategy, have students use a flowchart to find common denominators before solving fraction addition problems. Explain that students can use a flowchart to show the steps and decisions used to find common denominators. Use the prepared transparency, and demonstrate how to read the flowchart on the *Math Masters* page.

Example:

Step 1 Write $\frac{7}{24} + \frac{5}{6}$ in the START circle.

Step 2 Point to the first triangle and ask: *Do the fractions have a common denominator?* No

Step 3 Follow the No side of the triangle.

Step 4 Point to the second triangle and ask: *Is one denominator a factor of the other?* Yes. 6 is a factor of 24.

Step 5 Follow the YES side of the triangle.

Step 6 Rename $\frac{5}{6}$ with a denominator of 24. $\frac{5 * 4}{6 * 4} = \frac{20}{24}$

Step 7 Follow the line that leads to the next rectangle.

Step 8 Add the numerators. $7 + 20 = 27$

Step 9 Write the solution. $\frac{7}{24} + \frac{20}{24} = \frac{27}{24}$, $1\frac{3}{24}$, or $1\frac{1}{8}$

Have students use the flowchart as they solve the following problems:

- $\frac{13}{15} + \frac{8}{15}$ $\frac{21}{15}$, $1\frac{6}{15}$, or $1\frac{2}{5}$
- $\frac{18}{24} + \frac{5}{6}$ $\frac{38}{24}$, $1\frac{14}{24}$, or $1\frac{7}{12}$
- $\frac{3}{4} + \frac{3}{7}$ $\frac{33}{28}$, or $1\frac{5}{28}$
- $\frac{3}{8} + \frac{13}{18}$ $\frac{79}{72}$, or $1\frac{7}{72}$

Adjusting the Activity

Have students list the steps they take as they decide whether to use the QCD or to find the least common denominator.

AUDITORY ◆ **KINESTHETIC** ◆ **TACTILE** ◆ **VISUAL**

ENRICHMENT

Exploring Equivalent Fractions

SMALL-GROUP ACTIVITY

15–30 Min

PROBLEM SOLVING

(*Math Masters*, p. 228)

To extend students' understanding of equivalent fractions, have them explore fraction-to-decimal conversions using a calculator. Have students enter $\frac{3}{4}$ on their calculators and then locate and press the key that will convert the display to an equivalent decimal. On many calculators, this key is labeled F↔D. Ask: *Will equivalent fractions convert to the same decimal?* Explain that in this exploration students will work to support their responses.

Have each student write a fraction. Make adjustments so there are no duplicates. Students complete *Math Masters*, page 228. They use their fractions to make a list of 10 equivalent fractions, use their calculators to convert the fractions to decimals, and summarize their results.

Discuss students' summaries. Equivalent fractions name the same amount. They can also be defined as fractions that have the same decimal result when their numerators are divided by their denominators.

EXTRA PRACTICE

5-Minute Math

SMALL-GROUP ACTIVITY

5–15 Min

To offer students more experience with using a calculator to add fractions, see *5-Minute Math*, pages 26, 98, 99, and 113.

Math Masters, p. 227

1. Do equivalent fractions convert to the same decimal? Yes

2. Complete the fraction column in the table so there are 10 equivalent fractions.

3. Use your calculator to convert each fraction to a decimal. Write the display in the decimal column. (Don't forget to use a repeat bar, if necessary.) Sample answers:

Fractions	Decimals
$\frac{3}{4}$	0.75
$\frac{6}{8}$	0.75
$\frac{9}{12}$	0.75
$\frac{12}{16}$	0.75
$\frac{15}{20}$	0.75
$\frac{18}{24}$	0.75
$\frac{21}{28}$	0.75
$\frac{24}{32}$	0.75
$\frac{27}{36}$	0.75
$\frac{30}{40}$	0.75

4. Explain your results. Describe the relationship between the equivalent fractions and their decimal form. The equivalent fractions can all be renamed as $\frac{3}{4}$, the simplest form. Converted to a decimal, $\frac{3}{4}$ is equal to 0.75. So all equivalent fractions have the same decimal form.

Math Masters, p. 228

8·5 Fractions of Fractions

 Objective To introduce finding a fraction of a fraction.

Technology Resources www.everydaymathonline.com

ePresentations | eToolkit | Algorithms Practice | EM Facts Workshop Game™ | Family Letters | Assessment Management | Common Core State Standards | Curriculum Focal Points | Interactive Teacher's Lesson Guide

1 Teaching the Lesson

Key Concepts and Skills

• Use unit fractions to find a fraction of a number and to find the whole.
[Operations and Computation Goal 5]

• Use an area model to find fractions of fractions.
[Operations and Computation Goal 5]

Key Activities

Students solve fraction-of problems using number lines and folded-paper manipulatives.

Ongoing Assessment: Recognizing Student Achievement
Use journal page 259.
[Operations and Computation Goal 5]

Key Vocabulary

vertical ◆ horizontal

Materials

Math Journal 2, pp. 259–261
Student Reference Book, pp. 74 and 75
Math Masters, p. 414
Study Link 8·4
transparency of *Math Masters,* p. 434
(optional) ◆ 5 sheets of $8\frac{1}{2}$" by 11" paper per student ◆ slate ◆ scissors ◆ poster board ◆ Class Data Pad (optional)

2 Ongoing Learning & Practice

 Playing *Fraction Spin*
Math Journal 2, p. 262
Math Masters, p. 471
per partnership: large paper clip, 15 index cards (optional)
Students practice estimating sums and differences of fractions.

 Math Boxes 8·5
Math Journal 2, p. 263
Students practice and maintain skills through Math Box problems.

Study Link 8·5
Math Masters, p. 229
Students practice and maintain skills through Study Link activities.

3 Differentiation Options

READINESS
Modeling Equivalent Fractions
Math Masters, p. 230
Students use a fraction stick to model equivalent fractions.

ENRICHMENT
Summing the Squares
calculator ◆ Class Data Pad (optional)
Students use their calculators to find sums of fractions.

ELL SUPPORT
Building a Math Word Bank
Differentiation Handbook, p. 142
Students illustrate and write words related to the terms *horizontal* and *vertical.*

Advance Preparation

For Part 1, prepare a labeled diagram illustrating $\frac{3}{4}$ of $\frac{2}{3}$ on a poster or the Class Data Pad. (*See page 646.*)
Make a transparency of *Math Masters,* page 434. Have extra sheets of $8\frac{1}{2}$" by 11" paper available to students. For the Part 2 Adjusting the Activity, students will need 3" by 5" index cards cut in half vertically.

 Teacher's Reference Manual, **Grades 4–6** pp. 85–87

Getting Started

Mental Math and Reflexes

Have students solve the following fraction-of problems:

○○○ There are 12 counters in a set. How many counters are in $\frac{1}{2}$ of the set? 6

There are 10 counters in $\frac{1}{7}$ of a set. How many counters are in the whole set? 70

●●○ If $\frac{1}{2}$ of a set is 8, what is $\frac{1}{4}$ of the set? 4

If $\frac{3}{5}$ of a set is 18 counters, how many are in the whole set? 30

●●● If $\frac{3}{4}$ of a set is 6, what is $\frac{1}{8}$ of the set? 1

If 16 counters are $\frac{4}{5}$ of a set, how many are in $\frac{1}{4}$ of the set? 5

Math Message

Complete problems 1–11 on journal page 259.

Study Link 8·4 Follow-Up

Have partners compare answers and resolve differences.

---

1 Teaching the Lesson

▶ Math Message Follow-Up

WHOLE-CLASS DISCUSSION

(*Math Journal 2*, p. 259; *Math Masters*, p. 434)

Ask volunteers to present their solution strategies for Problems 1–10 on the board or on a transparency of *Math Masters*, page 434. Expect student approaches to be similar to the following:

▷ Use the number line. For Problem 3, divide the segment from 0 to 2 into 4 equal parts, and count 3 of those parts starting from 0.

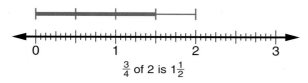

$\frac{3}{4}$ of 2 is $1\frac{1}{2}$

▷ For Problem 7, divide the segment from 0 to $\frac{3}{4}$ into 2 equal parts, and count 1 of those parts.

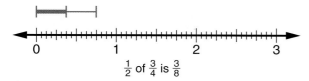

$\frac{1}{2}$ of $\frac{3}{4}$ is $\frac{3}{8}$

▷ Use addition. For Problem 3, add $\frac{3}{4}$ of 1 and $\frac{3}{4}$ of 1 to find $\frac{3}{4}$ of 2: $\frac{3}{4} + \frac{3}{4} = \frac{6}{4} = 1\frac{1}{2}$.

✔ Ongoing Assessment:
Recognizing Student Achievement

Journal Page 259 Problems 1–6

Use **journal page 259, Problems 1–6** to assess students' understanding of fractional parts on a number line. Students are making adequate progress if they correctly answer Problems 1–6. Some students might correctly answer Problems 7–10.

[*Operations and Computation Goal 5*]

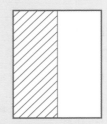

Sheet folded in half vertically

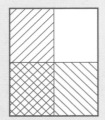

Sheet folded in quarters

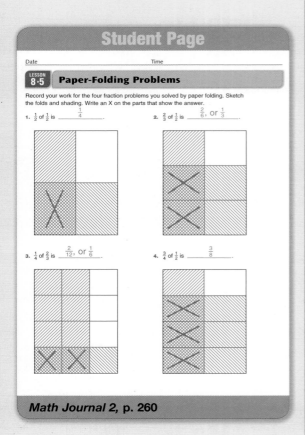
▶ **Using Unit Fractions to Find a Fraction of a Number**  WHOLE-CLASS ACTIVITY

(*Math Journal 2*, p. 259; *Student Reference Book*, pp. 74 and 75)

As a class, work through the examples in the *Student Reference Book*, pages 74 and 75. Then have students complete Problems 12–21 on journal page 259. Circulate and assist.

▶ **Modeling How to Find a Fraction of a Fraction**  PROBLEM SOLVING WHOLE-CLASS ACTIVITY ELL

Tell students that they are going to fold paper to solve problems that ask for a fraction of a fraction.

Example 1: Larry has $\frac{1}{2}$ of a fruit bar and wants to give half of it to his brother. How much of the whole fruit bar will Larry give to his brother? This problem can be solved by thinking of $\frac{1}{2}$ of $\frac{1}{2}$.

Ask students each to fold a sheet of paper into halves, either horizontally or vertically. Define **vertical** as the longer dimension of the paper and **horizontal** as the shorter dimension. To support English language learners, write *horizontal* and *vertical* on the board along with examples and discuss their meanings. Compare their results. It doesn't matter which way students fold their sheets in this example, but the way they fold them will be important in the next example.

Have students unfold their sheets, and show them how to orient the sheets so the halves are to the left and right of each other (rather than above and below each other). Shade the left half with diagonal marks. (*See margin.*)

Ask the students to fold their papers into halves in the opposite direction. (If the first fold was horizontal, the second fold will be vertical, and vice versa.) Have students unfold their sheets, orient them so the new halves are above and below each other, and shade the bottom half with diagonal marks that slant in the opposite direction to the first shading. (*See margin.*)

Ask a volunteer to give the answer and explain how this folded-paper model shows how much of the fruit bar Larry gave to his brother. Remind students that the sheet of paper represents the whole fruit bar, or ONE. Sample answer: Larry gave his brother $\frac{1}{4}$ of the fruit bar. Folding and shading the paper to represent $\frac{1}{2}$ of $\frac{1}{2}$ divided the whole into 4 equal parts. One of those 4 equal parts was shaded twice. This shows that $\frac{1}{2}$ of $\frac{1}{2}$ is $\frac{1}{4}$.

Students write $\frac{1}{2}$ *of* $\frac{1}{2}$ *is* $\frac{1}{4}$ on their folded papers.

Example 2: Ava has $\frac{1}{2}$ of a pizza. She eats $\frac{2}{3}$ of the pizza she has. How much of the whole pizza did she eat? This problem can be solved by thinking $\frac{2}{3}$ of $\frac{1}{2}$.

Ask students how they would fold and shade a sheet of paper to find $\frac{2}{3}$ of $\frac{1}{2}$. Refer to their suggestions as you lead students through the following steps:

1. Note that the denominator of the second fraction is 2. Fold a sheet of paper into halves, vertically. Unfold it and shade the left half.

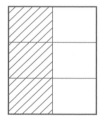

2. Note that the denominator of the first fraction is 3. Fold the sheet approximately into thirds, horizontally.

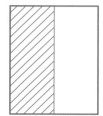

3. Unfold the sheet and use different shading to shade the bottom $\frac{2}{3}$ of the sheet, using the new folds. Explain that you are shading $\frac{2}{3}$ of the entire sheet and also $\frac{2}{3}$ of each half.

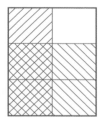

4. Write an X in each of the two parts of the sheet that was shaded twice. These parts represent $\frac{2}{3}$ of $\frac{1}{2}$.

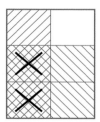

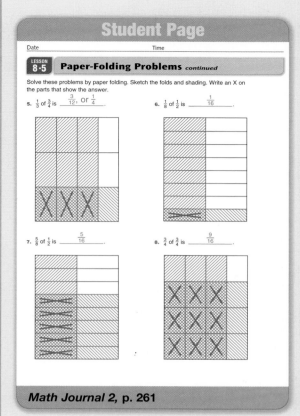
Adjusting the Activity

Have students find $\frac{1}{2}$ of $\frac{2}{3}$. Compare the answer and the folded-paper model to the model for $\frac{2}{3}$ of $\frac{1}{2}$. Students should conclude that $\frac{1}{2}$ of $\frac{2}{3}$ and $\frac{2}{3}$ of $\frac{1}{2}$ have the same answer.

AUDITORY ♦ KINESTHETIC ♦ TACTILE ♦ VISUAL

Links to the Future

The paper-folding model anticipates the area model that is developed in Lesson 8-6. Both models are used to prepare students for multiplying fractions.

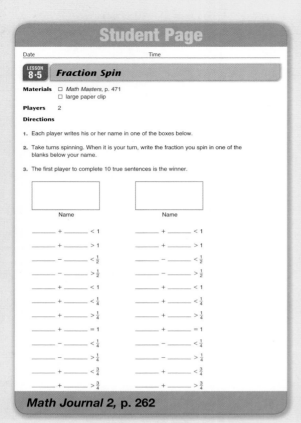

Math Journal 2, p. 262

Game Master

Name _____ Date _____ Time _____

Fraction Spin

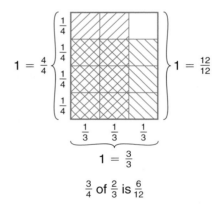

Math Masters, p. 471

Ask a volunteer to give the answer and explain how this folded-paper model shows how much of the whole pizza Ava ate. Remind students that the sheet of paper represents the whole pizza, or ONE. Sample answer: Ava ate $\frac{2}{6}$, or $\frac{1}{3}$, of the pizza. Folding and shading the paper to represent $\frac{2}{3}$ of $\frac{1}{2}$ divided the whole into 6 equal parts. Two of those 6 equal parts were shaded twice. This shows that $\frac{2}{3}$ of $\frac{1}{2}$ is $\frac{2}{6}$.

Ask: *How does the product $\frac{2}{6}$ compare to the two factors $\frac{2}{3}$ and $\frac{1}{2}$?* Sample answer: The product is smaller than both of the factors; the product $\frac{2}{6}$ is $\frac{2}{3}$ as much as $\frac{1}{2}$.

Have students write $\frac{2}{3}$ of $\frac{1}{2}$ is $\frac{2}{6}$ on their sheets.

▶ **Finding a Fraction of a Fraction** 👥 PARTNER ACTIVITY

(*Math Journal 2*, pp. 260 and 261; *Math Masters*, p. 414)

Have students fold paper to find $\frac{1}{4}$ of $\frac{2}{3}$ and $\frac{3}{4}$ of $\frac{1}{2}$. Circulate and assist. When most students have finished, ask volunteers to demonstrate their folded-paper model solutions.

Present the labeled diagram illustrating $\frac{3}{4}$ of $\frac{2}{3}$ that you prepared. Emphasize that the whole can be thought of as fourths, thirds, or twelfths, but the parts that are shaded twice represent twelfths.

$$1 = \frac{4}{4} \left\{ \begin{array}{c} \frac{1}{4} \\ \frac{1}{4} \\ \frac{1}{4} \\ \frac{1}{4} \end{array} \right. \underbrace{}_{\substack{\frac{1}{3}\ \frac{1}{3}\ \frac{1}{3} \\ 1 = \frac{3}{3}}} \left. \right\} 1 = \frac{12}{12}$$

$\frac{3}{4}$ of $\frac{2}{3}$ is $\frac{6}{12}$

Have students fold and shade a sheet of paper to show $\frac{3}{4}$ of $\frac{2}{3}$ and then cut out the rectangular pieces representing twelfths. Ask a volunteer if the answer on the diagram is in simplest form. No

Ask students to rearrange their pieces so they show the answer in simplest form. The answer in simplest form is $\frac{1}{2}$. Pieces should be arranged in 3 rows and 4 columns so that the pieces shaded twice represent $\frac{1}{2}$ because $\frac{6}{12} = \frac{3}{6} = \frac{1}{2}$.

Ask students to complete journal pages 260 and 261. Tell them to think of the rectangles as sheets of paper and to sketch the folds and shading. They should estimate where the folds are on each sketch and then fill in their answers.

After completing *Math Journal 2*, pages 260 and 261, have students write a number story that matches Problem 4, *Math Journal 2*, page 260 ($\frac{3}{4}$ of $\frac{1}{2}$) on an Exit Slip (*Math Masters*, page 414).

② Ongoing Learning & Practice

▶ Playing *Fraction Spin*

(*Math Journal 2*, p. 262; *Math Masters*, p. 471)

PARTNER ACTIVITY

Students play *Fraction Spin* to practice estimating sums and differences of fractions. Students will recognize *Fraction Spin* as being the same as *Mixed-Number Spin* from Lesson 8-3. This version has fractions only. Remind students to use benchmarks as they make their estimates.

Adjusting the Activity

Have students make a deck of 30 cards with fractions of their choice and a record sheet to match. Instead of using the spinner, partners take turns drawing cards and completing their record page.

To make a deck, partners need to decide on a range for their cards. They each make 15 cards for the deck. They can make the cards on 3 in. by 5 in. cards, cut in half.

AUDITORY ◆ KINESTHETIC ◆ TACTILE ◆ VISUAL

▶ Math Boxes 8·5

(*Math Journal 2*, p. 263)

INDEPENDENT ACTIVITY

Mixed Practice Math Boxes in this lesson are paired with Math Boxes in Lesson 8-7. The skills in Problems 4 and 5 preview Unit 9 content.

Writing/Reasoning Have students write a response to the following: *Write one of the false number sentences from Problem 2. Then write it correctly so it is true, and explain your solution.* Sample answer: $16 - (3 + 5) = 18$ is false because $16 - (3 + 5) = 8$. Remove the parentheses and follow the order of operations, $16 - 3 + 5 = 18$.

▶ Study Link 8·5

(*Math Masters*, p. 229)

INDEPENDENT ACTIVITY

Home Connection Students solve fraction-of-a-fraction problems.

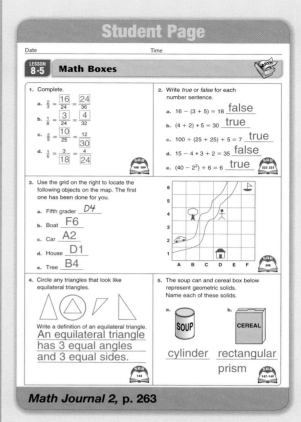

Math Journal 2, p. 263

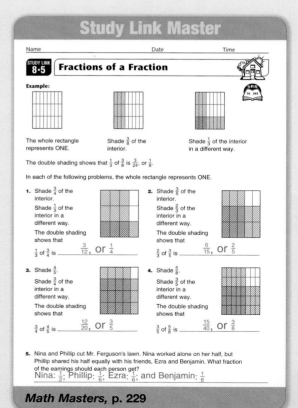

Math Masters, p. 229

Teaching Master

Name   Date   Time

LESSON 8·5 | **Equivalent Fractions**

Use the fraction stick to find equivalent fractions. A whole stick is worth 1.

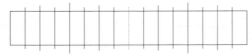

1. Divide the fraction stick into 4 equal parts.

   Find the equivalent fraction.

   $\frac{1}{2} = \frac{2}{4}$

2. Divide the fraction stick into 8 equal parts.

   Find the equivalent fractions.

   $\frac{1}{2} = \frac{2}{4} = \frac{4}{8}$

3. Divide the fraction stick into 16 equal parts.

   Find the equivalent fractions.

   $\frac{1}{2} = \frac{2}{4} = \frac{4}{8} = \frac{8}{16}$

Math Masters, p. 230

3 | Differentiation Options

READINESS

 SMALL-GROUP ACTIVITY

🕐 5–15 Min

▶ ## Modeling Equivalent Fractions

(*Math Masters*, p. 230)

To reinforce students' understanding of modeling fractional parts, work through the *Math Masters* page as a group. Discuss questions such as the following:

• When using a fraction stick, how do you know that two fractions are equivalent? The pieces are the same size.

• How could you express the whole as a fraction with a denominator of 8? $\frac{8}{8}$

• Explain how you can tell that a fraction represents 1 or the whole. The numerator and the denominator are the same.

ENRICHMENT

 SMALL-GROUP ACTIVITY

🕐 5–15 Min

▶ ## Summing the Squares

To extend students' ease in performing operations with fractions using a calculator, have them explore finding sums of fractions. Ask students for two numbers whose sum is 1. List these addition expressions on the board or Class Data Pad. Tell students to review the list, and ask: *If one of the fractions is squared, which sum is larger: the sum of the larger fraction squared and the smaller fraction, or the sum of the smaller fraction squared and the larger fraction?* Ask one group to find the sum after squaring the larger number and another group to find the sum after squaring the smaller number. Have a student from each group list the number sentences on the board.

For example: $\left(\frac{3}{4}\right)^2 + \frac{2}{8} = \frac{13}{16}$, and $\frac{3}{4} + \left(\frac{2}{8}\right)^2 = \frac{52}{64} = \frac{13}{16}$.

When students have completed the lists, discuss any problems or curiosities they encountered, and then discuss their findings. The sums are the same.

ELL SUPPORT

 SMALL-GROUP ACTIVITY

🕐 15–30 Min

▶ ## Building a Math Word Bank

(*Differentiation Handbook*, p. 142)

To provide language support for finding a fraction of a fraction, have students use the Word Bank Template found on *Differentiation Handbook*, page 142. Ask students to write the terms *horizontal* and *vertical,* draw pictures relating to each term, and write other related words. See the *Differentiation Handbook* for more information.

8·6 An Area Model for Fraction Multiplication

 Objective To develop a fraction multiplication algorithm.

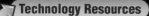

 Technology Resources www.everydaymathonline.com

								NCTM	iTLG
ePresentations	eToolkit	Algorithms Practice	EM Facts Workshop Game™	Family Letters	Assessment Management	Common Core State Standards	Curriculum Focal Points		Interactive Teacher's Lesson Guide

1 Teaching the Lesson

Key Concepts and Skills

- Use an area model to find fractions of fractions. [Operations and Computation Goal 5]

- Write number models for fraction multiplication problems shown with an area model.
  [Operations and Computation Goal 7]

- Describe the patterns in the area model for fraction multiplication.
  [Patterns, Functions, and Algebra Goal 1]

- Recognize the patterns in products when a number is multiplied by a fraction that is less than or equal to 1.
  [Patterns, Functions, and Algebra Goal 1]

Key Activities

Students solve problems using an area model for fraction multiplication. They use the area model and fraction multiplication patterns to derive the standard algorithm.

 Ongoing Assessment:
Informing Instruction See page 651.

 Ongoing Assessment:
Recognizing Student Achievement
Use journal page 265.
[Operations and Computation Goal 5]

Key Vocabulary

area model

Materials

Math Journal 2, pp. 264–266
Student Reference Book, p. 76
Study Link 8·5; transparency of
Math Masters, p. 231 (optional) ◆ slate

2 Ongoing Learning & Practice

Math Boxes 8·6
Math Journal 2, p. 267
Geometry Template
Students practice and maintain skills through Math Box problems.

Study Link 8·6
Math Masters, p. 232
Students practice and maintain skills through Study Link activities.

3 Differentiation Options

READINESS

Supporting Fraction Multiplication Concepts

Math Masters, p. 233
Students compare area models to reinforce the use of the word *of* to indicate multiplication.

EXTRA PRACTICE

Fraction Problems

Math Masters, p. 234
Students solve real-world number stories involving fractions.

Advance Preparation

For Part 1, make a transparency of *Math Masters,* page 231 for use in the discussion of journal page 265. The master is identical to the journal page.

 Teacher's Reference Manual, **Grades 4–6** pp. 143, 144, 220, 221

Getting Started

1 Teaching the Lesson

▶ Math Message Follow-Up

 WHOLE-CLASS DISCUSSION

(*Math Journal 2*, p. 264)

Ask a volunteer to demonstrate how to fold and shade a sheet of paper to solve the Math Message problem. Reinforce the demonstration by sketching the folds on the board or a transparency. The folded paper and sketch should show the paper folded into thirds in both directions. The whole has 9 parts, 2 of them shaded twice, so the answer is $\frac{2}{9}$. Have students complete Problem 2.

▶ Introducing the Word *of* to Mean *Multiply*

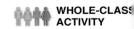 WHOLE-CLASS ACTIVITY

(*Math Journal 2*, p. 264)

Ask students what operation they used to solve the Mental Math and Reflexes problems. multiplication Point out that the number of coins in *3 sets of 4 coins* is equal to 3 times 4. Similarly, $\frac{2}{3}$ *of* $\frac{3}{4}$ is equal to $\frac{2}{3}$ times $\frac{3}{4}$. Students should record this as the answer to Problem 3 on the journal page. Have students complete the rest of the page and then compare answers with a partner.

▶ Using the Area Model for Fraction Multiplication

 PARTNER ACTIVITY

PROBLEM SOLVING

(*Math Journal 2*, p. 265)

On the board or a transparency, demonstrate how to solve $\frac{2}{3} * \frac{3}{4}$ from Problem 1 on journal page 265. Partition and shade a rectangle. Students should reproduce the shading in the rectangle at the top of the journal page.

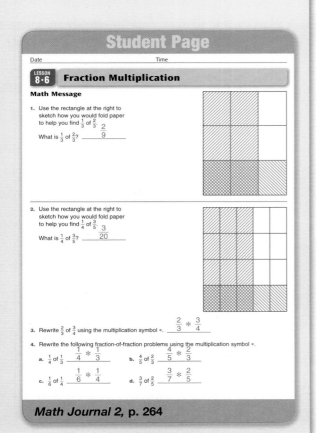

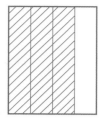

Figure 1   Figure 2

1. Note that the denominator of the second fraction is 4.

2. Divide the rectangle into fourths vertically. (*See Figure 1.*)

3. Shade the left $\frac{3}{4}$ of the interior of the rectangle.

4. Note that the denominator of the first fraction is 3.

5. Divide the rectangle into thirds horizontally. (*See Figure 2.*)

6. Use a different shading to shade the bottom $\frac{2}{3}$ of the interior.

7. Note the parts that have been shaded twice.

 Ongoing Assessment: Informing Instruction

Watch for students who have difficulty sketching the area models for the problems on the journal page. Have them first use the folded-paper method and then copy the results to the journal page.

Discuss the results:

- How does the diagram show the answer to $\frac{2}{3} * \frac{3}{4}$? The parts of the rectangle that were shaded first represent $\frac{3}{4}$ of the rectangle. The parts that were shaded second represent $\frac{2}{3}$ of the rectangle. The parts that have both shadings represent $\frac{2}{3}$ of $\frac{3}{4}$ of the rectangle. 6 parts out of 12 are shaded twice, so $\frac{2}{3}$ of $\frac{3}{4}$, or $\frac{2}{3} * \frac{3}{4}$, equals $\frac{6}{12}$, or $\frac{1}{2}$.

- How is this model similar to paper folding? The lines that divide the rectangle into fractional parts are just like the folds that divide the paper into fractional parts.

- Why would either of these models be called an **area model** for fraction multiplication? The doubly shaded part represents a fraction. The area of the doubly shaded part of the rectangle is a fraction of the area of the whole rectangle.

Have partners complete the journal page. Circulate and assist. When most students have finished, briefly review the answers.

 Ongoing Assessment: **Recognizing Student Achievement**

Journal Page 265 ★

Use **journal page 265** to assess students' understanding of the area model for fraction multiplication. Students are making adequate progress if their sketches accurately reflect the correct answers.

[Operations and Computation Goal 5]

Student Page

Date   Time

LESSON 8·6   An Area Model for Fraction Multiplication

1. Use the rectangle at the right to find $\frac{2}{3} * \frac{3}{4}$.

$\frac{2}{3} * \frac{3}{4} = \frac{6}{12}$, or $\frac{1}{2}$

Your completed drawing in Problem 1 is called an **area model.** Use area models to complete the remaining problems.

2.   3.   4.

$\frac{2}{3} * \frac{1}{5} = \frac{2}{15}$ $\frac{3}{4} * \frac{2}{5} = \frac{6}{20}$, or $\frac{3}{10}$ $\frac{1}{4} * \frac{5}{6} = \frac{5}{24}$

5.   6.   7.

$\frac{3}{8} * \frac{3}{5} = \frac{9}{40}$ $\frac{1}{2} * \frac{5}{8} = \frac{5}{16}$ $\frac{5}{6} * \frac{4}{5} = \frac{20}{30}$, or $\frac{2}{3}$

Explain how you sketched and shaded the rectangle to solve Problem 7.
I divided the rectangle into 5 sections vertically and shaded 4 of those sections. Then I divided the rectangle into 6 sections horizontally and shaded 5 of those sections. The 20 parts that are doubly shaded equal $\frac{20}{30}$ or $\frac{2}{3}$, which is the answer.

Math Journal 2, p. 265

Student Page

Date   Time

LESSON 8·6   An Algorithm for Fraction Multiplication

1. Look carefully at the fractions on journal page 265. What is the relationship between the numerators and the denominators of the two fractions being multiplied and the numerator and the denominator of their product?
The product of the two numerators is equal to the product numerator. The product of the two denominators is equal to the product denominator.

2. Describe a way to multiply two fractions. Multiply the numerators, and record the product as the product numerator. Multiply the denominators and record the product as the product denominator.

3. Multiply the following fractions using the algorithm discussed in class.

a. $\frac{1}{3} * \frac{1}{5} = \frac{1}{15}$ b. $\frac{2}{3} * \frac{1}{3} = \frac{2}{9}$

c. $\frac{3}{10} * \frac{7}{10} = \frac{21}{100}$ d. $\frac{5}{8} * \frac{1}{4} = \frac{5}{32}$

e. $\frac{3}{8} * \frac{5}{6} = \frac{15}{48}$, or $\frac{5}{16}$ f. $\frac{2}{5} * \frac{5}{12} = \frac{10}{60}$, or $\frac{1}{6}$

g. $\frac{4}{5} * \frac{2}{5} = \frac{8}{25}$ h. $\frac{4}{9} * \frac{3}{7} = \frac{12}{63}$, or $\frac{4}{21}$

i. $\frac{2}{4} * \frac{4}{8} = \frac{8}{32}$, or $\frac{1}{4}$ j. $\frac{3}{7} * \frac{5}{9} = \frac{15}{63}$, or $\frac{5}{21}$

k. $\frac{7}{9} * \frac{2}{6} = \frac{14}{54}$, or $\frac{7}{27}$ l. $\frac{2}{7} * \frac{9}{10} = \frac{18}{70}$, or $\frac{9}{35}$

4. Girls are one-half of the fifth-grade class. Two-tenths of these girls have red hair. Red-haired girls are what fraction of the fifth-grade class?
$\frac{2}{20}$, or $\frac{1}{10}$ of the fifth-grade class

Math Journal 2, p. 266

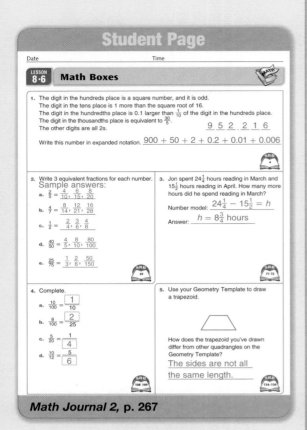

Student Page

Date _____ Time _____

1. The digit in the hundreds place is a square number, and it is odd.
   The digit in the tens place is 1 more than the square root of 16.
   The digit in the hundredths place is 0.1 larger than $\frac{1}{10}$ of the digit in the hundreds place.
   The digit in the thousandths place is equivalent to $\frac{30}{5}$.
   The other digits are all 2s.

   9 5 2 . 2 1 6

   Write this number in expanded notation. $900 + 50 + 2 + 0.2 + 0.01 + 0.006$

2. Write 3 equivalent fractions for each number.
   Sample answers:
   a. $\frac{2}{5} = \frac{4}{10}, \frac{6}{15}, \frac{8}{20}$
   b. $\frac{4}{7} = \frac{8}{14}, \frac{12}{21}, \frac{16}{28}$
   c. $\frac{1}{2} = \frac{2}{4}, \frac{3}{6}, \frac{4}{8}$
   d. $\frac{40}{50} = \frac{4}{5}, \frac{8}{10}, \frac{80}{100}$
   e. $\frac{25}{75} = \frac{1}{3}, \frac{2}{6}, \frac{50}{150}$

3. Jon spent $24\frac{1}{4}$ hours reading in March and $15\frac{1}{2}$ hours reading in April. How many more hours did he spend reading in March?

   Number model: $24\frac{1}{4} - 15\frac{1}{2} = h$

   Answer: $h = 8\frac{3}{4}$ hours

4. Complete.
   a. $\frac{10}{100} = \frac{1}{10}$
   b. $\frac{8}{100} = \frac{2}{25}$
   c. $\frac{5}{20} = \frac{1}{4}$
   d. $\frac{10}{12} = \frac{5}{6}$

5. Use your Geometry Template to draw a trapezoid.

   How does the trapezoid you've drawn differ from other quadrangles on the Geometry Template?
   The sides are not all the same length.

Math Journal 2, p. 267

After briefly reviewing answers, pose a few fraction multiplication number stories. *Suggestions:*

- Laura and her brother will paint $\frac{3}{4}$ of a wall. How much of the entire wall will each paint if they share the work equally? $\frac{3}{8}$ of the wall

- A tube of blue oil paint holds $\frac{5}{6}$ of an ounce of paint. It takes $\frac{3}{4}$ of the tube to paint the background of a sign. How many ounces of blue paint does it take to paint the background? $\frac{15}{24}$, or $\frac{5}{8}$ oz

▶ # Deriving a Fraction Multiplication Algorithm

PARTNER ACTIVITY

(*Math Journal 2*, p. 266; *Student Reference Book*, p. 76)

Have students work on Problems 1 and 2 on journal page 266. Discuss their answers. Students should notice that the product of the numerators is equal to the numerator of the product and that the product of the denominators is equal to the denominator of the product.

Ask volunteers to share their descriptions of a fraction multiplication algorithm from Problem 2. Explain that the relationships and descriptions are examples of the following general pattern: To multiply fractions, simply multiply the numerators and multiply the denominators. This pattern can be expressed as $\frac{a}{b} * \frac{c}{d} = \frac{a*c}{b*d}$. Remind students that b and d cannot be 0. Ask students to complete the journal page using this algorithm for fraction multiplication. Ask students to refer to *Student Reference Book*, page 76 as needed.

Circulate and assist. When most students have finished, have partners share answers and resolve differences.

NOTE Fraction multiplication is deceptively easy. One can easily learn by rote that to multiply fractions, one simply multiplies the numerators and multiplies the denominators. However, through modeling fractions by folding paper and shading rectangles students internalize concepts necessary to understand the meaning of expressions like $\frac{3}{4} * \frac{2}{3}$.

When students do not understand the reasons behind the fraction multiplication algorithm, they are more likely to add (or subtract or divide) numerators and denominators when they add (or subtract or divide) fractions. Students who understand what to do and why they are doing it will be better able to apply their knowledge in problem solving.

Multiplying a Fraction by 1

(*Math Journal 2*, p. 265)

Ask students to revisit Problem 1 on journal page 265. Remind them that they began by dividing the rectangle into fourths vertically and shading three of those four parts to show $\frac{3}{4}$ of the rectangle shaded. Then they divided the rectangle into thirds horizontally. Ask:

- How does dividing the rectangle into thirds (before applying the second round of shading) affect the number of parts in the rectangle and the number of parts that were shaded initially? Sample answer: Dividing the rectangle into thirds resulted in 3 times as many parts in all and 3 times as many parts shaded.

- Did this change how much of the rectangle was shaded? Explain. Sample answer: No, because the resulting fraction, $\frac{9}{12}$, is equivalent to the original fraction, $\frac{3}{4}$; the shaded amount of the rectangle remained the same.

Repeat the above discussion for Problem 5 ($\frac{3}{8} * \frac{3}{5}$) on journal page 265. Students should conclude that after the rectangle was divided into eighths horizontally, there were now 8 times as many parts in all and 8 times as many parts shaded. So, the $\frac{3}{5}$ of the rectangle that was initially shaded became $\frac{24}{40}$. Because $\frac{3}{5} = \frac{24}{40}$, the fractional part of the rectangle that was initially shaded did not change.

Help students conclude that when they divide rectangles into equal parts horizontally (or vertically if they began with horizontal partitions), they are in essence multiplying the numerator and the denominator of the original fraction by the same (nonzero) number.

Explain that this pattern can be expressed as $\frac{a}{b} = \frac{n*a}{n*b}$, where $b \neq 0$ and $n \neq 0$. Multiplying by $\frac{n}{n}$ does not change the value of the original fraction because it is equivalent to multiplying the fraction by 1. Ask students to try out this pattern on Problem 6.

Pose the following problems to provide additional practice multiplying by a fraction that has a value of 1.

- $1 * \frac{3}{4} = \frac{\square}{\square}$ $\frac{3}{4}$
- $\frac{4}{9} = \frac{\square * 4}{5 * 9}$ 5

- $\frac{5}{8} * \frac{\square}{\square} = \frac{15}{24}$ $\frac{3}{3}$
- $\frac{4 * 7}{4 * 10} = \frac{\square}{10}$ 7

▶ **Multiplying by a Fraction Less than 1**

(*Math Journal 2,* pp. 265 and 266)

Have students examine the drawings and the results in Problems 1–7 on journal page 265. Ask the following questions:

● In each problem, does the fractional part of the rectangle you shaded first represent the first fraction or the second fraction of the problem? It represents the second fraction.

● In each problem, how does the first fraction compare to 1? The first fraction in each problem is less than 1.

● In each problem, how would you compare the fractional part of the rectangle with double shading to the fractional part you shaded first? Sample answer: In each case, the fractional part with double shading is a portion of what I shaded first. So it is less than what I shaded first.

● In each problem, how does the product compare to the second fraction? Explain why that is the case. Sample answer: Each product is less than the second fraction. In each problem, we multiplied the second fraction by a fraction that is less than 1. So we were finding a portion of the second fraction.

Ask students to examine the results in Problem 3 on journal page 266. Ask: *Do the results support what we said about a fraction being multiplied by a number less than 1?* yes Ask students to describe the size of the product when you multiply a number by a fraction that is less than 1. Sample answer: When you multiply a number by a fraction that is less than 1, the product is less than the original number. For example, in Problem 3a, the product is a fraction, $\frac{1}{15}$, that is less than the original fraction, $\frac{1}{5}$.

② Ongoing Learning & Practice

▶ **Math Boxes 8·6**

INDEPENDENT ACTIVITY

(*Math Journal 2,* p. 267)

 Mixed Practice Math Boxes in this lesson are paired with Math Boxes in Lesson 8-8. The skill in Problem 5 previews Unit 9 content.

▶ **Study Link 8·6**

INDEPENDENT ACTIVITY

(*Math Masters,* p. 232)

 Home Connection Students solve fraction multiplication problems. They use the area model and the fraction multiplication algorithm.

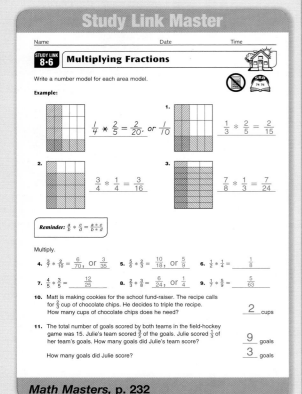

Math Masters, p. 232

③ Differentiation Options

READINESS

SMALL-GROUP ACTIVITY

5–15 Min

Supporting Fraction Multiplication Concepts

(*Math Masters*, p. 233)

To provide an additional model for the connection between the word *of* and multiplication, guide students through the activity on the *Math Masters* page.

Problem 1 Students review using multiplication to find the area of a rectangle and an area that is a fractional part of the rectangle. Point out that the numerators represent the length and width of the part of the rectangle that is shaded. Remind students that $\frac{1}{2}$ is equivalent to $\frac{2}{4}$. The denominators represent the length and width of the entire rectangle. The product of the fractions names the twice-shaded area of the rectangle.

Problem 2 Students find and shade a similar fractional part of a circle.

Review both problems by emphasizing that finding $\frac{1}{3}$ of $\frac{1}{2}$ of the rectangle is the same as finding $\frac{1}{3}$ of $\frac{1}{2}$ of the circle. Both problems can be solved using multiplication.

Pose several problems for students to solve using multiplication, and have them write the number sentences.

- $\frac{1}{5}$ of $\frac{1}{4}$ $\frac{1}{5} * \frac{1}{4} = \frac{1}{20}$
- $\frac{3}{5}$ of $\frac{1}{4}$ $\frac{3}{5} * \frac{1}{4} = \frac{3}{20}$
- $\frac{2}{5}$ of $\frac{3}{4}$ $\frac{2}{5} * \frac{3}{4} = \frac{6}{20}$, or $\frac{3}{10}$

EXTRA PRACTICE

INDEPENDENT ACTIVITY

5–15 Min

Fraction Problems

(*Math Masters*, p. 234)

Students solve real-world number stories involving fractions. They are asked to first write an open number model for each problem.

Name   Date   Time

LESSON 8·6 **Fraction Multiplication**

Problem 1

a. How many squares are in this grid? **12 squares**

b. How many squares represent $\frac{1}{3}$ of $\frac{1}{2}$ of the grid. **2 squares** Shade these squares.

c. Think of the total number of squares in the grid as the denominator and the shaded squares as the numerator, and write the fraction. $\frac{1}{3}$ of $\frac{1}{2}$ = $\frac{2}{12}$, or $\frac{1}{6}$

d. Write the number model you would use to find the area of this rectangle. *Reminder:* Area = length * width

Area = **3 * 4**

e. The number model to find the fractional part of the rectangle is the same as the number model to find the area of the rectangle. Write the number model you would use to find the fractional part of the rectangle. $\frac{1}{3} * \frac{1}{2}$

Problem 2

Linda bakes a peach pie. She serves $\frac{1}{2}$ of the pie for dessert. She saves $\frac{1}{3}$ of what is left for her mom.

a. Shade the circle to represent the piece of the pie that should be saved.

b. Think of the total number of pie pieces as the denominator and the shaded piece as the numerator, and write the fraction. $\frac{1}{6}$

c. Write a number sentence to show how you could find the fractional part of the pie that was saved without counting pie pieces. $\frac{1}{3} * \frac{1}{2} = p$

To find a fraction *of* a fraction, multiply.

Try This

Write and solve a number model to find the fractional part of the pie left after subtracting dessert and the piece saved for Linda's mom.

Sample answer: $1 - \left(\frac{1}{2} + \frac{1}{6}\right) = m$; $m = \frac{2}{6}$, or $\frac{1}{3}$

Math Masters, p. 233

Name   Date   Time

LESSON 8·6 **Fraction Problems**

1. Ailene is baking corn bread. She will cover $\frac{3}{4}$ of the cornbread with cheese. Then she plans to give $\frac{2}{3}$ of the cornbread with cheese to her friend Alex.

   a. Use the rectangle to show an area model for the problem.

   b. Write an open number model for the problem. Choose a letter to stand for the portion that will be given to Alex. $\frac{2}{3} * \frac{3}{4} = a$

   c. Ailene will give $\frac{1}{2}$ of the cornbread to Alex.

2. A recipe for granola bars calls for $\frac{1}{2}$ cup almonds. Cy is making $\frac{3}{4}$ of the recipe.

   a. Write an open number model to show how many ounces of almonds Cy will use. $\frac{3}{4} * \frac{1}{2} = a$

   b. Cy will use $\frac{3}{8}$ cup of almonds.

3. An ant weighs $\frac{1}{10}$ the weight of a crumb that it is carrying. Suppose the crumb weighs $\frac{3}{100}$ gram.

   a. Write an open number model to show the weight of the ant in grams. $\frac{1}{10} * \frac{3}{100} = a$

   b. The ant weighs $\frac{3}{1,000}$ gram.

4. Walker plans to hike a trail that is $\frac{8}{10}$ of a mile long. So far, he has walked $\frac{1}{4}$ that distance.

   a. Write an open number model for the problem. $\frac{1}{4} * \frac{8}{10} = w$

   b. So far, Walker has walked $\frac{1}{5}$ mi.

5. In Mrs. Ortiz's class, $\frac{9}{22}$ of the students are boys. Of the boys, $\frac{1}{9}$ are left-handed.

   a. Write an open number model to show how to find what fraction of the class are left-handed boys. $\frac{1}{9} * \frac{9}{22} = b$

   b. $\frac{1}{22}$ of the class are left-handed boys.

Math Masters, p. 234

8·7 Multiplication of Fractions and Whole Numbers

 Objective To provide experience finding the product of a whole number and a fraction.

 Technology Resources www.everydaymathonline.com

 ePresentations   eToolkit   Algorithms Practice   EM Facts Workshop Game™   Family Letters   Assessment Management   Common Core State Standards   Curriculum Focal Points   Interactive Teacher's Lesson Guide

---

1 Teaching the Lesson

Key Concepts and Skills

• Find fractions of a set.
[Number and Numeration Goal 2]

• Use given denominators to rename numbers as fractions.
[Number and Numeration Goal 5]

• Use an area model and a fraction multiplication algorithm to find fraction-by-whole-number products.
[Operations and Computation Goal 5]

Key Activities

Students use area models and a fraction multiplication algorithm to find the products of whole numbers and fractions.

Materials

Math Journal 2, pp. 268–270
Student Reference Book, p. 77
Study Link 8·6
slate ◆ Class Data Pad (optional)

2 Ongoing Learning & Practice

 Playing *Name That Number*
Student Reference Book, p. 325
per partnership: 4 each of number cards 0–9 (from the Everything Math Deck, if available), calculator (optional)
Students practice writing number sentences using order of operations.

 Math Boxes 8·7
Math Journal 2, p. 271
Students practice and maintain skills through Math Box problems.

 **Ongoing Assessment:
Recognizing Student Achievement**
Use Math Boxes, Problem 1.
[Number and Numeration Goal 5]

Study Link 8·7
Math Masters, p. 235
Students practice and maintain skills through Study Link activities.

3 Differentiation Options

READINESS
Writing Whole Numbers as Fractions
Students rename whole numbers as fractions and find common denominators.

ENRICHMENT
Simplifying Fraction Factors
Math Masters, p. 236
Class Data Pad (optional)
Students explore the use of the commutative property to simplify finding the product of fractions.

EXTRA PRACTICE
5-Minute Math
5-Minute Math™, pp. 23 and 185
Students practice multiplying fractions and whole numbers.

Advance Preparation

 Teacher's Reference Manual, Grades 4–6 pp. 85–87, 143, 144

Getting Started

Mental Math and Reflexes

Have students solve fraction-of problems. Remind them to think *of* when multiplying fractions.

●○○ $\frac{1}{5}$ of $1\frac{1}{2}$ $\frac{1}{10}$

$\frac{1}{8}$ of $1\frac{1}{2}$ $\frac{1}{16}$

$\frac{1}{2}$ of $\frac{2}{14}$ $\frac{1}{14}$

●●○ $\frac{2}{3}$ of $\frac{3}{4}$ $\frac{1}{2}$

$\frac{4}{5}$ of $\frac{4}{5}$ $\frac{16}{25}$

$\frac{8}{9} * \frac{2}{3}$ $\frac{16}{27}$

●●● $\frac{3}{14} * \frac{1}{3}$ $\frac{1}{14}$

$\frac{5}{9}$ of 12 $6\frac{2}{3}$

$\frac{6}{4} * \frac{2}{3}$ 1

Math Message

Complete journal page 268.

Study Link 8·6 Follow-Up

Have partners compare answers and resolve differences. Ask volunteers to share their solution strategies for Problems 10 and 11.

---

1 Teaching the Lesson

▶ Math Message Follow-Up

 WHOLE-CLASS DISCUSSION

(*Math Journal 2*, p. 268)

Algebraic Thinking Ask students whether they remember problems of this type from earlier grades. Point out that in the fifth grade they still solve the problems, but they also write the number models for calculations that solve the problems.

Review the problems by having volunteers rewrite each problem in the form $\frac{a}{b} * \frac{c}{d}$ on the board and then write the product.

1. $\frac{1}{6}$ of $1\frac{1}{6} * \frac{1}{1} = \frac{1}{6}$

2. **a.** $\frac{3}{4}$ of $1\frac{3}{4} * \frac{1}{1} = \frac{3}{4}$

   b. $\frac{2}{3}$ of $1\frac{2}{3} * \frac{1}{1} = \frac{2}{3}$

   c. $\frac{2}{2}$ of $1\frac{2}{2} * \frac{1}{1} = \frac{2}{2} = 1$

3. **a.** $\frac{1}{4}$ of $16\frac{1}{4} * \frac{16}{1} = \frac{16}{4} = 4$

   b. $\frac{1}{8}$ of $16\frac{1}{8} * \frac{16}{1} = \frac{16}{8} = 2$

4. **a.** $\frac{1}{2}$ of $\frac{1}{4}$ $\frac{1}{2} * \frac{1}{4} = \frac{1}{8}$

   b. $\frac{1}{8}$ of $\frac{1}{2}$ $\frac{1}{8} * \frac{1}{2} = \frac{1}{16}$

   c. $\frac{1}{2}$ of $\frac{1}{8}$ $\frac{1}{2} * \frac{1}{8} = \frac{1}{16}$

5. $\frac{5}{6}$ of $12\frac{5}{6} * \frac{12}{1} = \frac{60}{6} = 10$

▶ Using an Area Model to Represent the Product of a Fraction and a Whole Number

 WHOLE-CLASS ACTIVITY

(*Math Journal 2*, p. 269)

Pose this number story: *Sally made a cherry pie and a raspberry pie. Her family ate $\frac{2}{3}$ of the 2 pies. How much pie did they eat?* $1\frac{1}{3}$ pies Have students solve $\frac{2}{3} * 2 = ?$ on their slates.

Have volunteers show on the board or Class Data Pad how an area model might be used to represent this problem. The basic idea is that there are several wholes, each of which is divided into fractional parts. Summarize students' presentations using the steps on the next page:

Student Page

Date _____ Time _____

LESSON 8·7 A Blast from the Past

1. From *Kindergarten Everyday Mathematics*:

   This slice of pizza is what fraction of the whole pizza? $\frac{1}{6}$

2. From *First Grade Everyday Mathematics*:

   Write a fraction in each part of the diagrams below. Then color the figures as directed.

   a. $\frac{1}{4}$ $\frac{1}{4}$ $\frac{1}{4}$ $\frac{1}{4}$ Color $\frac{3}{4}$.

   b. $\frac{1}{3}$ $\frac{1}{3}$ $\frac{1}{3}$ Color $\frac{2}{3}$.

   c. $\frac{1}{2}$ $\frac{1}{2}$ Color $\frac{2}{2}$.

3. From *Second Grade Everyday Mathematics*:

   a. Color $\frac{1}{4}$ of the beads.

   b. Color $\frac{1}{8}$ of the beads.

4. From *Third Grade Everyday Mathematics*:

   a. $\frac{1}{2}$ of $\frac{1}{4} = \frac{1}{8}$ b. $\frac{1}{8}$ of $\frac{1}{2} = \frac{1}{16}$ c. $\frac{1}{2}$ of $\frac{1}{8} = \frac{1}{16}$

5. From *Fourth Grade Everyday Mathematics*:

   Cross out $\frac{5}{8}$ of the dimes.

Math Journal 2, p. 268

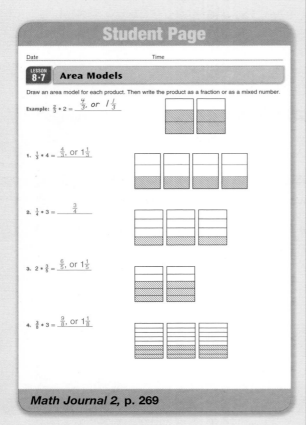

Math Journal 2, p. 269

Math Journal 2, p. 270

1. Draw a number of rectangles equal to the whole number. In this example, the whole is 2.

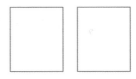

2. Note that the denominator of the fraction is 3. Divide both rectangles into thirds.

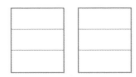

3. Note that the numerator of the fraction is 2. Shade $\frac{2}{3}$ of each rectangle.

In each rectangle, there are 3 parts; 2 of them are shaded. In the 2 rectangles, there are 4 shaded thirds altogether. So $\frac{2}{3} * 2 = \frac{4}{3}$ or $1\frac{1}{3}$.

Assign the journal page. When most students have finished, bring the class together to discuss answers.

Ask students to create number stories for Problems 1–4 to share with the class.

▶ Using an Algorithm to Multiply a Fraction and a Whole Number

PARTNER ACTIVITY

(*Math Journal 2*, p. 270; *Student Reference Book*, p. 77)

Algebraic Thinking Refer students to the top of journal page 270, and ask how this algorithm could be used to multiply a fraction and a whole number such as $\frac{2}{3} * 2$. Rewrite the whole number as a fraction. Remind students that any number can be thought of as a fraction with a denominator of 1.

Ask a volunteer to demonstrate using the algorithm to solve $\frac{2}{3} * 2$. $\frac{2}{3} * \frac{2}{1} = \frac{2 * 2}{3 * 1} = \frac{4}{3}$, or $1\frac{1}{3}$

Assign the journal page. Ask students to refer to *Student Reference Book*, page 77. Circulate and assist.

When students have completed the page, ask what patterns they notice about the numerators and denominators when multiplying fractions by whole numbers. The denominators in the products are always the same as the denominator of the fraction factor. The numerator is the product of the whole number and the numerator of the fraction factor.

Emphasize that, when rewriting the whole number as a fraction, the denominator is always 1. Ask students what true statement they can make about multiplying by 1. Any number times 1 is itself. Accordingly, the patterns for multiplying fractions by whole numbers can be represented as $\frac{a}{b} * c = \frac{a * c}{b}$.

2 Ongoing Learning & Practice

▶ Playing *Name That Number*

PARTNER ACTIVITY

(*Student Reference Book*, p. 325)

Students play *Name That Number* to practice writing number sentences using order of operations. Encourage them to find number sentences that use all five numbers. Students can use numbers as exponents or to form fractions.

▶ Math Boxes 8·7

INDEPENDENT ACTIVITY

(*Math Journal 2*, p. 271)

 Mixed Practice Math Boxes in this lesson are paired with Math Boxes in Lesson 8-5. The skills in Problems 4 and 5 preview Unit 9 content.

 Ongoing Assessment: Recognizing Student Achievement

Math Boxes Problem 1

Use **Math Boxes, Problem 1** to assess students' understanding of converting fractions to decimals and percents. Have students convert the fractions in Math Boxes, Problem 1 to the decimal and percent equivalents and then write a response to the following: *Explain your solution strategy.* Students are making adequate progress if their conversions are correct and their writing demonstrates an understanding of the role of the numerator and the denominator. Some students might refer to the fact that the fractions are equivalent; therefore, they have the same decimal and percent equivalents.

NOTE Students may use calculators. If they do, remind them to explain the part of the conversion process the calculator is performing.

[Number and Numeration Goal 5]

▶ Study Link 8·7

INDEPENDENT ACTIVITY

(*Math Masters*, p. 235)

 Home Connection Students solve problems to find a fraction of a whole number and a fraction of a fraction. They solve "What's My Rule?" problems and make a function table for fraction multiplication.

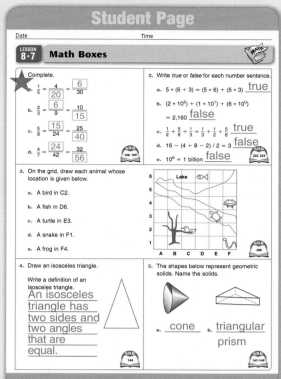

3 Differentiation Options

READINESS

SMALL-GROUP ACTIVITY

◑ 15–30 Min

▶ ## Writing Whole Numbers as Fractions

Algebraic Thinking To reinforce students' understanding of whole numbers written as fractions, guide them through the following activity:

▷ Remind students that any number can be thought of as a fraction with a denominator of 1. Write the examples on the board or Class Data Pad.

Examples: $3 = \frac{3}{1}$, $236 = \frac{236}{1}$, and $0.5 = \frac{0.5}{1}$

Ask students why this is true. The denominator represents how many parts it takes to make a whole. If it takes only 1 part, then the numerator represents *wholes*.

▷ When applying a multiplication algorithm to problems of the form $\frac{a}{b} * n$, where one factor is a fraction and the other factor is a whole number, think of the whole number as $\frac{n}{1}$.

▷ Ask students to write each number as a fraction on their slates. Then repeat the numbers, and ask students to rename each as a fraction with a denominator of 2.

$5 \quad \frac{5}{1}; \frac{10}{2}$ $\qquad$ $3.5 \quad \frac{3.5}{1}; \frac{7}{2}$ $\qquad$ $2 * 5 \quad \frac{10}{1}; \frac{20}{2}$

$7 \quad \frac{7}{1}; \frac{14}{2}$ $\qquad$ $1 \quad \frac{1}{1}; \frac{2}{2}$ $\qquad$ $100\% \quad \frac{1}{1}; \frac{2}{2}$

$140 \quad \frac{140}{1}; \frac{280}{2}$ $\qquad$ $0.5 \quad \frac{0.5}{1}; \frac{1}{2}$ $\qquad$ $2^3 \quad \frac{8}{1}; \frac{16}{2}$

ENRICHMENT

PARTNER ACTIVITY

◑ 15–30 Min

▶ ## Simplifying Fraction Factors
(*Math Masters*, p. 236)

To extend students' understanding of fraction multiplication and lowest terms, have students explore the process of reducing factors in fraction multiplication problems. When students have completed the *Math Masters* page, discuss any difficulties or curiosities they encountered.

EXTRA PRACTICE

SMALL-GROUP ACTIVITY

◔ 5–15 Min

▶ ## *5-Minute Math*

To offer students more experience with fractions and whole numbers, see *5-Minute Math*, pages 23 and 185.

Teaching Master

Name ___ Date ___ Time ___

LESSON 8·7 | **Simplifying Fraction Factors**

An Algorithm for Fraction Multiplication

$$\frac{a}{b} * \frac{c}{d} = \frac{a*c}{b*d}$$

The denominator of the product is the product of the factor denominators, and the numerator of the product is the product of the factor numerators.

The commutative property lets us write $\frac{a*c}{b*d}$ as $\frac{c*a}{d*b}$. Study the examples.

Example 1: $\frac{7}{8} * \frac{16}{21} = \frac{7*16}{8*21} = \frac{112}{168}; \frac{112}{168} \div \frac{8}{8} = \frac{14}{21}$ or $\frac{2}{3}$

Example 2: $\frac{7}{8} * \frac{16}{21} = \frac{7*16}{8*21} = \frac{16}{8} * \frac{7}{21} = \frac{2}{1} * \frac{1}{3} = \frac{2*1}{1*3} = \frac{2}{3}$

1. Describe the similarities and differences between Examples 1 and 2.
   Both examples have the same factors and products. Example 1 is renamed in simplest form after multiplying. Example 2 is renamed in simplest form before multiplying.

Example 3: $\frac{1}{8} * \frac{16}{21} = \frac{1*2}{1*3} = \frac{2}{3}$

2. Describe the similarities and differences between Examples 2 and 3.
   Both examples have the same factors and products. Example 3 has fewer steps than Example 2 because the fractions are reduced without rearranging them first.

Use what you have discovered to solve the following problems. Show your work.

3. $\frac{14}{60} * \frac{12}{21} = \underline{\frac{2}{15}}$ 4. $\frac{36}{88} * \frac{33}{72} = \underline{\frac{3}{16}}$ 5. $\frac{25}{54} * \frac{36}{45} = \underline{\frac{10}{27}}$

Math Masters, p. 236

8·8 Multiplication of Mixed Numbers

 Objective To introduce multiplication with mixed numbers.

Technology Resources www.everydaymathonline.com

ePresentations | eToolkit | Algorithms Practice | EM Facts Workshop Game™ | Family Letters | Assessment Management | Common Core State Standards | Curriculum Focal Points | Interactive Teacher's Lesson Guide

1 Teaching the Lesson

Key Concepts and Skills

- Convert between fractions and mixed numbers.
  [Number and Numeration Goal 5]

- Multiply mixed numbers.
  [Operations and Computation Goal 5]

- Use the partial-products algorithm to multiply whole numbers, fractions, and mixed numbers.
  [Operations and Computation Goal 5]

- Recognize the patterns in products when a number is multiplied by a fraction that is less than 1, equal to 1, or greater than 1.
  [Patterns, Functions, and Algebra Goal 1]

Key Activities

Students review conversions from mixed numbers to fractions and from fractions to mixed numbers. Then they multiply mixed numbers by applying the conversions and by using the partial-products method.

 Ongoing Assessment:
Informing Instruction See page 661.

 Ongoing Assessment:
Recognizing Student Achievement
Use an Exit Slip (*Math Masters*, page 414).
[Operations and Computation Goal 5]

Materials

Math Journal 2, pp. 272–274B
Student Reference Book, pp. 77–78B
Study Link 8·7
Math Masters, p. 414
slate

2 Ongoing Learning & Practice

Using Unit Fractions to Find a Fraction of a Number
Math Journal 2, p. 275
Students practice using unit fractions to find a fraction of a number.

 Math Boxes 8·8
Math Journal 2, p. 276
Students practice and maintain skills through Math Box problems.

 Study Link 8·8
Math Masters, p. 237
Students practice and maintain skills through Study Link activities.

3 Differentiation Options

READINESS

Ordering Improper Fractions
slate
Students review converting between fractions and mixed numbers and finding common denominators by ordering a set of improper fractions.

EXTRA PRACTICE

Playing *Frac-Tac-Toe*
Student Reference Book, pp. 309–311
Math Masters, pp. 472–484
per partnership: 4 each of number cards 0–10 (from the Everything Math Deck, if available), counters, calculator (optional)
Students practice converting between fractions, decimals, and percents.

Advance Preparation

For Part 1, draw several blank "What's My Rule?" rule boxes and tables on the board to use with the Study Link 8·7 Follow-Up.

 Teacher's Reference Manual, **Grades 4–6** pp. 143, 144

Getting Started

Mental Math and Reflexes

Have students write each mixed number as a fraction. *Suggestions:*

●○○ $1\frac{2}{3}$ $\frac{5}{3}$ ●●○ $6\frac{4}{7}$ $\frac{46}{7}$ ●●● $3\frac{7}{9}$ $\frac{34}{9}$

$8\frac{7}{10}$ $\frac{87}{10}$ $3\frac{5}{8}$ $\frac{29}{8}$ $5\frac{4}{5}$ $\frac{29}{5}$

Math Message

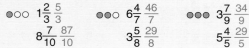

Complete journal page 272.

Study Link 8·7 Follow-Up

Have partners compare answers and resolve differences. Ask volunteers to write the incomplete version of their "What's My Rule?" table for the class to solve.

---

① Teaching the Lesson

▶ Math Message Follow-Up

WHOLE-CLASS DISCUSSION

(*Math Journal 2*, p. 272)

Ask students why the hexagons in the last row of the example on the journal page are divided into sixths. Sample answer: To add the 3 in $3 + \frac{5}{6}$, you need a common denominator. A simple way is to think of each whole as $\frac{6}{6}$. Ask volunteers to share their solution strategies for Problems 1–8.

▶ Multiplying with Mixed Numbers

WHOLE-CLASS ACTIVITY

PROBLEM SOLVING

(*Student Reference Book,* pp. 77 and 78)

Ask students how they would use the partial-products method to calculate $6 * 4\frac{3}{5}$. Discuss student responses as you summarize the following strategy:

▷ Calculate the partial products and add.

1. Think of $4\frac{3}{5}$ as $4 + \frac{3}{5}$. $6 * 4\frac{3}{5} = 6 * (4 + \frac{3}{5})$

2. Write the problem as the sum of $= (6 * 4) + (6 * \frac{3}{5})$
   partial products.

3. Calculate the partial products. $= 24 + \frac{18}{5}$

4. Convert $\frac{18}{5}$ to a mixed number. $= 24 + 3\frac{3}{5}$

5. Add. $= 27\frac{3}{5}$

Refer students to Step 2. Ask: *What property is used to rewrite the problem as the sum of partial products?* The Distributive Property. Write problems on the board or a transparency and ask students to find the missing value using the Distributive Property. *Suggestions*

- $4 * 3\frac{1}{2} = (4 * 3) + (4 * n)$ $\frac{1}{2}$ ● $4 * 3\frac{1}{2} = ?$ 14

- $8 * 2\frac{1}{4} = (8 * n) + (8 * \frac{1}{4})$ 2   ● $8 * 2\frac{1}{4} = ?$ 18

Ask students to refer to the example on *Student Reference Book,* page 78.

Student Page

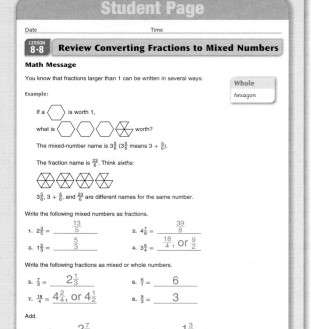

Date   Time

LESSON 8·8   **Review Converting Fractions to Mixed Numbers**

Math Message

You know that fractions larger than 1 can be written in several ways.

Example:

If a ⬡ is worth 1,

what is ⬡⬡⬡⬡ worth?

The mixed-number name is $3\frac{5}{6}$ ($3\frac{5}{6}$ means $3 + \frac{5}{6}$).

The fraction name is $\frac{23}{6}$. Think *sixths:*

$3\frac{5}{6}$, $3 + \frac{5}{6}$, and $\frac{23}{6}$ are different names for the same number.

Write the following mixed numbers as fractions.

1. $2\frac{3}{5} =$ $\frac{13}{5}$ 2. $4\frac{7}{8} =$ $\frac{39}{8}$

3. $1\frac{2}{3} =$ $\frac{5}{3}$ 4. $3\frac{6}{4} =$ $\frac{18}{4}$, or $\frac{9}{2}$

Write the following fractions as mixed or whole numbers.

5. $\frac{7}{3} =$ $2\frac{1}{3}$ 6. $\frac{6}{1} =$ 6

7. $\frac{18}{4} =$ $4\frac{2}{4}$, or $4\frac{1}{2}$ 8. $\frac{9}{3} =$ 3

Add.

9. $2 + \frac{7}{8} =$ $2\frac{7}{8}$ 10. $1 + \frac{3}{4} =$ $1\frac{3}{4}$

11. $3 + \frac{3}{5} =$ $3\frac{3}{5}$ 12. $6 + 2\frac{1}{3} =$ $8\frac{1}{3}$

Whole
hexagon

Math Journal 2, p. 272

Ask students how they might use improper fractions to calculate $6 * 4\frac{3}{5}$. Again, discuss student responses as you summarize the following strategy:

Convert whole numbers and mixed numbers to improper fractions.

1. Think of 6 as $\frac{6}{1}$ and $4\frac{3}{5}$ as $\frac{23}{5}$.

2. Rewrite the problem as fraction multiplication.
$$6 * 4\frac{3}{5} = \frac{6}{1} * \frac{23}{5}$$

3. Use a fraction multiplication algorithm.
$$= \frac{6 * 23}{1 * 5}$$

4. Multiply.
$$= \frac{138}{5}$$

5. Simplify the answer by converting $\frac{138}{5}$ to a mixed number.
$$= 27\frac{3}{5}$$

Ask students to refer to the second example on *Student Reference Book*, page 77.

Ask students to suggest advantages and disadvantages for each method. Expect a variety of responses. Sample answers: The partial-products method lets you work with smaller numbers but has more calculations. The improper-fraction method lets you multiply fractions where one of the denominators will be one, but you have a larger number to divide to simplify the answer.

Ask students to work through two or three additional examples, using either of the above strategies or others of their own choosing. After each problem, ask volunteers to share their solution strategies. *Suggestions:*

- $4 * \frac{3}{5}$ $2\frac{2}{5}$
- $2\frac{1}{4} * \frac{2}{3}$ $1\frac{1}{2}$
- $2\frac{2}{3} * 3$ 8

Ask: *What observations can you make regarding the factors in the three problems and the products?* Sample answers: When you multiply a nonzero whole number by a fraction less than 1 (as in $4 * \frac{3}{5} = 2\frac{2}{5}$), the product will be smaller than the whole number. When you multiply a nonzero number by a number greater than 1 (as in $2\frac{2}{3} * 3 = 8$), the product will be greater than the given number.

Pose some number stories for students to solve. *Suggestions:*

- Three students are making necklaces in art class. Each necklace needs $4\frac{3}{8}$ feet of string. How much string is needed for the three students to each make one necklace? $12\frac{9}{8}$, or $13\frac{1}{8}$ ft

- The top of a rectangular pencil case has a width of $2\frac{3}{8}$ inches and a length of 8 inches. What is the area of the top? $16\frac{24}{8}$, or 19 sq in.

Ongoing Assessment: Informing Instruction

Watch for students who have difficulty organizing partial products when multiplying two mixed numbers. Show them the diagram below, and have them write the partial products.

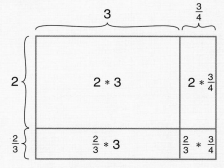

$$2 * 3 = 6 = 6$$
$$\frac{2}{3} * 3 = \frac{6}{3} = 2$$
$$2 * \frac{3}{4} = \frac{6}{4} = 1\frac{1}{2}$$
$$\frac{2}{3} * \frac{3}{4} = \frac{6}{12} = \frac{1}{2}$$
$$9\frac{2}{2}, \text{ or } 10$$

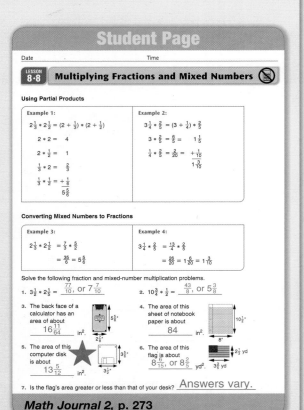

Student Page

Date _____ Time _____

LESSON 8·8 Multiplying Fractions and Mixed Numbers

Using Partial Products

Example 1:
$2\frac{1}{3} * 2\frac{1}{2} = (2 + \frac{1}{3}) * (2 + \frac{1}{2})$

$2 * 2 = 4$
$2 * \frac{1}{2} = 1$
$\frac{1}{3} * 2 = \frac{2}{3}$
$\frac{1}{3} * \frac{1}{2} = +\frac{1}{6}$
$5\frac{5}{6}$

Example 2:
$3\frac{1}{4} * \frac{2}{5} = (3 + \frac{1}{4}) * \frac{2}{5}$

$3 * \frac{2}{5} = \frac{6}{5} = 1\frac{1}{5}$
$\frac{1}{4} * \frac{2}{5} = \frac{2}{20} = +\frac{1}{10}$
$1\frac{3}{10}$

Converting Mixed Numbers to Fractions

Example 3:
$2\frac{1}{3} * 2\frac{1}{2} = \frac{7}{3} * \frac{5}{2}$
$= \frac{35}{6} = 5\frac{5}{6}$

Example 4:
$3\frac{1}{4} * \frac{2}{5} = \frac{13}{4} * \frac{2}{5}$
$= \frac{26}{20} = 1\frac{6}{20} = 1\frac{3}{10}$

Solve the following fraction and mixed-number multiplication problems.

1. $3\frac{1}{2} * 2\frac{1}{5} = \frac{77}{10}$, or $7\frac{7}{10}$

2. $10\frac{3}{4} * \frac{1}{2} = \frac{43}{8}$, or $5\frac{3}{8}$

3. The back face of a calculator has an area of about $16\frac{11}{64}$ in².

4. The area of this sheet of notebook paper is about 84 in².

5. The area of this computer disk is about $13\frac{5}{12}$ in².

6. The area of this flag is about $8\frac{6}{15}$, or $8\frac{2}{5}$ yd².

7. Is the flag's area greater or less than that of your desk? Answers vary.

Math Journal 2, p. 273

Student Page

Date _____ Time _____

LESSON 8·8 Track Records on the Moon and the Planets

Every moon and planet in our solar system pulls objects toward it with a force called **gravity**.

In a recent Olympic games, the winning high jump was 7 feet 8 inches, or $7\frac{2}{3}$ feet. The winning pole vault was 19 feet. Suppose that the Olympics were held on Earth's Moon, or on Jupiter, Mars, or Venus. What height might we expect for a winning high jump or a winning pole vault?

1. On the Moon, one could jump about 6 times as high as on Earth. What would be the height of the winning …
   high jump? About **46** feet   pole vault? About **114** feet

2. On Jupiter, one could jump about $\frac{3}{4}$ as high as on Earth. What would be the height of the winning …
   high jump? About $\frac{69}{24}$, or $2\frac{7}{8}$ feet   pole vault? About $\frac{57}{8}$, or $7\frac{1}{8}$ feet

3. On Mars, one could jump about $2\frac{2}{5}$ times as high as on Earth. What would be the height of the winning …
   high jump? About $\frac{184}{9}$, or $20\frac{4}{9}$ feet   pole vault? About $\frac{152}{3}$, or $50\frac{2}{3}$ feet

4. On Venus, one could jump about $1\frac{1}{7}$ times as high as on Earth. What would be the height of the winning …
   high jump? About $\frac{184}{21}$, or $8\frac{16}{21}$ feet   pole vault? About $\frac{152}{7}$, or $21\frac{5}{7}$ feet

5. Is Jupiter's pull of gravity stronger or weaker than Earth's? Explain your reasoning.
   Sample answer: Because you can't jump as high on Jupiter as you can on Earth, the gravity pulling you back on Jupiter must be stronger.

Try This

6. The winning pole-vault height given above was rounded to the nearest whole number. The actual winning height was 19 feet $\frac{1}{4}$ inch. If you used this actual measurement, about how many feet high would the winning jump be …
   on the Moon? $114\frac{1}{8}$ on Jupiter? $7\frac{17}{128}$
   on Mars? $50\frac{13}{18}$ on Venus? $21\frac{31}{42}$

Math Journal 2, p. 274

▶ **Multiplying Fractions and Mixed Numbers**

 PARTNER ACTIVITY

(*Math Journal 2,* pp. 273 and 274)

Assign both journal pages. Encourage students to consider the numbers in each problem and then to use the method that is most efficient for that problem. Circulate and assist.

✓ Ongoing Assessment:
Recognizing Student Achievement

Exit Slip ★

Use an **Exit Slip** (*Math Masters,* page 414) to assess students' understanding of multiplication with mixed numbers. Have students explain how they solved Problem 5 on journal page 273. Students are making adequate progress if they correctly reference using partial products, improper fractions, or a method of their own.

[Operations and Computation Goal 5]

▶ **Interpreting Multiplication as Resizing (Scaling)**

 **WHOLE-CLASS DISCUSSION**

(*Math Journal 2,* p. 274A; *Student Reference Book,* pp. 78A and 78B)

Explain to students that when they make an enlarged or reduced copy of an image using a photocopy machine, they are *resizing* or *scaling* the image. Ask students to tell where they have used the word *scale* in everyday life. Sample responses: I weigh things on a scale; an axis on a graph has a scale; I put together scale models; a map is a scale drawing. Conclude by pointing out that although scale models and scale drawings often are smaller than the original, scaling refers to the process of reducing, enlarging, or maintaining the same size. Ask students to refer to the examples on *Student Reference Book,* pages 78A and 78B.

Pose the following situations to students. Have students tell if the situation involves *enlarging, reducing,* or *making a copy that is the same size.* Also have students explain their answers.

● You make a copy that is $\frac{3}{4}$ the size of the original. Reducing; Sample answer: $\frac{3}{4}$ is less than 1, so the copy will be smaller than the original.

● You make a copy that is $1\frac{1}{2}$ times the size of the original. Enlarging; Sample answer: The copy will be the same size plus a half size more, so the copy will be larger than the original.

● You make a copy that is 100% of the original size. Same size; Sample answer: 100% means one whole, so the copy will be full size.

Explain that the enlargement or reduction of an image is measured with numbers called size-change, or scale, factors. Work through Problems 1 and 2 on *Math Journal 2*, page 274A as a class. Be sure the following points are discussed (for positive numbers):

▷ When you multiply a given number by a number greater than 1, the product is greater than the original number.

▷ When you multiply a given number by a number less than 1, the product is less than the original number.

▷ When you multiply a given number by a number equal to 1, the product is equal to the original number.

Then assign the rest of the journal page. Circulate and assist. After students complete the journal page, write the following expressions on the board.

$$3\frac{1}{2} * \frac{3}{4} \qquad 2\frac{5}{8} * \frac{3}{4} \qquad \frac{9}{10} * \frac{3}{4} \qquad \frac{9}{100} * \frac{3}{4} \qquad \frac{3}{3} * \frac{3}{4}$$

Ask students to determine, without performing any calculations, which of these expressions would result in the largest product and which would result in the smallest product. Ask them to explain their answers. Sample answers: In each case, $\frac{3}{4}$ is multiplied by a number. The largest number that $\frac{3}{4}$ is multiplied by is $3\frac{1}{2}$, so $3\frac{1}{2} * \frac{3}{4}$ would result in the largest product. The smallest number that $\frac{3}{4}$ is multiplied by is $\frac{9}{100}$, so $\frac{9}{100} * \frac{3}{4}$ would result in the smallest product. Ask: *Without doing any calculations, compare $\frac{3}{4}$ with the product of $3\frac{1}{2} * \frac{3}{4}$ and the product of $\frac{9}{100} * \frac{3}{4}$.* Sample answers: $3\frac{1}{2} * \frac{3}{4}$ is $3\frac{1}{2}$ times as large as $\frac{3}{4}$; $\frac{9}{100} * \frac{3}{4}$ is much smaller than $\frac{3}{4}$; it is $\frac{9}{100}$ the size of $\frac{3}{4}$.

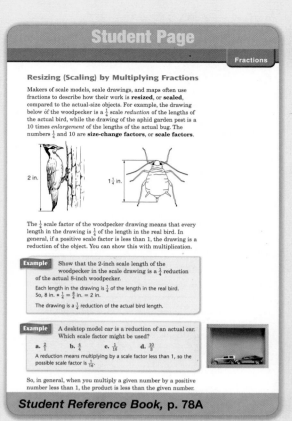
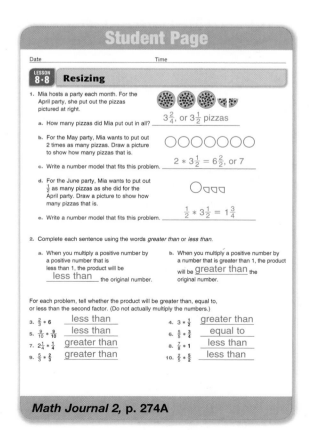
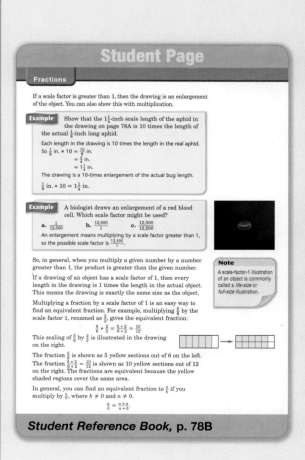

Student Page

Date _____ Time _____

LESSON 8·8 Fraction Problems

1. Horse races are measured in *furlongs* (1 furlong = $\frac{1}{8}$ mile). The Kentucky Derby is 10 furlongs long. What is the distance of the Kentucky Derby in miles?
   $1\frac{2}{8}$ miles, or $1\frac{1}{4}$ miles

   furlongs 0 ⊢⊢⊢⊢⊢⊢⊢⊢⊢⊢⊢⊢⊢⊢⊢⊢⊢ 16
   miles 0   1   2

2. Last week, Aaron earned $8 doing chores while Dara earned $2\frac{1}{2}$ times that much money.
   a. Write an open number model to show how much money Dara earned last week. $8 * 2\frac{1}{2} = d$
   b. How much money did Dara earn last week? $20

3. A recipe for punch calls for $4\frac{1}{2}$ cups of ginger ale. The recipe serves 20 people. Judy would like to make enough punch for $1\frac{1}{2}$ times that many people.
   a. Write an open number model to show how much ginger ale Judy will use. $1\frac{1}{2} * 4\frac{1}{2} = g$
   b. How much ginger ale will Judy use? $6\frac{3}{4}$ cups
   c. How many people does Judy plan on serving? 30 people

4. Dwayne is thinking of a number. If you multiply his number by $2\frac{12}{13}$, the product will be greater than $2\frac{12}{13}$. What do you know about Dwayne's number?
   His number is greater than 1.

5. What is the perimeter of the square at the right? 23 ft $5\frac{3}{4}$ ft

Try This

6. A U.S. presidential dollar coin weighs $8\frac{1}{10}$ grams. The coin is $\frac{1}{50}$ nickel, $\frac{35}{1,000}$ manganese, $\frac{3}{50}$ zinc, and the rest copper. If you made a circle graph to show the metals that make up the coin, how much of the circle would represent copper? Explain your answer.
   The metals other than copper make up $\frac{1}{50} + \frac{35}{1,000} + \frac{3}{50} =$
   $\frac{115}{1,000}$, or $\frac{23}{200}$, of the circle. So, copper represents
   $1 - \frac{23}{200} = \frac{177}{200}$ of the circle.

Math Journal 2, p. 274B

Student Page

Date _____ Time _____

LESSON 8·8 Finding Fractions of a Number

One way to find a fraction of a number is to use a **unit fraction**. A unit fraction is a fraction with 1 in the numerator. You can also use a diagram to help you understand the problem.

Example: What is $\frac{7}{8}$ of 32?
   $\frac{1}{8}$ of 32 is 4. So $\frac{7}{8}$ of 32 is 7 * 4 = 28.

   32
   ⊓⊓⊓⊓⊓⊓⊓⊓
   ?

Solve.

1. $\frac{1}{5}$ of 75 = 15
2. $\frac{2}{5}$ of 75 = 30
3. $\frac{4}{5}$ of 75 = 60
4. $\frac{1}{8}$ of 120 = 15
5. $\frac{3}{8}$ of 120 = 45
6. $\frac{5}{8}$ of 120 = 75

Solve Problems 7–18. They come from a math book that was published in 1904.

First think of $\frac{1}{3}$ of each of these numbers, and then state $\frac{2}{3}$ of each.

7. 9 6
8. 6 4
9. 12 8
10. 3 2
11. 21 14
12. 30 20

First think of $\frac{1}{4}$ of each of these numbers, and then state $\frac{3}{4}$ of each.

13. 32 24
14. 40 30
15. 12 9
16. 24 18
17. 20 15
18. 28 21

19. Lydia has 7 pages of a 12-page song memorized. Has she memorized more than $\frac{2}{3}$ of the song? No

20. A CD that normally sells for $15 is on sale for $\frac{1}{3}$ off. What is the sale price? $10

21. Christine bought a coat for $\frac{1}{4}$ off the regular price. She saved $20. What did she pay for the coat? $60

22. Seri bought 12 avocados on sale for $8.28. What is the unit price, the cost for 1 avocado? $0.69

Math Journal 2, p. 275

▶ **Fraction Problems**    INDEPENDENT ACTIVITY

(*Math Journal 2*, p. 274B)

Students solve real-world number stories involving fractions. They use a visual model or write an open number model to help them solve each problem.

2 Ongoing Learning & Practice

▶ **Using Unit Fractions to Find a Fraction of a Number**    INDEPENDENT ACTIVITY

(*Math Journal 2*, p. 275)

Students practice using unit fractions to find the fraction of a number.

▶ **Math Boxes 8·8**    INDEPENDENT ACTIVITY

(*Math Journal 2*, p. 276)

Mixed Practice Math Boxes in this lesson are paired with Math Boxes in Lesson 8-6. The skill in Problem 5 previews Unit 9 content.

Writing/Reasoning Have students write a response to the following: *Explain how to use the division rule for finding equivalent fractions to solve Problem 4b.* Sample answer: The division rule states that you can rename a fraction by dividing the numerator and the denominator by the same nonzero number. I divided the numerator and the denominator by 2 to rename the fraction $\frac{4}{50}$; $\frac{4 \div 2}{50 \div 2} = \frac{2}{25}$.

▶ **Study Link 8·8**    INDEPENDENT ACTIVITY

(*Math Masters*, p. 237)

Home Connection Students practice multiplying fractions and mixed numbers. They find the areas of rectangles, triangles, and parallelograms.

3 Differentiation Options

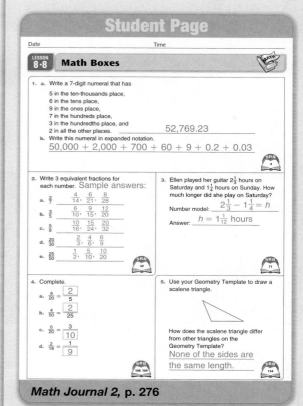

Math Journal 2, p. 276

READINESS

▶ Ordering Improper Fractions

SMALL-GROUP ACTIVITY

15–30 Min

To review converting between fractions and mixed numbers and finding common denominators, have students order a set of improper fractions. Write the following fractions on the board: $\frac{7}{2}, \frac{4}{1}, \frac{7}{3}$, and $\frac{11}{6}$. Ask students to suggest how to order the fractions from least to greatest. Expect that students will suggest the same strategies they used with proper fractions, such as putting the numbers in order and then comparing them to a reference. Use their responses to discuss and demonstrate the following methods:

▷ Rename each improper fraction as an equivalent fraction with a common denominator. Ask students what common denominator to use. Sample answer: Use 6 because the other denominators are all factors of 6. Have volunteers rename the fractions and write the equivalent fractions on the board underneath the first list of fractions. $\frac{21}{6}, \frac{24}{6}, \frac{14}{6}, \frac{11}{6}$

▷ Write each fraction as a whole or mixed number. Ask volunteers to write these mixed numbers on the board underneath the second list. $3\frac{1}{2}, 4, 2\frac{1}{3}, 1\frac{5}{6}$

Ask students to order the 3 lists on their slates. $\frac{11}{6}, \frac{7}{3}, \frac{7}{2}, \frac{4}{1}$; $\frac{11}{6}, \frac{14}{6}, \frac{21}{6}, \frac{24}{6}$; and $1\frac{5}{6}, 2\frac{1}{3}, 3\frac{1}{2}, 4$ Discuss any difficulties or curiosities that students encountered.

EXTRA PRACTICE

▶ Playing *Frac-Tac-Toe*

PARTNER ACTIVITY

15–30 Min

(*Student Reference Book*, pp. 309–311; *Math Masters*, pp. 472–484)

Students play a favorite version of *Frac-Tac-Toe* to practice converting between fractions, decimals, and percents.

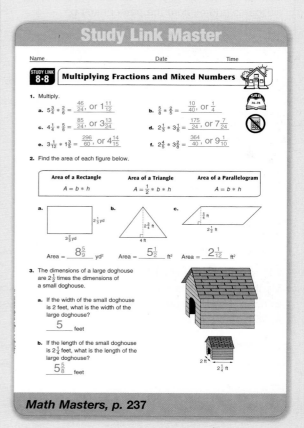

Math Masters, p. 237

8·9 Finding a Percent of a Number

1 Teaching the Lesson

Key Concepts and Skills

- Calculate percents and discounts, and describe strategies used.
  [Number and Numeration Goal 2]

- Convert between fractions, decimals, and percents.
  [Number and Numeration Goal 5]

- Use ratios expressed as percents to solve problems.
  [Operations and Computation Goal 7]

Key Activities

Students estimate and then calculate the percent of a number using fractions and decimals. They identify and calculate percent discounts and explore the percent key on their calculators.

 Ongoing Assessment:
Recognizing Student Achievement
Use Mental Math and Reflexes.
[Number and Numeration Goal 5]

Key Vocabulary

discount

Materials

Math Journal 2, pp. 277 and 278
Student Reference Book, pp. 263–265
Study Link 8·8
slate ◆ calculator ◆ overhead calculator (optional)

2 Ongoing Learning & Practice

 Math Boxes 8·9
Math Journal 2, p. 279
Students practice and maintain skills through Math Box problems.

 Study Link 8·9
Math Masters, p. 238
Students practice and maintain skills through Study Link activities.

3 Differentiation Options

READINESS

Finding the Percent of a Number
Math Masters, p. 239
calculator (optional)
Students use unit fractions to review finding the percent of a number.

ENRICHMENT

Calculating Discounts
Math Masters, p. 240
Students explore a variety of situations involving discounts.

Advance Preparation

Many calculators have a percent key, but not all calculators work the same. For Part 1, familiarize yourself with the use of the percent key on the calculators used by your class. Directions for the TI-15 and Casio *fx*-55 have been provided.

 Teacher's Reference Manual, **Grades 4–6** pp. 69–71, 153, 154

Getting Started

Math Message

It would cost $150,000 to rent a large amusement park for a private party. Would you rather have this price reduced by $35,000 or discounted 25%?

Study Link 8·8 Follow-Up

Have partners compare answers and resolve differences.

Ongoing Assessment:
Recognizing Student Achievement

Mental Math and Reflexes ★

Use the **Mental Math and Reflexes** problems to assess students' facility with converting between fractions, decimals, and percents and expressing fractions in simplest form. Students are making adequate progress if they have correctly written both the decimal and the fraction.

[Number and Numeration Goal 5]

---

1 Teaching the Lesson

▶ Math Message Follow-Up

 **WHOLE-CLASS DISCUSSION**

Have small groups share their solution strategies and then choose one strategy to represent the group. Ask volunteers to present the group strategies. A 25% discount is $37,500; therefore, it is a better deal than a $35,000 discount.

▶ Finding the Percent of a Number

 **WHOLE-CLASS DISCUSSION**

Pose the following percent-of-a-number problem: *The flu hit Roosevelt School hard. 40% of the 480 students were absent at least one day last week. How many students were absent at least one day?*

Write *40% of 480 = students absent at least one day* on the board or a transparency. Ask students to share their solution strategies for this problem. Expect a variety of responses such as the following:

▷ *The unit-percent approach.* 480 is 100%, or the whole.

    1% of 480 is 4.8.

    40% of 480 is 40 * 4.8, or 192.

Student Page

Date _____ Time _____

LESSON 8·9 Finding a Percent of a Number

1. The Madison Middle School boys' basketball team has played 5 games. The table at the right shows the number of shots taken by each player and the percent of shots that were baskets. Study the example. Then calculate the number of baskets made by each player.

Player	Shots Taken	Percent Made	Baskets
Bill	15	40%	6
Amit	40	30%	12
Josh	25	60%	15
Kevin	8	75%	6
Mike	60	25%	15
Zheng	44	25%	11
André	50	10%	5
David	25	20%	5
Bob	18	50%	9
Lars	15	20%	3
Justin	28	25%	7

Example:

Bill took 15 shots.
He made a basket on 40% of these shots.

$40\% = \frac{40}{100}$, or $\frac{4}{10}$

$\frac{4}{10}$ of 15 $= \frac{4}{10} * \frac{15}{1} = \frac{4*15}{10*1} = \frac{60}{10} = 6$

Bill made 6 baskets.

Sample answers:

2. On the basis of shooting ability, which five players would you select as the starting lineup for the next basketball game?

Bill, Amit, Josh, Kevin, and Bob

Explain your choices.
They have the highest percent of baskets made.

3. Which player(s) would you encourage to shoot more often? Kevin
Why? Of the few shots taken, he has made baskets 75% of the time.

4. Which player(s) would you encourage to pass more often? André
Why? Of the many shots taken, he has made baskets only 10% of the time.

Math Journal 2, p. 277

Student Page

Date _____ Time _____

LESSON 8·9 Calculating a Discount

Example: The list price for a toaster is $45. The toaster is sold at a 12% discount (12% off the list price). What are the savings? (**Reminder:** $12\% = \frac{12}{100} = 0.12$)

Paper and pencil:

12% of $45 $= \frac{12}{100} * 45 = \frac{12}{100} * \frac{45}{1}$

$= \frac{12*45}{100*1} = \frac{540}{100}$

$= \$5.40$

Calculator A: Enter 0.12 ⊗ 45 ⌨ and interpret the answer of 5.4 as $5.40.

Calculator B: Enter 0.12 ⊠ 45 ⊟ and interpret the answer of 5.4 as $5.40.

First use your percent sense to estimate the discount for each item in the table below. The **discount** is the amount by which the list price of an item is reduced. It is the amount the customer saves.

Then use your calculator or paper and pencil to calculate the discount. (If necessary, round to the nearest cent.)
Sample answers:

Item	List Price	Percent of Discount	Estimated Discount	Calculated Discount
Clock radio	$33.00	20%	$6.00	$6.60
Calculator	$60.00	7%	$4.00	$4.20
Sweater	$20.00	42%	$8.00	$8.40
Tent	$180.00	30%	$54.00	$54.00
Bicycle	$200.00	17%	$30.00	$34.00
Computer	$980.00	25%	$250.00	$245.00
Skis	$325.00	18%	$65.00	$58.50
Double CD	$29.99	15%	$4.50	$4.50
Jacket	$110.00	55%	$55.00	$60.50

Math Journal 2, p. 278

Remind students that to find 1%, they could divide the whole by 100 or think: *What times 100 equals the whole?*

▷ *The 10-percent approach.* 480 is 100%, or the whole.

10% of 480 is 48.

40% of 480 is 4 * 48, or 192.

Remind students that to find 10%, they could divide the whole by 10 or think: *What times 10 equals 480?*

▷ *The equivalent-fraction approach.* 40% is equal to $\frac{2}{5}$.

40% of 480 is the same as $\frac{2}{5}$ of 480, or $\frac{2}{5} * 480$, which is 192.

▷ *The equivalent-decimal approach.* 40% is equal to 0.40.

40% of 480 is the same as 0.40 of 480, or 0.40 * 480, which is 192.

 Links to the Future

This lesson stresses the use of equivalent fractions and equivalent decimals. Lesson 8-10 will address unit percents.

▶ **Using Fractions to Find the Percent of a Number** PARTNER ACTIVITY

(*Math Journal 2*, p. 277)

Work through the example at the top of the journal page as a class. Emphasize the following points:

▷ A percent can be thought of as a fraction with a denominator of 100.

Example: 43% is $\frac{43}{100}$; 99% is $\frac{99}{100}$; 7% is $\frac{7}{100}$; and 100% is $\frac{100}{100}$, or 1.

▷ Many commonly used percents are equivalent to easy fractions: $25\% = \frac{1}{4}$, $50\% = \frac{1}{2}$, and so on.

▷ Finding the percent of a number can be thought of as finding a fraction of that number.

Example: 50% of 18 is $\frac{50}{100}$ or $\frac{1}{2}$ of 18, or $\frac{1}{2} * 18$; and 25% of 28 is $\frac{1}{4}$ of 28, or $\frac{1}{4} * 28$.

NOTE Some students might write number models in the form 60% * 25, rather than $\frac{60}{100} * 25$, $\frac{6}{10} * 25$, or 0.6 * 25. All of these notations are acceptable.

Assign the journal page. Circulate and assist.

▶ **Calculating a Percent Discount** PARTNER ACTIVITY

(*Math Journal 2*, p. 278)   PROBLEM SOLVING

Refer students to journal page 278. As a class, work through the example at the top of the page. Remind students that a **discount** is the amount to be subtracted from a given whole. In this case, it is by how much the list price is reduced.

Ask students to complete the Estimated Discount column of the table on journal page 278. When most students have finished, have volunteers share their solution strategies. *For example:*

Clock radio: 20% of $33

▷ 20% is equal to $\frac{1}{5}$. One-fifth of $33 is between $6 and $7.

Computer: 25% of $980

▷ $980 is about $1,000. So 25% of $980 is about $\frac{1}{4}$ of $1,000, or $250.

Jacket: 55% of $110

▷ 55% is about $\frac{1}{2}$. So 55% of $110 is about $55.

Ask students to calculate and record the actual discount using any method they choose. Encourage them to try calculator and paper-and-pencil calculations.

Exploring the Percent Key on a Calculator

PARTNER ACTIVITY

(*Student Reference Book,* pp. 263–265)

Refer students to *Student Reference Book,* pages 263–265. As a class, discuss the examples for using the percent key to solve percent-of problems and to display percents as decimals and as fractions in simplest form. If your class calculators differ from the *Student Reference Book* examples, demonstrate the key sequences using an overhead calculator or by drawing them on the board.

Ask students to use the percent key on their calculators to find 25% of 180. 45 Have volunteers share the key sequences they entered. Partners then make up and solve percent-of problems.

2 Ongoing Learning & Practice

Math Boxes 8·9

INDEPENDENT ACTIVITY

(*Math Journal 2,* p. 279)

 Mixed Practice Math Boxes in this lesson are paired with Math Boxes in Lesson 8-11. The skill in Problem 5 previews Unit 9 content.

 Writing/Reasoning Have students write a response to the following: *How can you tell that the shape you drew in Problem 5 has a set of perpendicular sides? How could you change plotted point (4,2) to make parallel sides?* Sample answer: It has perpendicular sides because two of the sides form a right angle. I could change (4,2) to (6,2) to make one set of parallel sides.

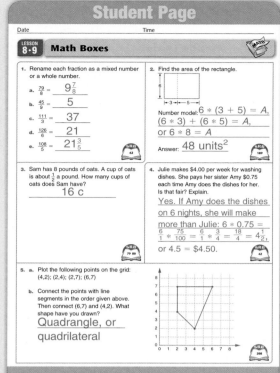

Math Journal 2, p. 279

Math Masters, p. 238

Teaching Master

Name　　　　　　　Date　　　　　　　Time

LESSON 8·9 **Finding the Percent of a Number**

The unit percent is 1% or 0.01.
For example, the unit percent of
100 is 1; the unit percent of
200 is 2; the unit percent of
10 is 0.1.

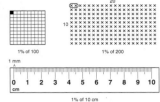

1% of 100　　　　1% of 200

1% of 10 cm

Another way to think of the unit percent of a number is to think: *What number times 100
equals the whole?* For example, 1 * 100 = 100; 2 * 100 = 200; 0.1 * 100 = 10

To find the unit percent of a whole, multiply by 0.01 or $\frac{1}{100}$.

Solve.

1. 1% of 84 __0.84__　2. 1% of 35 __0.35__　3. 1% of 628 __6.28__

The unit percent can be used to find other percents of a whole. For example, if you want to
find 8% of 200:

◆ Calculate the unit percent: 1% of 200 = 200 * 0.01 = 2
◆ Check your answer: 2 * 100 = 200.
◆ Multiply your answer by the percent you are finding: 2 * 8 = 16; 8% of 200 = 16

Solve.

4. 19% of 84 __15.96__　5. 72% of 35 __25.2__　6. 37% of 628 __232.36__

7. Think about the steps you followed in Problems 4–6. First you multiplied the unit
percent by 0.01, and then you multiplied the product by the number of percents. How
can you find the percent of a number by multiplying only once? Provide an example.

I can change the percent to a fraction and
multiply the number by that fraction.
19% of 84: $\frac{19}{100} * 84 = \frac{19}{100} * \frac{84}{1} = \frac{1,596}{100} = 15.96$

Math Masters, p. 239

Teaching Master

Name　　　　　　　Date　　　　　　　Time

LESSON 8·9 **Calculating Discounts**

There are 2 steps to finding a discounted total:

◆ Calculate the amount that represents the percent of discount.
◆ Subtract the calculated discount from the original total. This is the discounted total.

Calculate the discounted total for the following problems. Show your work on the
back of this sheet.

1. A computer store has an Internet special for their customers. If Carla spends $50.00 or
more, she gets 10% off her order. The shipping and handling charge is 4% of the original
total. Carla buys $68.00 in software. What is her total charge?

__$63.92__; Discount: 68 * 0.10 = 6.80; shipping and handling:
68 * 0.04 = 2.72; total charge: 68.00 + 2.72 − 6.80 = 63.92

2. The Hartfield School District wants to get the government discount for telephone service.
The discount is based on the percent of students qualifying for the National School Lunch
Program. 32% of students in this urban district qualify. The district pays about $3,500 per
month for telephone service. Use the table below to find how much the district would save.

Percent of Students	Urban Discount	Rural Discount
Less than 1%	20%	25%
1% to 19%	40%	50%
20% to 34%	50%	60%
35% to 49%	60%	70%
50% to 74%	80%	80%
75% to 100%	90%	90%

The Hartfield School District is eligible for a __50%__ discount. The district will save
about __$1,750.00__ per month for its telephone service. With the government discount,
the district will pay about __$1,750.00__ per month.

3. At the Goose Island Family Restaurant, if the original bill is $75.00 or more, the kids'
meals are discounted 3%. If the original bill is $95.70, with $23.00 for kids' meals, what is
the discounted amount? __$0.69__ What is the discounted total? __$95.01__

Math Masters, p. 240

Writing/Reasoning Have students write a response to the
following: *Explain how to rename an improper fraction as
a mixed number. Use Problem 1a as an example.* Sample
answer: To rename $\frac{79}{8}$ as a mixed number, first find how many
groups of 8 are in 79. There are 9 groups of 8 because 9 * 8 = 72.
Then subtract 72 from 79. The difference is the fraction part of
the mixed number. It tells how many eighths are left: $\frac{79}{8} - \frac{72}{8} = \frac{7}{8}$.
So $\frac{79}{8} = 9 + \frac{7}{8}$, or $9\frac{7}{8}$.

▶ **Study Link 8·9**

**INDEPENDENT
ACTIVITY**

(*Math Masters,* p. 238)

Home Connection Students convert between fractions,
decimals, and percents. Then they estimate and calculate
discounts for various items.

3 Differentiation Options

READINESS

**SMALL-GROUP
ACTIVITY**

15–30 Min

▶ **Finding the Percent of
a Number**

(*Math Masters,* p. 239)

To review finding the percent of a number, have students use
unit fractions. Ask students to describe a unit fraction. Sample
answer: A unit fraction has a 1 as its numerator and names
one of the equal parts that make the whole. Have a volunteer
use counters to demonstrate how to use the unit fraction to
find $\frac{3}{4}$ of 20. $\frac{1}{4}$ of 20 is 5 because 20 divided by 4 equals 5. So, $\frac{3}{4}$ of
20 is 5 * 3, or 15.

Explain that the unit percent is similar to a unit fraction. You
can find the percent of a whole by finding the unit percent and
multiplying. Have students use mental math, paper and pencil,
and/or calculators to complete the *Math Masters* page.

ENRICHMENT

**PARTNER
ACTIVITY**

15–30 Min

▶ **Calculating Discounts**

(*Math Masters,* p. 240)

To apply students' understanding of calculating percents,
have them find and calculate the discounts for a variety of
situations. Students solve number stories by calculating
the percent discount and the discounted total.

8·10 Relating Fractional Units to the Whole

Objective To provide practice finding the whole, given a fraction or a percent of the whole.

1 Teaching the Lesson

Key Concepts and Skills

• Use unit fractions and unit percents to find the whole.
[Number and Numeration Goal 2]

• Use unit fractions to solve fraction-of problems and unit percents to solve percent-of problems.
[Number and Numeration Goal 2]

• Find the unit fraction or unit percent of a given whole.
[Number and Numeration Goal 2]

• Convert between fractions and percents.
[Number and Numeration Goal 5]

Key Activities

Students identify the whole as a multiple of a unit fraction or unit percent of the whole. They practice using unit fractions or unit percents to find the whole.

 Ongoing Assessment:
Recognizing Student Achievement
Use journal page 280.
[Number and Numeration Goal 2]

Key Vocabulary

unit fraction ◆ unit percent

Materials

Math Journal 2, pp. 280–282
Student Reference Book, pp. 52 and 75
Study Link 8·9
transparency of *Math Masters,* p. 435 ◆
slate ◆ Class Data Pad

2 Ongoing Learning & Practice

 Playing *Factor Captor*
Student Reference Book, p. 306
Math Masters, pp. 454 and 455
calculator ◆ paper and pencil ◆ per partnership: 70 counters (for Grid 2) or 110 counters (for Grid 1–110)
Students find factors and multiples of numbers.

 Math Boxes 8·10
Math Journal 2, p. 283
ruler
Students practice and maintain skills through Math Box problems.

Study Link 8·10
Math Masters, p. 241
Students practice and maintain skills through Study Link activities.

3 Differentiation Options

READINESS
Finding the Fraction and the Percent of a Number
Math Masters, p. 242
Students identify the errors in fraction-of and percent-of problems.

ENRICHMENT
Finding the Fraction and the Percent of a Number
Math Masters, p. 243
Students identify appropriate and inappropriate methods to solve fraction-of and percent-of problems.

Advance Preparation

For Part 1, make a transparency of *Math Masters,* page 435.

 Teacher's Reference Manual, **Grades 4–6** pp. 62, 63, 69–71

Getting Started

Mental Math and Reflexes

Have students solve fraction-of problems.

- ●○○ How many days are $\frac{2}{7}$ of a week? 2 days

  How many counters are $\frac{2}{6}$ of 18 counters? 6 counters

- ●●○ How many seconds are $\frac{1}{6}$ of a minute? 10 seconds

  How many fluid ounces are $\frac{3}{4}$ of a cup? 6 ounces

- ●●● How many millimeters are $\frac{4}{5}$ of a centimeter? 8 mm

  How many inches are $\frac{4}{9}$ of 2 yards? 32 inches

Math Message

Complete the problems on journal page 280.

Study Link 8·9 Follow-Up

Have partners compare answers and resolve differences.

---

1 Teaching the Lesson

▶ ### Math Message Follow-Up

 WHOLE-CLASS DISCUSSION

(*Math Journal 2*, p. 280)

Algebraic Thinking Ask volunteers to share their solution strategies for finding the whole in the Math Message problems.

Have volunteers write the definitions of a **unit fraction** and a **unit percent** on the Class Data Pad. Any fraction with a numerator of 1 is a unit fraction. The unit percent is 1% of the whole. Ask: *Which of the problems on the journal page reference a unit fraction, and which problems reference the unit percent?* The fractions in Problems 1–4 are unit fractions, and the percents in Problems 5 and 6 are unit percents. Point out that in Problem 7, 10% can be rewritten as a unit fraction since $10\% = \frac{10}{100} = \frac{1}{10}$.

Guide students to conclude that if a unit fraction ($\frac{1}{n}$) is known, the whole is equal to the value of $\frac{1}{n}$ times the denominator (n). If the unit percent is known, the whole is equal to the value of 1% times 100.

Ongoing Assessment: Recognizing Student Achievement

Journal Page 280

Use **journal page 280,** to assess students' facility with using unit fractions and unit percents to solve problems. Students are making adequate progress if they correctly solve Problems 1–6. Some students will be able to solve Problems 7–9 correctly.

[Number and Numeration Goal 2]

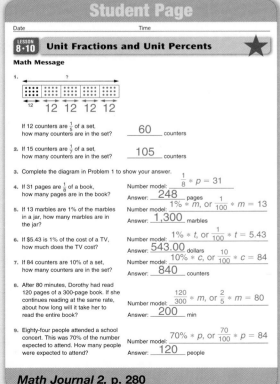

Using Unit Fractions to Find the Whole

(*Math Journal 2*, p. 281; *Student Reference Book*, p. 75)

PARTNER ACTIVITY

PROBLEM SOLVING

Algebraic Thinking Refer students to *Student Reference Book*, page 75, and work through the examples as a class. Emphasize how the meaning of the fractions in the examples is used to find the value of a unit fraction. Finding this value can be the key to an efficient solution.

Use your slate procedures, and have students solve the Check Your Understanding problems.

- **Problem 1** $\frac{1}{2}$ of 44 cookies = 22 cookies
- **Problem 2** $\frac{2}{3}$ of 9 cookies = 6 cookies
- **Problem 3** $\frac{3}{4}$ of 20 cookies = 15 cookies

Assign Problem 1 on journal page 281.

Adjusting the Activity

Have students draw pictures to help them find the solutions. For example, for Problem 1a on the journal page, draw a large rectangle to represent a cookie jar. Divide the rectangle in half. Write 31 in each of the halves. Then it's easy to see that there are 62 cookies in the jar. For fractions that are not unit fractions, divide the rectangle into equal parts. In Problem 1b, for example, figure out how many cookies go in each fifth by dividing 36 by 3. 12 Write 12 in each fifth, and find the total. 60

AUDITORY   ◆   KINESTHETIC   ◆   TACTILE   ◆   VISUAL

Using Unit Percents to Find the Whole

(*Math Journal 2*, pp. 281 and 282; *Student Reference Book*, p. 52; *Math Masters*, p. 435)

PARTNER ACTIVITY

PROBLEM SOLVING

Algebraic Thinking When students have completed Problem 1 on journal page 281, refer them to *Student Reference Book*, page 52, and work through the examples as a class. Emphasize the similarity between the first solution in the examples and the unit-fraction problems already discussed.

Point out that the second solution in the examples presents another method, which uses the given percent information to find the value of a unit percent (1%). Use your prepared transparency of *Math Masters*, page 435. Shade 60 squares and label the drawing *60% of the total is 120.* Explain that if you know the value of a given percent, you can find the value of the unit percent by dividing.

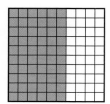

Date _____   Time _____

LESSON 8·10   **Using Units to Find the Whole**

1. Six jars are filled with cookies. The number of cookies in each jar is not known. For each clue given below, find the number of cookies in the jar.

Clue	Number of Cookies in Jar
a. $\frac{1}{2}$ jar contains 31 cookies.	62
b. $\frac{3}{5}$ jar contains 36 cookies.	60
c. $\frac{2}{8}$ jar contains 10 cookies.	40
d. $\frac{3}{8}$ jar contains 21 cookies.	56
e. $\frac{4}{7}$ jar contains 64 cookies.	112
f. $\frac{3}{11}$ jar contains 45 cookies.	165

2. Use your percent sense to estimate the list price for each item. Then calculate the list price.

Sale Price	Percent of List Price	Estimated List Price	Calculated List Price
$120.00	60%	$180.00	$200.00
$100.00	50%	Sample answers: $200.00	$200.00
$255.00	85%	$325.00	$300.00
$450.00	90%	$495.00	$500.00

3. Use the given rule to complete the table.

Rule out = 25% of in

in	out
44	11
100	25
64	16
124	31
304	76
116	29

4. Find the rule. Then complete the table.

Rule out = 40% of in

in	out
100	40
45	18
60	24
80	32
40	16
125	50

Math Journal 2, p. 281

Date _____   Time _____

LESSON 8·10   **Using Units to Find the WHOLE** *continued*

5. Alan is walking to a friend's house. He covered $\frac{6}{10}$ of the distance in 48 minutes. If he continues at the same speed, about how long will the entire walk take? **80 min**

6. 27 is $\frac{3}{4}$ of what number? **36**

7. $\frac{3}{8}$ is $\frac{3}{4}$ of what number? **$\frac{4}{8}$, or $\frac{1}{2}$**

8. 16 is 25% of what number? **64**

9. 40 is 80% of what number? **50**

The problems below are from an arithmetic book published in 1906. Solve the problems.

10. If the average coal miner works $\frac{2}{3}$ of a month with 30 days, how many days during the month does he work? **20** days

11. A recipe for fudge calls for $\frac{1}{4}$ of a cake of chocolate. If a cake costs 20¢, find the cost of the chocolate cake called for by the recipe. **5** ¢

12. A collection of mail that required 6 hours for a postman to make with a horse and wagon was made in an automobile in $\frac{5}{12}$ the time. How long did the automobile take? **$2\frac{1}{2}$** hours

13. How many corks per day does a machine in Spain make from the bark of a cork tree if it makes $\frac{1}{3}$ of a sack of 15,000 corks in that time? **5,000** corks

Source: Milne's *Progressive Arithmetic*

14. Alice baked a batch of cookies. 24 cookies are 40% of the total batch. Complete the table showing the number of cookies for each percent.

%	10%	20%	30%	40%	50%	60%	70%	80%	90%	100%
Cookies	6	12	18	24	30	36	42	48	54	60

15. Explain how you found 100% or the total number of cookies Alice baked. **Sample answer: I found the unit percent by dividing 24 by 4 to get 6, or 10% of the total. Then I multiplied 6 by 10 to get 60, or 100%.**

Math Journal 2, p. 282

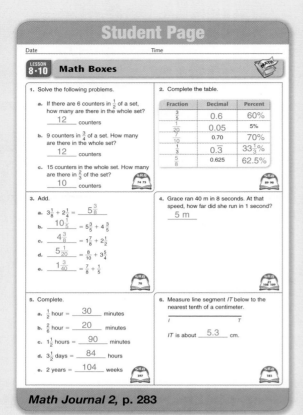

Math Journal 2, p. 283

Math Masters, p. 241

Ask: *If the value of these shaded squares is 120, how would you find what each square is worth?* Expect students to respond that they would think *What times 60 equals 120?* or divide 120 by 60. Remind students that fractions can be used to represent division. So $\frac{120}{60}$ represents $120 \div 60 = 2$. Ask students: *What is the percent of 1 square?* 1% This is the unit percent. The value of the unit percent is 2.

Refer students to Solution 2 in the first example. When the value of the unit percent is known, you can find the whole by multiplying this value by 100. If 1% is worth $2, then the whole, or 100%, is $2 * 100 = $200.

Erase the transparency and shade 80 squares. Label the drawing *80% of the total is $40.* Ask: *What is 1%, if 80% equals $40?* $0.50 If 1% is worth $0.50, then the whole, or 100%, is $0.50 * 100 = $50.

Have students complete the table in Problem 2 on journal page 281 in two steps:

1. Estimate the list price for each item.

2. Calculate the list price.

Assign students to complete journal pages 281 and 282. Most, but not all, of these problems involve finding the whole when a fraction or percent is known. Circulate and assist.

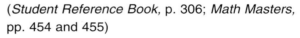

2 Ongoing Learning & Practice

▶ **Playing** *Factor Captor*

PARTNER ACTIVITY

(*Student Reference Book,* p. 306; *Math Masters,* pp. 454 and 455)

Students practice multiplication and division facts and factorization skills by playing *Factor Captor*. They can use either Grid 2 or Grid 1–110.

▶ **Math Boxes 8·10**

INDEPENDENT ACTIVITY

(*Math Journal 2*, p. 283)

Mixed Practice Math Boxes in this lesson are paired with Math Boxes in Lesson 8-12. The skill in Problem 6 previews Unit 9 content.

▶ **Study Link 8·10**

INDEPENDENT ACTIVITY

(*Math Masters*, p. 241)

Home Connection Students practice using unit fractions to solve problems. They complete "What's My Rule?" tables.

3 Differentiation Options

READINESS

 SMALL-GROUP ACTIVITY

 15–30 Min

Finding the Fraction and the Percent of a Number

(*Math Masters*, p. 242)

To review how to find the fraction and the percent of a number, have students identify and correct the errors in fraction-of and percent-of problems. Suggest that students describe the errors by telling what should have been done. When students have finished, have them share their descriptions of the errors in the two tables.

ENRICHMENT

 PARTNER ACTIVITY

15–30 Min

Finding the Fraction and the Percent of a Number

(*Math Masters*, p. 243)

To apply students' understanding of finding the fraction and the percent of a number, have students identify appropriate and inappropriate methods to solve fraction-of and percent-of problems. Allow time to discuss students' explanations in Problems 3 and 6.

Teaching Master

Name _____ Date _____ Time _____

LESSON 8·10 **Fraction of and Percent of a Number**

George practiced finding the fraction of and the percent of a number. He completed the tables below. George thinks there is something wrong with his answers, but he doesn't know how to fix it.

$\frac{1}{4}$ of 12 =	3
$\frac{2}{4}$ of 12 =	6
$\frac{3}{4}$ of 12 =	12
$\frac{4}{4}$ of 12 =	24

20% of 40 =	6
40% of 40 =	12
60% of 40 =	18
80% of 40 =	24
100% of 40 =	30

1. Study George's tables and then explain how he should correct his work.

When he found $\frac{3}{4}$ of 12, he should have multiplied 3 by the numerator instead of by the denominator. When he found $\frac{4}{4}$ of 12, he should have multiplied 3 by 4 instead of just doubling his answer for $\frac{3}{4}$, or he should have noticed that $\frac{4}{4}$ = 1. 10% of 40 = 4, so 20% of 40 is 8 and not 6. If he had calculated the unit percent correctly, he could have calculated all of the other percents correctly.

2. Write the correct answers.

$\frac{1}{4}$ of 12 =	3
$\frac{2}{4}$ of 12 =	6
$\frac{3}{4}$ of 12 =	9
$\frac{4}{4}$ of 12 =	12

20% of 40 =	8
40% of 40 =	16
60% of 40 =	24
80% of 40 =	32
100% of 40 =	40

Math Masters, p. 242

Teaching Master

Name _____ Date _____ Time _____

LESSON 8·10 **Fraction and Percent of a Number Methods**

1. Alton collected 252 marbles but lost $\frac{4}{7}$ of them on his way to school. When he arrived at school, how many marbles did Alton have left? **108 marbles**

Explain how you found your answer.

I found the number of marbles that he lost and then subtracted that from the total.

2. Circle the letter of each method below that you could use to solve Problem 1.

a. You can find $\frac{4}{7}$ of 252 by multiplying 252 • $\frac{4}{7}$ and simplifying.

b. You can find $\frac{4}{7}$ of 252 by dividing 252 by 4 and multiplying the result by 7.

c. You can find the unit fraction by dividing 252 by 7, and then find $\frac{4}{7}$ of 252 by multiplying the unit fraction value by 4.

3. For any method you did *not* circle, explain why it will not work.

Choice b will not work. Dividing 252 by 4 finds fourths, not sevenths.

4. The regular price for in-line skates is $125 at a local store. The store was having a promotion: Buy one pair of in-line skates and get a second pair for 75% of the regular price. How much would a second pair of in-line skates cost? **$93.75**

Explain how you found your answer.

75% = $\frac{3}{4}$. I used the unit fraction, 125 ÷ 4, and multiplied that by 3.

5. Circle the letter of each method below that you could use to solve Problem 4.

a. You can rename 75% as a fraction and then multiply $125 by the fraction to find 75% of $125.

b. You can find the cost of the second pair by multiplying $125 by $\frac{1}{4}$ and subtracting the product from $125.

c. You can find the cost of the second pair by dividing $125 by 4.

6. For any method you did *not* circle, explain why it will not work.

When you divide $125 by 4, you are finding $\frac{1}{4}$ of the price, the amount of the discount.

Math Masters, p. 243

8·11 American Tour: Rural and Urban

Objectives To provide experience with locating information on maps and charts and using percents to make estimates.

Technology Resources www.everydaymathonline.com

 ePresentations
 eToolkit
 Algorithms Practice
 EM Facts Workshop Game™
 Family Letters
 Assessment Management
 Common Core State Standards
 Curriculum Focal Points
 Interactive Teacher's Lesson Guide

1 Teaching the Lesson

Key Concepts and Skills

- Use unit fractions to solve fraction-of problems and unit percents to solve percent-of problems.
  [Number and Numeration Goal 2]

- Find the unit fraction or unit percent of a given whole.
  [Number and Numeration Goal 2]

- Collect and organize data from maps and charts.
  [Data and Chance Goal 1]

Key Activities

Students examine various representations of the total population and area of the United States, including the rural and urban population distributions and household sizes in 1790, 1850, 1900, and 2000. They use percents to estimate the number of rural and urban Americans for each year.

Materials

Math Journal 2, pp. 284–286
Student Reference Book, pp. 350, 351, and 376
Study Link 8·10
transparency of *Math Masters,* p. 244 ◆ slate

2 Ongoing Learning & Practice

 Playing *Fraction Capture*
Math Journal 1, p. 198
Math Masters, pp. 460 and 461
per partnership: 2 six-sided dice
Students practice comparing fractions and finding equivalent fractions.

 Ongoing Assessment:
Recognizing Student Achievement
Use *Math Masters,* page 461.
[Number and Numeration Goal 5;
Operations and Computation Goal 4]

 Math Boxes 8·11
Math Journal 2, p. 287
Students practice and maintain skills through Math Box problems.

 Study Link 8·11
Math Masters, p. 245
Students practice and maintain skills through Study Link activities.

3 Differentiation Options

READINESS

Using a Calculator to Find Percents of a Number

Student Reference Book, pp. 50 and 53
Math Masters, p. 246
calculator
Students use a calculator to find percents of numbers and to find the whole from a given percent.

ENRICHMENT

Charting Changes in Food Consumption

Student Reference Book, p. 363
Math Masters, p. 247
2 different-colored pencils
Students use chart data to make a line graph.

Advance Preparation

For Part 1, prepare a transparency of *Math Masters,* page 244 or draw the tables from it on the board. Make a large display version of the table, Estimated Rural and Urban Populations, on journal page 286, and post it in the classroom American Tour display. Find or estimate the population of your school's community, and display a newspaper or magazine report on a government survey.

 Teacher's Reference Manual, **Grades 4–6** pp. 62, 63, 69–71, 160–167

Getting Started

Math Message

Answer Problems 1–5 on journal page 284.

Study Link 8·10 Follow-Up

Have partners compare answers and resolve differences.

---

1   Teaching the Lesson

▶ Math Message Follow-Up

WHOLE-CLASS ACTIVITY

(*Math Journal 2*, p. 284; *Math Masters*, p. 244)

Collect and tabulate the results for Problems 1–4 in the tables on your transparency of *Math Masters*, page 244 or in the tables you have drawn on the board.

Number in Household	Number of Students
1–2	
3–5	
6 or more	

Table from *Math Masters*, page 244

Ask students to calculate the percent of students who belong to each household size. Add these percents to the table and discuss why one might report such results as percents. Percents allow for easier comparisons with other similar data sets of different sizes.

Ask why people might be interested in information like this. Companies that design and sell products conduct research to gather detailed information about potential buyers. The government uses such information to identify services that people might need.

Explain that the government has been gathering basic information about people for hundreds of years. In addition to the decennial census, there are also numerous other surveys. Suggest that students pay attention to how often the daily newspapers or news magazines and television news broadcasts present the results of a government survey.

Teaching Master

Name   Date   Time

LESSON 8·11   Classroom Survey

Number in Household	Number of Students
1–2	
3–5	
6 or more	

Language at Home	Number of Students
English	
Spanish	
Other	

Handedness	Number of Students
right	
left	

Years at Current Address	Number of Students
0 or 1	
2	
3	
4	
5	
6 or more	

Math Masters, p. 244

▶ **Investigating Data in the American Tour**

WHOLE-CLASS DISCUSSION

(*Student Reference Book,* pp. 350, 351, and 376)

Social Studies Link Have students examine the information about the United States in 1790, 1850, 1900, and 2000 on pages 350, 351, and 376 in the American Tour section of the *Student Reference Book.* Ask students to note one or two things that interest them in the displays and to be prepared to share their findings with the class. As they examine the pages, ask students to consider how some of the displays show parts of a whole.

After a few minutes, discuss the data displays. *Suggestions:*

▷ Ask students to share questions they have about the displays. Briefly discuss possible answers.

▷ Compare the U.S. household size data on page 376 of the *Student Reference Book* with the corresponding data for your class. Ask which year of the U.S. data most closely resembles your class data.

▷ In the four Population Distribution graphs on pages 350 and 351 of the *Student Reference Book,* the relative size (area) of each state indicates the portion of the total population living in that state at that time.

▷ In the four Urban/Rural graphs on page 376 of the *Student Reference Book,* the size of a sector indicates the portion of the total population living in that type of region at that time.

▷ In the four Household Size graphs on page 376 of the *Student Reference Book,* the length of each part of the bar shows the portion of the total population living in households of the given size at that time.

▶ **Solving Percent-of-a-Number Problems**

PARTNER ACTIVITY

(*Math Journal 2,* p. 284)

Ask students to solve Problems 6–8 on journal page 284. Circulate and assist. When most students have finished, ask volunteers to demonstrate their solution strategies.

▶ **Estimating Rural and Urban Populations**

SMALL-GROUP ACTIVITY

ELL

(*Math Journal 2,* pp. 285 and 286; *Student Reference Book,* pp. 350, 351, and 376)

Divide the class into eight groups. Assign one of the following populations to each group:

▷ Urban/1790   ▷ Rural/1790

▷ Urban/1850   ▷ Rural/1850

Date _____ Time _____

LESSON 8·11   Class Survey

1. How many people live in your home? Answers vary for Problems 1–4.
   ○ 1–2 people   ○ 3–5 people   ○ 6 or more people

2. What language do you speak at home?
   ○ English   ○ Spanish   ○ Other: _____

3. Are you right-handed or left-handed?
   ○ right-handed   ○ left-handed

4. How long have you lived at your current address? (Round to the nearest year.)
   _____ years

5. Pick one of the questions above. Tell why someone you don't know might be interested in your answer to the question you picked.
   Sample answers: People and companies who sell products want information about potential buyers. The government uses information to identify services that people might need.

6. Fifteen percent of the 20 students in Ms. Swanson's class were left-handed.
   How many students were left-handed? __3__ students

7. About 85% of the 600 students at Emerson Middle School speak English at home. Another 10% speak Spanish, and 5% speak other languages. About how many students speak each language at home?
   English: __510__ students
   Spanish: __60__ students
   Other: __30__ students

8. The government reported that about 5% of 148,000,000 workers do not have jobs.
   How many workers were jobless? __7,400,000__ workers

Math Journal 2, p. 284

▷ Urban/1900　　　▷ Rural/1900

▷ Urban/2000　　　▷ Rural/2000

Explain that each group will complete journal page 285. They will need to use the information on pages 350, 351, and 376 of the *Student Reference Book* and estimate the number of people living in the United States in their assigned region type, either rural or urban. On pages 350 and 351, the total population is given, and on page 376, a circle graph tells what percents of the population lived in urban and rural regions for each of the four years. To support English language learners, discuss the meanings of *rural* and *urban,* and give examples.

Suggest that students answer the first question based on their knowledge, and use Problems 2–5 to help lead them through the population estimation problem. Do not, however, guide students through the activity. Students will need to work together to complete the following steps:

1. Locate the necessary information.

2. Use the given percent to obtain a whole-number estimate for their assigned urban or rural population (rounded to the nearest hundred thousand).

When all the groups have made their estimates, have each group announce its results. Record the results on the board or a transparency. Ask the class whether each estimate is reasonable. If an estimate does not appear reasonable, ask the class to check it.

When the class has agreed on all estimates, students record them in the table on journal page 286. Have a volunteer record the estimates in the table prepared earlier. (*See Advance Preparation.*) Post the table and display your newspaper or magazine clippings of the results of government surveys in the classroom American Tour display.

Ask students to use the information in the table to answer the remaining questions on journal page 286.

Adjusting the Activity

Have students make posters for the classroom American Tour display. Ask students to gather information from other pages of the American Tour section in the *Student Reference Book* that they find interesting. Students then write a paragraph to share their interest or ask a question about the information.

AUDITORY ◆ KINESTHETIC ◆ TACTILE ◆ VISUAL

Date　　　　　　　Time

LESSON 8·11　Rural and Urban Populations

The U.S. Census Bureau classifies where people live according to the following rule: **Rural** areas are communities having fewer than 2,500 people each. **Urban** areas are communities having 2,500 or more people each.

1. According to the Census Bureau's definition, do you live in a rural or an urban area? Answers vary.

How did you decide? Sample answer: I live in an urban area because there are 500 students in my school and at least 4 other schools in my town. That makes about 2,500 people, not counting adults.

Today more than three out of every four residents in the United States live in areas the Census Bureau defines as urban. This was not always the case. When the United States was formed, it was a rural nation.

Work with your classmates and use the information in the *Student Reference Book,* pages 350, 351, and 376 to examine the transformation of the United States from a rural to an urban nation. Answers vary.

2. My group is to estimate the number of people living in _____ areas in (rural or urban)
(1790, 1850, 1900, or 2000)

3. The total U.S. population in _____ was _____.
(1790, 1850, 1900, or 2000)

4. Estimate: The number of people living in _____ areas in (rural or urban)
_____ was about _____.
(1790, 1850, 1900, or 2000)
Make sure your answer is rounded to the nearest 100,000.

5. Our estimation strategy was _____

Math Journal 2, p. 285

Date　　　　　　　Time

LESSON 8·11　Rural and Urban Populations *continued*

6. Use the estimates from the groups in your class to complete the following table.

| Estimated Rural and Urban Populations, 1790–2000 | | |
Year	Estimated Rural Population	Estimated Urban Population
1790	3,700,000	200,000
1850	19,700,000	3,500,000
1900	45,700,000	30,500,000
2000	59,100,000	222,322,000

7. Is it fair to say that for more than half our nation's history, the **majority** of the population lived in rural areas?

Vocabulary
majority means *more than one-half of a count*

Explain your answer.
Sample answer: Yes. For at least 110 years (from 1790 to 1900), more than half the population lived in rural areas. 110 years is more than half of the time from 1790 to 2000.

8. About how many times larger was the rural population in 2000 than in 1790? About 15 to 20 times larger

9. About how many times larger was the urban population in 2000 than in 1790? About 1,000 times larger

10. In which decade do you think the urban population became larger than the rural population? Sample answer: By 1920, 51% of the population was urban.

Math Journal 2, p. 286

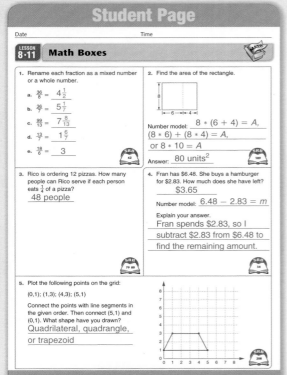

Math Journal 2, p. 287

Fraction Review

Write three equivalent fractions for each fraction. Sample answers:

1. $\frac{7}{8}$ $\frac{14}{16}, \frac{28}{32}, \frac{35}{40}$

2. $\frac{3}{4}$ $\frac{6}{8}, \frac{9}{12}, \frac{12}{16}$

3. $\frac{6}{12}$ $\frac{1}{2}, \frac{2}{4}, \frac{3}{6}$

4. $\frac{2}{3}$ $\frac{4}{6}, \frac{6}{9}, \frac{8}{12}$

Circle the fraction that is closer to $\frac{1}{2}$.

5. $\frac{3}{8}$ or $\frac{4}{5}$

6. $\frac{4}{7}$ or $\frac{5}{9}$

7. $\frac{7}{8}$ or $\frac{7}{9}$

8. $\frac{4}{10}$ or $\frac{7}{12}$

9. Explain how you found your answer for Problem 8.
Sample answer: I changed $\frac{4}{10}$ and $\frac{7}{12}$ to fractions with
a common denominator, $\frac{4}{10} = \frac{24}{60}$ and $\frac{7}{12} = \frac{35}{60}$. Because
$\frac{1}{2} = \frac{30}{60}, \frac{7}{12}$ is $\frac{5}{60}$ away from $\frac{1}{2}$, and $\frac{4}{10}$ is $\frac{6}{60}$ away from $\frac{1}{2}$.
So $\frac{7}{12}$ is closer to $\frac{1}{2}$.

Solve. Write your answers in simplest form.

10. $1\frac{7}{12} = \frac{5}{6} + \frac{3}{4}$

11. $\frac{7}{9} - \frac{1}{6} = \frac{11}{18}$

12. $8 - \frac{2}{3} = 7\frac{1}{3}$

13. $\frac{7}{8} - \frac{1}{6} = \frac{17}{24}$

14. $\frac{3}{4}$ of $\frac{2}{5}$ is $\frac{3}{10}$.

15. $4 * \frac{5}{6} = 3\frac{1}{3}$

Practice

16. $64,072 - 15,978 = 48,094$

17. $2,297 \div 45 \rightarrow 51\ R2$

18. $1,674 - 1,204 = 470$

19. $326 + 684 + 934 = 1,944$

Math Masters, p. 245

2 Ongoing Learning & Practice

▶ **Playing *Fraction Capture***   **PARTNER ACTIVITY**

(*Math Journal 1*, p. 198; *Math Masters*, pp. 460 and 461)

Students play *Fraction Capture* from Lesson 6-9 to practice comparing fractions and finding equivalent fractions. The rules are on *Math Journal 1*, page 198, and the gameboard is on *Math Masters*, page 460. Remind students of the importance of using the benchmark of $\frac{1}{2}$ when playing the game.

Ongoing Assessment:
Recognizing Student Achievement

Math Masters Page 461

Use the **Record Sheet** for *Fraction Capture* (*Math Masters*, page 461) to assess students' ability to use equivalent fractions. Have students record the numbers on the dice for each roll and the fractions they covered on the gameboard. Students are making adequate progress if they record pairs of fractions with sums greater than the benchmark of $\frac{1}{2}$. Some students might be able to identify expressions containing more than 2 fractions accurately.

[Number and Numeration Goal 5; Operations and Computation Goal 4]

▶ **Math Boxes 8·11**   **INDEPENDENT ACTIVITY**

(*Math Journal 2*, p. 287)

Mixed Practice Math Boxes in this lesson are paired with Math Boxes in Lesson 8-9. The skill in Problem 5 previews Unit 9 content.

▶ **Study Link 8·11**   **INDEPENDENT ACTIVITY**

(*Math Masters*, p. 245)

Home Connection Students find equivalent fractions. They practice adding, subtracting, and multiplying fractions.

3 Differentiation Options

READINESS   **SMALL-GROUP ACTIVITY**

▶ **Using a Calculator to Find Percents of a Number**    **15–30 Min**

(*Student Reference Book*, pp. 50 and 53; *Math Masters*, p. 246)

To apply students' understanding of finding the percent of a number and using a percent to find the whole, have students use calculators to complete the *Math Masters* page. Discuss the calculator examples on *Student Reference Book*, pages 50 and 53. As students work on the *Math Masters* page, point out how to read and interpret their calculator displays. Remind them to use the fix function to round.

Work through the example for finding the unit percent as a group. Explain that using number-and-word notation provides fewer digits to key into the calculator.

ENRICHMENT

Charting Changes in Food Consumption

PARTNER ACTIVITY

15–30 Min

(*Student Reference Book,* p. 363; *Math Masters,* p. 247)

Portfolio Ideas

To apply students' facility with locating information on data displays and their understanding of organizing data in tables and line graphs, have them use information from page 363 of the *Student Reference Book* to make a table of Americans' grape and carrot consumption from 1970 through 2000. Then they make a line graph to show the changes in consumption during this period. Point out that *per capita* means "for each person." Remind students to indicate the color they use for each food in the key boxes.

Discuss students' conclusions from Problem 3. Consider having students' post their line graphs in the class American Tour display.

Teaching Master

Name _____ Date _____ Time _____

LESSON 8·11 Using a Calculator with Percents

Finding the percent of a number is the same as multiplying the number by the percent. Usually, it's easiest to change the percent to a decimal and use a calculator.

Example: What is 65% of 55?

$65\% = \frac{65}{100} = 0.65$

Write the fraction and decimal for each percent.

1. $18\% = \frac{18}{100} = 0.18$ 2. $60\% = \frac{60}{100} = 0.6$

3. $89\% = \frac{89}{100} = 0.89$ 4. $7.5\% = \frac{7.5}{100} = 0.075$

Use your calculator and the percents in Problem 1 to find the percent of 55 by multiplying 55 by each decimal.

Example: 55 ∗ 0.65

5. 18% of 55 = 9.9   6. 60% of 55 = 33

7. 89% of 55 = 48.95   8. 7.5% of 55 = 4.125

9. Write the calculator key sequence that you used. Sample answers:

 0 · 1 8 × 5 5 Enter=, or 0 · 1 8 × 5 5 =

Sometimes you know a percent and how much it's worth, but you don't know what the ONE is. Use a unit percent strategy first to find 1%, and then multiply by 100 to get 100%.

Example: 60 million is 37% of what number?

60 ÷ 37 = 1.6216216

1.6216216 ∗ 100 = 162.16216

Using the fix function   1.6216216 ∗ 100 = 162 (rounded to the nearest whole number)

37% of 162 million is 59.94 million, or 60 million (rounded to the nearest ten million).

Use your calculator and unit percents to solve the following problems.

10. 42% of 43 = 18   11. 87% of 75 = 65

12. 63% of 44 million = 28 million

Math Masters, p. 246

Teaching Master

Name _____ Date _____ Time _____

LESSON 8·11 Charting Changes in Consumption

Many times the information that interests you has to be located in data displays with much more data than you need. Use the information on *Student Reference Book*, page 363 to complete the table below.

1. Per Capita Consumption of Carrots and Grapes
(title)

Foods	1970	1980	1990	2000
Carrots	6	6	8	10
Grapes	2.5	3.5	8	7

Line graphs can make it easier to compare changes in data over time. Use the data from your table in Problem 1 to make a line graph of the pounds of carrots and grapes eaten per person, per year in the United States. Use one color for the carrots data and a different color for the grapes data. Indicate your choices by coloring in the boxes of the graph key.

2. Carrots & Grapes Consumed
title

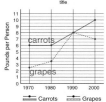

◼◼◼ Carrots ▭▭▭ Grapes

3. What is one conclusion you could draw from the data in your line graph?
Sample answer: People are consuming more carrots and grapes today than in 1970.

Math Masters, p. 247

8·12 Fraction Division

Objective To introduce division of fractions and relate the operation of division to multiplication.

Technology Resources
www.everydaymathonline.com

 ePresentations

 eToolkit

 Algorithms Practice

 EM Facts Workshop Game™

 Family Letters

 Assessment Management

 Common Core State Standards

 Curriculum Focal Points

 Interactive Teacher's Lesson Guide

---

1 Teaching the Lesson

Key Concepts and Skills

- Find common denominators for pairs of fractions. [Number and Numeration Goal 5]
- Use diagrams and visual models for division of fractions problems. [Operations and Computation Goal 5]
- Solve number stories involving division of a fraction by a whole number, division of a whole number by a fraction, and division of a fraction by a fraction. [Operations and Computation Goal 5]
- Write equations to model number stories. [Patterns, Functions, and Algebra Goal 2]

Key Activities

Students use diagrams and visual models to divide fractions. They solve number stories involving division of a fraction by a whole number, division of a whole number by a fraction, and division of a fraction by a fraction. Students use visual fraction models and equations to represent the problem.

 Ongoing Assessment: Informing Instruction See page 683.

Ongoing Assessment: Recognizing Student Achievement Use journal page 289.
[Operations and Computation Goal 5]

Materials

Math Journal 2, pp. 288–289B
transparency of *Math Masters*, p. 440B
Student Reference Book, pp. 79–80B
Study Link 8·11
slate or half-sheets of paper

2 Ongoing Learning & Practice

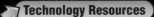 **Math Boxes 8·12**
Math Journal 2, p. 290
Students practice and maintain skills through Math Box problems.

 Study Link 8·12
Math Masters, p. 248
Students practice and maintain skills through Study Link activities.

3 Differentiation Options

READINESS

Playing *Build-It*
Student Reference Book, p. 300
Math Masters, pp. 446 and 447
per partnership: 1 six-sided die
Students compare and order fractions and rename mixed numbers as fractions.

ENRICHMENT

Exploring the Meaning of the Reciprocal
Math Masters, p. 249
calculator
Students explore the meaning of the reciprocal.

EXTRA PRACTICE

Dividing with Unit Fractions
Math Masters, p. 253B
Students practice using visual models to divide fractions.

Advance Preparation

 Teacher's Reference Manual, **Grades 4–6** pp. 144–147

Getting Started

1 Teaching the Lesson

▶ **Math Message Follow-Up**

WHOLE-CLASS DISCUSSION

(*Math Journal 2*, p. 288: *Math Masters*, p. 248)

Discuss students' solutions. Use a transparency of *Math Masters,* page 440B to illustrate Problems 1a–1c.

Problem 1a

Problem 1b

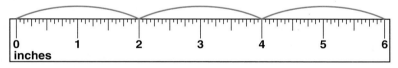

Problem 1c

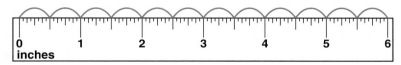

Point out that each problem on the journal page asks: *How many x's are in y?* Ask students to translate each problem into a question of this form. Record the questions on the board.

1. **a.** How many 2s are in 6?

   b. How many $\frac{1}{2}$s are in 6?

   c. How many $\frac{1}{8}$s are in $\frac{3}{4}$?

2. **a.** How many 2s are in 10?

   b. How many $\frac{1}{2}$s are in 10?

Refer students to the illustrations and questions for Problems 1 and 2, and ask what division open number sentence fits the first question. $6 \div 2 = s$

Continue for the other problems, writing the division open number sentence next to each question on the board. Ask students to refer to the visual models, if needed.

1. **a.** How many 2s are in 6? $6 \div 2 = s$

   b. How many $\frac{1}{2}$s are in 6? $6 \div \frac{1}{2} = s$

   c. How many $\frac{1}{8}$s are in $\frac{3}{4}$? $\frac{3}{4} \div \frac{1}{8} = s$

2. **a.** How many 2s are in 10? $10 \div 2 = b$

   b. How many $\frac{1}{2}$s are in 10? $10 \div \frac{1}{2} = b$

NOTE The division number models use b (for the number of boxes) and s (for the number of segments) to represent the unknowns. Students may prefer to use other letters or symbols. To avoid confusion in this introduction to division of fractions, the number models use $\div$ rather than / to show division.

▶ Dividing with Unit Fractions

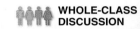

(Math Journal 2, p. 289; Student Reference Book, pp. 79 and 80A)

Read and discuss the first example on page 79 of the *Student Reference Book* on dividing a whole number by a unit fraction. A unit fraction is a fraction with a numerator of 1. Briefly discuss the solution.

▷ Draw 3 rectangles on the board, and ask students to copy the rectangles on a sheet of paper or slate.

▷ Ask students to use the rectangles to illustrate the following problem: *Jane has 3 loaves of banana bread to share with her friends. If she cuts each loaf into $\frac{1}{4}$s, how many quarter loaves will she have to share with her friends?*

Students should conclude that one way to illustrate the solution is to divide each of the rectangles into 4 equal parts.

$$3 \div \frac{1}{4} = 12$$

Ask:

- How many $\frac{1}{4}$s are in 3? 12

- What number model represents this problem? $3 \div \frac{1}{4} = 12$

Ask students to write $3 \div \frac{1}{4} = 12$ below their rectangles.

A unit fraction can also be divided by a whole number. Read and discuss the examples on page 80A of the *Student Reference Book*.

Draw a rectangle on the board, and divide it into 5 equal parts with $\frac{1}{5}$ shaded. Ask students to draw the same diagram on a piece of paper or slate.

Tell students that you can represent a unit fraction (such as $\frac{1}{5}$) being divided by a whole number (such as 3) by drawing a model for the fraction and then cutting it up into smaller equal parts. Pose the following problem: *Three family members equally share $\frac{1}{5}$ of a loaf of corn bread. How much of the loaf of corn bread will each person get?*

Have students divide their rectangles to show how the corn bread can be divided to find the solution to the problem.

Ongoing Assessment:
Informing Instruction

Watch for students who record the answer as $\frac{1}{3}$. Have students draw the line for thirds to extend across the rectangle in order to visualize the total number of parts out of 15.

Have a volunteer come to the board to show the solution. The student should divide the shaded fifth into three equal parts using horizontal lines. If necessary, model the lines extended all the way across the larger rectangle, with one small part double shaded. Explain that because the family only has $\frac{1}{5}$ of a loaf to begin with, when it is divided into three equal parts, each part of the corn bread that is cut up is $\frac{1}{15}$ of the entire loaf. So each person will get $\frac{1}{15}$ of the loaf of corn bread.

$$\frac{1}{5} \div 3 = \frac{1}{15} \left\{ \vphantom{\begin{array}{c} \\ \\ \\ \end{array}} \right.$$

Ask: *What number model represents this problem?* $\frac{1}{5} \div 3 = \frac{1}{15}$

Ask students to write "$\frac{1}{5} \div 3 = \frac{1}{15}$" below their rectangles.

Date _____ Time _____

LESSON 8·12   **Relationship Between Multiplication and Division**

1. Each division number sentence on the left can be solved by using a related multiplication sentence on the right. Draw a line to connect each number sentence on the left with its related number sentence on the right.

Division	Multiplication
a. $5 \div \frac{1}{4} = n$	$n * 4\frac{1}{5} = 4\frac{1}{5}$
b. $\frac{1}{5} \div 4 = n$	$n * 4 = \frac{1}{5}$
c. $4 \div \frac{1}{5} = n$	$n * \frac{1}{4} = 5$
d. $\frac{9}{10} \div \frac{3}{5} = n$	$n * \frac{9}{10} = \frac{3}{5}$
e. $\frac{3}{5} \div \frac{9}{10} = n$	$n * \frac{1}{5} = 4$
f. $4\frac{1}{5} \div 4\frac{1}{5} = n$	$n * \frac{3}{5} = \frac{9}{10}$

2. Solve the following division number sentences (from above). Use the related multiplication sentences to help you find each quotient.

a. $5 \div \frac{1}{4} = $ __20__
b. $\frac{1}{5} \div 4 = $ __$\frac{1}{20}$__
c. $4 \div \frac{1}{5} = $ __20__
d. $4\frac{1}{5} \div 4\frac{1}{5} = $ __1__

3. How is dividing 5 by $\frac{1}{4}$ different from dividing $\frac{1}{5}$ by 4? Sample answers: Dividing 5 by $\frac{1}{4}$ results in a quotient that is greater than 5. Dividing $\frac{1}{5}$ by 4 results in a quotient that is less than $\frac{1}{5}$. With $5 \div \frac{1}{4}$, you are finding how many $\frac{1}{4}$s are in 5. With $\frac{1}{5} \div 4$, you are finding how many 4s are in $\frac{1}{5}$, which is a very tiny number.

4. Write a number story for $5 \div \frac{1}{4}$. Answers vary.

5. Write a number story for $\frac{1}{5} \div 4$. Answers vary.

Math Journal 2, p. 289A

Have students read through Problems 1–4 on journal page 289. Ask them to describe how Problems 1 and 2 are different from Problems 3 and 4. Sample answer: In Problems 1 and 2, you are dividing a whole number by a unit fraction. In Problems 3 and 4, you are dividing a unit fraction by a whole number.

Have students solve Problems 1–6. Circulate and assist. Briefly discuss solutions.

Ongoing Assessment:
Recognizing Student Achievement

Journal Page 289

Use **journal page 289, Problems 1 and 2** to assess students' ability to divide a whole number by a unit fraction using a visual model. Students are making adequate progress if they are able to solve Problems 1 and 2. Some students may be able to solve Problems 3 and 4, which involve dividing a unit fraction by a whole number.

[Operations and Computation Goal 5]

▶ ## Relationship between Multiplication and Division

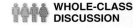
WHOLE-CLASS DISCUSSION

(*Math Journal 2*, p. 289A)

Another way to solve a fraction division problem is to think about it as a related fraction multiplication problem. Remind students of the relationship between multiplication and division. For example, to solve $63 \div 7$, you can think: *What number times 7 is 63? or $n * 7 = 63$.* 9

Write the following problems on the board to show how the relationship helps when dividing with fractions.

- To solve $\frac{1}{10} \div 5$, think: *What number times 5 is $\frac{1}{10}$? Or $n * 5 = \frac{1}{10}$.* $\frac{1}{50}$

- To solve $6 \div \frac{1}{5}$, think: *What number times $\frac{1}{5}$ is 6? Or $n * \frac{1}{5} = 6$.* 30

- To solve $6 \div \frac{2}{3}$, think: *What number times $\frac{2}{3}$ is 6? Or $n * \frac{2}{3} = 6$.* 9

- To solve $\frac{1}{10} \div \frac{3}{10}$, think: *What number times $\frac{3}{10}$ is $\frac{1}{10}$? Or $n * \frac{3}{10} = \frac{1}{10}$.* $\frac{1}{3}$

Ask students to solve the problems on journal page 289A. Circulate and assist.

▶ ## Introducing Common Denominator Division

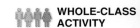
WHOLE-CLASS ACTIVITY

(*Math Journal 2*, p. 289B)

Draw four circles on the board, and ask students to copy these circles on a sheet of paper. Ask them to solve the problem $4 \div \frac{2}{3}$ and to illustrate their solution using the four circles.

After a few minutes, bring the class together to discuss their solutions. Use the students' responses to emphasize that one method for obtaining the solution is to divide each of the circles into 3 equal parts. As you illustrate this method on the board, point out that dividing each circle into 3 equal parts is equivalent to renaming each whole as $\frac{3}{3}$. This shows that 4 wholes is equivalent to $\frac{12}{3}$.

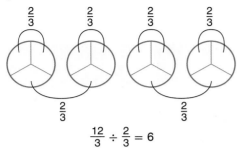

$$\frac{12}{3} \div \frac{2}{3} = 6$$

Write $\frac{12}{3} \div \frac{2}{3} = 6$ under the circles on the board. Students will readily see that there are 6 groups of $\frac{2}{3}$. Emphasize that the answer is the result of dividing the numerators $12 \div 2 = 6$.

Guide the discussion toward the following algorithm for division with fractions:

Step 1 Rename the numbers using a common denominator.

Step 2 Divide the numerators, and divide the denominators.

Discuss the examples at the top of journal page 289B. Point out that this method works for fractions divided by fractions or for mixed numbers or whole numbers divided by fractions. Use the following example to show that this method also works for fractions divided by whole numbers.

$$\frac{1}{8} \div 6 = \frac{1}{8} \div \frac{48}{8}$$
$$= \frac{1 \div 48}{8 \div 8}$$
$$= \frac{1 \div 48}{1}$$
$$= \frac{1}{48}$$

Solve Problems 1–3 on journal page 289B as a class. Ask students to come up to the board to record their steps.

Problem	Solution
$4 \div \frac{4}{5} = ?$	$4 \div \frac{4}{5} = \frac{20}{5} \div \frac{4}{5} = 20 \div 4 = 5$
$\frac{5}{6} \div \frac{1}{18} = ?$	$\frac{5}{6} \div \frac{1}{18} = \frac{15}{18} \div \frac{1}{18} = 15 \div 1 = 15$
$3\frac{1}{3} \div \frac{5}{6} = ?$	$3\frac{1}{3} \div \frac{5}{6} = \frac{10}{3} \div \frac{5}{6} = \frac{20}{6} \div \frac{5}{6} = 20 \div 5 = 4$

 Links to the Future

The algorithm introduced in this lesson focuses students on the meaning of division with fractions. The standard algorithm that involves multiplying by the reciprocal will be introduced in *Sixth Grade Everyday Mathematics*.

Student Page

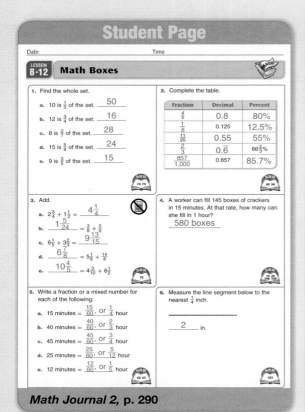

Math Journal 2, p. 290

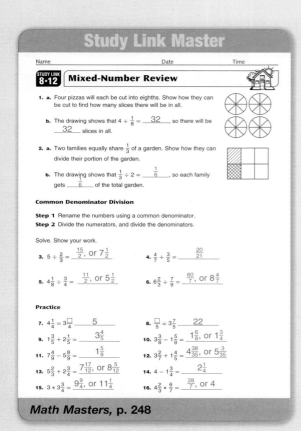

Math Masters, p. 248

▶ # Practicing Common Denominator Division

(*Math Journal 2*, p. 289B)

Assign Problems 1–10 on the journal page. Have students work with a partner. Circulate and assist. Briefly share solutions as needed.

2 Ongoing Learning & Practice

▶ # Math Boxes 8·12

(*Math Journal 2*, p. 290)

Mixed Practice Math Boxes in this lesson are paired with Math Boxes in Lesson 8-10. The skill in Problem 6 previews Unit 9 content.

▶ # Study Link 8·12

(*Math Masters*, p. 248)

Home Connection Students practice operations with fractions and mixed numbers.

3 Differentiation Options

▶ # Playing *Build-It*

(*Student Reference Book*, p. 300; *Math Masters*, pp. 446 and 447)

To practice comparing and ordering fractions and renaming mixed numbers as fractions, have students play this variation of *Build-It*. If students did not keep their Fraction Cards, they will need to cut the cards from *Math Masters*, page 446.

Students play the game as introduced in Lesson 8-1 except that at the end of each round, they toss a six-sided die to determine a whole-number part for each of their 5 fractions. Students then rename the mixed numbers as fractions. For example, after tossing a 3, the fractions $\frac{1}{5}$, $\frac{1}{4}$, $\frac{1}{3}$, $\frac{7}{12}$, and $\frac{5}{6}$ would become $3\frac{1}{5}$, $3\frac{1}{4}$, $3\frac{1}{3}$, $3\frac{7}{12}$, and $3\frac{5}{6}$. Renamed as fractions, the list would be $\frac{16}{5}$, $\frac{13}{4}$, $\frac{10}{3}$, $\frac{43}{12}$, and $\frac{23}{6}$.

Exploring the Meaning of the Reciprocal

(*Math Masters*, p. 249)

Portfolio
Ideas

To explore the relationship between a number and its reciprocal, have students use what they know about fractions, fraction multiplication, and their calculators to find the reciprocals of numbers.

When students have finished the *Math Masters* page, ask them to describe the pattern for finding the reciprocal of a number. Guide students to see that the reciprocal of a fraction is the fraction with the numerator and denominator interchanged, or inverted. For example, the reciprocal of $\frac{4}{9}$ is $\frac{9}{4}$, and $\frac{4}{9} * \frac{9}{4} = \frac{36}{36} = 1$. The reciprocal of a whole number is a unit fraction that has the whole number as its denominator. For example, the reciprocal of 8 is $\frac{1}{8}$, so $8 * \frac{1}{8} = \frac{8}{8} = 1$.

PARTNER ACTIVITY
15–30 Min

Dividing with Unit Fractions

(*Math Masters*, p. 253B)

Students practice using visual models to divide fractions.

PARTNER ACTIVITY
5–15 Min

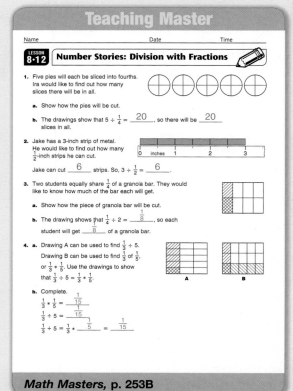

Teaching Master

LESSON 8·12 — Exploring the Meaning of the Reciprocal

Lamont and Maribel have to divide fractions. Lamont doesn't want to use common denominators. He thinks using the reciprocal is faster, but he's not sure what a reciprocal is. Maribel looks it up on the Internet and finds this: One number is the **reciprocal** of another number if their product is 1.

Example 1:	Example 2:
$3 * ? = 1$	$\frac{1}{2} * ? = 1$
$3 * \frac{1}{3} = \frac{3}{3} = 1$	$\frac{1}{2} * 2 = \frac{2}{2} = 1$
$\frac{1}{3}$ is the reciprocal of 3	2 is the reciprocal of $\frac{1}{2}$
3 is the reciprocal of $\frac{1}{3}$	$\frac{1}{2}$ is the reciprocal of 2

1. Find the reciprocals.
   a. 6 $\frac{1}{6}$ b. $\frac{1}{7}$ 7   c. 20 $\frac{1}{20}$ d. $\frac{1}{9}$ 9

2. What do you think would be the reciprocal of $\frac{5}{6}$? $\frac{6}{5}$

Reciprocals on a Calculator

On all scientific calculators, you can find a reciprocal of a number by raising the number to the −1 power.

3. Write each number in standard notation as a decimal and a fraction.
   a. 8^{-1} 0.125 $\frac{1}{8}$ b. 5^{-2} 0.04 $\frac{1}{25}$ c. 2^{-3} 0.125 $\frac{1}{8}$

4. Write the key sequence you could use to find the reciprocal of 36.

5. Write the key sequence you could use to find the reciprocal of $\frac{3}{7}$.

6. What pattern do you see for the reciprocal of a fraction?
   Once the original number is written as a fraction, the reciprocal is the original fraction written with the numerator as the denominator and the denominator as the numerator.

***Math Masters*, p. 249**

Teaching Master

LESSON 8·12 — Number Stories: Division with Fractions

1. Five pies will each be sliced into fourths. Ira would like to find out how many slices there will be in all.
   a. Show how the pies will be cut.
   b. The drawings show that $5 \div \frac{1}{4} =$ 20, so there will be 20 slices in all.

2. Jake has a 3-inch strip of metal. He would like to find out how many $\frac{1}{2}$-inch strips he can cut.
   Jake can cut 6 strips. So, $3 \div \frac{1}{2} =$ 6.

3. Two students equally share $\frac{1}{4}$ of a granola bar. They would like to know how much of the bar each will get.
   a. Show how the piece of granola bar will be cut.
   b. The drawing shows that $\frac{1}{4} \div 2 =$ $\frac{1}{8}$, so each student will get $\frac{1}{8}$ of a granola bar.

4. a. Drawing A can be used to find $\frac{1}{3} \div 5$. Drawing B can be used to find $\frac{1}{3}$ of $\frac{1}{5}$, or $\frac{1}{3} * \frac{1}{5}$. Use the drawings to show that $\frac{1}{3} \div 5 = \frac{1}{3} * \frac{1}{5}$.
   b. Complete.
   $\frac{1}{3} * \frac{1}{5} =$ $\frac{1}{15}$
   $\frac{1}{3} \div 5 =$ $\frac{1}{15}$
   $\frac{1}{3} \div 5 = \frac{1}{3} *$ $\frac{1}{5}$ = $\frac{1}{15}$

***Math Masters*, p. 253B**

8·13 Progress Check 8

⌖ **Objective** To assess students' progress on mathematical content through the end of Unit 8.

---

1 Looking Back: Cumulative Assessment

Input student data from Progress Check 8 into the **Assessment Management Spreadsheets**.

Materials
- ◆ Study Link 8◆12
- ◆ *Assessment Handbook,* pp. 110–117, 190–193, 223, and 274–277
- ◆ slate; ruler

CONTENT ASSESSED	LESSON(S)	SELF	ORAL/SLATE	WRITTEN PART A	WRITTEN PART B	OPEN RESPONSE
Find a percent of a number. [Number and Numeration Goal 2]	8·9–8·11	7	4		25	
Convert among fractions, decimals, and percents. [Number and Numeration Goal 5]	8·7, 8·9	1		1, 2		
Convert between fractions and mixed or whole numbers. [Number and Numeration Goal 5]	8·3, 8·4, 8·8, 8·12	6	1	15–18		
Find common denominators and equivalent fractions. [Number and Numeration Goal 5]	8·12	2	3	3, 4, 8–11, 13, 19		✔
Order and compare fractions using benchmarks. [Number and Numeration Goal 6]	8·1, 8·4	3		5, 6, 20		
Use an algorithm to add fractions and mixed numbers. [Operations and Computation Goal 4]	8·2, 8·4	5		8, 11, 13		✔
Use an algorithm to subtract fractions and mixed numbers. [Operations and Computation Goal 4]	8·3	4		7, 9, 10, 12, 14	22, 23	
Multiply fractions and mixed numbers. [Operations and Computation Goal 5]	8·5–8·7	8	2		21, 24, 26, 27	
Divide fractions. [Operations and Computation Goal 5]					28, 29	
Measure to the nearest $\frac{1}{4}$ inch. [Measurement and Reference Frames Goal 1]				7		

---

2 Looking Ahead: Preparing for Unit 9

 Math Boxes 8◆13

 Study Link 8◆13: Unit 9 Family Letter

Materials
- ◆ *Math Journal 2,* p. 291
- ◆ *Math Masters,* pp. 250–253
- ◆ calculator

Getting Started

Math Message • Self Assessment

Complete the Self Assessment (Assessment Handbook, *p. 190*).

Study Link 8·12 Follow-Up

Briefly review students' answers.

---

1 **Looking Back: Cumulative Assessment**

▶ Math Message Follow-Up

(Self Assessment, *Assessment Handbook*, p. 190)

INDEPENDENT ACTIVITY

The Self Assessment offers students the opportunity to reflect upon their progress.

▶ Oral and Slate Assessments

SMALL-GROUP ACTIVITY

Problems 1 and 3 provide summative information and can be used for grading purposes. Problems 2 and 4 provide formative information that can be useful in planning future instruction.

Oral Assessment

1. Students show thumbs up if the fractions and mixed numbers are equivalent and thumbs down if they are not equivalent. *Suggestions:*

   - $\frac{4}{3}$ and $1\frac{1}{3}$ up
   - $1\frac{3}{4}$ and $\frac{13}{4}$ down
   - $\frac{14}{8}$ and $1\frac{1}{2}$ down
   - $\frac{8}{3}$ and $2\frac{2}{3}$ up
   - $1\frac{7}{10}$ and $\frac{17}{100}$ down

2. Students show thumbs up if the product is correct and thumbs down if the product is not correct. *Suggestions:*

   - $\frac{1}{2} * \frac{2}{5} = \frac{2}{10}$ up
   - $\frac{1}{4} * \frac{2}{3} = \frac{3}{7}$ down
   - $\frac{7}{8} * \frac{1}{3} = \frac{8}{11}$ down
   - $\frac{3}{4} * \frac{2}{5} = \frac{6}{20}$ up
   - $\frac{6}{8} * \frac{1}{2} = \frac{6}{16}$ up

Assessment Master

Name _____ Date _____ Time _____

LESSON 8·13 **Self Assessment** *Progress Check 8*

Think about each skill listed below. Assess your own progress by checking the most appropriate box.

Skills	I can do this on my own and explain how to do it.	I can do this on my own.	I can do this if I get help or look at an example.
1. Convert among fractions, decimals, and percents.			
2. Find common denominators.			
3. Order and compare fractions.			
4. Use an algorithm to subtract mixed numbers with like denominators.			
5. Use an algorithm to add mixed numbers.			
6. Convert between fractions and mixed or whole numbers.			
7. Find a percent of a number.			
8. Use an algorithm to multiply fractions and mixed numbers.			
9. Divide fractions.			

Assessment Handbook, p. 190

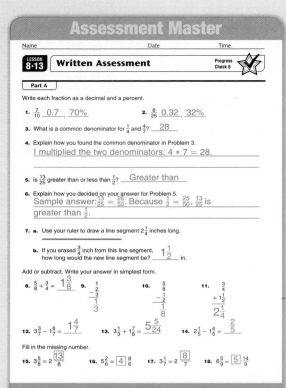

Assessment Handbook, p. 191

Slate Assessment

3. Find a common denominator for pairs of fractions. *Suggestions:*

- $\frac{3}{8}$ and $\frac{3}{4}$ eighths
- $\frac{5}{6}$ and $\frac{3}{4}$ twelfths
- $\frac{2}{5}$ and $\frac{7}{15}$ fifteenths
- $\frac{3}{10}$ and $\frac{4}{7}$ seventieths
- $\frac{5}{7}$ and $\frac{3}{5}$ thirty-fifths

4. Find the percent of numbers. *Suggestions:*

- 10% of 100 10
- 35% of 1,000,000 350,000
- 40% of 1,000 400
- 24% of 1,000 240
- 66% of 10,000 6,600

▶ Written Assessment

 INDEPENDENT ACTIVITY

(*Assessment Handbook*, pp. 191 and 192)

Part A   Recognizing Student Achievement

Problems 1–20 provide summative information and may be used for grading purposes.

Problem(s)	Description
1, 2	Convert among fractions, decimals, and percents.
3, 4, 8–11, 13, 19	Find common denominators.
5, 6, 20	Order and compare fractions.
7, 9, 10, 12, 14	Use an algorithm to subtract fractions and mixed numbers with like and unlike denominators.
7	Measure to the nearest $\frac{1}{4}$ inch.
8, 11, 13	Use an algorithm to add mixed numbers.
15–18	Convert between fractions and whole or mixed numbers.

Part B   Informing Instruction

Problems 21–29 provide formative information that can be useful in planning future instruction.

Problem(s)	Description
22, 23	Use an algorithm to subtract mixed numbers.
25	Find a percent of a number.
21, 24, 26, 27	Multiply fractions and mixed numbers.
28, 29	Divide fractions.

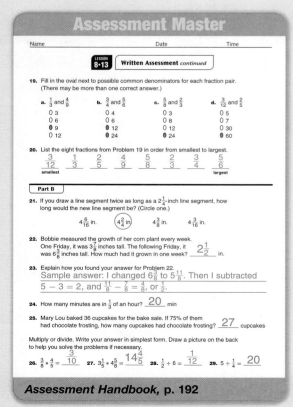

Assessment Handbook, p. 192

Use the checklists on pages 275 and 277 of the *Assessment Handbook* to record results. Then input the data into the **Assessment Management Spreadsheets** to keep an ongoing record of students' progress toward Grade-Level Goals.

▶ Open Response

(*Assessment Handbook*, p. 193)

Writing Egyptian Fractions

 The open-response item requires students to apply skills and concepts from Unit 8 to solve a multistep problem. See *Assessment Handbook*, pages 113–117 for rubrics and students' work samples for this problem.

---

(2) Looking Ahead: Preparing for Unit 9

▶ Math Boxes 8·13

INDEPENDENT ACTIVITY

(*Math Journal 2*, p. 291)

 Mixed Practice This Math Boxes page previews Unit 9 content.

▶ Study Link 8·13: Unit 9 Family Letter

INDEPENDENT ACTIVITY

(*Math Masters*, pp. 250–253)

Home Connection The Unit 9 Family Letter provides parents and guardians with information and activities related to Unit 9 topics.

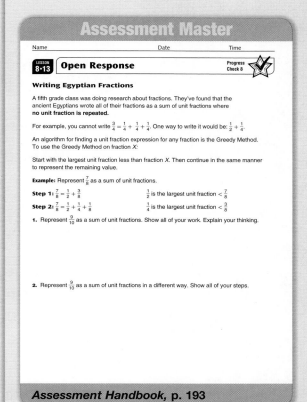

Assessment Handbook, p. 193

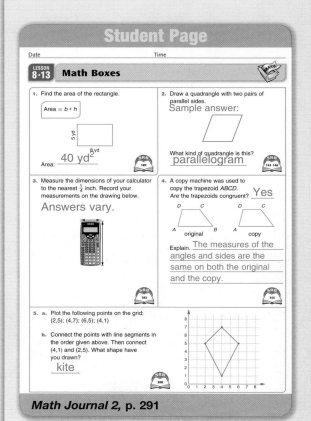

Math Journal 2, p. 291

Coordinates, Area, Volume, and Capacity

Overview

In Unit 9, students will practice plotting points on a coordinate grid and be introduced to transformations of figures in a plane. The area of rectangles is reviewed and then used as a starting point to find areas of triangles and parallelograms. Volume and capacity concepts are also reviewed and extended. Unit 9 has three main areas of focus:

◆ To work with coordinate graphs,

◆ To extend area concepts, and

◆ To develop a formula for volume and consider capacity relationships.

CCSS Linking to the Common Core State Standards

The content of Unit 9 addresses the Common Core State Standards for Mathematics in *Measurement and Data* and *Geometry*. The correlation of the Common Core State Standards to the *Everyday Mathematics* Grade 5 lessons begins on page CS1.

▶ Contents

Learning In Perspective

	Lesson Objectives	Links to the Past	Links to the Future
9·1	To reinforce students' understanding of coordinate grid structures and vocabulary.	In fourth grade, students locate points specified by ordered number pairs on the first quadrant of a coordinate grid.	In sixth grade, students plot ordered number pairs on a coordinate grid.
9·2	To reinforce plotting coordinates and the relationships between ordered number pairs and transformations of figures in a plane.	In fourth grade, students practice identifying lines of reflection and are guided in discovering the basic properties of reflection.	In sixth grade, students plot ordered number pairs and solve problems about polygons on a coordinate grid.
9·3	To reinforce plotting coordinates and the relationships between ordered number pairs and transformations of figures in a plane.	In fourth grade, students are guided in the application of reflections, rotations, and translations.	In sixth grade, students explore the relationship between endpoints and midpoints of line segments drawn on coordinate grids. They perform isometry transformations with figures on a coordinate grid.
9·4	To reinforce students' understanding of area concepts and units of area.	In fourth grade, students review the meaning of area as the measure of surface in square units and find the area of a figure by counting grid squares.	In sixth grade, students use graphing to investigate the relationship between area and perimeter.
9·5	To introduce the rectangle method for finding areas of polygons.	In fourth grade, students develop formulas for the area of a rectangle, a parallelogram, and a triangle.	In sixth grade, students examine how formulas are derived.
9·6	To provide experiences with the use of formulas for the areas of triangles and parallelograms.	In fourth grade, students develop formulas for the area of a rectangle, a parallelogram, and a triangle.	In sixth grade, students evaluate formulas.
9·7	To reinforce the use of sampling to make estimates.	In fourth grade, students do experiments to help determine expected outcomes and results.	In sixth grade, students determine whether a sample is random or biased.
9·8	To provide experiences with using a formula for the volume of rectangular prisms.	In fourth grade, students are guided in the development and use of a formula for finding the volume of a rectangular prism.	In sixth grade, students review volume formulas for rectangular prisms, cylinders, and spheres.
9·9	To provide experiences with using a formula for the volume of right prisms.	In fourth grade, students find the volume of rectangular prisms by counting cubic units and develop a formula for the volume of a rectangular prism.	In sixth grade, students apply volume formulas for rectangular prisms, cylinders, and spheres.
9·10	To reinforce the relationships among the liter, milliliter, and cubic centimeter.	In fourth grade, students review concepts and units of volume and customary units of capacity.	In sixth grade, students maintain and apply skills related to volume and capacity.

Key Concepts and Skills	Grade 5 Goals*
9·1 Translate numbers written in scientific notation into standard notation and number-and-word notation.	Number and Numeration Goal 1
Use ordered pairs of numbers to name, locate, and plot points in the first quadrant of a coordinate grid.	Measurement and Reference Frames Goal 4
9·2 Identify decimals on a number line.	Number and Numeration Goal 1
Plot points in the first quadrant of a coordinate grid.	Measurement and Reference Frames Goal 4
Use rules to generate transformations of plane figures on a coordinate grid.	Geometry Goal 3
9·3 Plot points in three quadrants of a coordinate grid.	Measurement and Reference Frames Goal 4
Construct congruent figures on a coordinate grid.	Geometry Goal 2
Describe reflections and translations of plane figures.	Geometry Goal 3
9·4 Multiply fractions and mixed numbers to find the area of a rectangle.	Operations and Computation Goal 5
Use a formula to calculate the areas of rectangles.	Measurement and Reference Frames Goal 2
Compare inch and centimeter measures for length and area.	Measurement and Reference Frames Goal 3
9·5 Use polygonal properties to support strategies for finding the areas of the polygons.	Measurement and Reference Frames Goal 2
Describe relationships between U.S. customary and metric square units.	Measurement and Reference Frames Goal 3
9·6 Investigate and use formulas to find the areas of triangles and parallelograms.	Measurement and Reference Frames Goal 2
Identify and define the base and height of triangles and parallelograms.	Geometry Goal 2
9·7 Use sampling to make an estimate for surface area problems.	Operations and Computation Goal 6
Collect and organize data.	Data and Chance Goal 1
Use latitude and longitude coordinates to locate points on Earth.	Measurement and Reference Frames Goal 4
9·8 Use formulas ($l * w * h$ or $B * h$) to calculate the volumes of rectangular prisms.	Measurement and Reference Frames Goal 2
Define the base and height of a rectangular prism.	Geometry Goal 2
Explore the properties of rectangular prisms.	Geometry Goal 2
Write number sentences with variables to model volume problems.	Patterns, Functions, and Algebra Goal 2
9·9 Use a formula to calculate the volumes of prisms.	Measurement and Reference Frames Goal 2
Define and classify prisms according to common properties.	Geometry Goal 2
9·10 Explore relationships between units of length and units of capacity.	Measurement and Reference Frames Goal 3
Investigate relationships and conversions between units of capacity and volume.	Measurement and Reference Frames Goal 3
Describe patterns in relationships between the dimensions and volume of rectangular prisms.	Measurement and Reference Frames Goal 3

*See the Appendix for a complete list of Grade 5 Goals.

A Balanced Curriculum

Ongoing Practice

Everyday Mathematics provides numerous opportunities for ongoing practice. These activities are embedded throughout the lessons:

 Mental Math and Reflexes activities promote speed and accuracy in mental computation.

 Math Boxes offer mixed practice and are paired across lessons as shown in the brackets below. This makes them useful as assessment tools. The last one or two boxes on each page preview the next unit's content.

Mixed practice	[9•1, 9•3], [9•2, 9•4], [9•5, 9•7], [9•6, 9•9], [9•8, 9•10]
Mixed practice with multiple choice	9•1, 9•2, 9•3, 9•4, 9•6, 9•9
Mixed practice with writing/reasoning opportunity	9•1, 9•2, 9•3, 9•4, 9•5, 9•6, 9•7, 9•8, 9•9, 9•10

 Study Links are daily homework assignments that review the content of the lesson and often contain ongoing facts practice or computation practice.

 5-Minute Math problems are offered for additional practice in Lessons 9•4, 9•6, 9•8, and 9•9.

 EM Facts Workshop Game provides online practice of basic facts and computation.

EXTRA PRACTICE **Extra Practice** activities are included in Lessons 9•2, 9•4, 9•5, 9•6, 9•7, 9•8, 9•9, and 9•10.

Practice through Games

Games are an essential component of practice in the *Everyday Mathematics* program. Games offer skills practice and promote strategic thinking. See the *Differentiation Handbook* for ways to adapt games to meet students' needs.

Lesson	Game	Skill Practiced
9•1, 9•3	*Hidden Treasure*	Naming and plotting ordered number pairs [MRF Goal 4]
9•5	*Frac-Tac-Toe*	Converting between fractions, decimals, and percents [NN Goal 5]
9•6	*Fraction Action, Fraction Friction*	Estimating sums of fractions using benchmarks [OC Goals 4 and 6]
9•9	*Polygon Capture*	Identifying properties of polygons [GEO Goal 2]

[NN] Number and Numeration
[MRF] Measurement and Reference Frames

[OC] Operations and Computation
[GEO] Geometry

[DC] Data and Chance
[PFA] Patterns, Functions, and Algebra

Problem Solving

Experts at problem solving and mathematical modeling generally do these things:

- Identify the problem.
- Decide what information is needed to solve the problem.
- Play with and study the data to find patterns and meaning.
- Identify and use mathematical procedures to solve the problem.
- Decide whether the solution makes sense and whether it can be applied to other problems.

The table below lists some of the opportunities in this unit for students to practice these strategies.

Lesson	Activity
9◆1	Match a number story to a graph that best represents the story.
9◆2, 9◆3	Draw transformations of a given picture on a coordinate grid.
9◆4	Solve number stories involving the area of rectangles.
9◆5	Find the areas of triangles and parallelograms using the rectangle method.
9◆6	Develop formulas for the area of triangles and the area of parallelograms.
9◆7	Estimate Earth's water surface area.
9◆7	Write the whole numbers from 1 to 100 using only four 4s.
9◆8	Develop a formula for the volume of a rectangular prism.
9◆10	Find the dimensions of an open box with the greatest possible volume.

*Lessons that teach **through** problem solving, not just **about** problem solving*

See Chapter 18: Problem Solving in the *Teacher's Reference Manual* for more information.

The Language of Mathematics

Everyday Mathematics provides lesson-specific suggestions to help all students acquire, process, and express mathematical ideas. Throughout Unit 9, there are lesson-specific language development notes that address the needs of English language learners, indicated by **ELL**.

ELL SUPPORT Activities to support English language learners are in Part 3 of Lessons 9◆1, 9◆2, 9◆3, 9◆4, 9◆9, and 9◆10.

The *English Learners Handbook* and the *Differentiation Handbook* have suggestions for promoting language development and acquisition of mathematics vocabulary. See Unit 9 in each handbook.

Literacy Connection

Room for Ripley, by Stuart J. Murphy, HarperCollins, 1999

G is for Googol, by David M. Schwartz, Tricycle Press, 1998

Spaghetti and Meatballs for All, by Marilyn Burns, Scholastic, 2008

For more literacy connections, see the *Home Connection Handbook,* Grades 4–6.

Cross-Curricular Links

Social Studies – Lesson 9◆2   **Literature** – Lessons 9◆5, 9◆10

Unit 9 Vocabulary

altitude	longitude
area	milliliter (mL)
Associative Property of Multiplication	opposite of a number
axes	ordered number pair
base	ordered pair of numbers
base (of a rectangular prism)	origin
capacity	perpendicular
coordinate	personal references
coordinate grid	prism
cubic centimeter	quart (qt)
cubic unit	rectangle method
cup (c)	rectangular prism
face	reflection
formula	square units
height	translation
height (of a rectangular prism)	variable
	vertical axis
horizontal axis	volume
latitude	volume (of a container)
liter (L)	

Balanced Assessment

✓ Daily Assessments

◆ **Recognizing Student Achievement** – A daily assessment that is included in every lesson to evaluate students' progress toward the Grade 5 Grade-Level Goals.

◆ **Informing Instruction** – Notes that appear throughout the unit to help anticipate students' common errors and suggest appropriate problem-solving strategies.

Lesson	Recognizing Student Achievement	Informing Instruction
9·1	Translate numbers written in scientific notation into standard notation and number-and-word notation. [NN Goal 1]	
9·2	Plot ordered number pairs and identify decimals on a number line. [NN Goal 1 and MRF Goal 4]	
9·3	Plot points on a coordinate grid and correctly graph transformations. [MRF Goal 4]	
9·4	Calculate and accurately explain how to find area. [MRF Goal 2]	Shade the grid in Problem 1 to show how much floor is covered.
9·5	Draw a line segment congruent to a given line segment and explain why the two line segments are congruent. [GEO Goal 2]	
9·6	Write both the equation and word sentence for the area formulas for triangles and parallelograms. [MRF Goal 2]	
9·7	Solve fraction-of problems and identify the numbers that represent the unit fraction of a set. [NN Goal 2]	
9·8	Find common denominators and correctly identify the least common denominators. [NN Goal 5]	Make a table for problems to correctly match given dimensions to formula variables.
9·9	Correctly match polygons with their properties. [GEO Goal 2]	
9·10	Explain the distinction between volume and capacity and provide examples by listing things measured in cubic centimeters and things measured in milliliters. [MRF Goal 3]	Cut a 1 cm by 1 cm square out of each of the four corners of a grid to make a pattern for an open box that is 1 centimeter in height.

[NN] Number and Numeration   [OC] Operations and Computation   [DC] Data and Chance
[MRF] Measurement and Reference Frames   [GEO] Geometry   [PFA] Patterns, Functions, and Algebra

Portfolio Opportunities

The following lessons provide opportunities to gather samples of students' mathematical writings, drawings, and creations to add balance to the assessment process: Lessons 9·1, 9·2, 9·3, 9·4, 9·5, 9·6, 9·7, 9·8, 9·9, 9·10, and 9·11. See pages 16 and 17 in the *Assessment Handbook* for more information about portfolios and how to use them.

Unit Assessment

Progress Check 9 – A cumulative assessment of concepts and skills taught in Unit 9 and in previous units, providing information for evaluating students' progress and planning for future instruction. These assessments include oral/slate, written, and open-response activities, as shown below in the sample Progress Check lesson opener.

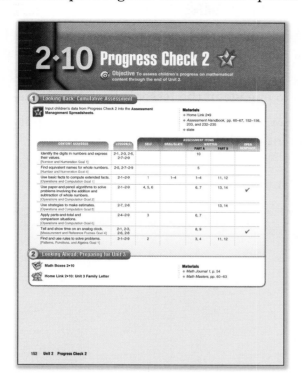

Core Assessment Resources

Assessment Handbook

- ◆ **Unit 9 Assessment Overview,** pages 118–125
- ◆ **Unit 9 Assessment Masters,** pages 194–198
- ◆ **Unit 9 Individual Profiles of Progress,** pages 278, 279, and 302
- ◆ **Unit 9 Class Checklists,** pages 280, 281, and 303
- ◆ **Quarterly Checklist: Quarter 3,** pages 298 and 299
- ◆ **Math Logs,** pages 306–308
- ◆ **Exit Slip,** page 311
- ◆ **Other Student Assessment Forms,** pages 304, 305, 309, and 310

Assessment Management Spreadsheets

The Assessment Management Spreadsheets consist of the Digital Class Checklists and Individual Profile of Progress Checklists. Use them to monitor, record, and report student progress.

Addressing All Needs

Differentiated Instruction

 Adjusting the Activity – suggests adaptations that target advanced learners, English language learners, or learners who need additional instructional support.

ELL SUPPORT / **ELL** – provides lesson-specific suggestions to help English language learners understand and process the mathematical content.

READINESS – accesses students' prior knowledge or previews content that prepares students to engage in the lesson's Part 1 activities.

EXTRA PRACTICE – provides additional opportunities to apply the mathematical content of the lesson.

ENRICHMENT – enables students to apply or further explore the mathematical content of the lesson.

Lesson	Adjusting the Activity	ELL Support/ ELL	Readiness	Extra Practice	Enrichment
9•1		•	•		•
9•2		•	•	•	•
9•3		•	•		•
9•4		•	•	•	•
9•5	•		•	•	
9•6	•		•	•	•
9•7				•	•
9•8	•	•	•	•	•
9•9		•	•	•	•
9•10		•	•	•	

▷ Additional Resources

Differentiation Handbook
Provides ideas and strategies for differentiating instruction.
Pages 106–112

English Learners Handbook
Contains lesson-specific comprehension strategies.
Pages 82–91

Multilingual Handbook
Previews concepts and vocabulary. It is written in six languages.
Pages 163–182

Planning Tips

Multiage Classroom

Companion Lessons from Grades 4 and 6 can help you meet instructional needs of a multiage classroom. The full Scope and Sequence can be found in the Appendix.

Grade 4		6•8	6•8	8•3	1•4, 1•5, 1•8	1•8, 8•3, 8•6–8•8	8•8	11•5		11•7	
Grade 5	9•1	9•2	9•3	9•4	9•5	9•6	9•7	9•8	9•9	9•10	9•11
Grade 6				9•8	5•10, 9•8	3•4, 5•10, 9•8	1•10, 9•8	9•9	9•9		

Pacing for Success

Pacing depends on a number of factors, such as students' individual needs and how long your school has been using *Everyday Mathematics*. At the beginning of Unit 9, you may want to use tools available at www.everydaymathonline.com to help you set your pace.

Home Support

Unit 9 Family Letter (English/Spanish) provides families with an overview, Do-Anytime Activities, Building Skills through Games, a list of vocabulary, and answers to the daily homework (Study Links). Family Letters in English, Spanish, and seven other languages are also available online.

Study Links are the daily homework assignments. They consist of active projects and ongoing review problems.

▶ Home Support Resources

Home Connection Handbook
Offers ideas and reproducible masters for communicating with families. See Table of Contents for unit information.

Student Reference Book
Provides a resource for students and parents.
Pages 80A, 80B, 158, 188, 190, 191, 195–197, 208–210, 309–312, 319, 328, 384, 396

Technology Resources

Algorithms Practice

EM Facts Workshop Game™

Family Letters

Interactive Teacher's Lesson Guide

www.everydaymathonline.com

Materials

Technology Resources   www.everydaymathonline.com

ePresentations | eToolkit | Algorithms Practice | EM Facts Workshop Game™ | Family Letters | Assessment Management | Common Core State Standards | Curriculum Focal Points | Interactive Teacher's Lesson Guide

Lesson	Masters	Manipulative Kit	Other Items
9·1	Game Master, p. 485 Transparencies of *Math Masters*, pp. 437, 438, and 485 Study Link Master, p. 254 Teaching Masters, pp. 255 and 256 *Differentiation Handbook,* p. 142	slate	Class Data Pad; straightedge; red pencil or crayon; Geometry Template; compass
9·2	Transparency of *Math Masters*, p. 260 Study Link Master, p. 257 Teaching Masters, pp. 258 and 259 Teaching Aid Master, p. 438		straightedge; Geometry Template
9·3	Study Link Master, p. 261 Game Master, p. 486 Teaching Masters, pp. 262–264	slate; 4 metersticks; compass	Class Data Pad*; straightedge; Geometry Template; per partnership: 1 red pencil or crayon; masking tape; markers; calculator
9·4	Teaching Aid Masters, pp. 414 and 436 Transparency of *Math Masters,* p. 436 Study Link Master, p. 265 Teaching Masters, pp. 266, 267, and 293A *Differentiation Handbook,* p. 142	slate; per partnership: 2 six-sided dice	Class Data Pad; inch ruler; roll of paper towels, wax paper, or aluminum foil*; 3 different-colored pencils or markers; scissors; per partnership: 36 centimeter cubes
9·5	Transparency of *Math Masters*, p. 436 Study Link Master, p. 268 Game Masters, pp. 472–484 Teaching Aid Master, p. 436	slate; per partnership: 4 each of number cards 0–10	per partnership: 2 different-colored counters, Geometry Template, construction paper, scissors, 4 sheets of unlined paper; *Spaghetti and Meatballs for All*
9·6	Study Link Master, p. 269 Game Master, p. 459 Teaching Masters, pp. 270–273	2 pattern block triangles	Class Data Pad; straightedge; colored pencil; tape or glue; scissors; per partnership: calculator
9·7	Teaching Masters, pp. 274, 275, 277, and 278 Study Link Master, p. 276	slate	Class Data Pad*; Probability Meter; world map or globe; stick-on note; calculator; Geometry Template
9·8	Study Link Master, p. 279 Teaching Masters, pp. 280 and 281 Teaching Aid Master, p. 429	slate	scissors; transparent tape; 24 centimeter cubes; per partnership: one stick-on note, pad of unused stick-on notes, centimeter cube
9·9	Teaching Masters, pp. 282, 283, and 285–288 Study Link Master, p. 284 Game Masters, pp. 494–496*; p. 497 *Differentiation Handbook,* p. 142		Class Data Pad; demonstration materials: metric ruler, foam board, knife, tape*; scissors; tape or glue
9·10	Teaching Aid Masters, pp. 414 and 436 Study Link Master, p. 289	slate; base-10 flats or longs	Class Data Pad*; scissors; transparent tape; 1-liter cube; water-tight liter box; 1-liter pitcher; measuring cup; *Room for Ripley;* per group: 5 different-sized containers; 5 volume-measuring tools; macaroni, centimeter cubes, or other small items to fill containers
9·11	Assessment Masters, pp. 194–198 Study Link Masters, pp. 290–293	slate	

*Denotes optional materials

Mathematical Background

The discussion below highlights the major content areas presented in Unit 9 and helps establish instructional priorities.

Coordinate Graphs (Lessons 9•1–9•3)

When we use map models of our world, we are usually locating ourselves on 2-dimensional surfaces (including surfaces of spheres). To do so, two pieces of information, or "coordinates," are needed to specify each location—one coordinate for each dimension.

In *Fourth Grade Everyday Mathematics,* students used map coordinates to identify regions on a map and to identify a point where two grid lines intersect. Additionally, students were introduced to the coordinate grid system of latitude and longitude used to locate points on Earth's surface.

Lessons 9-1 through 9-3 provide students with practice in plotting and reading the location of ordered number pairs on a coordinate grid. Negative and fractional coordinates, as well as positive whole-number coordinates, are included. Students are introduced to the game *Hidden Treasure* (similar to the commercially available Battleship™). Additionally, Lessons 9-2 and 9-3 expose students to transformations of geometric figures through the application of a designated rule.

In Lessons 9-2 and 9-3, students also explore how the boundary (perimeter), area, and angle measures of a figure are affected when the figure is transformed mathematically—enlarged, reduced, translated, or reflected. Students often confuse perimeter with area. Perimeter is a measure of length or distance; area is a measure of surface. You can illustrate perimeter with a trundle wheel that measures the boundary of a surface, and area with the sweep of a paint roller across a surface. Perimeter is measured in units of length—the number of unit line segments from one point to another. Area is measured in square units— the number of unit squares needed to cover a surface. Review these basic differences often.

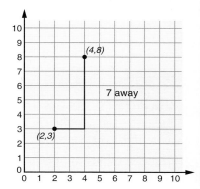

Students practice plotting and reading ordered number pairs by playing *Hidden Treasure.*

 PROFESSIONAL DEVELOPMENT To learn more about coordinate graphs, see Section 15.3 of the *Teacher's Reference Manual.*

A trundle wheel can be used to measure the boundary (perimeter) of a large surface.

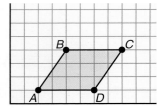

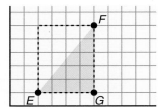

Formulas for Area (Lessons 9♦4–9♦6)

It is important to note that, like other numerical measures, area always includes both a number and a unit. Units of area are typically square units based on some linear unit (for example, square yard, square meter, or square mile).

In Lesson 9-4, students review two methods for finding the area of a rectangular figure. They count the total number of unit squares and fractions of unit squares that fit neatly inside the rectangle. Additionally, students use the formula $A = b * h$, where A represents the area of the rectangle, b represents the length of the base, and h represents the height.

In Lesson 9-5, students explore the rectangle method for finding the area of nonrectangular polygons. As a result of this exploration, students generate formulas for the area of a triangle and a parallelogram in Lesson 9-6.

PROFESSIONAL DEVELOPMENT For additional information about formulas for area, see Section 14.4.2 of the *Teacher's Reference Manual*.

Area Explorations (Lesson 9♦7)

In the exploration "Earth's Water Surface," students review locating places on Earth with latitude and longitude. Then they use latitude and longitude in a sampling experiment that enables them to estimate, without measuring, the percent of Earth's surface that is covered by water.

PROFESSIONAL DEVELOPMENT For more area explorations, see Section 14.4 of the *Teacher's Reference Manual*.

Pacific Ocean

Atlantic Ocean

What percentage of Earth's surface is covered by water?

Volume and Capacity (Lessons 9◆8–9◆10)

Students review and extend their knowledge of volume (the amount of space an object takes up) and capacity (the amount of material a container can hold).

Lesson 9-8 involves building a 3-dimensional shape with identical cubic blocks (or filling it completely with such blocks), and then counting the blocks. If the shape is bounded by a rectangular prism, it is natural to build it as one layer of blocks, count the blocks in that layer, and then multiply by the number of layers it would take to fill the prism.

Since the number of blocks in the base layer corresponds to the area of the base (often expressed as $l * w$), that process is easily linked to either of the two standard formulas for the volume of a rectangular prism: $V = l * w * h$ (the product of the length and width of the rectangular base and the height perpendicular to that base) or $V = B * h$ (the product of the area of the base and the height perpendicular to that base).

Both formulas work fine; however, $V = B * h$ can be applied more easily to nonrectangular prisms and then to formulas for pyramids and cones. For example, it is difficult to build or fill a triangular prism (or a cylinder) with cubes, but it is easy to find the area of the triangular base, and then imagine that base rising along the height dimension to generate the volume.

In Lesson 9-10, the capacity relationship 1 liter = 1,000 milliliters = 1,000 cubic centimeters is demonstrated. Students also practice converting between U.S. customary measures of capacity (fluid ounce, cup, pint, quart, gallon).

 You can learn more about volume and capacity in Section 14.5 of the *Teacher's Reference Manual.*

Project Note

Use Project 9, Adding Volumes of Solid Figures, to find the volume of two non-overlapping right rectangular prisms.

Note

Traditionally, linear measures are represented in formulas by lowercase letters, and areas and volumes by uppercase letters. For example, *b* might be used to represent the length of the base of a rectangle, and *B* to represent the area of the base.

9·1 Hidden Treasure: A Coordinate Game

 Objective To reinforce students' understanding of coordinate grid structures and vocabulary.

Technology Resources www.everydaymathonline.com

ePresentations

eToolkit

Algorithms Practice

EM Facts Workshop Game™

Family Letters

Assessment Management

Common Core State Standards

Curriculum Focal Points

Interactive Teacher's Lesson Guide

---

1 Teaching the Lesson

Key Concepts and Skills

- Translate numbers written in scientific notation into standard notation and number-and-word notation.
  [Number and Numeration Goal 1]

- Use ordered pairs of numbers to name, locate, and plot points in the first quadrant of a coordinate grid.
  [Measurement and Reference Frames Goal 4]

Key Activities

Students review coordinate grids, ordered number pairs, and coordinates. They use coordinate grids to graph a picture by choosing and connecting ordered number pairs. Students practice naming and plotting ordered number pairs by playing *Hidden Treasure*.

Ongoing Assessment: Recognizing Student Achievement Use Mental Math and Reflexes.
[Number and Numeration Goal 1]

Key Vocabulary

coordinate grid ◆ axes ◆ perpendicular ◆ origin ◆ ordered pair of numbers ◆ vertical axis ◆ horizontal axis ◆ coordinate

Materials

Math Journal 2, pp. 292 and 293
Student Reference Book, pp. 208 and 319
Math Masters, p. 485
transparencies of *Math Masters,* pp. 437, 438, and 485 ◆ Class Data Pad ◆ slate ◆ straightedge ◆ red pencil or crayon

2 Ongoing Learning & Practice

Matching Number Stories to Graphs

Math Journal 2, p. 294
Students match number stories to line graphs and explain their solution strategies.

 ### Math Boxes 9·1

Math Journal 2, p. 295
Geometry Template ◆ compass
Students practice and maintain skills through Math Box problems.

 ### Study Link 9·1

Math Masters, p. 254
straightedge
Students practice and maintain skills through Study Link activities.

3 Differentiation Options

READINESS
Finding Locations on a Map
Math Masters, p. 255
Students locate points on a map.

ENRICHMENT
Finding Distances
Math Masters, p. 256
straightedge
Students use gridlines to identify point-to-point distances on a grid.

ELL SUPPORT
Building a Math Word Bank
Differentiation Handbook, p. 142
Students write, define, and illustrate the terms *horizontal axis* and *vertical axis.*

Advance Preparation

For Part 1, make transparencies of *Math Masters,* pages 437, 438, and 485. Copies of *Math Masters,* page 485 can be used as additional *Hidden Treasure* gameboards. For a mathematics and literacy connection, obtain a copy of *G Is for Googol: A Math Alphabet Book* by David M. Schwartz (Tricycle Press, 1998).

 Teacher's Reference Manual, Grades 4–6 pp. 249, 250

Getting Started

Mental Math and Reflexes

Have students write numbers in standard notation and number-and-word notation. Ask students to explain how they determined the number of zeros to attach when writing the number in standard notation. *Suggestions:*

●○○ $3 * 10^3$ 3,000; 3 thousand

     $5 * 10^2$ 500; 5 hundred

●●○ $9 * 10^5$ 900,000; 9 hundred thousand

     $7 * 10^6$ 7,000,000; 7 million

●●● $6.5 * 10^4$ 65,000; 6.5 ten thousand

     $3.9 * 10^5$ 390,000; 3.9 hundred thousand

Math Message

Plot the following points on the small coordinate grid on journal page 292:

$(4,0); (0,4); (0,0); (5,1\frac{1}{2}); (1.25, 4.75)$

Ongoing Assessment: Recognizing Student Achievement

Mental Math and Reflexes

Use the **Mental Math and Reflexes** problems to assess students' ability to translate numbers written in scientific notation into standard notation and number-and-word notation. Students are making adequate progress if they correctly write each number in standard notation.

[Number and Numeration Goal 1]

---

1 Teaching the Lesson

► Math Message Follow-Up

WHOLE-CLASS ACTIVITY

(*Math Journal 2*, p. 292; *Student Reference Book*, p. 208; *Math Masters*, p. 437)

Use a transparency of *Math Masters*, page 437 to illustrate the following concepts:

▷ A plane is a flat surface that extends forever. A rectangular **coordinate grid** is used to name points in a plane.

▷ The coordinate grid is formed by two number lines called **axes**.

▷ The number lines intersect at right angles at their 0 points. The two number lines are **perpendicular**.

▷ The point where the lines meet (0,0) is called the **origin**.

▷ Every point on a coordinate grid can be named by an **ordered pair of numbers**. The first number in the pair is always the horizontal distance of the point from the **vertical axis**. The second number in the pair is always the vertical distance of the point from the **horizontal axis**.

Interactive whiteboard-ready ePresentations are available at www.everydaymathonline.com to help you teach the lesson.

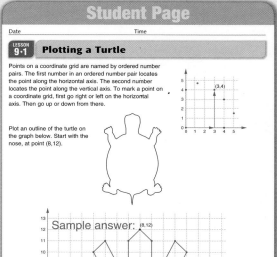

Student Page

Date   Time

LESSON 9·1 Plotting a Turtle

Points on a coordinate grid are named by ordered number pairs. The first number in an ordered number pair locates the point along the horizontal axis. The second number locates the point along the vertical axis. To mark a point on a coordinate grid, first go right or left on the horizontal axis. Then go up or down from there.

Plot an outline of the turtle on the graph below. Start with the nose, at point (8,12).

Sample answer: (8,12)

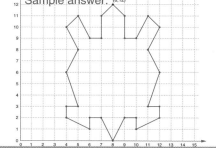

Math Journal 2, p. 292

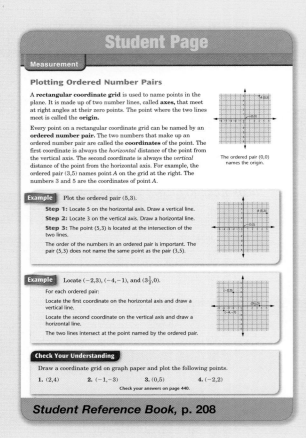

Student Reference Book, p. 208

▷ The numbers in an ordered pair are the **coordinates** of the corresponding point. To plot the coordinates of a point, first move left or right along the horizontal axis, and then move up or down along the vertical axis.

▷ One or both coordinates may be a whole number, fraction, decimal, or mixed number.

▷ When one of the coordinates is 0, the point lies directly on an axis.

Ask volunteers to use the transparency to demonstrate and explain how to plot the Math Message points. Encourage students to make use of the Key Vocabulary terms in their explanations.

Write (3,4) and (4,3) on the board. Ask: *Do these coordinates name the same point?* No *Why?* The position of the numbers in an ordered pair determines the axis to be used for each of the coordinates. Unless the numbers are in the same positions in both ordered pairs, they will name different points.

Ask students to suggest ways to remember which axis the coordinates refer to in an ordered number pair. Write their suggestions on the Class Data Pad. *For example:*

▷ Alphabetically, *horizontal* comes before *vertical*.

▷ Think about painting the side of a house. You must move the ladder to where you want to paint before climbing up.

▷ Think about an elevator building. You go across the ground floor first and find the elevator to take you up to where you want to go.

▷ Think of the proverb: You must crawl before you can walk. Crawling is horizontal. Walking is vertical.

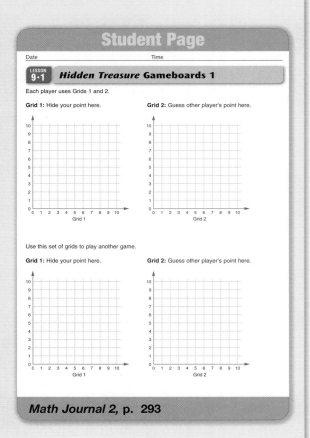

Math Journal 2, p. 293

▶ Graphing a Picture

👥👥👥 **WHOLE-CLASS ACTIVITY**

(*Math Journal 2*, p. 292; *Math Masters*, p. 438)

Tell students that they are going to graph a representation of the turtle shown at the top of journal page 292 as a class. Use the transparency of *Math Masters*, page 438 to model plotting and connecting points. Begin the picture by having students mark and label the point at (8,12), which is the tip of the turtle's nose.

Ask volunteers to suggest whole-number coordinates for the next point on the turtle graph. Have students mark that point on their own graphs and then use a straightedge to connect it to the previous point.

Continue until an outline of the turtle has been drawn on the graph. Remind students that it is not important that their graphs exactly match the picture. Rather, they should choose points that will be a close representation of the picture.

Ask students to label the coordinates of 4 points on their graphs.

Playing the *Hidden Treasure* Game

👥 **PARTNER ACTIVITY**

(*Math Journal 2*, p. 293; *Student Reference Book*, p. 319; *Math Masters*, p. 485)

Ask students whether they have ever played Hot and Cold. It is a game where Player A leaves the room while the others hide some object. Then Player A returns and has to locate the object. The others provide clues by saying whether Player A is "hot" or "cold." The farther away from the object, the "colder" Player A becomes. The closer to the object, the "warmer" Player A becomes. The game continues until Player A locates the object.

Tell students that *Hidden Treasure* is a game that is similar to Hot and Cold. Go over the rules on page 319 of the *Student Reference Book*. Be sure students understand the directions.

Use a transparency of the gameboard (*Math Masters*, p. 485) to play a sample round showing students how to complete the grids and how to answer a player's guesses.

Have partners play two or more games. Players write in their own journals, using one of the two gameboards on journal page 293. Note that a gameboard consists of two grids.

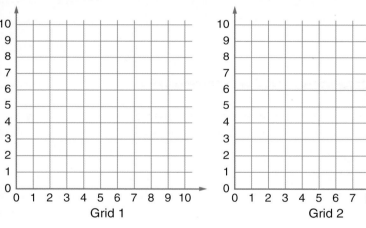

Grid 1: Hide your point here.
Grid 2: Guess other player's point here.

Circulate and assist. Pass out copies of *Math Masters*, page 485 if additional gameboards are needed.

2 Ongoing Learning & Practice

Matching Number Stories to Graphs

👤 **INDEPENDENT ACTIVITY**

🧩 **PROBLEM SOLVING**

(*Math Journal 2*, p. 294)

Students match number stories to line graphs and explain their solution strategies. They also identify the rule that describes one of the stories.

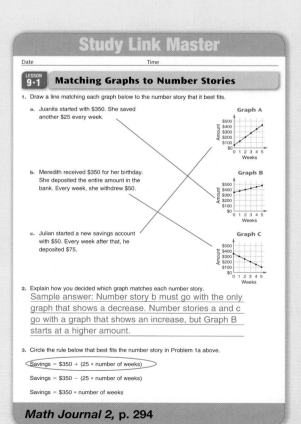

Student Reference Book, p. 319

Study Link Master

Date _____ Time _____

LESSON 9·1   Matching Graphs to Number Stories

1. Draw a line matching each graph below to the number story that it best fits.

   a. Juanita started with $350. She saved another $25 every week.

   b. Meredith received $350 for her birthday. She deposited the entire amount in the bank. Every week, she withdrew $50.

   c. Julian started a new savings account with $50. Every week after that, he deposited $75.

   Graph A
   Graph B
   Graph C

2. Explain how you decided which graph matches each number story.
   Sample answer: Number story b must go with the only graph that shows a decrease. Number stories a and c go with a graph that shows an increase, but Graph B starts at a higher amount.

3. Circle the rule below that best fits the number story in Problem 1a above.

   (Savings = $350 + (25 * number of weeks))

   Savings = $350 − (25 * number of weeks)

   Savings = $350 * number of weeks

Math Journal 2, p. 294

Student Page

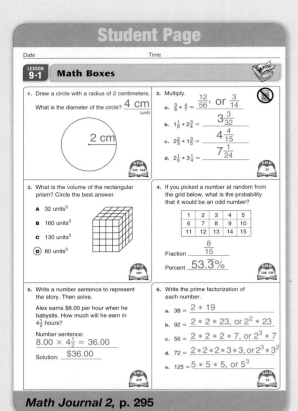

Date _____ Time _____

LESSON 9·1 Math Boxes

1. Draw a circle with a radius of 2 centimeters.
   What is the diameter of the circle? **4 cm** (unit)

   2 cm

2. Multiply.

   a. $\frac{3}{8} * \frac{4}{7} = \frac{12}{56}$, or $\frac{3}{14}$

   b. $1\frac{1}{8} * 2\frac{3}{4} = 3\frac{3}{32}$

   c. $2\frac{2}{3} * 1\frac{3}{5} = 4\frac{4}{15}$

   d. $2\frac{1}{6} * 3\frac{1}{4} = 7\frac{1}{24}$

3. What is the volume of the rectangular prism? Circle the best answer.

   A 32 units³

   B 160 units³

   C 130 units³

   (D) 80 units³

4. If you picked a number at random from the grid below, what is the probability that it would be an odd number?

1	2	3	4	5
6	7	8	9	10
11	12	13	14	15

   Fraction $\frac{8}{15}$

   Percent **53.3%**

5. Write a number sentence to represent the story. Then solve.

   Alex earns $8.00 per hour when he babysits. How much will he earn in $4\frac{1}{2}$ hours?

   Number sentence:

   $8.00 \times 4\frac{1}{2} = 36.00$

   Solution: $36.00

6. Write the prime factorization of each number.

   a. 38 **2 * 19**

   b. 92 **2 * 2 * 23, or 2^2 * 23**

   c. 56 **2 * 2 * 2 * 7, or 2^3 * 7**

   d. 72 **2 * 2 * 2 * 3 * 3, or 2^3 * 3^2**

   e. 125 **5 * 5 * 5, or 5^3**

Math Journal 2, p. 295

Study Link Master

Name _____ Date _____ Time _____

STUDY LINK 9·1 Plotting Points

1. Plot the following points on the grid below. After you plot each point, draw a line segment to connect it to the last point you plotted.
   Reminder: Use your straightedge!

   (3,6); (11,11); (15,11); (15,7); (7,2); (3,2); (3,6); (7,6)

   Draw a line segment connecting (7,6) and (7,2).
   Draw a line segment connecting (7,6) and (15,11).

2. What 3-dimensional shape could this drawing represent? **Rectangular prism**

3. a. What ordered pair would name the missing vertex to represent a prism? **(11,7)**

   b. Draw the missing vertex, and then add dashed lines for the missing edges.

   Practice

   4. 3,745 + 8,761 + 791 = **13,297**

   5. 3.745 + 87.61 + 781 = **872.355**

   6. $4\frac{3}{8} + 5\frac{7}{8} = $ **$10\frac{2}{8}$, or $10\frac{1}{4}$**

   7. $\frac{1}{5} + \frac{3}{4} = $ **$\frac{19}{20}$**

Math Masters, p. 254

Math Boxes 9·1

(*Math Journal 2*, p. 295)

INDEPENDENT ACTIVITY

Mixed Practice Math Boxes in this lesson are paired with Math Boxes in Lesson 9-3. The skill in Problem 5 previews Unit 10 content.

Writing/Reasoning Have students write a response to the following: *Explain how you solved Problem 2d. How might you check your answer?* Sample answer: I renamed $2\frac{1}{6}$ as $\frac{13}{6}$ and renamed $3\frac{1}{4}$ as $\frac{13}{4}$. I multiplied $\frac{13}{6} * \frac{13}{4} = \frac{169}{24}$. Then I divided 169 by 24 to rename the product as a mixed number. $169 \div 24 = 7\frac{1}{24}$. To check my answer, I would use my calculator to divide $7\frac{1}{24} \div 3\frac{1}{4} = 2\frac{1}{6}$. Ask students to write a number story for Problem 2d. Answers vary.

Study Link 9·1

(*Math Masters*, p. 254)

INDEPENDENT ACTIVITY

Home Connection Students practice plotting points on a coordinate grid.

---

(3) Differentiation Options

READINESS

INDEPENDENT ACTIVITY

▶ Finding Locations on a Map

5–15 Min

(*Math Masters*, p. 255)

To provide experience with coordinate grids, have students identify locations on a map using ordered pairs of numbers. Students used a similar map structure to name points using ordered pairs of numbers in *Fourth Grade Everyday Mathematics*.

When students have finished, ask volunteers to share their solution strategies. Discuss which locations could be named with more than one point and why. Some locations are areas that contain several points, and other locations are a single place at a single point.

ENRICHMENT

INDEPENDENT ACTIVITY

▶ Finding Distances

15–30 Min

(*Math Masters*, p. 256)

To apply students' understanding of coordinate grids, have them use a grid to compare and analyze distances. Students compare distances across diagonals with distances where only lines along the grid and square corners are allowed.

When students have finished, ask them to connect the points they plotted in Problem 4. Ask: *What shape was formed?* A square Discuss why the points did not form a circle. With a circle drawn on a grid, some of the points would be on a diagonal from the center. Because diagonals are not allowed, the shape couldn't be a circle. Explain that this shape is a *taxicab circle* because all of the points are equidistant from the center point.

Taxicab geometry was developed by Russian mathematician, Hermann Minkowski. Consider assigning students to explore the interactive taxicab geometry activity on the Annenberg Foundation Web site at http://www.learner.org/teacherslab/math/geometry/shape/taxicab/.

ELL SUPPORT

SMALL-GROUP ACTIVITY

5–15 Min

Building a Math Word Bank

(Differentiation Handbook, p. 142)

To provide language support for coordinate grids, have students use the Word Bank Template found on *Differentiation Handbook,* page 142. Ask students to write the terms *horizontal axis* and *vertical axis,* draw pictures relating to the terms, and write other related words. See the *Differentiation Handbook* for more information. Point out the unusual spelling of the plural, *axes,* and distinguish this meaning from the plural of the cutting tool, *ax.*

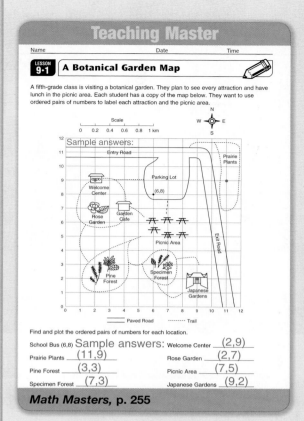

Teaching Master

Name   Date   Time

LESSON 9·1 **A Botanical Garden Map**

A fifth-grade class is visiting a botanical garden. They plan to see every attraction and have lunch in the picnic area. Each student has a copy of the map below. They want to use ordered pairs of numbers to label each attraction and the picnic area.

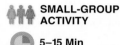

Find and plot the ordered pairs of numbers for each location.

Sample answers:

School Bus (6,8)		Welcome Center	(2,9)
Prairie Plants	(11,9)	Rose Garden	(2,7)
Pine Forest	(3,3)	Picnic Area	(7,5)
Specimen Forest	(7,3)	Japanese Gardens	(9,2)

Math Masters, p. 255

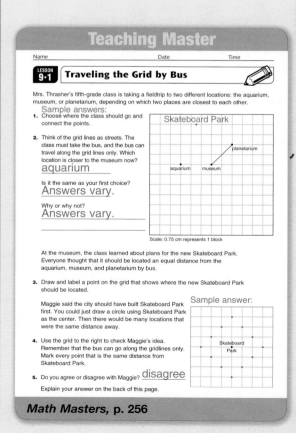

Teaching Master

Name   Date   Time

LESSON 9·1 **Traveling the Grid by Bus**

Mrs. Thrasher's fifth-grade class is taking a fieldtrip to two different locations: the aquarium, museum, or planetarium, depending on which two places are closest to each other.

Sample answers:
1. Choose where the class should go and connect the points.

2. Think of the grid lines as streets. The class must take the bus, and the bus can travel along the grid lines only. Which location is closer to the museum now?
   aquarium

   Is it the same as your first choice?
   Answers vary.

   Why or why not?
   Answers vary.

Scale: 0.75 cm represents 1 block

At the museum, the class learned about plans for the new Skateboard Park. Everyone thought that it should be located an equal distance from the aquarium, museum, and planetarium by bus.

3. Draw and label a point on the grid that shows where the new Skateboard Park should be located.

   Maggie said the city should have built Skateboard Park first. You could just draw a circle using Skateboard Park as the center. Then there would be many locations that were the same distance away.

4. Use the grid to the right to check Maggie's idea. Remember that the bus can go along the gridlines only. Mark every point that is the same distance from Skateboard Park.

5. Do you agree or disagree with Maggie? disagree

   Explain your answer on the back of this page.

Sample answer:

Math Masters, p. 256

9·2 Coordinate Graphs: Part 1

Objective To reinforce plotting coordinates and the relationships between ordered number pairs and transformations of figures in a plane.

Technology Resources www.everydaymathonline.com

 ePresentations

 eToolkit

 Algorithms Practice

 EM Facts Workshop Game™

 Family Letters

 Assessment Management

 Common Core State Standards

 Curriculum Focal Points

 Interactive Teacher's Lesson Guide

1 Teaching the Lesson

Key Concepts and Skills

- Identify decimals on a number line.
  [Number and Numeration Goal 1]

- Plot points in the first quadrant of a coordinate grid.
  [Measurement and Reference Frames Goal 4]

- Use rules to generate transformations of plane figures on a coordinate grid.
  [Geometry Goal 3]

Key Activities

Students plot and read ordered number pairs to graph figures. They investigate changing number pairs to transform figures.

 Ongoing Assessment: Recognizing Student Achievement Use journal page 298.
[Number and Numeration Goal 1; Measurement and Reference Frames Goal 4]

Key Vocabulary

ordered number pair ◆ coordinates

Materials

Math Journal 2, pp. 296–298
Study Link 9·1
transparency of *Math Masters,* p. 260 ◆
straightedge

2 Ongoing Learning & Practice

 **Math Boxes 9·2**
Math Journal 2, p. 299
Students practice and maintain skills through Math Box problems.

 Study Link 9·2
Math Masters, p. 257
straightedge
Students practice and maintain skills through Study Link activities.

3 Differentiation Options

READINESS
Locating Points on a Number Line
Geometry Template or ruler
Students locate decimals on a number line by plotting points between whole numbers.

ENRICHMENT
Scaling Graphs
Math Masters, p. 259
Students explore transformations on a coordinate grid by creating rules to change the values of ordered number pairs.

EXTRA PRACTICE
Plotting Pictures
Math Masters, p. 258
Geometry Template or straightedge
Students create and graph pictures on a coordinate grid.

ELL SUPPORT
Differentiating Points Defined by Ordered Number Pairs
Math Masters, p. 438
Students plot ordered number pairs on a coordinate grid to demonstrate the meaning of the order of the numbers in the pair.

Advance Preparation

For Part 1, make a transparency of *Math Masters,* page 260.

 Teacher's Reference Manual, Grades 4–6 pp. 199, 249, 250

Getting Started

Mental Math and Reflexes

Have students list all of the whole number factors of each number and write their prime factorizations on a sheet of paper. Remind them to use factor rainbows and factor trees. *Suggestions:*

- ●○○ **16** 1, 2, 4, 8, 16; 2 * 2 * 2 * 2
  12 1, 2, 3, 4, 6, 12; 2 * 2 * 3
- ●●○ **42** 1, 2, 3, 6, 7, 14, 21, 42; 2 * 3 * 7
  14 1, 2, 7, 14; 2 * 7
- ●●● **70** 1, 2, 5, 7, 10, 14, 35, 70; 2 * 5 * 7
  120 1, 2, 3, 4, 5, 6, 8, 10, 12, 15, 20, 24, 30, 40, 60, 120; 2 * 2 * 2 * 3 * 5

Math Message

Complete Problem 1 on journal page 298.

Study Link 9·1 Follow-Up

Have partners compare answers and resolve any differences.

---

1 Teaching the Lesson

▶ Math Message Follow-Up

 WHOLE-CLASS DISCUSSION

(*Math Journal 2*, p. 298; *Math Masters*, p. 260)

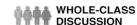 **Social Studies Link** Have volunteers plot the points for an outline map of the 48 contiguous U.S. states on a transparency of *Math Masters,* page 260.

Reinforce that, in an **ordered number pair,** the first **coordinate** locates the point along the horizontal axis, and the second coordinate locates the point along the vertical axis.

▶ Locating, Plotting, and Reading Number Pairs

 PARTNER ACTIVITY

(*Math Journal 2*, p. 298)

Have students complete journal page 298. Circulate and assist. When most students have completed the journal page, ask them to share any difficulties or curiosities they encountered.

Point out that coordinates can be located between consecutive whole numbers on the number line. For example, (7.5,5.5); (11,2.5); and (12.5,4) on the outline map.

 Ongoing Assessment: Recognizing Student Achievement

Journal page 298 Problems 2 and 3

Use **journal page 298, Problems 2 and 3** to assess students' abilities to plot ordered number pairs and to identify decimals on a number line. Students are making adequate progress if they correctly complete Problems 2 and 3.

[Number and Numeration Goal 1; Measurement and Reference Frames Goal 4]

Student Page

Date _____ Time _____

LESSON 9·2 Plotting a Map

1. **a.** Plot the following ordered number pairs on the grid:

   (21,14); (17,11); (17,13); (15,14); (2,16); (1,11); (2,8); (3,6); (7.5,5.5); (11,2.5); (12.5,4)

   b. Connect all the points in the same order in which they were plotted. Then connect (12.5,4) to (17.5,5) and (21.5,15.5) to (21,14). When you have finished, you should see an outline map of the continental United States.

   [grid with points labeled: Billings, Montana; Salt Lake City, Utah; Chicago, Illinois; Denver, Colorado; Atlanta, Georgia; Dallas, Texas; U.S.–Mexican Border]

   ★ Write the coordinates of each city.
   a. Chicago, Illinois (15 , 11)   b. Atlanta, Georgia (17 , 7)
   c. Dallas, Texas (12 , 6)   d. Denver, Colorado (7.5 , 9.5)

   ★ Plot each city on the grid and write the city name.
   a. Billings, Montana (7.5,13)   b. Salt Lake City, Utah (5.5,10.5)

4. The U.S.–Mexican border is shown by line segments from (3,6) to (7.5,5.5) and from (7.5,5.5) to (11,2.5). Write the border name on the grid.

Math Journal 2, p. 298

Date _____ Time _____

LESSON 9·2 Sailboat Graphs

1. **a.** Using the ordered number pairs listed in the column titled Original Sailboat in the table below, plot the ordered number pairs on the grid titled Original Sailboat on the next page.

   b. Connect the points in the same order that you plot them. You should see the outline of a sailboat.

2. Fill in the missing coordinates in the last three columns of the table. Use the rule given in each column to calculate the ordered number pairs.

Original Sailboat	New Sailboat 1 — Rule: Double each number of the original pair.	New Sailboat 2 — Rule: Double the first number of the original pair.	New Sailboat 3 — Rule: Double the second number of the original pair.
(8,1)	(16,2)	(16,1)	(8,2)
(5,1)	(10,2)	(10,1)	(5,2)
(5,7)	(10,14)	(10,7)	(5,14)
(1,2)	(2 , 4)	(2 , 2)	(1 , 4)
(5,1)	(10 , 2)	(10 , 1)	(5 , 2)
(0,1)	(0 , 2)	(0 , 1)	(0 , 2)
(2,0)	(4 , 0)	(4 , 0)	(2 , 0)
(7,0)	(14 , 0)	(14 , 0)	(7 , 0)
(8,1)	(16 , 2)	(16 , 1)	(8 , 2)

3. **a.** Plot the ordered number pairs for New Sailboat 1 on the next page. Connect the points in the same order that you plot them.

   b. Then plot the ordered number pairs for New Sailboat 2, and connect the points.

   c. Finally, plot the ordered number pairs for New Sailboat 3, and connect the points.

Math Journal 2, p. 296

Date _____ Time _____

LESSON 9·2 Sailboat Graphs *continued*

Original Sailboat

New Sailboat 1

New Sailboat 2

New Sailboat 3

Math Journal 2, p. 297

▶ **Plotting Ordered Number Pairs and Transforming Figures**

PARTNER ACTIVITY

PROBLEM SOLVING

(*Math Journal 2,* pp. 296 and 297)

Ask students to plot and connect the number pairs as described in Problem 1 on journal page 296. Verify that they have drawn the outline of a sailboat.

Discuss the rules and the examples in the table in Problem 2. Emphasize how to use the rules to create new ordered number pairs. Point out that one of the rules changes both coordinates, and that other rules change only one coordinate. Have students complete the table, and then plot the coordinates for three new sailboats, as described in Problem 3. Circulate and assist.

▶ **Discussing the Results of Operations on Number Pairs**

WHOLE-CLASS DISCUSSION

(*Math Journal 2,* pp. 296 and 297)

Ask students to describe the changes from the original sailboat to each of the new sailboats. Student responses might include the following:

▷ New Sailboat 1 is twice as high and twice as wide as the original sailboat—the sailboat stretched in both directions.

▷ New Sailboat 2 is twice as wide, but no higher than before—the sailboat stretched left and right, but not up and down.

▷ New Sailboat 3 is twice as high, but no wider than before—the sailboat stretched up and down, but not left and right.

Ask small groups to first compare angles in the new sailboats to angles in the original sailboat, and then compare the areas of the new sailboats to the area of the original sailboat. Students may choose to estimate or measure the angles. One approach for comparing areas would be to take a small part of the sailboat—for example, the boat minus the sail—and determine the area by counting squares.

When most groups have finished, ask volunteers to report the group findings. The angles remain the same for New Sailboat 1, but change for New Sailboats 2 and 3. The area doubles for New Sailboat 2; doubles for New Sailboat 3; and quadruples for New Sailboat 1.

Without drawing the new sailboats, ask students how they could use the rules stated in Problem 2 to predict how the angles and area of each new sailboat would change from those of the original sailboat. If both coordinates change, the angles will remain the same. If only one of the coordinates changes, the angles will change. If both coordinates are doubled (or halved) the area will be four times larger (or smaller). If only one of the coordinates is doubled (or halved), the area will be two times larger (or smaller).

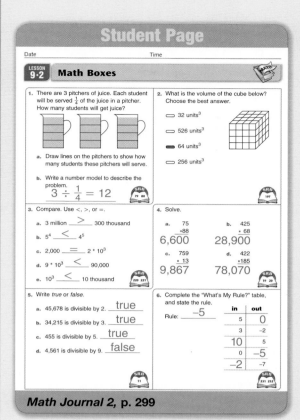

Date   Time

LESSON
9·2   **Math Boxes**

1. There are 3 pitchers of juice. Each student will be served $\frac{1}{4}$ of the juice in a pitcher. How many students will get juice?

   a. Draw lines on the pitchers to show how many students these pitchers will serve.

   b. Write a number model to describe the problem.
   $$3 \div \frac{1}{4} = 12$$

2. What is the volume of the cube below? Choose the best answer.

   ⬡ 32 units³
   ⬡ 526 units³
   ▬ 64 units³
   ⬡ 256 units³

3. Compare. Use <, >, or =.

   a. 3 million $>$ 300 thousand
   b. 5^4 $<$ 4^5
   c. 2,000 $=$ $2 * 10^3$
   d. $9 * 10^3$ $<$ 90,000
   e. 10^3 $<$ 10 thousand

4. Solve.

   a. 75
      *88
      6,600

   b. 425
      + 68
      28,900

   c. 759
      * 13
      9,867

   d. 422
      *185
      78,070

5. Write *true* or *false*.

   a. 45,678 is divisible by 2. true
   b. 34,215 is divisible by 3. true
   c. 455 is divisible by 5. true
   d. 4,561 is divisible by 9. false

6. Complete the "What's My Rule?" table, and state the rule.

   Rule: -5

in	out
5	0
3	−2
10	5
0	−5
−2	−7

Math Journal 2, p. 299

---

② Ongoing Learning & Practice

▶ Math Boxes 9·2
(*Math Journal 2,* p. 299)

INDEPENDENT ACTIVITY

 Mixed Practice Math Boxes in this lesson are paired with Math Boxes in Lesson 9-4. The skill in Problem 6 previews Unit 10 content.

 Writing/Reasoning Have students write a response to the following: *Explain the strategy and reasoning you would use to solve Problem 4c with the standard multiplication algorithm.* Answers vary.

 Writing/Reasoning Have students write a response to the following: *Explain your solution strategy for completing the table and finding the rule for Problem 6.* Sample answer: I looked for a pattern between the *in* column numbers and the *out* column numbers. Since $3 - 5 = -2$, I know that the rule is $- 5$.

▶ Study Link 9·2
(*Math Masters,* p. 257)

INDEPENDENT ACTIVITY

 Home Connection Students plot points to graph a triangle and a parallelogram on the first quadrant of a coordinate grid.

---

③ Differentiation Options

READINESS

SMALL-GROUP ACTIVITY

◑ 15–30 Min

▶ Locating Points on a Number Line

To explore locating decimals on a number line, have students plot points between whole numbers. Students draw, mark, and label a 5-inch line segment to show each inch mark from 0 to 5 inches. Then students plot a set of points on their line segments. They should estimate the approximate locations, place the points, and then check their placement with a ruler.

Suggestions: 2.5; 1.25; 3.75; 4.5; 1.5.

Name   Date   Time

STUDY LINK
9·2   **Plotting Figures on a Coordinate Grid**

Sample answers:
1. Plot three points, and make a triangle on the grid below. Label the points as *A*, *B*, and *C*. List the coordinates of the points you've drawn.

   A: (8 , 16)   B: (0 , 5)   C: (16 , 5)

2. Circle the name of the kind of triangle you drew.

   scalene   equilateral   (isosceles)

3. Plot four points, and make a parallelogram on the grid below. Label the points as *M*, *N*, *O*, and *P*. List the coordinates of the points you've drawn.

   M: (6 , 15)   N: (1 , 12)   O: (3 , 1)   P: (8 , 4)

4. Circle another name for the parallelogram you've drawn.

   (quadrangle)   rhombus   rectangle   square

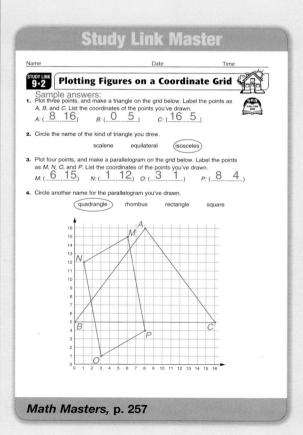

Math Masters, p. 257

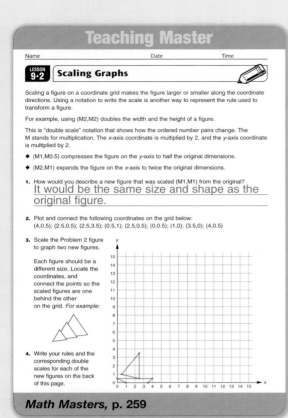

Math Masters, p. 259

Math Masters, p. 258

PARTNER ACTIVITY

15–30 Min

▶ Scaling Graphs

(*Math Masters*, p. 259)

To extend students' understanding of transforming figures on a coordinate grid, have them create rules to change given ordered number pairs. Partners graph the coordinates for given figures, create rules to enlarge the figure, and graph the new figures. They also write the rule and the corresponding "double scale" for each new figure.

When students are finished, discuss how they adjusted the coordinates so that the figures would be located one behind the other. Students will need to apply their rule to the coordinate values and then adjust the values to position the figures appropriately by increasing the *x* and *y* values to shift and raise the new figures.

NOTE Transformations that change the size of a new figure from the original are called *dilations,* and those that change the position of a new figure in relation to the original are called *translations.*

EXTRA PRACTICE

PARTNER ACTIVITY

15–30 Min

▶ Plotting Pictures

(*Math Masters*, p. 258)

Portfolio Ideas

Students draw a simple picture on a grid and list the point they plotted to make their drawing. They give their list of ordered pairs to a partner who reproduces the drawing by plotting and connecting the points on a blank grid.

ELL SUPPORT

PARTNER ACTIVITY

5–15 Min

▶ Differentiating Points Defined by Ordered Number Pairs

(*Math Masters*, p. 438)

To differentiate between the points defined by ordered number pairs that have the same numbers in reverse order, have students plot and label (6,2) and (2,6) on the first quadrant of a coordinate grid. Ask students to label the coordinate grid with the following terms: *horizontal axis, ordered number pair,* and *vertical axis.* Ask students to write a response to the following: *How would you explain to a friend that (6,2) and (2,6) have two different locations on the coordinate grid?* The position of the numbers in an ordered number pair are very important. The first number is the horizontal distance of the point from the verticle axis, and the second number is the vertical distance from the horizontal axis. The point at (6,2) is a different distance from the vertical and horizontal axes than the point at (2,6).

Planning Ahead

Students will study area in Lesson 9-4. Display full-size paper models of the most commonly used unit squares: 1 square inch, 1 square foot, 1 square yard, 1 square centimeter, and 1 square meter. These can be made from butcher paper, pages from the Class Data Pad, or newspapers. The square inch and square centimeter can be cut from *Math Masters,* pages 429 and 436. Label each square in two ways, for example—1 square inch and 1 in^2; 1 square meter and 1 m^2. Use the display to emphasize the relationships between the square units. For example, a square yard fits inside a square meter. A square yard is equal to 9 square feet, and a square foot is equal to 144 (12 * 12) square inches.

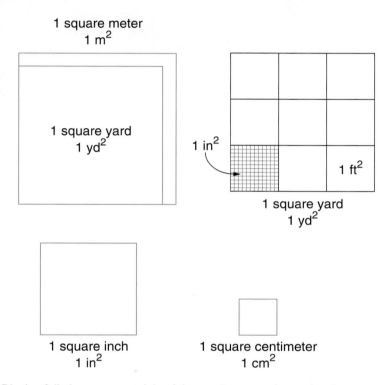

Display full-size paper models of the most commonly used unit squares.

9·3 Coordinate Graphs: Part 2

 Objective To reinforce plotting coordinates and the relationships between ordered number pairs and transformations of figures in a plane.

---

1 Teaching the Lesson

Key Concepts and Skills

• Plot points in three quadrants of a coordinate grid.
[Measurement and Reference Frames Goal 4]

• Construct congruent figures on a coordinate grid.
[Geometry Goal 2]

• Describe reflections and translations of plane figures.
[Geometry Goal 3]

Key Activities

Students plot ordered number pairs to graph figures in three quadrants of a coordinate grid. They investigate changing ordered number pairs to transform figures.

 Ongoing Assessment:
Recognizing Student Achievement
Use journal page 301.
[Measurement and Reference Frames Goal 4]

Key Vocabulary

opposite of a number ◆ translation ◆ reflection

Materials

Math Journal 2, pp. 300 and 301
Student Reference Book, pp. 158 and 384
Study Link 9·2
Class Data Pad (optional) ◆ straightedge ◆ calculator ◆ slate

2 Ongoing Learning & Practice

 Playing *Hidden Treasure*

Math Journal 2, p. 302
Student Reference Book, p. 319
Math Masters, p. 486
per partnership: 2 pencils, 1 red pencil or crayon
Students practice naming and plotting ordered number pairs in all four quadrants on a coordinate grid.

 Math Boxes 9·3

Math Journal 2, p. 303
Geometry Template or ruler ◆ compass
Students practice and maintain skills through Math Box problems.

Study Link 9·3

Math Masters, p. 261
Students practice and maintain skills through Study Link activities.

3 Differentiation Options

READINESS

Building a Coordinate Grid

Math Masters, p. 262
straightedge ◆ 4 metersticks ◆ masking tape ◆ markers
Students use metersticks to create four-quadrant coordinate grids and explore the ordered number pairs for points in each quadrant.

ENRICHMENT

Exploring the Line of Reflection

Math Masters, pp. 263 and 264
Students explore the line of reflection on a coordinate grid.

ELL SUPPORT

Defining Geometry Transformations

Students make posters to define and illustrate the terms *reflection* and *translation.*

Advance Preparation

For Part 2, make copies of *Math Masters,* page 486 to use as additional *Hidden Treasure* gameboards.
For the optional Readiness activity in Part 3, make and cut in half copies of *Math Masters,* page 262.

 Teacher's Reference Manual, **Grades 4–6** pp. 196–199, 249, 250

Getting Started

Math Message

The Divers Club and the Rock Climbers Club compete against each other by drawing cards that tell the depths for dives and the heights for climbs. Which of the distances below are for the divers and which are for the climbers?

−175 ft

70 ft

−200 ft

3,600 ft

Study Link 9·2 Follow-Up

Have partners compare their answers and resolve any differences.

1 Teaching the Lesson

Math Message Follow-Up

WHOLE-CLASS DISCUSSION

(*Student Reference Book,* p. 384)

Ask volunteers to share their solution strategies. Altitude is measured in relation to sea level (0 ft), so the negative numbers are for the divers and the positive numbers are for the climbers.

Refer students to *Student Reference Book,* page 384. Ask students to use the table to find the highest and lowest elevations in the United States. Mount McKinley, 20,320 ft and Death Valley, −282 ft Ask: *Would the Divers Club be able to dive in Death Valley?* no Explain that below sea level does not have to be underwater. Negative elevations represent the distance below sea level—on land or water.

Sea level is a reference position, much like zero on a thermometer or a number line, which separates positive and negative values. Numbers that are the same distance from the reference position in opposing directions are called opposites. The **opposite** of a positive number is a negative number, and the opposite of a negative number is a positive number. For example, the opposite of +7 is −7, and the opposite of −26 is +26 or 26.

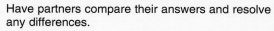

Student Page

American Tour

Highest and Lowest Elevations in the United States

State	Highest Point	Altitude (ft)	Lowest Point	Elevation (ft)
Alabama	Cheaha Mountain	2,405	Gulf of Mexico	Sea level
Alaska	Mount McKinley	20,320	Pacific Ocean	Sea level
Arizona	Humphreys Peak	12,633	Colorado River	70
Arkansas	Magazine Mountain	2,753	Ouachita River	55
California	Mount Whitney	14,494	Death Valley	−282
Colorado	Mount Elbert	14,433	Arikaree River	3,315
Connecticut	Mount Frissell	2,380	Long Island Sound	Sea level
Delaware	Ebright Road (New Castle Co)	448	Atlantic Ocean	Sea level
Florida	Sec. 30, T6N, R20W (Walton Co)¹	345	Atlantic Ocean	Sea level
Georgia	Brasstown Bald	4,784	Atlantic Ocean	Sea level
Hawaii	Mauna Kea	13,796	Pacific Ocean	Sea level
Idaho	Borah Peak	12,662	Snake River	710
Illinois	Charles Mound	1,235	Mississippi River	279
Indiana	Franklin Township (Wayne Co)	1,257	Ohio River	320
Iowa	Sec. 29, T100N, R41W (Osceola Co)¹	1,670	Mississippi River	480
Kansas	Mount Sunflower	4,039	Verdigris River	679
Kentucky	Black Mountain	4,139	Mississippi River	257
Louisiana	Driskill Mountain	535	New Orleans	−8
Maine	Mount Katahdin	5,267	Atlantic Ocean	Sea level
Maryland	Backbone Mountain	3,360	Atlantic Ocean	Sea level
Massachusetts	Mount Greylock	3,487	Atlantic Ocean	Sea level
Michigan	Mount Arvon	1,979	Lake Erie	571
Minnesota	Eagle Mountain	2,301	Lake Superior	600
Mississippi	Woodall Mountain	806	Gulf of Mexico	Sea level
Missouri	Taum Sauk Mountain	1,772	St. Francis River	230
Montana	Granite Peak	12,799	Kootenai River	1,800
Nebraska	Johnson Township (Kimball Co)	5,424	Missouri River	840
Nevada	Boundary Peak	13,143	Colorado River	479
New Hampshire	Mount Washington	6,288	Atlantic Ocean	Sea level
New Jersey	High Point	1,803	Atlantic Ocean	Sea level
New Mexico	Wheeler Peak	13,161	Red Bluff Reservoir	2,842
New York	Mount Marcy	5,344	Atlantic Ocean	Sea level
North Carolina	Mount Mitchell	6,684	Atlantic Ocean	Sea level
North Dakota	White Butte	3,506	Red River	750
Ohio	Campbell Hill	1,549	Ohio River	455
Oklahoma	Black Mesa	4,973	Little River	289
Oregon	Mount Hood	11,239	Pacific Ocean	Sea level
Pennsylvania	Mount Davis	3,213	Delaware River	Sea level
Rhode Island	Jerimoth Hill	812	Atlantic Ocean	Sea level
South Carolina	Sassafras Mountain	3,560	Atlantic Ocean	Sea level
South Dakota	Harney Peak	7,242	Big Stone Lake	966
Tennessee	Clingmans Dome	6,643	Mississippi River	178
Texas	Guadalupe Peak	8,749	Gulf of Mexico	Sea level
Utah	Kings Peak	13,528	Beaverdam Wash	2,000
Vermont	Mount Mansfield	4,393	Lake Champlain	95
Virginia	Mount Rogers	5,729	Atlantic Ocean	Sea level
Washington	Mount Rainier	14,410	Pacific Ocean	Sea level
West Virginia	Spruce Knob	4,861	Potomac River	240
Wisconsin	Timms Hill	1,951	Lake Michigan	579
Wyoming	Gannett Peak	13,804	Belle Fourche River	3,099

¹ Sec. means Section; T means Township; R means Range; N means North; and W means West.

Student Reference Book, p. 384

Date _____ Time _____

LESSON 9·3 **More Sailboat Graphs**

1. a. Using the ordered number pairs listed in the column titled Original Sailboat in the table below, plot the ordered number pairs on the grid on the next page.

   b. Connect the points in the same order that they were plotted. You should see the outline of a sailboat. Write *original* in the sail.

2. Fill in the missing coordinates in the last three columns of the table.
   Use the rule given in each column to calculate the ordered number pairs.

Original Sailboat	New Sailboat 1 Rule: Add 10 to the first number of the original pair.	New Sailboat 2 Rule: Change the first number of the original pair to the opposite number.	New Sailboat 3 Rule: Change the second number of the original pair to the opposite number.
(9,3)	(19,3)	(−9,3)	(9,−3)
(6,3)	(16,3)	(−6,3)	(6,−3)
(6,9)	(16,9)	(−6,9)	(6,−9)
(2,4)	(12, 4)	(−2, 4)	(2, −4)
(6,3)	(16, 3)	(−6, 3)	(6, −3)
(1,3)	(11, 3)	(−1, 3)	(1, −3)
(3,2)	(13, 2)	(−3, 2)	(3, −2)
(8,2)	(18, 2)	(−8, 2)	(8, −2)
(9,3)	(19, 3)	(−9, 3)	(9, −3)

3. a. Plot the ordered number pairs for New Sailboat 1 on the next page. Connect the points in the same order that you plot them. Write the number 1 in the sail.

   b. Then plot the ordered number pairs for New Sailboat 2 and connect the points. Write the number 2 in the sail.

   c. Finally, plot the ordered number pairs for New Sailboat 3 and connect the points. Write the number 3 in the sail.

Math Journal 2, p. 300

Date _____ Time _____

LESSON 9·3 **More Sailboat Graphs** *continued*

4. Use the following rule to create a new sailboat figure on the coordinate grid above:

   Rule: Add 10 to the second number of the original pair. Leave the first number unchanged.

   Try to plot the new coordinates without listing them. Write the number 4 in the sail.

Math Journal 2, p. 301

▶ Plotting Ordered Number Pairs and Transforming Figures

PARTNER ACTIVITY

ELL

PROBLEM SOLVING

(*Math Journal 2*, pp. 300 and 301)

Journal pages 300 and 301 are similar to the journal pages in Lesson 9-2. To support English language learners, explain that in that lesson, the transformations resulted in enlargements of the figure, making the figures bigger in one or two dimensions. In this lesson, the transformations result in *translations* and *reflections* of the figure.

Assign the journal pages. Remind students to connect the points in the same order that they were plotted. Circulate and assist.

Ongoing Assessment:
Recognizing Student Achievement

Journal Page 301

Use **journal page 301** to assess students' ability to plot points on a coordinate grid. Students are making adequate progress if they have correctly graphed New Sailboats 1 and 4.

[Measurement and Reference Frames Goal 4]

▶ Discussing Operations on Ordered Number Pairs

WHOLE-CLASS DISCUSSION

ELL

(*Math Journal 2*, pp. 300 and 301; *Student Reference Book*, p. 158)

Ask students to describe the changes from the original sailboat to the new sailboats. Student responses might include the following:

▷ New Sailboat 1 looks the same as the original, but has moved to the right.

▷ New Sailboat 2 looks the same size as the original, but seems to be moving in the opposite direction; it looks like it was flipped over toward the left.

▷ New Sailboat 3 looks like the reflection you would see in a mirror or in the water on a calm day.

▷ New Sailboat 4 looks the same as the original, but has moved up 10 units.

Explain that New Sailboats 1 and 4 are called **translations** of the original sailboat. New Sailboats 2 and 3 are called **reflections** of the original sailboat. To support English language learners, write these terms on the board or Class Data Pad along with examples.

To review *rotation,* have students read page 158 in the *Student Reference Book,* and then ask students to solve Check Your Understanding, Problem 2.

② Ongoing Learning & Practice

▶ Playing *Hidden Treasure*

PARTNER ACTIVITY

(*Math Journal 2*, p. 302; *Student Reference Book*, p. 319; *Math Masters*, p. 486)

Hidden Treasure was introduced in Lesson 9-1. The rules of the game are unchanged. However, the gameboard (*Math Journal 2*, page 302) now includes both positive and negative quadrants of the coordinate grid.

Circulate and assist. Pass out copies of *Math Masters*, page 486 if additional gameboards are needed.

▶ Math Boxes 9·3

INDEPENDENT ACTIVITY

(*Math Journal 2*, p. 303)

 Mixed Practice Math Boxes in this lesson are paired with Math Boxes in Lesson 9-1. The skill in Problem 5 previews Unit 10 content.

 Writing/Reasoning Have students write a response to the following: *Explain how you could determine the volume of the rectangular prism in Problem 3 by counting the unit cubes. Then write a number model for the formula you could use to find the volume.* Sample answers: I could count the number of unit cubes in the bottom layer first. There are 15 unit cubes in the bottom layer. The height is 3, so there are three layers of 15, so the volume is 45 units^3. The length is 5, the width is 3, and the height is 3. The formula is $V = l * w * h$. The number model is 45 units$^3 = 5 * 3 * 3$.

▶ Study Link 9·3

INDEPENDENT ACTIVITY

(*Math Masters*, p. 261)

 Home Connection Students plot points and their reflections on a grid.

③ Differentiation Options

READINESS

▶ Building a Coordinate Grid

SMALL-GROUP ACTIVITY

🕐 **5–15 Min**

(*Math Masters*, p. 262)

To provide a concrete model for the structure of coordinate grids, have students use metersticks to build a coordinate grid and analyze the signs of the coordinates in each quadrant.

Date   Time

LESSON 9·3   *Hidden Treasure* **Gameboards 2**

Each player uses Grids 1 and 2.

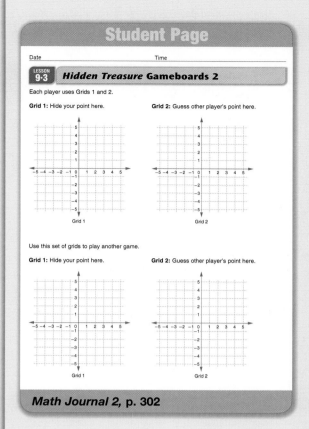

Grid 1: Hide your point here.   **Grid 2:** Guess other player's point here.

Use this set of grids to play another game.

Grid 1: Hide your point here.   **Grid 2:** Guess other player's point here.

Math Journal 2, p. 302

Date   Time

LESSON 9·3   **Math Boxes**

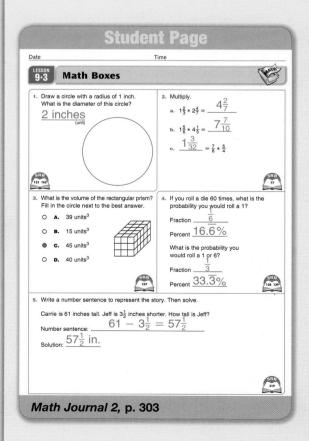

1. Draw a circle with a radius of 1 inch. What is the diameter of this circle?

2 inches (unit)

2. Multiply.
   a. $1\frac{2}{3} * 2\frac{4}{7} = $ __$4\frac{2}{7}$__
   b. $1\frac{5}{6} * 4\frac{1}{5} = $ __$7\frac{7}{10}$__
   c. __$1\frac{3}{32}$__ $= \frac{7}{8} * \frac{5}{4}$

3. What is the volume of the rectangular prism? Fill in the circle next to the best answer.
   ○ A. 39 units^3
   ○ B. 15 units^3
   ● C. 45 units^3
   ○ D. 40 units^3

4. If you roll a die 60 times, what is the probability you would roll a 1?
   Fraction __$\frac{1}{6}$__
   Percent __16.6%__
   What is the probability you would roll a 1 or 6?
   Fraction __$\frac{1}{3}$__
   Percent __33.3%__

5. Write a number sentence to represent the story. Then solve.
   Carrie is 61 inches tall. Jeff is $3\frac{1}{2}$ inches shorter. How tall is Jeff?
   Number sentence: __$61 - 3\frac{1}{2} = 57\frac{1}{2}$__
   Solution: __$57\frac{1}{2}$ in.__

Math Journal 2, p. 303

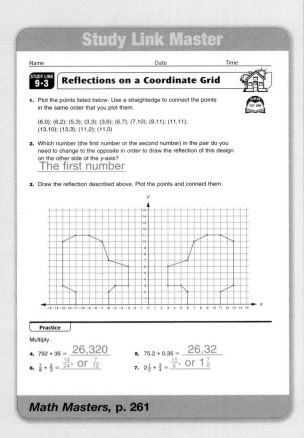
Have students use masking tape and markers to label two metersticks positive and two metersticks negative. Explain that the metersticks will represent the horizontal and vertical axes of a coordinate grid. Lay the sticks on the floor, and label the center as 0 and the ends as either x or y. Have students position themselves so that their view of the grid has the positive quadrant at the upper right.

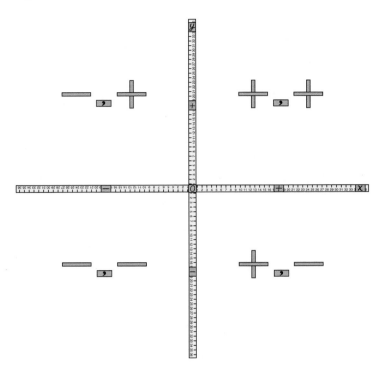

Ask students to compare the meterstick model with the rectangular coordinate grid on *Math Masters,* page 262 for similarities and differences. Expect students to remark that one difference is that the numbers on the negative parts of the model axes are upside down. Explain that for this activity they don't have to read the numbers but should pay attention to which sections are negative.

Ask a volunteer to step from one quadrant to the next until you say "Stop." Ask: *What types of numbers would name a point in this part of the grid?* Sample answers: 2 positive numbers; 2 negative numbers; 1 positive and 1 negative; or 1 negative and 1 positive Use masking tape to mark the quadrant accordingly. Repeat for all quadrants.

Remind students that the first coordinate is located on the horizontal axis (x-axis) and the second coordinate is located on the vertical axis (y-axis). Ask a volunteer to move into one quadrant on the model, and then ask a member of the group to give the coordinates of a point that could be in the same quadrant. If the student answers correctly, he or she gets to move onto the grid and call on someone else. Continue until each person in the group has had an opportunity to name coordinates.

Ask students to complete *Math Masters,* page 262.

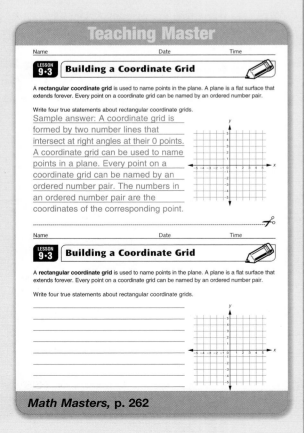

Exploring the Line of Reflection

(*Math Masters,* pp. 263 and 264)

To extend students' understanding of transformations on a coordinate grid, have them record coordinates and plot reflections for their first initials.

When students have completed both pages (*Math Masters,* pages 263 and 264), ask volunteers to share the rules they recorded on page 264. Discuss how they identified the rules and the relationship between matching points. Ask: *Is Image 3 a reflection of Image 1?* Yes *Why, or why not?* All the points in Image 3 and their matching points in Image 1 are the same distance from the line of symmetry. *Is Image 3 a reflection of the Preimage? Why or why not?* No. Image 3 and the Preimage do not share a line of reflection.

Defining Geometry Transformations

To provide language support for geometry transformations, have students illustrate the terms *reflection* and *translation*. Then have students write brief definitions in their own words. Combine the illustrations and definitions on posters for display during Unit 9.

Teaching Master

Name _____ Date _____ Time _____

LESSON 9·3 Exploring the Line of Reflection

In geometry, when a line divides a figure into two parts that look exactly alike, but are facing opposite directions, the figure is said to be symmetric. The line is called a *line of symmetry* for the figure. Think of the line of symmetry as a line of reflection. The left side and its reflection together form the figure.

The line of reflection may also be used to produce a new figure that has the same size and shape. The original figure is called the preimage and the new figure is called the image. The preimage and the image are reversed, and each point and its matching point are the same distance from the line of reflection.

Reflect the left side to get the figure shown on the right.   line of symmetry

1. Graph the initial of your first name on the coordinate grid below. Record the coordinates.

Answers vary.

Example:	Preimage Coordinates		Preimage Coordinates
	(3,1)		
	(1,1)		
	(1,8)		
	(3,8)		
	(7,3)		
	(7,8)		
	(9,8)		
	(9,1)		
	(7,1)		
	(3,6)		

2. Follow the instructions on *Math Masters,* page 264 to graph reflections of your initial.

***Math Masters,* p. 263**

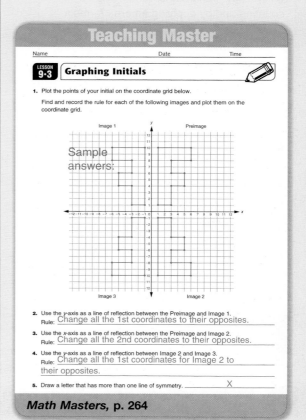

Teaching Master

Name _____ Date _____ Time _____

LESSON 9·3 Graphing Initials

1. Plot the points of your initial on the coordinate grid below.

Find and record the rule for each of the following images and plot them on the coordinate grid.

Image 1   Preimage

Sample answers:

Image 3   Image 2

2. Use the *y*-axis as a line of reflection between the Preimage and Image 1.
   Rule: Change all the 1st coordinates to their opposites.

3. Use the *x*-axis as a line of reflection between the Preimage and Image 2.
   Rule: Change all the 2nd coordinates to their opposites.

4. Use the *y*-axis as a line of reflection between Image 2 and Image 3.
   Rule: Change all the 1st coordinates for Image 2 to their opposites.

5. Draw a letter that has more than one line of symmetry. _____ X

***Math Masters,* p. 264**

9·4 Areas of Rectangles

 Objective To reinforce students' understanding of area concepts and units of area.

Technology Resources www.everydaymathonline.com

 ePresentations   eToolkit   Algorithms Practice   EM Facts Workshop Game™   Family Letters   Assessment Management   Common Core State Standards   Curriculum Focal Points   Interactive Teacher's Lesson Guide

---

1 Teaching the Lesson

Key Concepts and Skills

- Multiply fractions and mixed numbers to find the area of a rectangle.
  [Operations and Computation Goal 5]

- Use a formula to calculate the areas of rectangles.
  [Measurement and Reference Frames Goal 2]

- Compare inch and centimeter measures for length and area.
  [Measurement and Reference Frames Goal 3]

Key Activities

Students review area concepts and the names and notations for common area units. They find areas of rectangles by counting and by applying an area formula.

 Ongoing Assessment:
Informing Instruction See page 725.

 Ongoing Assessment:
Recognizing Student Achievement
Use an Exit Slip (*Math Masters,* page 414). [Measurement and Reference Frames Goal 2]

Key Vocabulary

area ◆ square units ◆ base ◆ height ◆ formula ◆ variable

Materials

Math Journal 2, pp. 304 and 305
Student Reference Book, p. 188
Study Link 9·3 ◆ Math Masters, p. 414
transparency of *Math Masters,* p. 436 ◆ Class Data Pad ◆ inch ruler ◆ slate ◆ roll of paper towels, wax paper, or aluminum foil (optional)

2 Ongoing Learning & Practice

Fraction Division Review

Math Journal 2, p. 306
Student Reference Book, pp. 80–80B
Students use visual models and number stories to solve fraction problems.

 Math Boxes 9·4

Math Journal 2, p. 307
Students practice and maintain skills through Math Box problems.

 Study Link 9·4

Math Masters, p. 265
Students practice and maintain skills through Study Link activities.

3 Differentiation Options

READINESS

Comparing Perimeter and Area

Math Masters, p. 266
per partnership: 2 six-sided dice, 36 centimeter cubes
Students use centimeter grids to compare the perimeters and areas of rectangles.

ENRICHMENT

Comparing Perimeter and Area for Irregular Figures

Math Masters, pp. 267 and 436
3 different-colored pencils or markers ◆ scissors
Students compare the perimeters and areas of irregular polygons.

EXTRA PRACTICE

5-Minute Math

5-Minute Math™, p. 212
Students calculate the areas of rectangles.

EXTRA PRACTICE

Area: Tiling and Using a Formula

Math Masters, pp. 293A and 436
Students find the areas of rectangles with fractional units by tiling and using a formula.

ELL SUPPORT

Building a Math Word Bank

Differentiation Handbook, p. 142
Students define and illustrate the terms *length, height, base,* and *width.*

Advance Preparation

For Part 1, display a set of unit squares. (*See Planning Ahead, Lesson 9-2.*) Use a roll of paper or foil to demonstrate carpet rolls for *Math Journal 2,* page 305, Problem 2.

 Teacher's Reference Manual, **Grades 4–6** pp. 220–222, 233, 234, 236

Getting Started

Mental Math and Reflexes

Have students write fractions as equivalent decimals and percents. *Suggestions:*

○●○○ $\frac{2}{3}$ $0.\overline{66}$; $66\frac{2}{3}\%$

$\frac{4}{5}$ 0.8; 80%

○○●○ $\frac{8}{25}$ 0.32; 32%

$\frac{19}{20}$ 0.95; 95%

○○○● $\frac{24}{50}$ 0.48; 48%

$\frac{3}{8}$ 0.375; 37.5%

Math Message

Read page 188 of the Student Reference Book, *and write two important facts about area.*

Study Link 9·3 Follow-Up

Have partners compare answers and resolve any differences.

---

1 Teaching the Lesson

▶ Math Message Follow-Up

 **WHOLE-CLASS DISCUSSION**

(*Student Reference Book*, p. 188)

Ask volunteers to share what they wrote about area. Use their responses and the display of common units of area to review basic area concepts. Emphasize the following points:

▷ **Area** is a measure of the surface, or region, inside a closed boundary. It is the number of whole and partial unit squares needed to cover the region without gaps or overlaps.

> **NOTE** It is more precise to talk about the area of a rectangular region, the area of a triangular region, and so on. However, it is customary to refer to area in terms of the figure that is the boundary: the area of a rectangle, the area of a triangle, and so on.

▷ Area is measured in **square units.** There are many units to choose from, and some choices make more sense than others.

Call students' attention to the classroom display of unit squares and to alternative ways of writing the units: *square inch, sq in.,* or *in^2; square meter, sq m,* or *m^2;* and so on.

Ask students to share the relationships they observe among the units—for example, a square meter is larger than a square yard. There are 9 square feet in a square yard and 144 square inches in a square foot. A square inch is larger than a square centimeter.

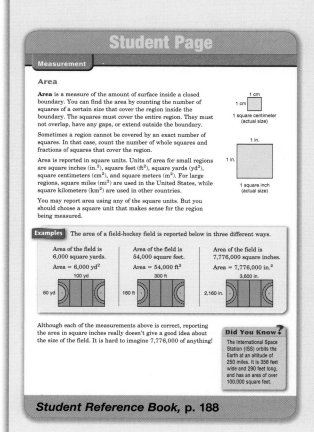

Student Page

Measurement

Area

Area is a measure of the amount of surface inside a closed boundary. You can find the area by counting the number of squares of a certain size that cover the region inside the boundary. The squares must cover the entire region. They must not overlap, have any gaps, or extend outside the boundary.

Sometimes a region cannot be covered by an exact number of squares. In that case, count the number of whole squares and fractions of squares that cover the region.

Area is reported in square units. Units of area for small regions are square inches (in.²), square feet (ft²), square yards (yd²), square centimeters (cm²), and square meters (m²). For large regions, square miles (mi²) are used in the United States, while square kilometers (km²) are used in other countries.

You may report area using any of the square units. But you should choose a square unit that makes sense for the region being measured.

Examples The area of a field-hockey field is reported below in three different ways.

Area of the field is 6,000 square yards.	Area of the field is 54,000 square feet.	Area of the field is 7,776,000 square inches.
Area = 6,000 yd²	Area = 54,000 ft²	Area = 7,776,000 in.²

Although each of the measurements above is correct, reporting the area in square inches really doesn't give a good idea about the size of the field. It is hard to imagine 7,776,000 of anything!

Did You Know?
The International Space Station (ISS) orbits the Earth at an altitude of 250 miles. It is 356 feet wide and 290 feet long, and has an area of over 100,000 square feet.

Student Reference Book, p. 188

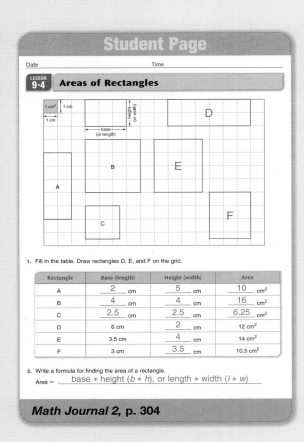

Date _____ Time _____

1. Fill in the table. Draw rectangles D, E, and F on the grid.

Rectangle	Base (length)	Height (width)	Area
A	2 cm	5 cm	10 cm²
B	4 cm	4 cm	16 cm²
C	2.5 cm	2.5 cm	6.25 cm²
D	6 cm	2 cm	12 cm²
E	3.5 cm	4 cm	14 cm²
F	3 cm	3.5 cm	10.5 cm²

2. Write a formula for finding the area of a rectangle.

Area = ___base * height (b * h), or length * width (l * w)___

Math Journal 2, p. 304

▶ # Finding the Area of a Rectangle

(*Math Journal 2*, p. 304)

Ask volunteers to define the terms **base** and **height.** The term *base* is often used to mean both a side of a figure and the length of that side. The *height* of a rectangle is the length of a side adjacent to the base.

Ask students to decide upon the phrasing of a common definition for these vocabulary terms. Record the student definitions on the Class Data Pad.

Ask a volunteer to draw a rectangle on the board and label the base and height.

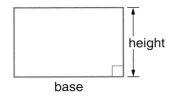

In *Fourth Grade Everyday Mathematics,* students found the area of a rectangle by counting unit squares. Then they developed a formula for finding the area of a rectangle. Expect that students might use either method—formula or counting squares—to find the areas of the rectangles on journal page 304.

With the counting method, some rectangles enclose partial grid squares, and students must count and add the full and partial squares to find areas. For example, rectangle C encloses 4 full squares (4 cm²), 4 half-squares ($4 * \frac{1}{2} = 2$ cm²), and 1 quarter-square ($\frac{1}{4}$ cm²). Its total area is $4 + 2 + \frac{1}{4} = 6\frac{1}{4}$ cm².

4 full squares	4 cm²
4 half-squares	2 cm² Each half-square has an area of $\frac{1}{2}$ cm².
+1 quarter-square	$\frac{1}{4}$ cm² The quarter-square is $\frac{1}{2}$ cm long and $\frac{1}{2}$ cm wide.
total area	$6\frac{1}{4}$ cm²

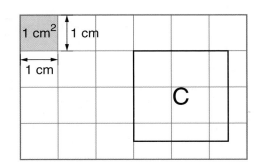

Assign journal page 304, Problem 1. Circulate and assist.

Discussing Formulas for the Area of a Rectangle

WHOLE-CLASS DISCUSSION

(*Math Journal 2,* p. 304; *Math Masters,* p. 436)

Algebraic Thinking Ask volunteers to give the dimensions of rectangles A–F as other volunteers draw the rectangles on a transparency of *Math Masters,* page 436.

Ask: *What do you notice about the relationship between the base and height and the actual area of each figure?* The base multiplied by the height is equal to the area.

Reinforce this rule:

> If the length of the base and the height of a rectangle are known, the area can be found by multiplying the length of the base by the height.

Such a rule is called a **formula.** The formula can be written in abbreviated form as:

$$A = b * h,$$

where A stands for the area, b stands for the length of the base, and h stands for the height. Ask students to complete Problem 2 on journal page 304. Remind students that letters used in this way are called **variables.** Add the abbreviated formula to the definitions on the Class Data Pad, and have students write the abbreviated formula after their answers for Problem 2 on journal page 304.

Refer students to the rectangles drawn on the transparency. Have students apply the formula for the rectangles in Problem 1. Ask volunteers to record a number model for the area of each rectangle on the transparency. For example, 2 cm * 5 cm = 10 cm². Have students check their total count of the squares with the product from the number model. For rectangles C and E, ask students to think about the decimals as fractions ($2\frac{1}{2}$ cm * $2\frac{1}{2}$ cm = $6\frac{1}{4}$ cm², and 4 cm * $3\frac{1}{2}$ cm = 14 cm²).

Ask partners to estimate, in inches, the length of the sides of the rectangles on journal page 304. Then have students measure the sides of rectangle C using their inch rulers. (Each side of rectangle C is about 1 inch long.) Ask students what the area of rectangle C is when the unit is inches. 1 square inch Point out that there are about 2.5, or $2\frac{1}{2}$ centimeters in 1 inch, and about 6.25, or $6\frac{1}{4}$ square centimeters in 1 square inch.

Applying the Area Formulas

INDEPENDENT ACTIVITY

PROBLEM SOLVING

(*Math Journal 2,* p. 305)

Have students complete journal page 305. Circulate and assist.

NOTE An alternative formula for the area of a rectangle is $A = l * w$, where l stands for the length and w stands for the width of the rectangle. Students are familiar with both versions of the formula from *Fourth Grade Everyday Mathematics.*

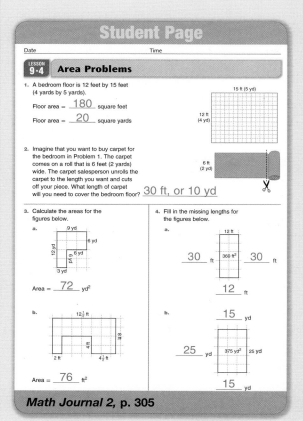

Student Page

Math Journal 2, p. 305

Student Page

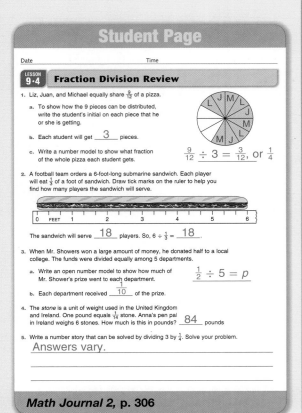

Date _____ Time _____

LESSON 9·4 **Fraction Division Review**

1. Liz, Juan, and Michael equally share $\frac{9}{12}$ of a pizza.

   a. To show how the 9 pieces can be distributed, write the student's initial on each piece that he or she is getting.

   b. Each student will get __3__ pieces.

   c. Write a number model to show what fraction of the whole pizza each student gets.

   $\frac{9}{12} \div 3 = \frac{3}{12}$, or $\frac{1}{4}$

2. A football team orders a 6-foot-long submarine sandwich. Each player will eat $\frac{1}{3}$ of a foot of sandwich. Draw tick marks on the ruler to help you find how many players the sandwich will serve.

   The sandwich will serve __18__ players. So, $6 \div \frac{1}{3} =$ __18__.

3. When Mr. Showers won a large amount of money, he donated half to a local college. The funds were divided equally among 5 departments.

   a. Write an open number model to show how much of Mr. Shower's prize went to each department.

   $\frac{1}{2} \div 5 = p$

   b. Each department received __$\frac{1}{10}$__ of the prize.

4. The *stone* is a unit of weight used in the United Kingdom and Ireland. One pound equals $\frac{1}{14}$ stone. Anna's pen pal in Ireland weighs 6 stones. How much is this in pounds? __84__ pounds

5. Write a number story that can be solved by dividing 3 by $\frac{1}{4}$. Solve your problem.

   Answers vary.

Math Journal 2, p. 306

Student Page

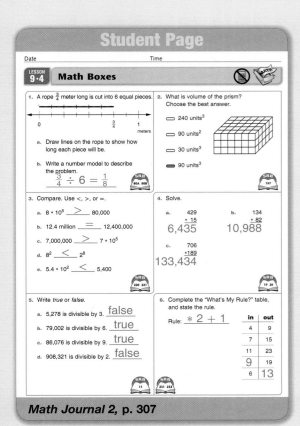

Date _____ Time _____

LESSON 9·4 **Math Boxes**

1. A rope $\frac{3}{4}$ meter long is cut into 6 equal pieces.

   a. Draw lines on the rope to show how long each piece is.

   b. Write a number model to describe the problem.

   $\frac{3}{4} \div 6 = \frac{1}{8}$

2. What is volume of the prism? Choose the best answer.

   ⬜ 240 units³
   ⬜ 90 units²
   ⬜ 30 units³
   ⬛ 90 units³

3. Compare. Use <, >, or =.

   a. $8 * 10^5$ __>__ 80,000

   b. 12.4 million __=__ 12,400,000

   c. 7,000,000 __>__ $7 * 10^5$

   d. 8^2 __<__ 2^8

   e. $5.4 * 10^2$ __<__ 5,400

4. Solve.

   a. 429 * 15 = **6,435**

   b. 134 * 82 = **10,988**

   c. 706 * 189 = **133,434**

5. Write *true* or *false*.

   a. 5,278 is divisible by 3. __false__

   b. 79,002 is divisible by 6. __true__

   c. 86,076 is divisible by 9. __true__

   d. 908,321 is divisible by 2. __false__

6. Complete the "What's My Rule?" table, and state the rule.

   Rule: $* 2 + 1$

in	out
4	9
7	15
11	23
9	19
6	13

Math Journal 2, p. 307

★ Ongoing Assessment: Informing Instruction

Watch for students who hesitate with Problem 2. Ask: *Which unit makes more sense to work with, feet or yards?* yards Refer students to Problem 1 and ask how many yards of carpet are needed. 20 square yards Illustrate Problem 2 using a roll of paper towels, waxed paper, or aluminum foil to demonstrate how a piece of carpet is cut from a roll. As the "carpet" unrolls, the area increases. For example, in Problem 2, each foot unrolled adds an additional 6 square feet or 2 square yards. As you unroll the model, have students shade the grid in Problem 1 to show how much floor is covered. Prompt students to tell you where to cut the model.

When most students have completed the journal page, ask volunteers to share their solution strategies. Ask questions like the following:

● In Problem 2, how will you cut the carpet to make it fit the bedroom? If students determine that they will need a piece of carpet 30 feet or 10 yards long, they will need to cut it in half to fit the bedroom. Each of the two pieces will be 2 yards by 5 yards.

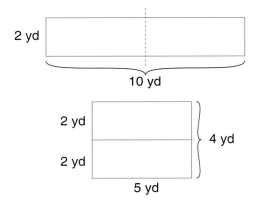

● In Problem 4, how did you find the missing lengths? Encourage students to use multiplication/division relationships and open number sentences. For example, $360 \div 12 = h$, or $25 * b = 375$.

★ Ongoing Assessment: Recognizing Student Achievement

Exit Slip ★

Use an **Exit Slip** (*Math Masters,* page 414) to assess students' ability to calculate area. Have students write a response to the following: *Explain how you found the area for the figure in Problem 3b on journal page 305.* Students are making adequate progress if they multiply the side lengths to find the areas of the rectangles in order to find the total area.

[Measurement and Reference Frames Goal 2]

② Ongoing Learning & Practice

▶ ## Fraction Division Review

PARTNER ACTIVITY

(*Math Journal 2*, p. 306; *Student Reference Book*, pp. 80–80B)

Have students review information about fraction division problems on pages 80–80B of the *Student Reference Book*. Discuss the use of visual models and number stories. Then have students complete the journal page.

▶ ## Math Boxes 9·4

INDEPENDENT ACTIVITY

(*Math Journal 2*, p. 307)

 Mixed Practice Math Boxes in this lesson are paired with Math Boxes in Lesson 9-2. The skill in Problem 6 previews Unit 10 content.

 Writing/Reasoning Have students write a response to the following: *Explain how you could determine the volume of the rectangular prism in Problem 2 by counting the unit cubes. Then write a number model for the formula you could use to find the volume.* Sample answers: I could count the number of unit cubes in the bottom layer first. The width is 6 and the length of the base is 5. So there are 30 unit cubes in the bottom layer. The height is 3, so there are three layers of 30. The volume is 90 units^3. The formula is $B * h = V$. The number model is $(5 * 6) * 3 = 90$ units^3.

▶ ## Study Link 9·4

INDEPENDENT ACTIVITY

(*Math Masters*, p. 265)

 Home Connection Students solve area problems.

③ Differentiation Options

READINESS

▶ ## Comparing Perimeter and Area

PARTNER ACTIVITY

5–15 Min

(*Math Masters*, p. 266)

To support students' understanding of perimeter and area, have partners roll 2 six-sided dice to determine the dimensions of a rectangle. They draw a rectangle with those dimensions and find the perimeter and area of the rectangle. Partners then find other rectangles with the same area, but different perimeters. They repeat this process until the table on page 266 is completed.

Discuss what conclusions can be drawn from the table. Sample answers: Different perimeters can have the same area; the dimensions are factor pairs for the area.

Name   Date   Time

STUDY LINK 9·4   More Area Problems

1. Rashid can paint 2 square feet of fence in 10 minutes. Fill in the missing parts to tell how long it will take him to paint a fence that is 6 feet high by 25 feet long. Rashid will be able to paint ___150 sq ft___ of fence in __12 hr 30 min__.
   (area)   (hours/minutes)

2. Regina wants to cover one wall of her room with wallpaper. The wall is 9 feet high and 15 feet wide. There is a doorway in the wall that is 3 feet wide and 7 feet tall. How many square feet of wallpaper will she need to buy?
   ___114 square feet___

Calculate the areas for the figures below.

Area = ___80___ yd²   Area = ___33___ ft²

Fill in the missing lengths for the figures below.

Math Masters, p. 265

Name   Date   Time

LESSON 9·4   Comparing Perimeter and Area

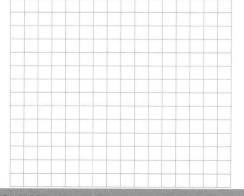

◆ Roll 2 six-sided dice. The numbers on top are the lengths of 2 sides of a rectangle.
◆ Draw the rectangle in the grid below.
◆ Record the perimeter and the area of the rectangle in the table.
◆ Use centimeter cubes to find other rectangles that have the same area, but different perimeters. Draw the rectangles and record their perimeters and areas in the table.
◆ Repeat until you have filled the table. You might need to roll the dice several times.

Rectangle	Perimeter	Area
A	Answers vary.	
B		
C		
D		
E		
F		

Math Masters, p. 266

PARTNER ACTIVITY   15–30 Min

▶ Comparing Perimeter and Area for Irregular Figures

(*Math Masters,* pp. 267 and 436)

To apply students' understanding of perimeter and area to irregular figures, have partners divide rectangles and compare the relationship between perimeter and area. When students have finished, have them share the parts they cut from their rectangles and discuss questions such as the following:

- Can you use the area of a figure to predict the perimeter of that figure? No

- Can you use the perimeter of a figure to predict the area of that figure? No

Guide students to conclude that perimeter and area are independent measures.

SMALL-GROUP ACTIVITY   5–15 Min

▶ *5-Minute Math*

To offer students more experience with calculating the area of rectangles, see *5-Minute Math,* page 212.

PARTNER ACTIVITY   15–30 Min

▶ Area: Tiling and Using a Formula

(*Math Masters,* pp. 293A and 436)

To find the area, students use grid paper to tile rectangles that have fractional side lengths. They also use the formula for the area of a rectangle to show that both methods produce the same result.

SMALL-GROUP ACTIVITY   5–15 Min

▶ Building a Math Word Bank

(*Differentiation Handbook,* p. 142)

To provide language support for area, have students use the Word Bank Template found on *Differentiation Handbook,* page 142. Ask students to write the terms *length, height, base,* and *width;* draw pictures relating to each term; and write other related words. See the *Differentiation Handbook* for more information.

9·5 The Rectangle Method for Finding Area

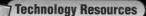

Objective To introduce the rectangle method for finding areas of polygons.

Technology Resources www.everydaymathonline.com

ePresentations

eToolkit

Algorithms Practice

EM Facts Workshop Game™

Family Letters

Assessment Management

Common Core State Standards

Curriculum Focal Points

Interactive Teacher's Lesson Guide

---

1 Teaching the Lesson

Key Concepts and Skills

- Use polygonal properties to support strategies for finding the areas of polygons.
[Measurement and Reference Frames Goal 2]

- Describe relationships between U.S. customary and metric square units.
[Measurement and Reference Frames Goal 3]

Key Activities

Students identify personal references for square units. They use a rectangle method to find the areas of triangles and parallelograms.

Key Vocabulary

personal references ◆ rectangle method

Materials

Math Journal 2, pp. 308–310
Student Reference Book, pp. 190 and 191
Study Link 9·4
transparency of *Math Masters,* p. 436 ◆ slate

2 Ongoing Learning & Practice

Playing *Frac-Tac-Toe*

Student Reference Book, pp. 309–311
Math Masters, pp. 472–484
per partnership: 4 each of number cards 0–10 (from the Everything Math Deck, if available), 2 different-colored counters or pennies
Students practice converting among fractions, decimals, and percents.

Math Boxes 9·5

Math Journal 2, p. 311
Geometry Template or ruler
Students practice and maintain skills through Math Box problems.

Ongoing Assessment:
Recognizing Student Achievement
Use Math Boxes, Problem 2.
[Geometry Goal 2]

Study Link 9·5

Math Masters, p. 268
Students practice and maintain skills through Study Link activities.

3 Differentiation Options

READINESS

Building Rectangles

per partnership: construction paper, scissors, 4 sheets of unlined paper
Students construct rectangles by arranging triangles.

EXTRA PRACTICE

Reading *Spaghetti and Meatballs for All*

Math Masters, p. 436
Students investigate perimeter and area relationships by completing an activity from the book.

Advance Preparation

For Part 1, assign small groups for the Math Message activity.

For the optional Readiness activity in Part 3, obtain the book *Spaghetti and Meatballs for All* by Marilyn Burns (Scholastic, 1997).

 Teacher's Reference Manual, **Grades 4–6** pp. 214–218, 220, 221, 233, 234, 236

Getting Started

Mental Math and Reflexes

Have students practice solving extended multiplication facts.
Suggestions:

●○○ 5 [80s] = ? 400   ●●○ 50 [80s] = ? 4,000   ●●● 700 [60s] = ? 42,000

7 [60s] = ? 420   70 [60s] = ? 4,200   500 [80s] = ? 40,000

9 [40s] = ? 360   90 [40s] = ? 3,600   900 [40s] = ? 36,000

Math Message

Work with your small group to read and complete journal page 308.

Study Link 9·4 Follow-Up

Have partners compare answers and resolve any differences.

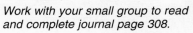

1 Teaching the Lesson

▶ ## Math Message Follow-Up

 WHOLE-CLASS DISCUSSION

(*Math Journal 2,* p. 308)

Ask groups to share their **personal references** for the five square units. Some may mention the same object as a personal reference for both 1 square yard and 1 square meter. This is reasonable; 1 meter is only about 10% longer than 1 yard, and 1 square meter is only about 20% larger than 1 square yard.

▶ ## Finding the Area of a Nonrectangular Figure

 PARTNER ACTIVITY

(*Math Journal 2,* p. 309)

Read the text at the top of journal page 309 as a class. Verify that students understand the assignment and then ask partners to complete the journal page. As you circulate and assist, encourage students to develop their own strategies for finding the area of a nonrectangular figure. Use questions to remind students of the properties of the figures and the meaning of area. For example, ask whether there is a relationship between the length of the sides of a triangle and the length of the sides of a rectangle.

▶ ## Introducing the Rectangle Method for Finding Area

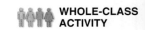 **WHOLE-CLASS ACTIVITY**

(*Math Journal 2,* p. 309; *Student Reference Book,* pp. 190 and 191; *Math Masters,* p. 436)

Ask students to share their strategies for finding the area of the figures on journal page 309, and survey students for any partial solution strategies or strategies they tried that were not successful. Relate student responses, as applicable, to the **rectangle method** for finding area.

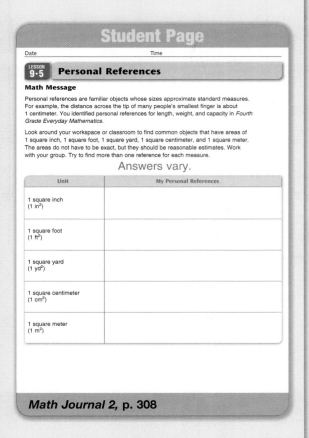

Math Journal 2, p. 308

The two most frequently used strategies to implement the rectangle method are described on pages 190 and 191 of the *Student Reference Book*. Have partners study the examples on these pages. Then demonstrate each strategy on a transparency of the centimeter grid on *Math Masters*, page 436.

Strategy 1: Add the parts.

Explain that the easiest application of the method is to find the area of a right triangle because the formed rectangle will be divided into two congruent triangles. The area of one of these triangles is one-half the area of the rectangle.

With triangle *ABC*, it is possible to split the triangle into two parts that are right triangles. Demonstrate by shading each part differently and indicate the right angle. The goal is to find the areas of the two parts and to add them to get the total area of the figure. (*See Figure 1.*)

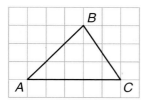 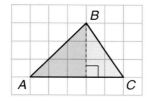

Figure 1

Draw a rectangle around the left part of the figure. The area of this rectangle is 9 square units. The shaded region is $\frac{1}{2}$ of the rectangular region, so its area is $4\frac{1}{2}$ square units. (*See Figure 2.*)

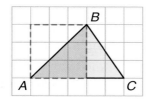

Figure 2

Draw a rectangle around the right part of the figure. The area of this rectangle is 6 square units. The shaded region is $\frac{1}{2}$ of the rectangular region, so its area is 3 square units. (*See Figure 3.*)

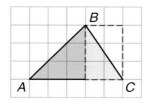

Figure 3

Since $4\frac{1}{2} + 3 = 7\frac{1}{2}$, the area of triangle *ABC* is $7\frac{1}{2}$ square units.

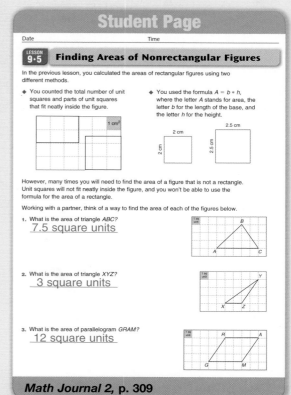

Strategy 2: Subtract the excess.

Some triangles cannot be split into two parts that are right triangles, as is the case with triangle *XYZ*. Now the goal is to enclose the entire figure within a rectangle, find the area of the interior parts of the rectangle that are not in the original figure, and subtract them from the area of the rectangle. The area remaining will be the area of the original figure.

Demonstrate this approach with triangle *XYZ*. Shade the interior parts that are not part of the original figure. (*See Figure 4.*)

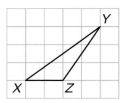 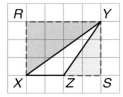

Figure 4

The area of rectangle *XRYS* is 12 square units. The blue-shaded region is a right triangle that is $\frac{1}{2}$ of the rectangular region, so its area is 6 square units. (*See Figure 5.*)

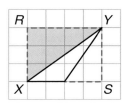

Figure 5

Draw a rectangle around the small, yellow-shaded triangular region. The area of the rectangle is 6 square units. The shaded region is again a right triangle that is $\frac{1}{2}$ of the rectangular region, so its area is 3 square units. (*See Figure 6.*)

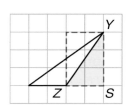

Figure 6

Because the area of the entire rectangle is 12 square units, and the combined areas of the two shaded triangular regions is 9 square units, the area of triangle *XYZ* is $12 - (6 + 3) = 3$ square units.

Draw a parallelogram on the board. Ask volunteers to show how they would apply the subtract-the-excess strategy to parallelograms.

Adjusting the Activity

Have students describe a right triangle, draw three different right triangles, and then use dotted lines to enclose each triangle within a rectangle.

AUDITORY ◆ KINESTHETIC ◆ TACTILE ◆ VISUAL

Using the Rectangle Method for Triangles and Parallelograms

(*Math Journal 2*, p. 310)

PARTNER ACTIVITY

PROBLEM SOLVING

Ask partners to complete journal page 310. Circulate and assist.

When most students have completed the journal page, have volunteers share their solution strategies.

2 Ongoing Learning & Practice

Playing *Frac-Tac-Toe*

PARTNER ACTIVITY

(*Student Reference Book*, pp. 309–311;
Math Masters, pp. 472–484)

Students practice converting among fractions, decimals, and percents by playing their favorite version of *Frac-Tac-Toe*.

Math Boxes 9·5

INDEPENDENT ACTIVITY

(*Math Journal 2*, p. 311)

Mixed Practice Math Boxes in this lesson are paired with Math Boxes in Lesson 9-7. The skill in Problem 5 previews Unit 10 content.

Writing/Reasoning Have students respond to the following: *In Problem 3c, find the equivalent measure in kilometers (km) and millimeters (mm). In Problem 3e, find the equivalent measure in meters (m) and kilometers (km). Explain what information you needed to make these conversions.* Problem 3c: 1 meter = 0.001 km = 1,000 mm. Problem 3e: 16 mm = 0.016 m = 0.000016 km. Sample answer: I needed to know how many millimeters are in a meter and how many meters are in a kilometer.

Ongoing Assessment:
Recognizing Student Achievement

Math Boxes Problem 2

Use **Math Boxes, Problem 2** to assess students' understanding of congruency. Students are making adequate progress if the drawn line segment and their written explanations show that congruent line segments have the same length.

[Geometry Goal 2]

Study Link 9·5

INDEPENDENT ACTIVITY

(*Math Masters*, p. 268)

Home Connection Students find the area of nonrectangular regions using the rectangle method.

Date _____ Time _____

LESSON 9·5 Math Boxes

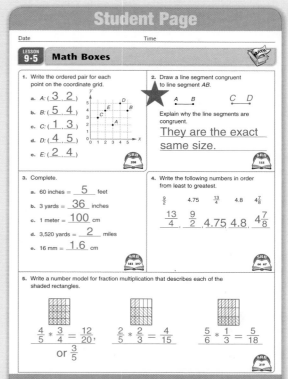

1. Write the ordered pair for each point on the coordinate grid.
   a. A: (3 , 2)
   b. B: (5 , 4)
   c. C: (1 , 3)
   d. D: (4 , 5)
   e. E: (2 , 4)

2. Draw a line segment congruent to line segment *AB*.

   A B   C D

   Explain why the line segments are congruent.
   They are the exact same size.

3. Complete.
   a. 60 inches = __5__ feet
   b. 3 yards = __36__ inches
   c. 1 meter = __100__ cm
   d. 3,520 yards = __2__ miles
   e. 16 mm = __1.6__ cm

4. Write the following numbers in order from least to greatest.

   $\frac{9}{2}$ 4.75 $\frac{13}{4}$ 4.8 $4\frac{7}{8}$

   $\frac{13}{4}$, $\frac{9}{2}$, 4.75 , 4.8 , $4\frac{7}{8}$

5. Write a number model for fraction multiplication that describes each of the shaded rectangles.

   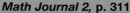

   $\frac{4}{5} * \frac{3}{4} = \frac{12}{20}$, or $\frac{3}{5}$

   $\frac{2}{5} * \frac{2}{3} = \frac{4}{15}$

   $\frac{5}{6} * \frac{1}{3} = \frac{5}{18}$

Math Journal 2, p. 311

Name _____ Date _____ Time _____

STUDY LINK 9·5 The Rectangle Method

Use the rectangle method to find the area of each figure below.

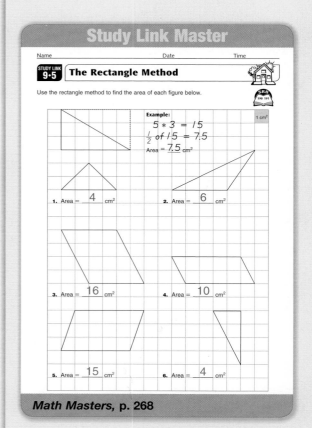

Example:
5 * 3 = 15
$\frac{1}{2}$ of 15 = 7.5
Area = 7.5 cm²

1 cm²

1. Area = __4__ cm²
2. Area = __6__ cm²
3. Area = __16__ cm²
4. Area = __10__ cm²
5. Area = __15__ cm²
6. Area = __4__ cm²

Math Masters, p. 268

PARTNER ACTIVITY

5–15 Min

▶ Building Rectangles

To support visualizing triangles enclosed within rectangles, have students construct rectangles by cutting, tracing, and drawing triangles. Ask students to use construction paper to cut out a triangle of their choice and trace it on a piece of unlined paper. Partners then take turns adding to the traced figures by drawing other triangles until the figure is a rectangle.

Ask partners to share their drawings with the group and discuss their solution strategies. Encourage students to share their decisions about how to draw each subsequent triangle. Ask students what true statements they can make about the rectangles. For example, if you start with an equilateral triangle, you need 2 more triangles to make the rectangle.

Consider having students make posters of their cut triangles and the drawn rectangles for display.

WHOLE-CLASS ACTIVITY

15–30 Min

▶ Reading *Spaghetti and Meatballs for All*

(*Math Masters*, p. 436)

Literature Link To further explore perimeter and area, read the story and complete the following activity from the Extending Children's Learning section, at the end of the book. Have students use grid paper to draw possible table arrangements to seat 12, 16, 24, 36, or any number of people (*n*). Encourage students to find the fewest and the largest possible table arrangements in each case.

Number of Guests	Tables Needed	
	Fewest	Most
12	3	5
16	4	7
24	6	11
36	9	17
n	$n \div 4$	$(n - 2) \div 2$

Spaghetti and Meatballs for All

Summary: This is the story of a family dinner where the seating is rearranged to accommodate each new arrival of guests.

Objective To provide experiences with the use of formulas for the areas of triangles and parallelograms.

Technology Resources www.everydaymathonline.com

 Presentations

 eToolkit

  Algorithms Practice

 EM Facts Workshop Game™

 Family Letters

 Assessment Management

 Common Core State Standards

 Curriculum Focal Points

 Interactive Teacher's Lesson Guide

---

1 Teaching the Lesson

Key Concepts and Skills

• Investigate and use formulas to find the areas of triangles and parallelograms.
[Measurement and Reference Frames Goal 2]

• Identify and define the base and height of triangles and parallelograms.
[Geometry Goal 2]

Key Activities

Students define and identify the base and height for triangles and parallelograms. They develop and use formulas for the area of a triangle and a parallelogram.

 Ongoing Assessment:
Recognizing Student Achievement
Use journal page 314.
[Measurement and Reference Frames Goal 2]

Key Vocabulary

base ◆ height ◆ perpendicular ◆ altitude

Materials

Math Journal 2, pp. 312–314
Study Link 9·5
Class Data Pad

2 Ongoing Learning & Practice

 Playing *Fraction Action, Fraction Friction*
Student Reference Book, p. 312
Math Masters, p. 459
per partnership: calculator
Students practice using estimation and paper-and-pencil computation to add fractions with unlike denominators.

Math Boxes 9·6
Math Journal 2, p. 315
straightedge ◆ colored pencil
Students practice and maintain skills through Math Box problems.

Study Link 9·6
Math Masters, p. 269
Students practice and maintain skills through Study Link activities.

3 Differentiation Options

READINESS

Exploring the Areas of Parallelograms and Triangles
Math Masters, pp. 270–272
2 pattern block triangles ◆ tape or glue ◆ scissors
Students derive the area formulas for parallelograms and triangles.

ENRICHMENT

Calculating Area
Math Masters, p. 273
Students calculate the area of a nonrectangular path.

EXTRA PRACTICE

5-Minute Math
5-Minute Math™, p. 51
Students find the areas of triangles.

Advance Preparation

 Teacher's Reference Manual, **Grades 4–6** pp. 220–222

Getting Started

Mental Math and Reflexes

Give the following directions: Thumbs up means *more than,* thumbs down means *less than,* and a fist means *about the same as.* Students show the appropriate signal after each problem. *Suggestions:*

⚫◯◯ Is the area of your journal greater than, less than, or about the same as 1 square foot? Thumbs down; less than; $8\frac{1}{2}$ in. * 11 in. = 93.5 in², or about 0.6 ft²

⚫⚫◯ Is the area of the board greater than, less than, or about the same as 1 square meter? Thumbs up; greater than

⚫⚫⚫ Is the area of the seat of your chair greater than, less than, or about the same as 4 square feet? Thumbs down; less than

Math Message

Complete journal page 312.

Study Link 9·5 Follow-Up

Have partners share answers and resolve any differences.

---

1 Teaching the Lesson

▶ Math Message Follow-Up

WHOLE-CLASS DISCUSSION

(*Math Journal 2,* p. 312)

Have volunteers share their definitions for the base and height of triangle and a parallelogram. Ask students for the phrasing that the class should use as common definitions for these vocabulary terms. Record the agreed upon definitions on the Class Data Pad. Emphasize the following points:

▷ The **base** can be any side. A triangle has 3 possible bases. A parallelogram has 4 possible bases. The base is often chosen to be the side that the figure "sits" on.

▷ The word *base* is also used to mean the length of one side of a figure.

▷ The **height** of a figure is the shortest distance between a base and the vertex opposite that base.

▷ A dashed line segment shows height. It is **perpendicular** to the base, so it meets the base at a right angle.

▷ The height can be shown by a line segment that is outside of the figure when the triangle is obtuse. Thus, the line segment is perpendicular to an extension of the base.

▷ The height of a figure is sometimes called the **altitude** of the figure.

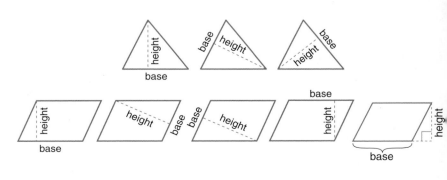

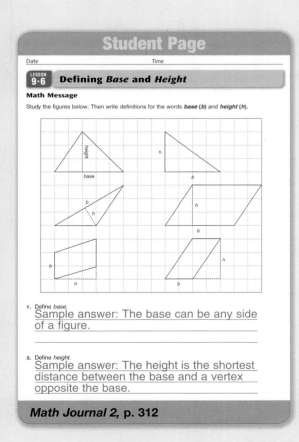

Student Page

Date   Time

LESSON 9·6 Defining *Base* and *Height*

Math Message

Study the figures below. Then write definitions for the words *base (b)* and *height (h)*.

1. Define *base.*
   Sample answer: The base can be any side of a figure.

2. Define *height.*
   Sample answer: The height is the shortest distance between the base and a vertex opposite the base.

Math Journal 2, p. 312

Identifying Base and Height

 PARTNER ACTIVITY

(*Math Journal 2*, p. 313)

Have students select and label a base on each of the figures on journal page 313. Tell them NOT to select any side that intersects one or more grid lines as the base of a figure.

In figures A and B, have students label the height. For the other figures, have them draw and label a dashed line segment perpendicular to the base to indicate the corresponding height. Remind students that some heights may be shown by dashed lines outside of the figure. Circulate and assist.

Using the Rectangle Method for Triangles and Parallelograms

 PARTNER ACTIVITY

(*Math Journal 2*, pp. 313 and 314)

Ask students to use dashed lines to draw the rectangles that enclose each of the triangles on journal page 313 and then use the rectangle method to fill in the column under *Area* on journal page 314. Circulate and assist.

When most students have completed the Area column, ask volunteers to share their solution strategies.

Developing Area Formulas for Triangles and Parallelograms

 **WHOLE-CLASS ACTIVITY**

PROBLEM SOLVING

(*Math Journal 2*, pp. 313 and 314)

Algebraic Thinking Have students fill in the columns under *base* and *height* in the table on journal page 314 and then complete the rest of the table.

When students have finished, ask them to use the information in the table to complete the journal page. They should record the formulas both as word sentences and as equations with variables. The word *base* may be used to mean the length of a base. Circulate and assist.

> ⬆ **Adjusting the Activity**
>
> Have students compare the table information with the area of the rectangles they've drawn to enclose the triangles on journal page 313.
>
> A U D I T O R Y ♦ K I N E S T H E T I C ♦ T A C T I L E ♦ V I S U A L

Student Page

Date _____ Time _____

LESSON 9·6 The Rectangle Method

Math Journal 2, p. 313

Student Page

Date _____ Time _____

LESSON 9·6 Finding Areas of Triangles and Parallelograms

1. Fill in the table. All figures are shown on journal page 313.

Triangles	Area	base	height	base * height
A	3 cm²	3 cm	2 cm	6 cm²
B	2 cm²	4 cm	1 cm	4 cm²
C	10 cm²	5 cm	4 cm	20 cm²
D	8.125 cm²	6.5 cm	2.5 cm	16.25 cm²
E	6 cm²	3 cm	4 cm	12 cm²
F	4 cm²	2 cm	4 cm	8 cm²
Parallelograms	**Area**	**base**	**height**	**base * height**
G	6 cm²	3 cm	2 cm	6 cm²
H	12 cm²	6 cm	2 cm	12 cm²
I	4 cm²	2 cm	2 cm	4 cm²
J	14 cm²	3.5 cm	4 cm	14 cm²

2. Examine the results of Figures A–F. Propose a formula for the area of a triangle as an equation and as a word sentence.

★ Area of a triangle = $\frac{1}{2}(b * h)$. The area of a triangle is half of the product of the length of the base times the height.

3. Examine the results of Figures G–J. Propose a formula for the area of a parallelogram as an equation and as a word sentence.

★ Area of a parallelogram = $b * h$. The area of a parallelogram is the product of the length of the base times the height.

Math Journal 2, p. 314

Ask volunteers to write the equations and the word sentences for the two formulas on the board or Class Data Pad.

▷ The area of a triangle equals $\frac{1}{2}$ of the product of the (length of its) base times its height.

$A = \frac{1}{2}$ of $(b * h)$, $A = \frac{1}{2} * b * h$, or $A = \frac{1}{2} bh$ where b is the (length of the) base and h is the height.

▷ The area of a parallelogram is equal to the (length of its) base times its height.

$A = b * h$, or $A = bh$ where b is the (length of the) base and h is the height.

Ongoing Assessment:
Recognizing Student Achievement

Journal page 314, Problems 2 and 3

Use **journal page 314, Problems 2 and 3** to assess students' understanding of the area formulas for triangles and parallelograms. Students are making adequate progress if they have correctly written both the equation and the word sentence for each formula.

[Measurement and Reference Frames Goal 2]

---

2 Ongoing Learning & Practice

▶ Playing *Fraction Action, Fraction Friction*

PARTNER ACTIVITY

COMPUTATION PRACTICE

(*Student Reference Book,* p. 312; *Math Masters,* p. 459)

Students practice using estimation and paper-and-pencil computation to add fractions with unlike denominators by playing *Fraction Action, Fraction Friction*. Remind students to use benchmarks as they make their estimates.

▶ Math Boxes 9·6

INDEPENDENT ACTIVITY

(*Math Journal 2,* p. 315)

Mixed Practice Math Boxes in this lesson are paired with Math Boxes in Lesson 9-9. The skill in Problem 5 previews Unit 10 content.

Writing/Reasoning For Problem 1, have students plot a new set of points and connect them in order with line segments using a colored pencil. Dictate: (1,1), (1,−2), (−3,2), (−3,5). Have students write a response to the following: *What transformation of the original parallelogram results in the new parallelogram? Explain.* Sample answer: Rotation. The new parallelogram is made by rotating the original 90° clockwise around the point (1,1).

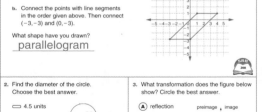

Study Link 9·6

(Math Masters, p. 269)

INDEPENDENT ACTIVITY

Home Connection Students practice using formulas to find the area of triangles and parallelograms.

3 Differentiation Options

READINESS

INDEPENDENT ACTIVITY

► Exploring the Areas of Parallelograms and Triangles

(Math Masters, pp. 270–272)

30+ Min

Algebraic Thinking To explore how the area formulas for parallelograms and triangles are derived, have students complete the following activity.

Ask students to fit two pattern block triangles together and name the new figure that is formed. parallelogram Explain that this relationship between parallelograms and triangles can be used to find their areas. Have students complete Math Masters, pages 270–272. Circulate and assist as needed.

ENRICHMENT

INDEPENDENT ACTIVITY

► Calculating Area

(Math Masters, p. 273)

15–30 Min

To apply students' understanding of the rectangle method and formulas for finding area, have them calculate the area of a path on a grid.

When students have finished, discuss their solution strategies. The problem may be approached in many ways. For example, some students might have used the rectangle method while others might have noticed that each horizontal row of the path forms a parallelogram with a base of 3 cm and a height of 1 cm; therefore, the area of each parallelogram is 3 cm². The full path is made up of 11 of these parallelograms, so its area is 11 ∗ 3 cm² or 33 cm².

Another model for this problem is to think of a large stack of playing cards—5 or more decks piled several inches high. First they are arranged neatly, so that the sides of the stack are straight up and down. Then the cards are pushed left and right to create a wavy stack that looks something like the picture on Math Masters, page 273 when the cards are viewed head-on.

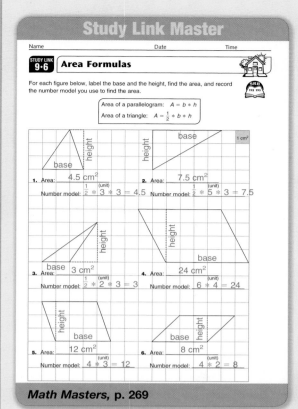

Math Masters, p. 269

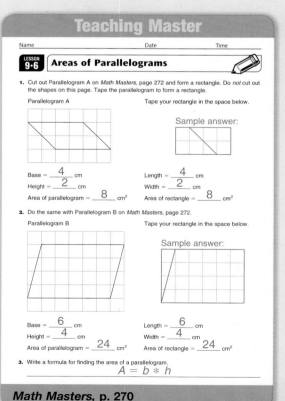

Math Masters, p. 270

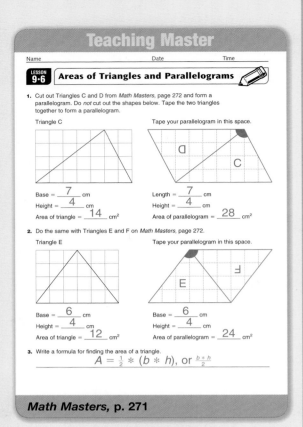

Math Masters, p. 271

When the vertical stack is viewed head-on, the rectangular area seen must be the same as the area seen when the wavy stack is viewed head-on since exactly the same cards are in both stacks. So the wavy stack of cards (or the path on the master) has the same area as the vertical stack of cards (or a path represented by a 3-centimeter-wide vertical strip on the grid).

 **EXTRA PRACTICE**

SMALL-GROUP ACTIVITY

5–15 Min

▶ *5-Minute Math*

To offer students more experience calculating the areas of triangles, see *5-Minute Math,* page 51.

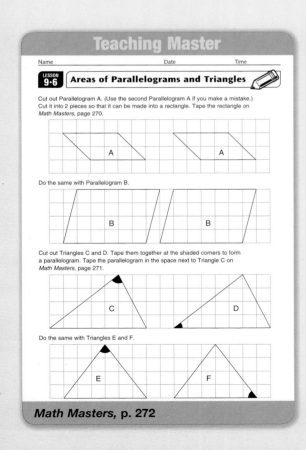

Math Masters, p. 272

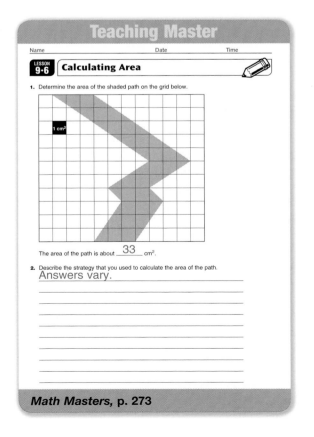

Math Masters, p. 273

9·7 Earth's Water Surface

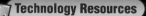 **Objective** To reinforce the use of sampling to make estimates.

Technology Resources www.everydaymathonline.com

 ePresentations   eToolkit   Algorithms Practice   EM Facts Workshop Game™   Family Letters   Assessment Management   Common Core State Standards   Curriculum Focal Points   Interactive Teacher's Lesson Guide

---

1 Teaching the Lesson

Key Concepts and Skills

- Use sampling to make an estimate for surface area problems.
  [Operations and Computation Goal 6]

- Collect and organize data.
  [Data and Chance Goal 1]

- Use latitude and longitude coordinates to locate points on Earth.
  [Measurement and Reference Frames Goal 4]

Key Activities

Students locate points on Earth's surface using latitude and longitude. They use a random set of points on Earth's surface to estimate the percent of Earth's surface that is covered by water.

 **Ongoing Assessment:
Recognizing Student Achievement**
Use Mental Math and Reflexes.
[Number and Numeration Goal 2]

Key Vocabulary

latitude ◆ longitude

Materials

Math Journal 2, p. 316
Student Reference Book, pp. 209 and 210
Study Link 9◆6
Math Masters, pp. 274 and 275
Class Data Pad (optional) ◆ Probability Meter
◆ slate ◆ world map or globe ◆ stick-on note

---

2 Ongoing Learning & Practice

Solving the Four-4s Problem

Math Journal 2, pp. 317–319
calculator
Students represent all the whole numbers from 1 through 100 using only four 4s.

 Math Boxes 9·7

Math Journal 2, p. 320
Student Reference Book, pp. 184 and 397 (optional)
Geometry Template or ruler
Students practice and maintain skills through Math Box problems.

 Study Link 9·7

Math Masters, p. 276
Students practice and maintain skills through Study Link activities.

---

3 Differentiation Options

ENRICHMENT

Estimating the Ground Level Area of the School

Math Masters, p. 277
Students develop and carry out a plan for estimating the school's land area.

EXTRA PRACTICE

Using Formulas to Find Area

Math Masters, p. 278
Students solve mixed area review problems using formulas.

Advance Preparation

For Part 1, cut the copies of *Math Masters,* pages 274 and 275 into small squares. Place the latitude and longitude cards into two containers labeled *latitude* and *longitude.* Gather world maps or globes. You will also need the Probability Meter and a stick-on note.

For the optional Enrichment activity in Part 3, sketch and make copies of a floor plan for the ground level of your school.

 Teacher's Reference Manual, Grades 4–6 pp. 69–71, 160–167, 254

Getting Started

Mental Math and Reflexes

Have students find the whole for a given fraction of a set.
Suggestions:

● ○ ○   If 12 counters are $\frac{1}{4}$ of a set, how many counters are in the set?
     48 counters

● ● ○   If 22 counters are $\frac{2}{3}$ of a set, how many counters are in the set?
     33 counters   How many are in $\frac{1}{3}$ of the set?   11 counters

● ● ●   If 15 counters are $\frac{3}{8}$ of a set, how many counters are in the set?
     40 counters   How many are in $\frac{1}{8}$ of the set?   5 counters

Math Message

Complete Problem 1 on journal page 316.

Study Link 9·6 Follow-Up

Ask volunteers to share their number sentences.

✓ **Ongoing Assessment:**
Recognizing Student Achievement

Mental Math and Reflexes

Use the **Mental Math and Reflexes** problems to assess students' ability to find a fraction of a set. Students are making adequate progress if they correctly identify the numbers that represent the unit fractions.

[Number and Numeration Goal 2]

---

1   Teaching the Lesson

▶ ## Math Message Follow-Up

👥 WHOLE-CLASS
DISCUSSION

(Math Journal 2, p. 316)

Ask volunteers to share their estimates and explanations for Problem 1 on journal page 316. If it is not mentioned, remind students that sampling is another way to make an estimate. In previous lessons this year, students used sampling to estimate the time it would take to travel certain distances and to tap a certain number of times. In this activity, they will use a random set of points on Earth's surface to estimate the percent of Earth's surface that is covered by water.

▶ ## Locating Points on Land or Water

👥 WHOLE-CLASS
ACTIVITY

(Math Journal 2, p. 316; Student Reference Book, pp. 209 and 210; Math Masters, pp. 274 and 275)

Refer students to *Student Reference Book,* pages 209 and 210. Ask questions such as the following:

● What are the lines that go east and west around Earth called?
Lines of latitude

Student Page

Date   Time

LESSON 9·7   **Earth's Water Surface**

Math Message   Answers vary.

1. **a.** What percent of Earth's surface do you think is covered by water?
   My estimate: _____

   b. Explain how you made your estimate.
   _____
   _____
   _____

A Sampling Experiment   Answers vary.

2. **a.** My location is at latitude _____ and longitude _____.

   b. Circle one.
   My location is on: land   water

   c. What fraction of the class has a water location? _____

   d. Percent of Earth's Surface that is covered by water:
   My class's estimate: _____

Follow-Up

3. **a.** Percent of Earth's surface that is covered by water:
   Actual figure: About 70%

   b. How does your class estimate compare to the actual figure?
   Answers vary.
   _____
   _____

Math Journal 2, p. 316

- What are the lines that go north and south around Earth called? Lines of longitude

- How are **latitude** and **longitude** measured and named? Latitude is measured and named in degrees north or south of the equator, and longitude is measured and named in degrees east or west of the prime meridian.

- What is a main use of latitude and longitude? To locate places on a map

Have each student draw one latitude card and one longitude card from the containers, write the coordinates on journal page 316, and return the cards to the containers. Ask students to use a world map or globe to locate the coordinates, determine whether that location is on land or on water, and circle the answer on the journal page.

Have students tally their results on the board or Class Data Pad as they finish. When all results are tallied, ask students what fraction of the class had a water location. Then have students convert the fraction to a decimal and a percent and record the percent on journal page 316. Have a volunteer post the percent on the Probability Meter. Ask students how they could interpret the percent.

For example, if 72% of the class reported a water location, the results could be interpreted in the following ways:

▷ This sampling indicates that about 72% of Earth's surface is covered by water.

▷ If you pick a random point on Earth, this sampling indicates that your chance of landing in water is about 72%.

Have students compare their original estimates of the percent of Earth's surface covered by water with the results of the sampling experiment. Also compare the class results with the actual value, which is approximately 70%. If the class results are very far from 70%, discuss the fact that this sometimes happens in sampling experiments, and move the marker on the Probability Meter to about 70%.

NOTE In statistics, this type of activity is called *Monte Carlo Sampling.* The middle value for the thousands of classes that will be doing this experiment will be about 70%, but a few results may differ considerably. Your results may be far from 70%—assure students that they have done nothing wrong.

Student Page

Date _____ Time _____

LESSON 9·7 The Four-4s Problem

Using only four 4s and any operation on your calculator, create expressions for values from 1 through 100. Do not use any other numbers except the ones listed in the rules below. You do not need to find an expression for every number. Some are quite difficult. Try to find as many as you can today, but keep working when you have free time. The rules are listed below:

♦ You must use four 4s in every expression.
♦ You can use two 4s to create 44 or $\frac{4}{4}$.
♦ You may use 4^0 ($4^0 = 1$).
♦ You may use $\sqrt{4}$ ($\sqrt{4} = 2$).
♦ You may use 4! (four factorial). ($4! = 4 * 3 * 2 * 1 = 24$)

Use parentheses as needed so that it is very clear what is to be done and in what order. Examples of expressions for some numbers are shown below. **Sample answers:**

$1 = \dfrac{4^0 * 4^0 * 4^0 * 4^0}{}$
$2 = \dfrac{\sqrt{4} * 4^0 * 4^0 * 4^0}{}$
$3 = \dfrac{(\sqrt{4} + 4^0) * \frac{4}{4}}{}$
$4 = \dfrac{4! - (4 * 4) - 4}{}$
$5 = \dfrac{\sqrt{4} + \sqrt{4} + \sqrt{4} - 4^0}{}$
$6 = \dfrac{(\sqrt{4} + \sqrt{4} + \sqrt{4}) * 4^0}{}$
$7 = \dfrac{\sqrt{4} + \sqrt{4} + \sqrt{4} + 4^0}{}$
$8 = \dfrac{(4 * 4) - 4 - 4}{}$
$9 = 4 + \sqrt{4} + \sqrt{4} + 4^0$
$10 = \dfrac{(4 * \sqrt{4}) + 4 - \sqrt{4}}{}$
$11 = \dfrac{4 + 4 + 4 - 4^0}{}$
$12 = \dfrac{(4 + 4 + 4) * 4^0}{}$
$13 = \dfrac{4 + 4 + 4 + 4^0}{}$
$14 = \dfrac{4 + 4 + 4 + \sqrt{4}}{}$
$15 = \dfrac{4! - 4 - 4 - 4^0}{}$

$16 = \dfrac{(4! - 4 - 4) * 4^0}{}$
$17 = \dfrac{(4 * 4) + \frac{4}{4}}{}$
$18 = \dfrac{((4 * 4) + \sqrt{4}) * 4^0}{}$
$19 = \dfrac{((4 * 4) + 4) - 4^0}{}$
$20 = \dfrac{((4 * 4) + 4) * 4^0}{}$
$21 = \dfrac{(4 * 4) + 4 + 4^0}{}$
$22 = \dfrac{(4 * 4) + 4 + \sqrt{4}}{}$
$23 = \dfrac{4! - \sqrt{4} + \frac{4}{4}}{}$
$24 = \dfrac{4! * \frac{4}{4} * 4^0}{}$
$25 = \dfrac{4! * \frac{4}{4} + 4^0}{}$
$26 = (4! + \sqrt{4}) * \frac{4}{4}$
$27 = \dfrac{4! + \sqrt{4} + \frac{4}{4}}{}$
$28 = \dfrac{44 - (4 * 4)}{}$
$29 = \dfrac{4! + 4 + \sqrt{4} - 4^0}{}$
$30 = \dfrac{(4! + 4 + \sqrt{4}) * 4^0}{}$

Math Journal 2, p. 317

Student Page

Date _____ Time _____

LESSON 9·7 The Four-4s Problem *continued*

$31 = \dfrac{4! + 4 + \sqrt{4} + 4^0}{}$
$32 = \dfrac{4! + 4 + \sqrt{4} + \sqrt{4}}{}$
$33 = \dfrac{4! + 4 + 4 + 4^0}{}$
$34 = \dfrac{4! + 4 + 4 + \sqrt{4}}{}$
$35 = \dfrac{(\frac{4!}{4})^{\sqrt{4}} - 4^0}{}$
$36 = \dfrac{4! + 4 + 4 + 4}{}$
$37 = \dfrac{(\frac{4!}{4})^{\sqrt{4}} + 4^0}{}$
$38 = \dfrac{44 - 4 - \sqrt{4}}{}$
$39 = \dfrac{44 - 4 - 4^0}{}$
$40 = \dfrac{(44 - 4) * 4^0}{}$
$41 = \dfrac{44 - 4 + 4^0}{}$
$42 = \dfrac{44 - 4 + \sqrt{4}}{}$
$43 = \dfrac{44 - \sqrt{4} + 4^0}{}$
$44 = \dfrac{44 * \frac{4}{4}}{}$
$45 = \dfrac{44 + \frac{4}{4}}{}$
$46 = \dfrac{(44 + \sqrt{4}) * 4^0}{}$
$47 = \dfrac{44 + \sqrt{4} + 4^0}{}$
$48 = \dfrac{44 + \sqrt{4} + \sqrt{4}}{}$
$49 = \dfrac{4! + 4! + \sqrt{4} - 4^0}{}$
$50 = \dfrac{(4! + 4! + \sqrt{4}) * 4^0}{}$
$51 = \dfrac{4! + 4! + \sqrt{4} + 4^0}{}$
$52 = \dfrac{4! + 4! + \sqrt{4} + \sqrt{4}}{}$
$53 = \dfrac{4! + 4! + 4 + 4^0}{}$
$54 = \dfrac{4! + 4! + 4 + \sqrt{4}}{}$
$55 = \dfrac{(\sqrt{4} * (4! + 4)) - 4^0}{}$
$56 = \dfrac{(\sqrt{4} * (4! + 4)) * 4^0}{}$

$57 = \dfrac{(\sqrt{4} * (4! + 4)) + 4^0}{}$
$58 = (\sqrt{4} * (4! + 4)) + \sqrt{4}$
$59 = \dfrac{\frac{4!}{0.4} - \frac{4}{4}}{}$
$60 = \dfrac{(\sqrt{4} * (4! + 4)) + 4}{}$
$61 = \dfrac{\frac{4!}{0.4} + \frac{4}{4}}{}$
$62 = \dfrac{(4 * 4 * 4) - \sqrt{4}}{}$
$63 = \dfrac{(4 * 4 * 4) - 4^0}{}$
$64 = \dfrac{(4 * 4 * 4) * 4^0}{}$
$65 = \dfrac{(4 * 4 * 4) + 4^0}{}$
$66 = \dfrac{(4 * 4 * 4) + \sqrt{4}}{}$
$67 = \dfrac{44 + 4! - 4^0}{}$
$68 = \dfrac{(4 * 4 * 4) + 4}{}$
$69 = \dfrac{44 + 4! + 4^0}{}$
$70 = \dfrac{44 + 4! + \sqrt{4}}{}$
$71 = \dfrac{((\sqrt{4} + 4^0) * 4!) - 4^0}{}$
$72 = \dfrac{4! * (\sqrt{4} + \frac{4}{4})}{}$
$73 = \dfrac{((\sqrt{4} + 4^0) * 4!) + 4^0}{}$
$74 = \dfrac{((\sqrt{4} + 4^0) * 4!) + \sqrt{4}}{}$
$75 = \dfrac{(4! + 4^0) * (\sqrt{4} + 4^0)}{}$
$76 = \dfrac{((\sqrt{4} + 4^0) * 4!) + 4}{}$
$77 = \dfrac{(\sqrt{4} + 4^0)^4 - 4}{}$
$78 = \dfrac{(4! + \sqrt{4}) * (\sqrt{4} + 4^0)}{}$
$79 = \dfrac{4 * (4! - 4) - 4^0}{}$
$80 = \dfrac{4 * 4 * (4 + 4^0)}{}$
$81 = \dfrac{4 * (4! - 4) + 4^0}{}$
$82 = \dfrac{4 * (4! - 4) + \sqrt{4}}{}$

Math Journal 2, p. 318

---

2 Ongoing Learning & Practice

▶ ## Solving the Four-4s Problem

PARTNER ACTIVITY

PROBLEM SOLVING

(*Math Journal 2*, pp. 317–319)

Students represent all of the whole numbers from 1 through 100 using only four 4s. They may use any of the operations in any combination to arrive at each target number. Note that this activity should be ongoing. Consider giving students a week or more to create expressions for as many of the numbers as possible. Include time that week for students to make a large class poster of the four-4s problem to record and display their solutions.

▶ ## Math Boxes 9·7

INDEPENDENT ACTIVITY

(*Math Journal 2*, p. 320; *Student Reference Book*, pp. 184 and 397)

Mixed Practice Math Boxes in this lesson are paired with Math Boxes in Lesson 9-5. The skill in Problem 5 previews Unit 10 content.

Writing/Reasoning Have students write a response to the following: *Explain your method of remembering the steps for plotting ordered number pairs on a coordinate grid.* Sample answer: I remember that alphabetically, horizontal comes before vertical, so I find the first coordinate on the horizontal axis and then look for the second coordinate on the vertical axis.

Writing/Reasoning Have students write a response to the following: *Write a fraction multiplication number story for Problem 5b.* Answers vary.

NOTE After students complete Problem 3 on *Math Journal 2*, page 320, you may want to provide additional practice converting units of measurement (including compound units such as square feet or square yards). Use problems similar to those on pages 184 and 397 of the *Student Reference Book*.

▶ ## Study Link 9·7

INDEPENDENT ACTIVITY

(*Math Masters*, p. 276)

Home Connection Students practice determining appropriate units of measure for area. They practice using formulas to find the areas of rectangles and triangles.

PARTNER ACTIVITY

Estimating the Ground Level Area of the School

30+ Min

(*Math Masters,* p. 277)

To apply students' understanding of sampling as an estimation strategy, have them estimate the ground level area of the school. The activity has three parts—planning, gathering data, and estimating—and can be done in one day or over several days.

1. Planning

Students work alone or with partners to develop a plan to estimate the ground area of the school. Have students share and discuss their plans.

Students who have done this activity have used a variety of strategies. *For example:*

▷ Students found the area of their classroom. They estimated that each classroom in the school had about the same area. Areas of the gym and lunchroom were reported in terms of how many classrooms would fit inside them. Students then estimated the ground level area of the entire school.

▷ Students measured the perimeter of the school by first finding the length of their strides and then walking around the outside of the school. They used these measures to estimate the ground level area of the school.

2. Gathering Data

Partners carry out their plans and record their results on a sketch of the floor plan. Consider having students gather data at some time other than the math period such as at recess or lunch.

3. Estimating

Partners use the gathered data to estimate the area of the first floor of the school.

Have partners present their findings to the class. Discuss the estimates with the class and ask how accurate they are. Ask: *Would students be surprised if the actual area were 10% more or less than their estimates, 20% more or less, and so on? What range of areas might the actual area fall between? What defines a good estimate?*

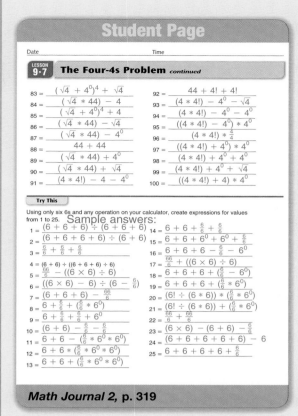

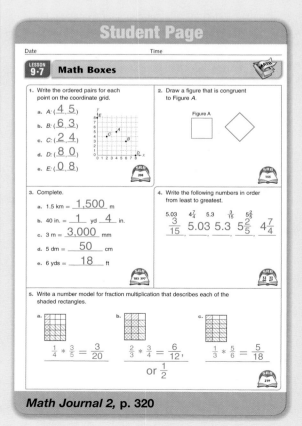

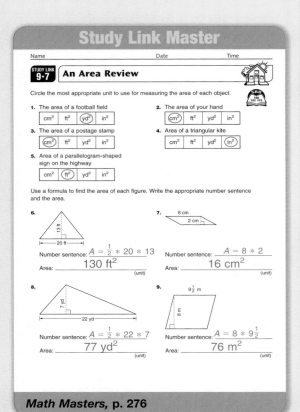

▶ # Using Formulas to Find Area

(*Math Masters*, p. 278)

Algebraic Thinking Students practice using formulas to find the area of nonrectangular figures. When students have finished, discuss how the formulas at the top of the page are related to the rectangle area formula for finding the area of a rectangle.

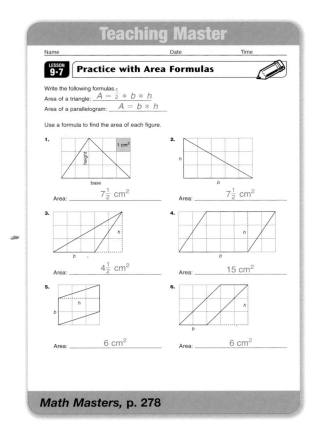

9·8 Volume of Rectangular Prisms

 Objective To provide experiences with using a formula for the volume of rectangular prisms.

---

10 **Technology Resources** www.everydaymathonline.com

ePresentations

eToolkit

Algorithms Practice

EM Facts Workshop Game™

Family Letters

Assessment Management

Common Core State Standards

Curriculum Focal Points

Interactive Teacher's Lesson Guide

---

1 Teaching the Lesson

Key Concepts and Skills

- Use formulas ($l * w * h$ or $B * h$) to calculate the volumes of rectangular prisms. [Measurement and Reference Frames Goal 2]

- Define the base and height of a rectangular prism. [Geometry Goal 2]

- Explore the properties of rectangular prisms. [Geometry Goal 2]

- Write number sentences with variables to model volume problems. [Patterns, Functions, and Algebra Goal 2]

Key Activities

Students discuss the difference between volume and area. They define *base* and *height* for a rectangular prism and develop a formula for the volume of a rectangular prism. Students use a formula to find volumes and to model a rectangular prism with a given volume.

Ongoing Assessment: Informing Instruction See page 751.

Key Vocabulary

volume ◆ cubic unit ◆ rectangular prism ◆ face ◆ base (of a rectangular prism) ◆ height (of a rectangular prism) ◆ Associative Property of Multiplication

Materials

Math Journal 2, pp. 321, 322, and Activity Sheet 8
Student Reference Book, pp. 195–197
Study Link 9·7
scissors ◆ transparent tape ◆ 36 centimeter cubes ◆ slate

2 Ongoing Learning & Practice

Math Boxes 9·8
Math Journal 2, p. 323
Students practice and maintain skills through Math Box problems.

Ongoing Assessment: Recognizing Student Achievement
Use Math Boxes, Problem 3.
[Number and Numeration Goal 5]

Study Link 9·8
Math Masters, p. 279
Students practice and maintain skills through Study Link activities.

3 Differentiation Options

READINESS

Analyzing Prism Nets for Cubes

Math Masters, pp. 280 and 429
Students investigate solid geometry concepts using cube diagrams.

ENRICHMENT

Finding the Volume of One Stick-On Note

Math Masters, p. 281
per partnership: one stick-on note, pad of unused stick-on notes, centimeter cube
Students compare the volume of a single stick-on note to the volume of a centimeter cube.

EXTRA PRACTICE

5-Minute Math

5-Minute Math™, pp. 52 and 214
Students calculate the volumes of prisms.

Advance Preparation

For Part 1, make models of the open boxes on Activity Sheet 8 to illustrate where to fold and where to tape the patterns for Boxes A and B. Have students save the boxes for use in Project 9.

 Teacher's Reference Manual, Grades 4–6 pp. 187–189, 222–225

Getting Started

Mental Math and Reflexes

Students practice rounding numbers. Have them write their answers on their slates. *Suggestions:*

●○○ Round 654 to the nearest hundred. 700

     Round 4,654.97 to the nearest whole number. 4,655

●●○ Round 67.072 to the nearest tenth. 67.1

     Round 3.452 to the nearest hundredth. 3.45

●●● Round 67% of 100 to the nearest ten. 70

     Round 8.006 to the nearest tenth. 8.0

Math Message

Write 2 questions that can be answered by reading Student Reference Book, *page 195.*

Study Link 9·7 Follow-Up

Ask volunteers to present the area formulas for a triangle and for a parallelogram and the number models they used to solve the Study Link Problems.

Project Note

For more practice finding the volume of rectangular prisms, see Project 9: Adding Volumes of Solid Figures.

(1) Teaching the Lesson

▶ Math Message Follow-Up

WHOLE-CLASS DISCUSSION
ELL

(*Student Reference Book,* p. 195)

Ask students to pose their questions for the class. Use the questions and responses to discuss the difference between area and volume. To support English language learners, write the key ideas on the board. Emphasize the following points:

▷ Shapes that are 2-dimensional are flat. The surfaces they enclose take up a certain amount of area, but they do not have any thickness, so they do not take up any space.

▷ Shapes that are 3-dimensional have length, width, *and* thickness, so they enclose a certain amount of space.

▷ The amount of surface inside a 2-dimensional shape is the area of the shape. Area is measured in square units, such as square inches, square feet, square centimeters, and so on.

▷ The amount of space enclosed by a 3-dimensional shape is the **volume** of the shape. Volume is measured in **cubic units,** such as cubic inches, cubic feet, cubic centimeters, and so on.

▷ The symbol used to indicate square units is the abbreviation of the unit name with a superscript 2, for example, in^2, ft^2, cm^2, m^2, and so on. For cubic units, the symbol is the abbreviation of the unit name with a superscript 3, for example, in^3, ft^3, cm^3, m^3, and so on. To support English language learners, discuss the meanings of the word *volume.* Students might have heard the word used in contexts involving sound level or a book. Emphasize that volume is also used in the mathematical context involving 3-dimensional shapes.

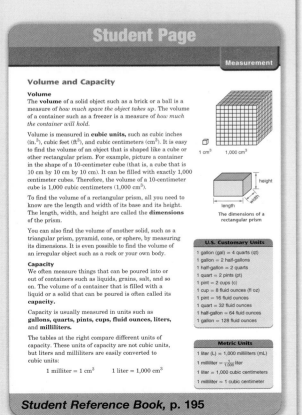

Student Page

Student Reference Book, p. 195

Defining Base and Height for Rectangular Prisms

WHOLE-CLASS DISCUSSION
ELL

(*Math Journal 2*, p. 321)

As a class, read the introduction on journal page 321. Have students study the figures and then write their own definitions for the base and height of a rectangular prism. Ask volunteers to share their definitions with the class. Use their responses to reinforce the following points:

▷ A **rectangular prism** is formed by six flat surfaces, or **faces,** that are rectangles. To support English language learners, compare the common meaning and the mathematical meaning of the word *face*.

▷ Any of the six faces of the prism can be a **base,** but the face that the prism "sits on" is often chosen as a base.

▷ The **height** (for a given base) is the shortest distance between the base and the opposite face.

Links to the Future

The names and properties of prisms will be revisited in more detail in Unit 11.

There are two types of prisms, right and oblique. (*See below.*) When the faces of a prism are all rectangles, it is a *right rectangular prism*. When the faces are not all rectangles, it is an *oblique rectangular prism*. Oblique prisms are not considered in *Fifth Grade Everyday Mathematics*.

Right rectangular prism   Oblique rectangular prism

Adjusting the Activity

ELL

Have students identify objects in the classroom that have the shape of rectangular prisms.

AUDITORY ◆ KINESTHETIC ◆ TACTILE ◆ VISUAL

Developing a Formula for Volume

WHOLE-CLASS ACTIVITY
PROBLEM SOLVING

(*Math Journal 2*, pp. 321, 322, and Activity Sheet 8; *Student Reference Book*, pp. 196 and 197)

Algebraic Thinking Give 24 centimeter cubes to each student. Ask students to tear out Activity Sheet 8 from the back of their journals and follow the directions on journal page 321 to answer Problems 2 and 3.

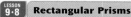 Student Page

Date _____ Time _____

LESSON 9·8 Rectangular Prisms

A **rectangular prism** is a geometric solid enclosed by six flat surfaces formed by rectangles. If each of the six rectangles is also a square, then the prism is a **cube.** The flat surfaces are called **faces** of the prism.

Bricks, paperback books, and most boxes are rectangular prisms. Dice and sugar cubes are examples of cubes.

Below are three different views of the same rectangular prism.

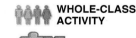

1. Study the figures above. Write your own definitions for **base** and **height.**

Base of a rectangular prism: Sample answer: Any face of the prism; usually the face the prism sits on

Height of a rectangular prism: Sample answer: The shortest distance between the base and the opposite face

Examine the patterns on Activity Sheet 6. These patterns will be used to construct open boxes—boxes that have no tops. Try to figure out how many centimeter cubes are needed to fill each box to the top. Do not cut out the patterns yet.
Answers vary.

2. I think that _____ centimeter cubes are needed to fill Box A to the top.

3. I think that _____ centimeter cubes are needed to fill Box B to the top.

Math Journal 2, p. 321

NOTE You may want to remind students that to be a prism, a polyhedron must have at least one pair of parallel and congruent faces, which can be called *bases*. Rectangular prisms have 3 pairs of parallel congruent faces. Therefore, when calculating the volume of a rectangular prism, any face can be chosen as the base.

When students have completed the problems, display your prepared models as guides for folding and taping the boxes. Direct students to do the following:

1. Cut out the pattern for Box A, fold it on the dashed lines, and tape it to make an open box.

2. Cover the bottom of Box A with one layer of centimeter cubes. Ask: *How many cubes are in this layer?* 8

3. Put a second layer of cubes on top of the first layer. Ask: *How many cubes are in the box now?* 16

4. Put a third layer on top of the second layer. Ask: *How many cubes are in the box now?* 24 *What is the volume of the box?* 24 cm^3

5. Cut out the pattern for Box B, fold it on the dashed lines, and tape it to make an open box.

6. Cover the bottom of Box B with one layer of cubes. Ask: *How many cubes are in this layer?* 9

Ask students to answer the following questions without putting any more cubes in the box:

- How many layers of cubes are needed to fill the box? 5

- How many centimeter cubes in all are needed to fill the box? 45 How did you find the answer? Sample answer: By multiplying the number of cubes in 1 layer by the number of layers.

- What is the volume of the box? 45 cm^3

Point out that the number of cubes in one layer is the same as the number of square centimeters in the base ($l * w$), and that the number of layers is the same as the height in centimeters of the box. Ask students how this information might be used in a formula to find the volume of the box. Multiply the area of the base by the height of the box.

This formula is written as $V = B * h$, where V represents the volume, B represents the area of the base, and h represents the height from that base. Ask students to write this formula at the top of journal page 322. Have students refer to pages 196 and 197 of the *Student Reference Book* as needed.

NOTE Traditionally, linear measures are represented in formulas by lowercase letters, and 2- and 3-dimensional measures are represented by uppercase letters. For example, *b* is used to represent the length of the base of a rectangle, and *B* is used to represent the area of the base of a prism.

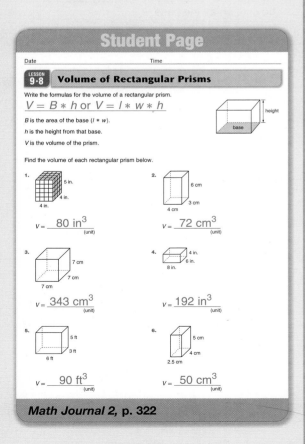

Another Formula for Volume of a Rectangular Prism

WHOLE-CLASS ACTIVITY

(*Student Reference Book,* pp. 196 and 197)

Ask students to review pages 196 and 197 of the *Student Reference Book.* Give each student 12 more centimeter cubes so each student has 36 cubes.

NOTE If you do not have 36 centimeter cubes per student, ask students to build the rectangular prisms in partnerships.

Ask students to use the centimeter cubes to do the following:

1. Build a rectangular prism with a base that is 4 cubes long and 3 cubes wide, and that is 1 cube high.
   Ask: *Describe a way you could determine the volume of the rectangular prism.* Sample answer: Multiply $4 * 3 * 1$ to obtain 12 cm^3. *What do the 4, 3, and 1 represent in the prism?* The length, width, and height

2. Build a second 4-by-3-by-1 rectangular prism. Place it on top of the original rectangular prism.
   Ask: *How could you determine the volume of the new rectangular prism?* Sample answers: Multiply $4 * 3 * 2$ to obtain 24 cm^3; multiply $12 * 2$ to get 24 cm^3.

3. Build a third 4-by-3-by-1 layer. Place it on top of the existing rectangular prism. Ask students to write a number model using three factors to find the volume of the new prism.
   $4 * 3 * 3 = 36$ cm^3

Now ask the following question: *Suppose you know the number of cubes in the length, width, and height of a rectangular prism. How could this information be used to write another formula for finding the volume of a rectangular prism?* Multiply: *length * width * height* $(l * w * h)$; $V = l * w * h$.

Have students write this formula at the top of journal page 322, next to the first formula they derived for finding the volume of a rectangular prism. Discuss why both formulas will result in the same volume.

Conclude by asking students to explain how they could use the new formula to find the volume of a cube. Sample answers: Replace each side-length letter in the formula with the length of a side of the cube. You could rewrite the formula as $V = s^3$, where s is the length of a side of the cube.

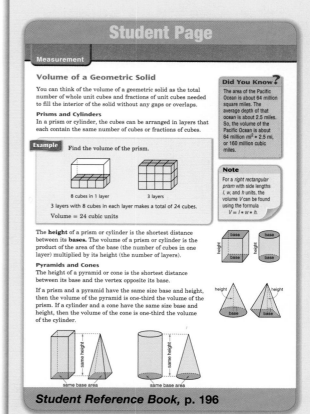

Student Reference Book, p. 196

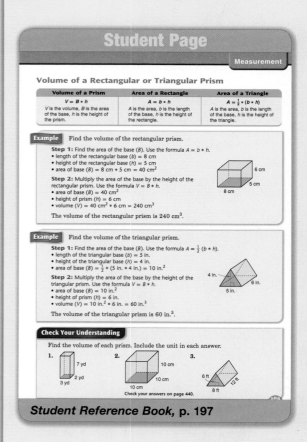

Student Reference Book, p. 197

▶ Building a Rectangular Prism with a Given Volume

Algebraic Thinking Ask students to use centimeter cubes to build the shape of a rectangular prism with a volume of 24 cm^3.

Ask: *What are the possible areas for the base* (B) *and the length of the height* (h) *from that base?* $B = 24$ cm^2, $h = 1$ cm; $B = 12$ cm^2, $h = 2$ cm; $B = 8$ cm^2, $h = 3$ cm; $B = 6$ cm^2, $h = 4$ cm; $B = 4$ cm^2, $h = 6$ cm; $B = 3$ cm^2, $h = 8$ cm; $B = 2$ cm^2, $h = 12$ cm; $B = 1$ cm^2, $h = 24$ cm

Ask students to use the cubes to make a rectangular prism that has a length of 3 cm, a width of 2 cm (base of 6 cm^2), and a height of 4 cm. Explain that the volume can be found as follows:

$$V = (l * w) * h = (3 * 2) * 4$$

Now ask students to carefully rotate their rectangular prism so that it now has a length of 4 cm, a width of 2 cm (base of 8 cm^2), and a height of 3 cm. Explain that the volume can be found as follows:

$$V = (l * w) * h = 3 * (2 * 4)$$

Ask: *What do the two rectangular prisms have in common?* Sample answer: The dimensions of the prisms have the same three measures, and each has a volume of 24 cm^3.

Guide students to conclude that if the measures of the three dimensions of two rectangular prisms are the same, the volumes are the same. Then point out that this is an illustration of the **Associative Property of Multiplication,** which means that changing the grouping of factors does not change the product.

$$\text{So, } (3 * 2) * 4 = 3 * (2 * 4)$$
$$6 * 4 \quad = \quad 3 * 8$$
$$24 \quad = \quad 24$$

Have students repeat this activity by comparing the volumes of two rectangular prisms that have dimensions of 2 cm, 3 cm, and 5 cm, but different bases.

▶ Finding the Volumes of Rectangular Prisms

(*Math Journal 2,* p. 322)

Algebraic Thinking Have students complete journal page 322 by calculating the volume of six rectangular prisms from the given dimensions.

Ongoing Assessment: Informing Instruction

Watch for students who are not correctly matching the given dimensions to the formula variables. Have them make and complete a table for the problems on journal page 322, such as the following:

Problem	V	B	h
1	80 in³	4 * 4	5
2	72 cm³	4 * 3	6
3	343 cm³	7 * 7	7
4	192 in³	8 * 6	4
5	90 ft³	6 * 3	5
6	50 cm³	2.5 * 4	5

2 Ongoing Learning & Practice

Math Boxes 9·8

INDEPENDENT ACTIVITY

(*Math Journal 2*, p. 323)

Mixed Practice Math Boxes in this lesson are paired with Math Boxes in Lesson 9-10. The skills in Problems 2 and 5 preview Unit 10 content.

Writing/Reasoning Have students write a response to the following: *Explain the strategy you used to solve Problem 1c and explain your reasoning.* Answers vary.

Ongoing Assessment: Recognizing Student Achievement

Math Boxes Problem 3 ★

Use **Math Boxes, Problem 3** to assess students' abilities to find common denominators and to write fractions in simplest form. Students are making adequate progress if they correctly identify the least common denominators.

[Number and Numeration Goal 5]

Study Link 9·8

INDEPENDENT ACTIVITY

(*Math Masters*, p. 279)

Home Connection Students find the volume of cube structures.

Student Page

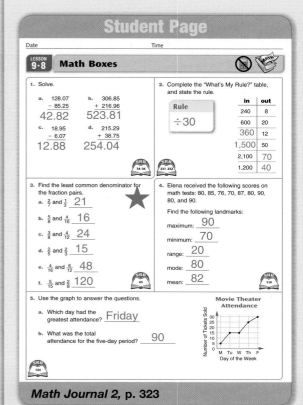

Math Journal 2, p. 323

Study Link Master

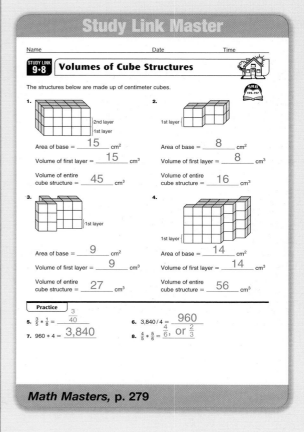

Math Masters, p. 279

Teaching Master

Name　　　　　　　　Date　　　　　　Time

LESSON 9·8 | Unfolding Prisms

If you could unfold a prism so that its faces are laid out as a set attached at their edges, you would have a flat diagram for the shape. Imagine unfolding a cube. There are many different ways that you could make diagrams, depending on how you unfold the cube.

Which of the following are diagrams that could be folded to make a cube? Write *yes* or *no* in the blank next to each diagram.

1. _No_

2. _No_

3. _Yes_

4. _Yes_

Math Masters, p. 280

Teaching Master

Name　　　　　　　　Date　　　　　　Time

LESSON 9·8 | Comparing Volume

What is the volume of one stick-on note? In other words, how much space is taken up by a single stick-on note? How does the volume of a stick-on note compare to the volume of a centimeter cube?

1. An unused pad of stick-on notes is an example of what shape?
   Rectangular prism

2. Estimate the volume of one stick-on note.
   Sample answer: About 0.75 cm³

3. Calculate the volume of one stick-on note. Volume = _Answers vary._

   Record your strategy.

4. Use a formula to calculate the volume of one centimeter cube. Volume = _1 cm³_

   Write the number sentence for this calculation.
   Volume = (1 cm ∗ 1 cm) ∗ 1 cm = 1 cm³

5. Explain how the volume of one stick-on note compares with the volume of one centimeter cube.
   Answers vary.

Math Masters, p. 281

---

3 Differentiation Options

READINESS

PARTNER ACTIVITY

🕐 5–15 Min

▶ Analyzing Prism Nets for Cubes

(*Math Masters*, pp. 280 and 429)

Portfolio Ideas
To stimulate students' ability to visualize, name, and describe geometric solids, have students look at diagrams to determine which shapes can and cannot be folded into cubes. Read and discuss the introduction as a group. As students choose which of the diagrams can be folded into a cube, provide inch grid paper so students may check their work.

Discuss students' solutions.

ENRICHMENT

PARTNER ACTIVITY

🕐 5–15 Min

▶ Finding the Volume of One Stick-On Note

(*Math Masters*, p. 281)

Portfolio Ideas
To apply students' understanding of how to find the volume of a rectangular prism, have partners compare the volume of a single stick-on note and that of a centimeter cube. Give each partnership one stick-on note, one unused pad of stick-on notes, and one centimeter cube. Ask students to estimate how the volume of the single stick-on note compares with the volume of the cube.

Have students record their strategies and solutions on *Math Masters*, page 281. When partners have completed the page, ask them to present their solutions.

NOTE One approach to finding the volume of a single stick-on note would be to measure the dimensions and find the volume of the unused pad of stick-on notes. A single stick-on note would represent a fraction of the pad.

EXTRA PRACTICE

SMALL-GROUP ACTIVITY

🕐 5–15 Min

▶ 5-Minute Math

To offer students more experience with calculating the volumes of prisms, see *5-Minute Math,* pages 52 and 214.

9·9 Volume of Right Prisms

Objective To provide experiences with using a formula for the volume of right prisms.

Technology Resources www.everydaymathonline.com

 ePresentations
 eToolkit
 Algorithms Practice
 EM Facts Workshop Game™
 Family Letters
 Assessment Management
 Common Core State Standards
 Curriculum Focal Points
 Interactive Teacher's Lesson Guide

---

1 Teaching the Lesson

Key Concepts and Skills

• Use a formula to calculate the volumes of prisms.
[Measurement and Reference Frames Goal 2]

• Define and classify prisms according to common properties.
[Geometry Goal 2]

Key Activities

Students examine a model of a prism to verify a formula for finding the volume of right prisms, and then use the volume formula to calculate the volumes of right prisms.

Key Vocabulary

prism ◆ face

Materials

Math Journal 2, pp. 324–325B
Study Link 9·8
Math Masters, pp. 282 and 283
Class Data Pad ◆ demonstration materials: metric ruler, foam board, knife, tape (optional)

2 Ongoing Learning & Practice

 Playing *Polygon Capture*
Student Reference Book, p. 328
Math Masters, pp. 494–496 (optional); p. 497
Polygon Capture Pieces and Property Cards (*Math Journal 1,* Activity Sheets 3 and 4)
Students practice identifying attributes of polygons.

 Ongoing Assessment:
Recognizing Student Achievement
Use *Math Masters,* page 497.
[Geometry Goal 2]

 Math Boxes 9·9
Math Journal 2, p. 326
Student Reference Book, p. 158
Students practice and maintain skills through Math Box problems.

Study Link 9·9
Math Masters, p. 284
Students practice and maintain skills through Study Link activities.

3 Differentiation Options

READINESS
Analyzing Prism Nets for Triangular Prisms
Math Masters, pp. 285 and 286
scissors ◆ tape or glue
Students build a triangular prism from a pattern.

ENRICHMENT
Building Nets
Math Masters, pp. 287 and 288
scissors ◆ tape or glue
Students explore the properties of prisms by building nets for prisms.

ELL SUPPORT
Building a Math Word Bank
Differentiation Handbook, p. 142
Students define and illustrate the term *prism*.

EXTRA PRACTICE
5-Minute Math
5-Minute Math™, pp. 214 and 215
Students calculate the volumes of rectangular prisms.

Advance Preparation

For Part 1, you will need two pieces of foam board, each at least 4 inches by 10 inches. Use the templates on *Math Masters,* pages 282 and 283 to draw and cut out a triangular prism and a parallelogram prism. With a pen or marker, draw the dashed lines (representing the heights of the bases). Draw a line segment connecting the midpoints of two sides of the triangle.

 Teacher's Reference Manual, **Grades 4–6** pp. 187–189, 222–225

Getting Started

Mental Math and Reflexes

Have students show thumbs up if the statement is true and thumbs down if the statement is false. *Suggestions:*

- ●○○ Prisms are 3-dimensional shapes. Thumbs up; true
- ●●○ A rectangular prism is formed by eight flat surfaces. Thumbs down; false

  The amount of space enclosed by a 3-dimensional shape is measured in cubic units. Thumbs up; true
- ●●● The volume of a prism is the area of its base. Thumbs down; false

Math Message

Are all of the cube structures shown on Study Link 9•8 rectangular prisms? Be prepared to explain your answer.

Study Link 9•8 Follow-Up

Have partners compare answers and resolve any differences.

---

1 Teaching the Lesson

▶ **Math Message Follow-Up**
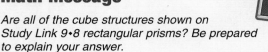 **WHOLE-CLASS DISCUSSION**

Ask volunteers to explain which of the cube structures on Study Link 9-8 are rectangular **prisms** and why.

▷ The structure in Problem 1 is a rectangular prism because all six surfaces are formed by rectangles.

▷ The other three structures are not rectangular prisms because their faces are not all rectangles. The bases are polygons, but not rectangles.

Remind students that geometric solids are hollow, but thinking of cube structures can help when measuring volume.

▷ All of the cube structures are prisms because each is a closed 3-dimensional figure made up of polygonal regions—the flat surfaces, or **faces**—and each has two congruent and parallel faces.

Ask students what the two congruent and parallel faces are called. Bases of the prism The other faces are formed by rectangles and connect the two bases. Ask volunteers to explain how a cube structure can be used to find the volume of a prism. Use their responses to emphasize the following points:

▷ You can think of each prism as being made up of layers of centimeter cubes with the same number of cubes in each layer. The number of layers is equivalent to the height of the prism.

▷ The number of cubes in the first layer is the same as the number of squares in the base (the area of the base).

▷ If you know the number of cubes in the first layer, then you can find the volume of the entire prism by multiplying the number of cubes in the first layer by the number of layers (the height of the prism).

Refer to Study Link 9-8, Problem 1, and pose the following question: *What would the volume of the prism be if it were 5 centimeters high?* 75 cm³ *2½ centimeters high?* 37.5 cm³ Have volunteers demonstrate their solution strategies on the board.

NOTE Slanted prisms are a second type of rectangular prism. They are distinguished from right prisms because all the lateral faces are not all rectangles and the lateral edges are not perpendicular to the bases. Slanted prisms are defined by transformations of a polygonal base.

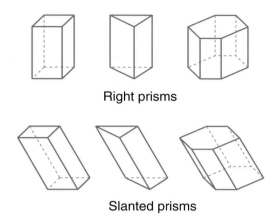

Right prisms

Slanted prisms

▶ Verifying the Volume Formula for Prisms

WHOLE-CLASS ACTIVITY

(*Math Masters,* pp. 282 and 283)

Algebraic Thinking Show students the two prisms that you cut out of foam board. Ask volunteers to describe the shapes. Expect that students might respond that the shapes are 3-dimensional figures, geometric solids, and/or prisms. Explain that prisms are named by the shapes of the bases. Ask: *What are the names of these two prisms?* Triangular prism and parallelogram prism Ask students how we know that the triangular faces on the triangular prism are the bases. Because the bases of a prism must be parallel and congruent

Write the formula $V = B * h$ on the Class Data Pad. Tell students that this formula can be used to calculate the volume of any prism regardless of its base shape. The volume of any prism is the product of the area of its base times its height. Write this definition under the formula.

Have volunteers use the following activity to verify the volume formula:

1. Use a metric ruler to measure the base and height of one of the parallelogram prism faces. This face will be one of the bases. Use these measures to calculate the area of the base (*B*).

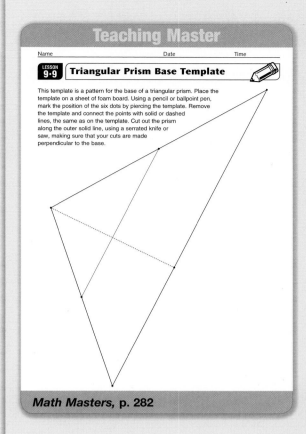
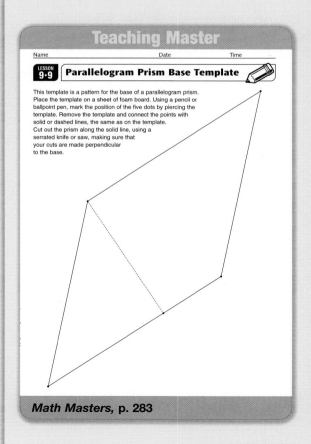

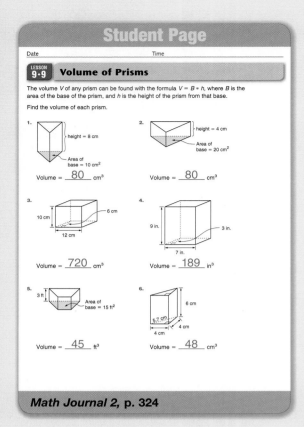

Date _____ Time _____

LESSON 9·9 **Volume of Prisms**

The volume V of any prism can be found with the formula $V = B * h$, where B is the area of the base of the prism, and h is the height of the prism from that base.

Find the volume of each prism.

1. height = 8 cm
Area of base = 10 cm²
Volume = __80__ cm³

2. height = 4 cm
Area of base = 20 cm²
Volume = __80__ cm³

3. 10 cm, 6 cm, 12 cm
Volume = __720__ cm³

4. 9 in., 3 in., 7 in.
Volume = __189__ in³

5. 3 ft, Area of base = 15 ft²
Volume = __45__ ft³

6. 6 cm, 5.7 cm, 4 cm, 4 cm
Volume = __48__ cm³

Math Journal 2, p. 324

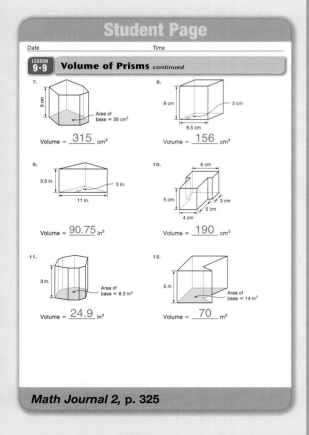

Date _____ Time _____

LESSON 9·9 **Volume of Prisms** *continued*

7. 9 cm, Area of base = 35 cm²
Volume = __315__ cm³

8. 8 cm, 3 cm, 6.5 cm
Volume = __156__ cm³

9. 5.5 in., 3 in., 11 in.
Volume = __90.75__ in³

10. 6 cm, 5 cm, 3 cm, 5 cm, 4 cm
Volume = __190__ cm³

11. 3 in., Area of base = 8.3 in²
Volume = __24.9__ in³

12. 5 m, Area of base = 14 m²
Volume = __70__ m³

Math Journal 2, p. 325

---

2. Measure the height (h) of the parallelogram prism. Record the area of the base (B) and the height (h) of the prism on the board.

3. Calculate the volume (V) of the prism, and record it on the board.

Cut the prism into two parts along the dashed height line. Move the triangular piece to the other end to form a rectangular prism. (*See Figure 1.*) Tape the two pieces together if you wish. Ask students if the volume of the prism has changed. No. Cutting and rearranging the prism has not changed its volume.

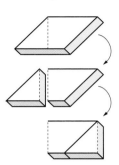

Figure 1

4. Use a metric ruler to measure the base and height of one of the rectangular prism faces. This face will be one of the bases. Use these measures to calculate the area of the base (B).

5. Measure the height (h) of the rectangular prism. Record the area of the base (B) and the height (h) of the rectangular prism on the board.

6. Calculate the volume (V) of the prism, and record it on the board.

Explain that when the parallelogram prism was cut and rearranged, the volume did not change. Because the formula $V = B * h$ applies to any prism, using this formula should result in the same volume for the parallelogram prism and the rectangular prism. Ask: *When applied to the parallelogram prism and the rectangular prism, did the formula* V = B * h *result in the same volume?* Yes

Repeat this procedure with the triangular prism. (*See Figure 2.*) This time cut the prism into three sections. First cut through the line connecting the midpoints of two sides. This creates a trapezoidal prism and a smaller triangular prism. Then cut the resulting triangular prism through the dashed height line, creating two smaller triangular prisms. Rotate and reattach these small triangular prisms at the ends of the trapezoidal prism to form a rectangular prism. Tape the pieces together if you wish.

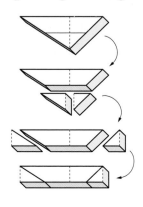

Figure 2

Finding the Volumes of Prisms

PARTNER ACTIVITY

(*Math Journal 2,* pp. 324 and 325)

Algebraic Thinking Have students complete journal pages 324 and 325.

Adding Volumes of Solids

WHOLE-CLASS ACTIVITY

(*Math Journal 2,* pp. 325A and 325B)

To solve problems on journal pages 325A and 325B, students find the volumes of rectangular prisms and then use those results to find the volumes of solid figures composed of two non-overlapping rectangular prisms. Write $3 \times 2 \times 4$ on the board. Ask:

- What does it mean if a rectangular prism has the dimensions $3 \times 2 \times 4$? Sample answer: The length is 3 units, the width is 2 units, and the height is 4 units.

- Does the notation suggest how you can find the volume? Yes Explain your answer. Sample answer: The notation suggests that you multiply the three dimensions together to find the volume.

Have students look at the prism in Problem 1, *Math Journal 2,* page 325A. Explain that this figure can be viewed as two rectangular prisms put together. Ask: *How could you find the volume of this solid using the formula for finding the volume of a rectangular prism?* Sample answer: Use the formula to find the volumes of the two smaller prisms, and then add the two volumes together.

Have students complete journal pages 325A and 325B. The solids on page 325A show stacks of cubes so students can count cubes to verify their results. The solids on page 325B provide the dimensions of the prisms but do not show the cubes.

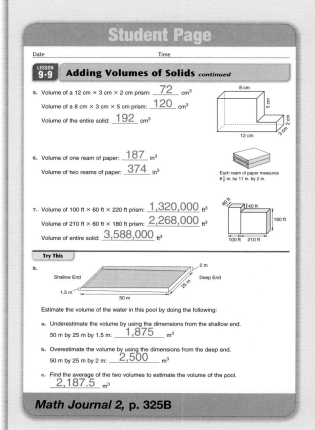

Math Journal 2, p. 325A

Math Journal 2, p. 325B

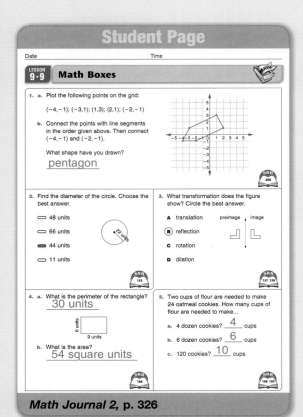

Student Page

Date   Time

LESSON 9·9   Math Boxes

1. a. Plot the following points on the grid:
   (−4,−1); (−3,1); (1,3); (2,1); (−2,−1)

   b. Connect the points with line segments in the order given above. Then connect (−4,−1) and (−2,−1).

   What shape have you drawn?
   __pentagon__

2. Find the diameter of the circle. Choose the best answer.
   ○ 48 units
   ○ 66 units
   ● 44 units
   ○ 11 units

   (circle labeled 22 units)

3. What transformation does the figure show? Circle the best answer.
   A translation   preimage   image
   (B) reflection
   C rotation
   D dilation

4. a. What is the perimeter of the rectangle?
   __30 units__

   (rectangle: 6 units by 9 units)

   b. What is the area?
   __54 square units__

5. Two cups of flour are needed to make 24 oatmeal cookies. How many cups of flour are needed to make...
   a. 4 dozen cookies? __4__ cups
   b. 6 dozen cookies? __6__ cups
   c. 120 cookies? __10__ cups

Math Journal 2, p. 326

▶ Playing *Polygon Capture*

PARTNER ACTIVITY

(*Student Reference Book,* p. 328; *Math Masters,* pp. 494–497)

Students practice identifying properties of polygons by playing *Polygon Capture*. Students first played this game in Unit 3 and stored the sets of *Polygon Capture* pieces and cards. If additional sets are needed, copy *Math Masters,* pages 494–496. Have students cut out the pieces and cards.

Ongoing Assessment:
Recognizing Student Achievement

Math Masters Page 497 ★

Use the **Record Sheet** from *Polygon Capture* (*Math Masters,* page 497) to assess students' ability to match polygons with their properties. On their first two draws of *Polygon Capture,* have students write the properties and list or draw all of the shapes that fit the properties. Students are making adequate progress if they have correctly matched properties and shapes.

[Geometry Goal 2]

▶ Math Boxes 9·9

INDEPENDENT ACTIVITY

(*Math Journal 2,* p. 326; *Student Reference Book,* p. 158)

Mixed Practice Math Boxes in this lesson are paired with Math Boxes in Lesson 9-6. The skill in Problem 5 previews Unit 10 content.

Writing/Reasoning Have students do the following: *Draw and label a preimage of a simple figure and then draw the image rotated 180° clockwise about a point.* Have students refer to *Student Reference Book,* page 158. Sample answer:

Preimage   Image

▶ Study Link 9·9

INDEPENDENT ACTIVITY

(*Math Masters,* p. 284)

Home Connection Students calculate the volume of various types of prisms.

Study Link Master

Name   Date   Time

STUDY LINK 9·9   Volumes of Prisms

The volume *V* of any prism can be found with the formula $V = B * h$, where *B* is the area of the base of the prism, and *h* is the height of the prism from that base.

1. (triangular prism: 6 cm, 4 cm, 6 cm)
   Volume = __72__ cm³

2. (rectangular prism: 5 cm, 4 cm, 7.2 cm)
   Volume = __144__ cm³

3. (triangular prism: 3.5 in., 5 in., 8 in.)
   Volume = __70__ in³

4. (prism: 4 cm, 6 cm, 3 cm, 5 cm, 3 cm)
   Volume = __162__ cm³

5. (prism: 3 in., Area of base = 15 in²)
   Volume = __45__ in³

6. (prism: 7 m, Area of base = 20 m²)
   Volume = __140__ m³

Practice

Solve each equation.

7. $36 * r = 144$ __4__

8. $3,577 − t = 3,822$ __−245__

9. $3,577 − m = 3,417$ __160__

10. $d * 68 = 340$ __5__

Math Masters, p. 284

3 Differentiation Options

READINESS

Analyzing Prism Nets for Triangular Prisms

SMALL-GROUP ACTIVITY

15–30 Min

(*Math Masters*, pp. 285 and 286)

To explore the properties of triangular prisms, have students build a prism from a net and identify other nets that will form a triangular prism. This activity mirrors activities in Lesson 9-8, except that students are now working with triangular prisms instead of cubes. Read and discuss the introduction on *Math Masters*, page 286 as a group.

Discuss students' solutions, and then have them identify the prism surfaces as either faces or bases.

ENRICHMENT

Building Nets

PARTNER ACTIVITY

30+ Min

(*Math Masters*, pp. 287 and 288)

To extend students' ability to visualize, name, and describe geometric solids, have students build nets for prisms. Partners cut out the individual shapes on *Math Masters*, page 287 and follow the instructions on *Math Masters*, page 288 to form nets for rectangular, triangular, pentagonal, hexagonal, or octagonal prisms.

Ask students to discuss any discoveries or curiosities they encountered during the activity. Consider having partners cut out and fold their completed nets to check the configurations.

ELL SUPPORT

Building A Math Word Bank

SMALL-GROUP ACTIVITY

5–15 Min

(*Differentiation Handbook*, p. 142)

To provide language support for volume, have students use the Word Bank Template found on *Differentiation Handbook*, page 142. Ask students to write the term *prism*, draw pictures related to the term, and write other related words. See the *Differentiation Handbook* for more information.

EXTRA PRACTICE

5-Minute Math

SMALL-GROUP ACTIVITY

5–15 Min

To offer students more experience calculating the volumes of rectangular prisms, see *5-Minute Math*, pages 214 and 215.

Teaching Master

Name   Date   Time

LESSON 9·9 Unfolding Geometric Solids

If you could unfold a prism so that its faces are laid out as a set attached at their edges, you would have a flat diagram for the shape. Imagine unfolding a triangular prism. There are different ways that you could make diagrams, depending on how you unfold the triangular prism.

Which of the following are diagrams that could be folded to make a triangular prism? Write *yes* or *no* in the blank under each diagram.

1.   Yes   2.   No

3.   Yes   4.   No

Math Masters, p. 286

Teaching Master

Name   Date   Time

LESSON 9·9 Using Faces and Bases

The flat diagram formed from unfolding a prism so that its faces are laid out flat and attached at their edges is called a **geometric net**. For a given prism, there are different nets, depending on how you think about unfolding the prism.

1. Cut out the figures on *Math Masters*, page 287. You and your partner will use the figures to build nets for the prisms below.

2. Take turns to select, draw, and place figures to form a net for a prism.

3. The partner who places the figure that completes the net states the number of faces and the number of bases. For example, if the net for a cube were completed, the partner would say, "4 faces, 2 bases." This ends the round.

4. A partner can also block the completion of a net. In this case, the partner would put down a figure that would prevent completing the net in the following placement and say "block." The blocked partner then has the opportunity to complete the net by placing two figures and stating the number of faces and bases. Again, this would end the round.

Example:

Student 1
Draw 1:

Student 2
Draw 2:

Student 1
Draw 3:

Student 2
Draw 4:

Student 1
Draw 5:

Student 1 states, "3 faces, 2 bases."

This ends the round.

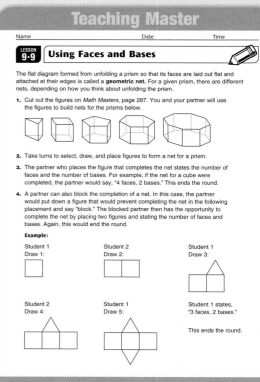

Math Masters, p. 288

9·10 Capacity: Liter, Milliliter, and Cubic Centimeter

 Objective To reinforce the relationships among the liter, milliliter, and cubic centimeter.

Technology Resources www.everydaymathonline.com

 ePresentations   eToolkit   Algorithms Practice   EM Facts Workshop Game™   Family Letters   Assessment Management   Common Core State Standards   Curriculum Focal Points  Interactive Teacher's Lesson Guide

---

1 Teaching the Lesson

Key Concepts and Skills

• Explore relationships between units of length and units of capacity. Investigate relationships and conversions between units of capacity and volume. Describe patterns in relationships between the dimensions and volume of rectangular prisms.
[Measurement and Reference Frames Goal 3]

Key Activities

Students verify that 1 L = 1,000 mL, a 1 L box actually holds 1 L, and 1 L = 1,000 cm³. They convert among units of volume and capacity and relate the dimensions of a prism to its volume.

 Ongoing Assessment:
Recognizing Student Achievement
Use an Exit Slip (*Math Masters,* p. 414).
[Measurement and Reference Frames Goal 3]

 Ongoing Assessment:
Informing Instruction See page 763.

Key Vocabulary

liter (L) ◆ capacity ◆ quart (qt) ◆ cup (c) ◆ milliliter (mL) ◆ cubic centimeter ◆ volume of a container

Materials

Math Journal 2, pp. 327–329
Study Link 9·9
Student Reference Book, pp. 196 and 197
Math Masters, pp. 414 and 436
Class Data Pad (optional) ◆ scissors ◆ transparent tape ◆ slate ◆ for demonstration: 1-liter cube, water-tight liter box, 1-liter pitcher, measuring cup, base-10 flats or longs

---

2 Ongoing Learning & Practice

Finding Areas of Rectangles with Fractional Measures

Math Journal 2, p. 330
Students find the areas of rectangles with fractional side lengths.

 Math Boxes 9·10

Math Journal 2, p. 331
Students practice and maintain skills through Math Box problems.

 Study Link 9·10

Math Masters, p. 289
Students practice and maintain skills through Study Link activities.

---

3 Differentiation Options

READINESS

Comparing the Capacity of Containers

per group: 5 different-sized containers; 5 volume-measuring tools; macaroni, centimeter cubes, or other small items to fill containers
Students explore the concept of capacity by comparing five different-sized containers.

EXTRA PRACTICE

Reading a Story about Volume

Room for Ripley
Students explain how they would calculate the volume of water needed to fill a fish tank.

ELL SUPPORT

Using Metric Prefix Multipliers

Student Reference Book, p. 396
Students use metric prefix multipliers to name quantities.

Advance Preparation

For Part 1, you will need a 1-liter cube, a water-tight liter box, a 1-liter pitcher, and a measuring cup that shows 1 cup and 250 mL. Gather a 1-liter bottle and other containers labeled with metric units of capacity. Make 2–4 copies of *Math Masters,* page 436 for each partnership. For the optional Extra Practice activity in Part 3, obtain a copy of **Room for Ripley** by Stuart J. Murphy (HarperCollins, 1999).

 Teacher's Reference Manual, Grades 4–6 pp. 216–218, 222–225

Getting Started

Mental Math and Reflexes

Have students record measurement equivalencies for units of capacity and volume on their slates. *Suggestions:*

●○○ 3 gallons equals how many pints? 24 pints

40 cups equals how many gallons? $2\frac{1}{2}$ gallons

●●○ 3 quarts equals how many fluid ounces? 96 fluid ounces

5 liters equals how many milliliters? 5,000 milliliters

●●● 700 cm³ equals how many milliliters? 700 milliliters

650 milliliters equals how many cubic centimeters? 650 cm³

Math Message

Which holds more, a 1-quart bottle or a 1-liter bottle? Be prepared to explain your answer.

Study Link 9·9 Follow-Up

Have partners compare their answers and resolve any differences.

---

1 Teaching the Lesson

Math Message Follow-Up

 **WHOLE-CLASS DISCUSSION** · ELL

Survey students for their answers to the Math Message problem. Ask volunteers to explain their solution strategies. Then show students the 1-liter bottle, and remind them that the **liter (L)** is a metric unit of capacity. Ask volunteers to define **capacity.** Capacity is the amount a container can hold. Demonstrate that 1 liter is a little more than 1 **quart (qt):**

▷ Remind students that 1 quart equals 4 **cups (c).**

▷ Measure 1 cup of water with a measuring cup and pour it into the 1-liter pitcher. Do this four times. Show students that 4 cups or 1 quart of water does not reach the 1-liter level.

To support English language learners and students new to the United States who might not be familiar with the U.S. customary units of capacity, show the appropriate containers as these units are discussed.

Demonstrating That 1 Liter Equals 1,000 Milliliters

 **WHOLE-CLASS DISCUSSION** · ELL

Liquids such as water, soft drinks, and fuel are often measured in liters. Smaller amounts of liquids are often measured in milliliters. Show students several containers whose labels give the capacity in **milliliters (mL).** Review the symbols for liter (L) and milliliter (mL). To support English language learners, distinguish between the use of a single letter to indicate a unit such as L for liter and the use of a single letter as a variable, such as in the formula $A = l * w$.

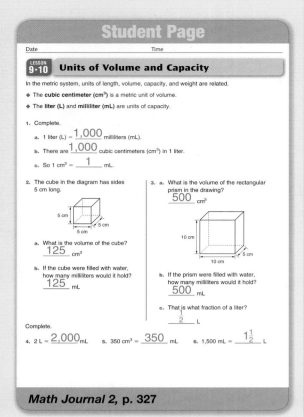

Math Journal 2, p. 327

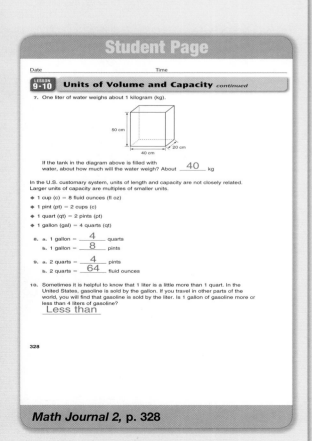

Math Journal 2, p. 328

▷ Demonstrate that there are 1,000 milliliters in 1 liter. Measure 250 milliliters of water with a measuring cup, and pour it into the 1-liter pitcher. Do this four times. Show students that the water reaches the 1-liter level.

Since 4 * 250 mL = 1,000 mL, then 1 liter = 1,000 milliliters.

▶ Demonstrating That 1 Liter Equals 1,000 cm³

 **WHOLE-CLASS DISCUSSION**

Model the relationship between 1 liter and 1,000 cubic centimeters:

▷ Demonstrate that a liter box actually holds 1 liter. Fill the 1-liter pitcher with water to the 1-liter level, and pour this into the liter box. Show students that the water is level with the top edge of the liter box. The liter box holds 1 liter of liquid.

▷ Demonstrate that a liter box holds 1,000 **cubic centimeters.** Count out and stack 10 flats (each 10 cm by 10 cm by 1 cm), or combine available flats with groups of 10 longs (each 10 cm by 1 cm by 1 cm) equivalent to 10 flats. Ask: *What is the volume of the cube structure?* 1,000 cm³ Next, fill the 1-liter box with the cube structure. Ask: *How much does the 1-liter box hold?* 1,000 cm³

Clarify that volume is the amount of space that a 3-dimensional object takes up. The **volume of a container** is a measure of how much the container will hold. The volume of a container that is filled with a liquid or a solid that can be poured is often called its capacity.

Capacity is usually measured in units such as gallons, quarts, pints, cups, fluid ounces, liters, and milliliters. These units of capacity are not cubic units, but liters and milliliters easily convert to cubic units.

Use questions similar to the following to summarize the discussions:

● 1 liter is equivalent to how many cubic centimeters? 1,000 cm³

● 1 liter is equivalent to how many milliliters? 1,000 milliliters

● What is the relationship between milliliters and cubic centimeters? 1 milliliter is equivalent to 1 cubic centimeter.

Write the following equivalencies on the board or on the Class Data Pad:

1 L = 1,000 mL

$1 \text{ mL} = \frac{1}{1,000} \text{ liter}$

1 L = 1,000 cm³

1 mL = 1 cm³

Solving Problems about Volume and Capacity

INDEPENDENT ACTIVITY

(*Math Journal 2*, pp. 327 and 328)

Assign journal pages 327 and 328. Students convert between metric units of volume and capacity and between U.S. customary units of capacity.

 Ongoing Assessment:
Recognizing Student Achievement

Exit Slip ⭐

Use an **Exit Slip** (*Math Masters,* page 414) to assess students' understanding of the distinction between volume and capacity. Have students explain the difference between volume and capacity, and have them list several examples of things that would be measured in cubic centimeters and several examples of things that would be measured in milliliters. Students are making adequate progress if they reference liquids that can be poured as being measured in milliliters, or a unit of capacity, and cubic centimeters as the measure of nonliquids, or the measure of how much space is taken up or enclosed.

[Measurement and Reference Frames Goal 3]

Exploring Volume

PARTNER ACTIVITY

(*Math Journal 2*, p. 329; *Student Reference Book,* pp. 196 and 197; *Math Masters*, p. 436)

PROBLEM SOLVING

Ask students to refer to the formulas for finding the volumes of rectangular prisms on pages 196 and 197 of the *Student Reference Book,* as needed. Ask volunteers to record the two formulas for finding the volume of a rectangular prism on the board.

$$V = l * w * h$$

$$V = B * h$$

Pass out several copies of *Math Masters,* page 436 (1 cm Grid Paper) to each partnership. Partners first cut out a 16 cm by 22 cm section of grid paper. Then on journal page 329 they try to find the dimensions of the open box with the greatest possible volume that can be made out of that section of grid paper. Remind students of the open-box patterns they used on Activity Sheet 8 in Lesson 9-8 and the nets they made in the Part 3 activities of Lesson 9-9. Finally, they record their discovery in Problem 2.

Date _____ Time _____

LESSON 9·10 **Open Boxes**

What are the dimensions of an open box—having the greatest possible volume—that can be made out of a single sheet of centimeter grid paper?

1. Use centimeter grid paper to experiment until you discover a pattern. Record your results in the table below.

Height of box	Length of base	Width of base	Volume of box
1 cm	20 cm	14 cm	280 cm³
2 cm	18 cm	12 cm	432 cm³
3 cm	16 cm	10 cm	480 cm³
4 cm	14 cm	8 cm	448 cm³
5 cm	12 cm	6 cm	360 cm³
6 cm	10 cm	4 cm	240 cm³
7 cm	8 cm	2 cm	112 cm³

2. What are the dimensions of the box with the greatest volume?

Height of box = _3_ cm   Length of base = _16_ cm

Width of base = _10_ cm   Volume of box = _480_ cm³

Math Journal 2, p. 329

 Ongoing Assessment:
Informing Instruction

Watch for students who have difficulty deciding how to cut the grid paper correctly to make boxes. Suggest that they cut a 1 cm by 1 cm square out of each of the four corners of the grid to make a pattern for an open box that is 1 centimeter in height, then cut a 2 cm by 2 cm square at each corner to make a pattern for an open box that is 2 cm in height, and so on.

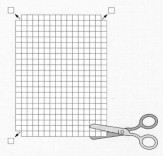

Students use *Math Masters*, page 436 to find the greatest possible volume of an open box.

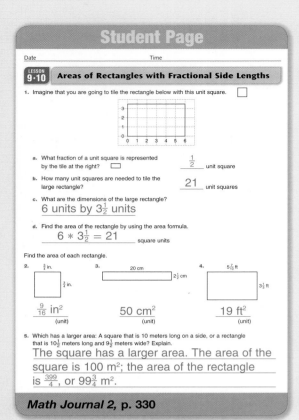

Student Page

Date _____ Time _____

LESSON 9·10 Areas of Rectangles with Fractional Side Lengths

1. Imagine that you are going to tile the rectangle below with this unit square. ☐

a. What fraction of a unit square is represented by the tile at the right? ☐ $\frac{1}{2}$ unit square

b. How many unit squares are needed to tile the large rectangle?   **21** unit squares

c. What are the dimensions of the large rectangle?   **6 units by $3\frac{1}{2}$ units**

d. Find the area of the rectangle by using the area formula. $6 * 3\frac{1}{2} = 21$ square units

Find the area of each rectangle.

2. $\frac{3}{4}$ in.
$\frac{3}{4}$ in.
$\frac{9}{16}$ in² (unit)

3. 20 cm
$2\frac{1}{2}$ cm
50 cm² (unit)

4. $5\frac{7}{10}$ ft
$3\frac{1}{3}$ ft
19 ft² (unit)

5. Which has a larger area: A square that is 10 meters long on a side, or a rectangle that is $10\frac{1}{2}$ meters long and $9\frac{1}{2}$ meters wide? Explain.
The square has a larger area. The area of the square is 100 m²; the area of the rectangle is $\frac{399}{4}$, or $99\frac{3}{4}$ m².

Math Journal 2, p. 330

▶ **Finding Areas of Rectangles with Fractional Measures**

INDEPENDENT ACTIVITY

(*Math Journal 2*, p. 330)

Students find the areas of rectangles with fractional side lengths.

▶ **Math Boxes 9·10**

INDEPENDENT ACTIVITY

(*Math Journal 2*, p. 331)

Mixed Practice Math Boxes in this lesson are paired with Math Boxes in Lesson 9-8. The skills in Problems 2 and 5 preview Unit 10 content.

Writing/Reasoning Have students write a response to the following: *Explain how you found the least common denominator for Problem 3.* Sample answer: I wrote the multiples for 20 (20, 40, 60, and so on) until I found a number that was divisible by 3 (60).

Writing/Reasoning Have students write a response to the following: *Explain the strategy you used to solve Problem 1d and the reasoning used.* Answers vary.

▶ **Study Link 9·10**

INDEPENDENT ACTIVITY

(*Math Masters*, p. 289)

Home Connection Students complete a page that reviews plotting points and calculating area.

READINESS

SMALL-GROUP ACTIVITY

▶ **Comparing the Capacity of Containers**

 15–30 Min

To explore the concept of capacity, have students compare the capacity of five different-sized containers. Ask students to predict which containers have the largest and smallest capacities. Then have students use fill material (macaroni, centimeter cubes) to compare the capacities of the five containers and to determine if their predictions were correct. Encourage students to continue to develop their personal references as they make and check their predictions.

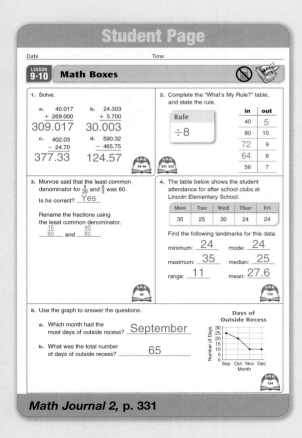

Student Page

Date _____ Time _____

LESSON 9·10 Math Boxes

1. Solve.

a. 40.017 + 269.000 = **309.017**   b. 24.303 + 5.700 = **30.003**

c. 402.03 − 24.70 = **377.33**   d. 590.32 − 465.75 = **124.57**

2. Complete the "What's My Rule?" table, and state the rule.

Rule: $\div 8$

in	out
40	5
80	10
72	9
64	8
56	7

3. Monroe said that the least common denominator for $\frac{5}{20}$ and $\frac{2}{3}$ was 60.

Is he correct? **Yes**

Rename the fractions using the least common denominator.
$\frac{15}{60}$ and $\frac{40}{60}$

4. The table below shows the student attendance for after school clubs at Lincoln Elementary School.

Mon	Tue	Wed	Thur	Fri
35	25	30	24	24

Find the following landmarks for this data.

minimum: **24**   mode: **24**

maximum: **35**   median: **25**

range: **11**   mean: **27.6**

5. Use the graph to answer the questions.

a. Which month had the most days of outside recess? **September**

b. What was the total number of days of outside recess? **65**

Days of Outside Recess

Math Journal 2, p. 331

Reading a Story about Volume

WHOLE-CLASS ACTIVITY

🕐 5–15 Min

Literature Link To explore volume, read the following book to the class. Explore the following question: *How much water does the fish tank hold?* Discuss how students would calculate the volume of water in the fish tank.

Room for Ripley

Summary: This book follows a boy's adventure to buy a fish and figure out how much water is needed in the fish tank.

ELL SUPPORT

Using Metric Prefix Multipliers

SMALL-GROUP ACTIVITY

🕐 5–15 Min

(*Student Reference Book,* p. 396)

To support language development for metric measurement, have students look at the prefixes table on *Student Reference Book,* page 396. Ask questions similar to the following:

- If a cycle is a wheel, how many wheels does a unicycle have? A bicycle? A tricycle? One wheel; two wheels; three wheels

- How many angles does a quadrangle have? four

- How many sides does a pentagon have? A hexagon? A heptagon? A nonagon? 5 sides; 6 sides; 7 sides; 9 sides

- How many liters are in a kiloliter? A milliliter? 1,000 liters; $\frac{1}{1,000}$ liter

Encourage students to look for the prefixes in number names. Consider having students illustrate some of the words and prefixes that they discuss.

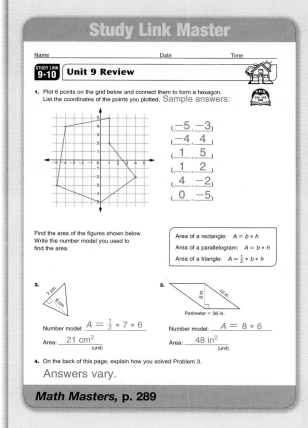

Study Link Master

Name   Date   Time

STUDY LINK 9·10 **Unit 9 Review**

1. Plot 6 points on the grid below and connect them to form a hexagon. List the coordinates of the points you plotted. Sample answers:

$(-5, -3)$
$(-4, 4)$
$(1, 5)$
$(1, 2)$
$(4, -2)$
$(0, -5)$

Find the area of the figures shown below. Write the number model you used to find the area.

Area of a rectangle: $A = b * h$
Area of a parallelogram: $A = b * h$
Area of a triangle: $A = \frac{1}{2} * b * h$

2. 7 cm, 6 cm

Number model: $A = \frac{1}{2} * 7 * 6$

Area: $21\ cm^2$ (unit)

3. 6 in., 10 in.
Perimeter = 36 in.

Number model: $A = 8 * 6$

Area: $48\ in^2$ (unit)

4. On the back of this page, explain how you solved Problem 3.

Answers vary.

Math Masters, p. 289

◎ Objective To assess students' progress on mathematical content through the end of Unit 9.

---

1 Looking Back: Cumulative Assessment

 Input student data from Progress Check 9 into the **Assessment Management Spreadsheets**.

Materials
- ◆ Study Link 9◆10
- ◆ *Assessment Handbook*, pp. 118–125, 194–198, 224, and 268–271
- ◆ slate

CONTENT ASSESSED	LESSON(S)	SELF	ORAL/SLATE	WRITTEN PART A	PART B	OPEN RESPONSE
Factor numbers. [Number and Numeration Goal 3]						✔
Understand the concepts of perimeter and area of a figure. [Measurement and Reference Frames Goal 2]	9·4, 9·5	2	1, 2	5, 11		✔
Use a formula to find the perimeters and areas of triangles and parallelograms. [Measurement and Reference Frames Goal 2]	9·5, 9·6	3	3	5–9, 13, 14		✔
Understand the concept of volume of a figure. [Measurement and Reference Frames Goal 2]	9·8–9·10	5	1, 2	14, 17	22	
Use a formula to find the volumes of prisms. [Measurement and Reference Frames Goal 2]	9·8, 9·9	6	4	16, 17	18–21	
Identify and plot ordered pairs on a coordinate grid. [Measurement and Reference Frames Goal 4]	9·1–9·3	1		1–4, 12, 13		
Identify the base and height of triangles and parallelograms. [Geometry Goal 2]	9·6	4		10, 15		
Understand and draw figure reflections. [Geometry Goal 3]	9·2, 9·3			2, 4		

---

2 Looking Ahead: Preparing for Unit 10

 Math Boxes 9◆11

 Study Link 9◆11: Unit 10 Family Letter

Materials
- ◆ *Math Journal 2*, p. 332
- ◆ *Math Masters*, pp. 290–293

Getting Started

1 Looking Back: Cumulative Assessment

Math Message Follow-Up

INDEPENDENT ACTIVITY

(Self Assessment, *Assessment Handbook,* p. 194)

The Self Assessment offers students the opportunity to reflect upon their progress.

Oral and Slate Assessments

SMALL-GROUP ACTIVITY

Problems 1 and 3 provide summative information and can be used for grading purposes. Problems 2 and 4 provide formative information that can be useful in planning future instruction.

Oral Assessment

1. Ask students to show thumbs up if the statement about area or volume is true and thumbs down if the statement is false. You may want to have students correct the incorrect statements. *Suggestions:*

   - Inches squared is a unit of volume. Thumbs down; false; unit of area

   - Area is found using two dimensions. Thumbs up; true

   - 64 cubic feet could describe area or volume. Thumbs down; false; describes volume

2. Ask students to show thumbs up if the situation involves finding the volume and thumbs down if the situation involves finding the area. *Suggestions:*

   - The amount of cereal a box would hold. Thumbs up; volume

   - The surface of a kitchen floor. Thumbs down; area

   - How much a moving box would hold. Thumbs up; volume

Assessment Master

Name _____ Date _____ Time _____

LESSON 9·11 **Self Assessment** — Progress Check 9

Think about each skill listed below. Assess your own progress by checking the most appropriate box.

Skills	I can do this on my own and explain how to do it.	I can do this on my own.	I can do this if I get help or look at an example.
1. Identify and plot ordered pairs on a one-quadrant and four-quadrant coordinate grid.			
2. Understand the concept of area of a figure.			
3. Use a formula to find the area of rectangles, triangles, and parallelograms.			
4. Identify the base and height of triangles and parallelograms.			
5. Understand the concept of volume of a figure.			
6. Use a formula to find the volume of prisms.			

Assessment Handbook, p. 194

Assessment Master

Name _____ Date _____ Time _____

LESSON 9·11 **Written Assessment** — Progress Check 9

Part A

Use the grid at the right for Problems 1–4.

1. **a.** Plot and label the following points:
   A: (1,1)   B: (2,3)   C: (5,3)   D: (4,1)

   b. Draw line segments to connect the points as follows:
   A to B, B to C, C to D, and D to A.

   c. Describe the figure you have drawn.
   Sample answer:
   A parallelogram with $\overline{BC}$ parallel to $\overline{AD}$ and $\overline{AB}$ parallel to $\overline{DC}$

2. Plot points on the grid to make a reflection of the figure. Begin with the reflection of point A at (1,−1).

3. Record the points you used below.

Point	Original Figure	Reflected Figure
A	(1,1)	(1 , −1)
B	(2,3)	(2 , −3)
C	(5,3)	(5 , −3)
D	(4,1)	(4 , −1)

4. Describe a rule for changing the points from the original figure to get the reflected figure.
   Sample answer: Change the second number in each number pair to its opposite.

Assessment Handbook, p. 195

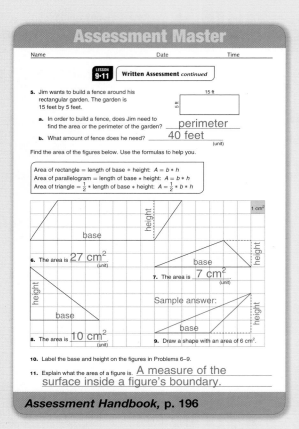

Assessment Master

Name _____ Date _____ Time _____

LESSON 9·11 Written Assessment *continued*

5. Jim wants to build a fence around his rectangular garden. The garden is 15 feet by 5 feet.

15 ft / 5 ft

a. In order to build a fence, does Jim need to find the area or the perimeter of the garden? __perimeter__

b. What amount of fence does he need? __40 feet__ (unit)

Find the area of the figures below. Use the formulas to help you.

Area of rectangle = length of base * height: $A = b * h$
Area of parallelogram = length of base * height: $A = b * h$
Area of triangle = $\frac{1}{2}$ * length of base * height: $A = \frac{1}{2} * b * h$

1 cm²

base / height

6. The area is __27 cm²__ (unit)

7. The area is __7 cm²__ (unit) base / height

height / base

8. The area is __10 cm²__ (unit)

Sample answer: base / height

9. Draw a shape with an area of 6 cm².

10. Label the base and height on the figures in Problems 6–9.

11. Explain what the area of a figure is. __A measure of the surface inside a figure's boundary.__

Assessment Handbook, p. 196

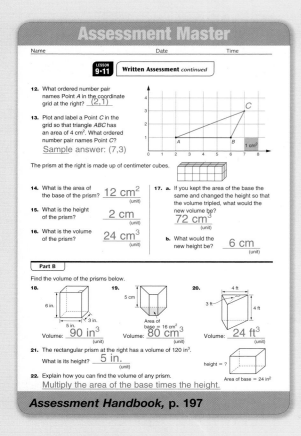

Assessment Master

Name _____ Date _____ Time _____

LESSON 9·11 Written Assessment *continued*

12. What ordered number pair names Point A in the coordinate grid at the right? __(2,1)__

13. Plot and label a Point C in the grid so that triangle ABC has an area of 4 cm². What ordered number pair names Point C? __Sample answer: (7,3)__

The prism at the right is made up of centimeter cubes.

14. What is the area of the base of the prism? __12 cm²__ (unit)

15. What is the height of the prism? __2 cm__ (unit)

16. What is the volume of the prism? __24 cm³__ (unit)

17. a. If you kept the area of the base the same and changed the height so that the volume tripled, what would the new volume be? __72 cm³__ (unit)

b. What would the new height be? __6 cm__ (unit)

Part B

Find the volume of the prisms below.

18. 6 in. / 5 in. / 3 in. Volume: __90 in³__ (unit)

19. 5 cm / Area of base = 16 cm² Volume: __80 cm³__ (unit)

20. 4 ft / 3 ft / 4 ft Volume: __24 ft³__ (unit)

21. The rectangular prism at the right has a volume of 120 in³. What is its height? __5 in.__ (unit) height = ? / Area of base = 24 in²

22. Explain how you can find the volume of any prism. __Multiply the area of the base times the height.__

Assessment Handbook, p. 197

768 Unit 9 Progress Check 9

Slate Assessment

3. Have students calculate the areas of rectangles with the given dimensions. *Suggestions:*

- The base is 9 centimeters and the height is 8 centimeters. 72 cm^2

- The base is 12 feet and the height is 3 yards. 12 yd^2, or 108 f

- The base is 5 meters and the perimeter is 22 meters. 30 m^2

4. Have students calculate the volumes of rectangular prisms wit the given dimensions. *Suggestions:*

- The length is 2 inches, the height is 4 inches, and the width i 3 inches. 24 in^3

- The height is 3 units, the length is 4 units, and the width is 3 units. 36 cubic units

▶ **Written Assessment**

(*Assessment Handbook*, pp. 195–197)

INDEPENDENT ACTIVITY

Part A   Recognizing Student Achievement

Problems 1–17 provide summative information and may be used fo grading purposes.

Problem(s)	Description
1–4, 12, 13	Identify and plot ordered pairs on a one and four-quadrant coordinate grid.
5, 11	Understand the concept of area of a figure.
6–9	Use a formula to find the areas of triangles a parallelograms.
10	Identify the base and height of triangles and parallelograms.
14, 15	Understand the concept of volume of a figure
16, 17	Use a formula to find the volume of prisms.

Part B   Informing Instruction

Problems 18–22 provide formative information that can be useful i planning future instruction.

Problem(s)	Description
18–21	Use a formula to find the volume of prisms
22	Understand the concept of volume for a figur

Use the checklists on pages 269 and 271 of the *Assessment Handbook* to record results. Then input the data into the **Assessment Management Spreadsheets** to keep an ongo record of students' progress toward Grade-Level Goals.

Open Response

(*Assessment Handbook,* p. 198)

INDEPENDENT ACTIVITY

Countertop Tiles

The open-response item requires students to apply skills and concepts from Unit 9 to solve a multistep problem. See *Assessment Handbook,* pages 121–125 for rubrics and students' work samples for this problem.

---

2 Looking Ahead: Preparing for Unit 10

Math Boxes 9·11

INDEPENDENT ACTIVITY

(*Math Journal 2,* p. 332)

Mixed Practice This Math Boxes page previews Unit 10 content.

Study Link 9·11: Unit 10 Family Letter

INDEPENDENT ACTIVITY

(*Math Masters,* pp. 290–293)

Home Connection The Unit 10 Family Letter provides parents and guardians with information and activities related to Unit 10 topics.

Name   Date   Time

LESSON 9·11 Open Response   Progress Check 9

Countertop Tiles

Rafael is covering two countertops with tiles. The tiles are three inches by six inches.

For each countertop:

◆ Decide whether Rafael will be able to cover the entire surface with whole tiles (no gaps and no overlaps).

◆ Record your work with labeled pictures, and explain in words why the countertop can or cannot be covered with the tiles.

1. Countertop A: 15 inches by 18 inches

2. Countertop B: 9 inches by 9 inches

3. Based on your work, what rule could be used to determine whether or not a countertop can be covered with three-inch-by-six-inch tiles without having to draw a plan?

Assessment Handbook, p. 198

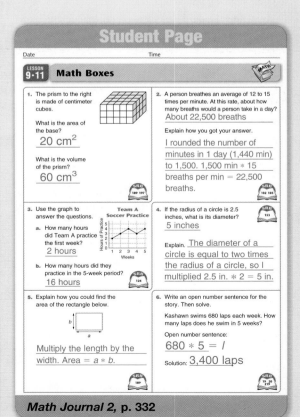

Date   Time

LESSON 9·11 Math Boxes

1. The prism to the right is made of centimeter cubes.

What is the area of the base?

20 cm²

What is the volume of the prism?

60 cm³

2. A person breathes an average of 12 to 15 times per minute. At this rate, about how many breaths would a person take in a day?

About 22,500 breaths

Explain how you got your answer.

I rounded the number of minutes in 1 day (1,440 min) to 1,500. 1,500 min * 15 breaths per min = 22,500 breaths.

3. Use the graph to answer the questions.

Team A Soccer Practice

a. How many hours did Team A practice the first week?

2 hours

b. How many hours did they practice in the 5-week period?

16 hours

4. If the radius of a circle is 2.5 inches, what is its diameter?

5 inches

Explain. The diameter of a circle is equal to two times the radius of a circle, so I multiplied 2.5 in. * 2 = 5 in.

5. Explain how you could find the area of the rectangle below.

Multiply the length by the width. Area = a * b.

6. Write an open number sentence for the story. Then solve.

Kashawn swims 680 laps each week. How many laps does he swim in 5 weeks?

Open number sentence:

680 * 5 = l

Solution: **3,400 laps**

Math Journal 2, p. 332

Using Data; Algebra Concepts and Skills

Overview

In Unit 10, students will be introduced to pre-algebra concepts and skills. They will concentrate on solving problems using a pan-balance model, which means making sure that a change to one side is compensated by a change to the other side. Students will also represent relationships as algebraic expressions that will help them generate input-output tables. Linking the data in the tables to corresponding points on a coordinate grid will help students better understand and interpret the data. Unit 10 has four main areas of focus:

◆ To solve equations using a pan-balance model,

◆ To represent relationships as algebraic expressions,

◆ To generate input-output tables, and

◆ To link data in tables to corresponding points on coordinate grids.

CCSS Linking to the Common Core State Standards

The content of Unit 10 addresses the Common Core State Standards for Mathematics in *Operations and Algebraic Thinking.* The correlation of the Common Core State Standards to the *Everyday Mathematics* Grade 5 lessons begins on page CS1.

▶ Contents

Learning In Perspective

	Lesson Objectives	Links to the Past	Links to the Future
10·1	To introduce a pan-balance approach for solving simple equations.	In fourth grade, students are introduced to vocabulary for open sentences.	In sixth grade, students model equation-solving techniques.
10·2	To develop a pan-balance approach for solving sets of two equations with two unknowns.	In fourth grade, students solve open number sentences.	In sixth grade, students use an equivalent equations method for solving equations.
10·3	To introduce the use of algebraic expressions to represent situations and describe rules.	In fourth grade, students solve "What's My Rule?" and Frames-and-Arrows problems.	In sixth grade, students write algebraic expressions for situations.
10·4	To develop representational forms for rates.	In fourth grade, students find unit rates.	In sixth grade, students model rate and ratio problems with proportions.
10·5	To provide experience with using a formula as a prediction tool.	In fourth grade, students develop and use a formula for the area of a rectangle.	In sixth grade, students simplify and solve equations.
10·6	To provide experiences with interpreting tables and graphs.	In fourth grade, students determine the maximum, minimum, range, and mode of a set of data.	In sixth grade, students use diagrams, formulas, and graphs for making predictions and drawing conclusions.
10·7	To provide experiences with interpreting line graphs.	In fourth grade, students find the median of a set of data and display data with line plots and graphs.	In sixth grade, students represent rates with data tables, rules expressed in words, formulas, and line graphs.
10·8	To provide experience with comparison ratios and the use of the irrational number π.	In third grade, children develop the "about 3 times" rule relating circumference and diameter.	In sixth grade, students apply appropriate uses of the irrational number π.
10·9	To introduce a formula to calculate the area of a circle.	In fourth grade, students develop a definition of a circle with paper folding.	In sixth grade, students apply a formula to calculate the area of a circle.

Key Concepts and Skills	Grade 5 Goals*

10·1
Use addition and subtraction to solve pan-balance problems.
Use multiplication and division to solve pan-balance problems.
Use a pan-balance model to solve linear equations with one unknown.

Operations and Computation Goal 1
Operations and Computation Goal 3
Patterns, Functions, and Algebra Goal 2

10·2
Use addition and subtraction to solve pan-balance problems.
Use multiplication and division to solve pan-balance problems.
Use a pan-balance model to solve linear equations with two unknowns.

Operations and Computation Goal 1
Operations and Computation Goal 3
Patterns, Functions, and Algebra Goal 2

10·3
Identify and use patterns in tables to solve problems.
Write algebraic expressions to model rules.
Use variables to write number models that describe situations.

Patterns, Functions, and Algebra Goal 1
Patterns, Functions, and Algebra Goal 1
Patterns, Functions, and Algebra Goal 2

10·4
Use table data to create line graphs.
Represent functions with tables, graphs, and formulas.
Extend patterns in graphs and tables to solve problems.

Data and Chance Goal 1
Patterns, Functions, and Algebra Goal 1
Patterns, Functions, and Algebra Goal 1

10·5
Construct line graphs that represent single sets of data.
Extend patterns in graphs and tables to solve problems.
Represent functions with tables, graphs, and formulas.

Data and Chance Goal 1
Patterns, Functions, and Algebra Goal 1
Patterns, Functions, and Algebra Goal 1

10·6
Construct line graphs that represent two sets of data.
Extend patterns in graphs and tables to solve problems.
Represent rates with formulas, tables, and graphs.

Data and Chance Goal 1
Patterns, Functions, and Algebra Goal 1
Patterns, Functions, and Algebra Goal 1

10·7
Read and analyze line graphs and answer questions based on the displayed data.
Identify and use patterns in graphs to match graphs with situations.

Data and Chance Goal 2
Patterns, Functions, and Algebra Goal 1

10·8
Use ratios to express relationships between dimensions of objects.
Find the median of a data set.
Use ratios to define π and describe the relationship between circumference and diameter.

Operations and Computation Goal 7
Data and Chance Goal 2
Measurement and Reference Frames Goal 2

10·9
Find the median of a data set.
Investigate and apply a formula for finding the area of a circle.
Use ratios to describe the relationship between radius and area.
Use patterns in a table to define the relationship between radius and area.

Data and Chance Goal 2
Measurement and Reference Frames Goal 2
Measurement and Reference Frames Goal 2
Patterns, Functions, and Algebra Goal 1

*See the Appendix for a complete list of Grade 5 Goals.

A Balanced Curriculum

Ongoing Practice

Everyday Mathematics provides numerous opportunities for ongoing practice. These activities are embedded throughout the lessons:

 Mental Math and Reflexes activities promote speed and accuracy in mental computation.

 Math Boxes offer mixed practice and are paired across lessons as shown in the brackets below. This makes them useful as assessment tools. The last one or two boxes on each page preview the next unit's content.

Mixed practice	[10•1, 10•3], [10•2, 10•4], [10•5, 10•7, 10•9], [10•6, 10•8]
Mixed practice with multiple choice	10•2, 10•4
Mixed practice with writing/reasoning opportunity	10•1, 10•2, 10•3, 10•4, 10•6, 10•9

 Study Links are daily homework assignments that review the content of the lesson and often contain ongoing facts practice or computation practice.

 5-Minute Math problems are offered for additional practice in Lessons 10•5 and 10•7.

 EM Facts Workshop Game provides online practice of basic facts and computation.

EXTRA PRACTICE **Extra Practice** activities are included in Lessons 10•1, 10•3, 10•4, 10•5, 10•7, and 10•9.

Practice through Games

Games are an essential component of practice in the *Everyday Mathematics* program. Games offer skills practice and promote strategic thinking. See the *Differentiation Handbook* for ways to adapt games to meet students' needs.

Lesson	Game	Skill Practiced
10•1, 10•7, 10•9	*First to 100*	Practicing solving open number sentences [PFA Goal 2]
10•3	*Name That Number*	Applying number properties, equivalent names, arithmetic operations, and basic facts [NN Goal 4 and PFA Goal 3]
10•6	*Mixed-Number Spin* or *Fraction Spin*	Estimating sums and differences of fractions and/or mixed numbers [OC Goals 4 and 6]

[NN] Number and Numeration [OC] Operations and Computation [DC] Data and Chance
[MRF] Measurement and Reference Frames [GEO] Geometry [PFA] Patterns, Functions, and Algebra

Problem Solving

Experts at problem solving and mathematical modeling generally do these things:

- Identify the problem.
- Decide what information is needed to solve the problem.
- Play with and study the data to find patterns and meaning.

- Identify and use mathematical procedures to solve the problem.
- Decide whether the solution makes sense and whether it can be applied to other problems.

The table below lists some of the opportunities in this unit for students to practice these strategies.

Lesson	Activity
10•1, 10•2	Solve pan-balance problems.
10•3	Write algebraic expressions to represent situations described in words.
10•4	Use different ways of representing rates to solve rate problems.
10•5	Predict when Old Faithful will erupt next.
10•7	Match descriptions of events with graphs that represent them.
10•8	Investigate the relationship between the circumference and diameter of a circle.
10•9	Investigate the relationship between the radius and the area of a circle.

Lessons that teach through problem solving, not just about problem solving

See Chapter 18: Problem Solving in the *Teacher's Reference Manual* for more information.

The Language of Mathematics

Everyday Mathematics provides lesson-specific suggestions to help all students acquire, process, and express mathematical ideas. Throughout Unit 10, there are lesson-specific language development notes that address the needs of English language learners, indicated by **ELL**.

ELL SUPPORT Activities to support English language learners are in Part 3 of Lessons 10•3, 10•4, and 10•8.

The *English Learners Handbook* and the *Differentiation Handbook* have suggestions for promoting language development and acquisition of mathematics vocabulary. See Unit 10 in each handbook.

Literacy Connection

The Librarian Who Measured the Earth, by Kathryn Lasky, Little Brown & Co., 1994

Sir Cumference and the First Round Table, by Cindy Neuschwander, Charlesbridge Publishing, 2002

Sir Cumference and the Dragon of Pi: A Math Adventure, by Cindy Neuschwander, Charlesbridge Publishing, 1999

For more literacy connections, see the *Home Connection Handbook,* Grades 4–6.

Unit 10 Vocabulary

algebraic expression
circumference
coordinates
diameter
formula
geyser
line graph
mystery graph
ordered number pairs
pan balance
pi (π)
predict
radius
rate
ratio
ratio comparison
variable

Cross-Curricular Links

Social Studies – Lesson 10•1   **Science** – Lesson 10•5
Literature – Lesson 10•8

Balanced Assessment

Daily Assessments

◆ **Recognizing Student Achievement** – A daily assessment that is included in every lesson to evaluate students' progress toward the Grade 5 Grade-Level Goals.

◆ **Informing Instruction** – Notes that appear throughout the unit to help anticipate students' common errors and suggest appropriate problem-solving strategies.

Lesson	Recognizing Student Achievement	Informing Instruction
10◆1	Apply a formula for volume. [MRF Goal 2]	Cross out objects that are removed with each change in a pan-balance problem. Write number models for expressions with shapes or variables.
10◆2	Solve equations using a pan-balance model. [PFA Goal 2]	
10◆3	Write algebraic expressions that model situations. [PFA Goal 2]	
10◆4	Use table data to plot points on a graph. [DC Goal 1]	
10◆5	Solve addition and subtraction open sentences containing negative and positive numbers. [PFA Goal 2]	
10◆6	Read and interpret graphs; be able to extend the lines to see an increase in time and distance. [DC Goal 2]	See the pattern in the computations used to complete Lupita's data in the table and write the computation in equation form.
10◆7	Interpret line graphs. [DC Goal 2]	Draw a graph on the board or Class Data Pad and ask questions about the visual representation of a situation.
10◆8	Explain and demonstrate accurate descriptions of area and perimeter. [MRF Goal 2]	
10◆9	Replace variables in number sentences and solve problems correctly. [PFA Goal 2]	Trace and measure larger objects.

[NN] Number and Numeration
[MRF] Measurement and Reference Frames

[OC] Operations and Computation
[GEO] Geometry

[DC] Data and Chance
[PFA] Patterns, Functions, and Algebra

Portfolio Opportunities

The following lessons provide opportunities to gather samples of students' mathematical writings, drawings, and creations to add balance to the assessment process: Lessons 10◆1, 10◆2, 10◆4, 10◆5, 10◆6, 10◆7, 10◆9, and 10◆10.

See pages 16 and 17 in the *Assessment Handbook* for more information about portfolios and how to use them.

Unit Assessment

Progress Check 10 – A cumulative assessment of concepts and skills taught in Unit 10 and in previous units, providing information for evaluating students' progress and planning for future instruction. These assessments include oral/slate, written, and open-response activities, as shown below in the sample Progress Check lesson opener.

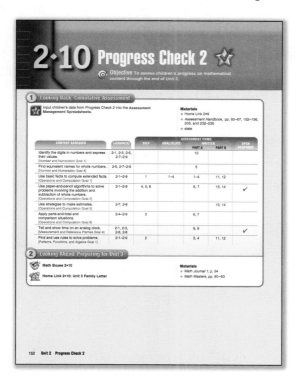

Core Assessment Resources

Assessment Handbook

- ◆ **Unit 10 Assessment Overview,** pages pages 126–133
- ◆ **Unit 10 Assessment Masters,** pages 199–204
- ◆ **Unit 10 Individual Profiles of Progress,** pages 282, 283, and 302
- ◆ **Unit 10 Class Checklists,** pages 284, 285, and 303
- ◆ **Math Logs,** pages 306–308
- ◆ **Exit Slip,** page 311
- ◆ **Other Student Assessment Forms,** pages 304, 305, 309, and 310

Assessment Management Spreadsheets

The Assessment Management Spreadsheets consist of the Digital Class Checklists and Individual Profile of Progress Checklists. Use them to monitor, record, and report student progress.

Addressing All Needs

Differentiated Instruction

 Adjusting the Activity – suggests adaptations that target advanced learners, English language learners, or learners who need additional instructional support.

ELL SUPPORT / **ELL** – provides lesson-specific suggestions to help English language learners understand and process the mathematical content.

READINESS – accesses students' prior knowledge or previews content that prepares students to engage in the lesson's Part 1 activities.

EXTRA PRACTICE – provides additional opportunities to apply the mathematical content of the lesson.

ENRICHMENT – enables students to apply or further explore the mathematical content of the lesson.

Lesson	Adjusting the Activity	ELL Support/ ELL	Readiness	Extra Practice	Enrichment
10◆1	●	●	●	●	●
10◆2	●	●	●		●
10◆3		●	●	●	●
10◆4		●		●	●
10◆5		●		●	●
10◆6	●	●	●	●	●
10◆7		●	●	●	●
10◆8		●	●		●
10◆9		●		●	●

▷ Additional Resources

Differentiation Handbook
Provides ideas and strategies for differentiating instruction.
Pages 113–119

English Learners Handbook
Contains lesson-specific comprehension strategies.
Pages 92–100

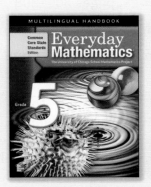

Multilingual Handbook
Previews concepts and vocabulary. It is written in six languages.
Pages 183–200

Planning Tips

Multiage Classroom

Companion Lessons from Grades 4 and 6 can help you meet instructional needs of a multiage classroom. The full Scope and Sequence can be found in the Appendix.

Grade 4			3◆7	2◆6, 12◆1, 12◆2			2◆6		8◆3
Grade 5	10◆1	10◆2	10◆3	10◆4	10◆5	10◆6	10◆7	10◆8	10◆9
Grade 6	6◆9, 6◆10	6◆9, 6◆10	3◆3	1◆4, 1◆6, 1◆7, 3◆5, 3◆10		1◆5, 1◆6, 3◆10	1◆4, 1◆6, 1◆7, 3◆5, 3◆9		9◆8

Pacing for Success

Pacing depends on a number of factors, such as students' individual needs and how long your school has been using *Everyday Mathematics*. At the beginning of Unit 10, you may want to use tools available at www.everydaymathonline.com to help you set your pace.

Home Support

Unit 10 Family Letter (English/Spanish) provides families with an overview, Do-Anytime Activities, Building Skills through Games, a list of vocabulary, and answers to the daily homework (Study Links). Family Letters in English, Spanish, and seven other languages are also available online.

Study Links are the daily homework assignments. They consist of active projects and ongoing review problems.

▶ **Home Support Resources**

Home Connection Handbook
Offers ideas and reproducible masters for communicating with families. See Table of Contents for unit information.

Student Reference Book
Provides a resource for students and parents.
Pages 112, 218, 308, 325, and Glossary

Technology Resources

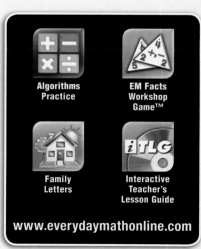

Algorithms Practice

EM Facts Workshop Game™

Family Letters

Interactive Teacher's Lesson Guide

www.everydaymathonline.com

▶ Materials

Technology Resources   www.everydaymathonline.com

ePresentations | eToolkit | Algorithms Practice | EM Facts Workshop Game™ | Family Letters | Assessment Management | Common Core State Standards | Curriculum Focal Points | Interactive Teacher's Lesson Guide

Lesson	Masters	Manipulative Kit	Other Items
10·1	Study Link Master, p. 294 Game Masters, pp. 456–458 Teaching Masters, pp. 295 and 296	for demonstration purposes: 4 trapezoid pattern blocks (or 4 quarters); pan balance; slate; per partnership: 2 six-sided dice	Class Data Pad*; for demonstration purposes: box of 100 standard 1" paper clips, 7 identical ballpoint pens; per partnership: calculator; small objects: nickels, pennies, paper clips, centimeter cubes, and so on; 30 pennies: 10 each from 1981, 1982, and 1983
10·2	Study Link Master, p. 297 Teaching Master, p. 298	for demonstration purposes: 3 identical compasses (pencils removed); slate; 1 or 2 pan balances	for demonstration purposes: box of 100 standard 1" paper clips, 3 identical ballpoint pens, 2 identical plastic 6" half-circle protractors, 1 plastic 12" ruler, Class Data Pad*
10·3	Study Link Master, p. 299 Teaching Masters, pp. 300 and 300A *Differentiation Handbook,* p. 142	slate; per partnership: 1 complete deck of number cards; compass	Class Data Pad; Geometry Template or ruler
10·4	Study Link Master, p. 301 Teaching Masters, pp. 300B, 302, and 303	slate	straightedge
10·5	Study Link Master, p. 304 Teaching Master, p. 305	slate	atlas or map of the United States; straightedge; calculator
10·6	Teaching Aid Masters, pp. 414 and 439 Study Link Master, p. 306 Teaching Masters, pp. 307–307B Game Masters, pp. 470, 471, 488, and 489	slate	Class Data Pad*; straightedge; 3–4 different-colored pencils or markers; per partnership: 1 large paper clip; per group: stopwatch; calculator
10·7	Study Link Master, p. 308 Game Masters, pp. 456–458 Teaching Masters, pp. 309–311	slate; per partnership: 2 six-sided dice	Class Data Pad*; calculator
10·8	Study Link Master, p. 312 Teaching Master, p. 313 *Differentiation Handbook,* p. 143	slate; per group: meterstick or metric tape measure	collection of round objects; for demonstration purposes: board compass, 1-foot piece of string; per group: 4-foot length of string; Class Data Pad*; *The Librarian Who Measured the Earth*; 5" by 8" pieces of paper or index cards; scissors; calculator
10·9	Teaching Aid Master, p. 436 Transparencies of *Math Masters,* pp. 314 and 436 Study Link Master, p. 315 Game Masters, pp. 456–458 Teaching Masters, pp. 316–318	slate; per partnership: 2 six-sided dice	collection of round objects from Lesson 10-8; metric ruler; scissors; colored pencil or marker; construction paper; glue or tape; calculator; Geometry Template
10·10	Assessment Masters, pp. 199–204 Study Link Masters, pp. 319–322	slate	ruler; calculator

*Denotes optional materials

> Mathematical Background

The discussion below highlights the major content ideas presented in Unit 10 and helps establish instructional priorities.

Pan-Balance Equations
(Lessons 10◆1 and 10◆2)

These lessons on solving equations build on previous informal experiences in *Everyday Mathematics.* Missing addends and factors are introduced in first and second grades $(5 + ? = 13)$. In third and fourth grades, more complicated equations are treated informally with puzzles ("I am a number x in $2x + 2 = 8$. What number am I?").

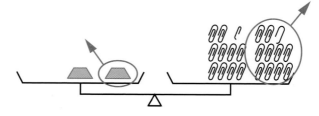

In Lessons 10-1 and 10-2, students solve pan-balance equations by acting out situations in which the weight of a single object is found by removing the same number of identical objects from each pan, or by removing the same fraction of objects from each pan—until the object in question is balanced with one or more "weights."

The pan balance is used more as a metaphor than as an actual measurement tool. By about the middle of sixth grade, this concrete image will be extended to a set of procedures by which even very complicated equations can be reduced to simple equations with obvious solutions.

 PROFESSIONAL DEVELOPMENT — For additional information about pan-balance equations, see Section 17.2.4 of the *Teacher's Reference Manual.*

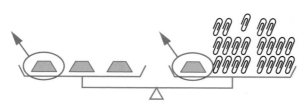

Removing one block from each pan will keep the pans balanced.

Removing one-half of the objects from each pan will keep the pans balanced.

Algebraic Expressions (Lesson 10◆3)

As noted in the discussion of pan-balance equations, students in K–3 *Everyday Mathematics* have worked with missing or unknown parts of number sentences. In *Fourth Grade Everyday Mathematics,* this work became more explicit; the term *variable* was introduced, and variables were used as "unknowns" in open sentences. Later, variables were used in formulas for finding the areas and perimeters of polygons. Lesson 10-3 deals with still another common use of variables: as a means of expressing the rule that links the numbers in a "What's My Rule?" table. ("What's My Rule?" is a routine introduced in Kindergarten.) Whereas in earlier grades, students used words to express the relationship between the inputs and outputs in the table, they now also use algebraic expressions containing variables. These input-output rules are known formally as "functions" and will receive more attention in subsequent units of *Everyday Mathematics*.

PROFESSIONAL DEVELOPMENT You can find additional information about algebraic expressions in Section 17.2.3 of the *Teacher's Reference Manual.*

Rules, Tables, and Graphs

(Lessons 10◆4, 10◆6, and 10◆7)

Lesson 10-4 reminds students that a rate describes a relationship between two quantities. For example, speed is a rate that describes the relationship between the time it takes to travel a distance and the distance traveled in that time. Students represent rates in the form of data tables, rules, and graphs.

In Lesson 10-6, students explore a real-world situation involving a race between two children. They use the information presented in the problem to develop a table of data. The table is then analyzed as students try to develop rules that will describe the relationship between each pair of data. Finally, the data are displayed in a graph. Emphasis is placed on the idea that the data table, rule, and graph are simply different ways of representing the same relationship.

In Lesson 10-7, students are presented with several mystery graphs and are asked to match each graph with the situation that best describes it. This lesson has been very popular with students in classrooms; they especially enjoy the Study Link in which they are given the opportunity to create their own mystery graphs.

PROFESSIONAL DEVELOPMENT More information about rules, tables, and graphs can be found in Section 12.2 of the *Teacher's Reference Manual.*

Laquita

Time	15	20	25	30
Speed	2	5	4	5

Krysta

Time	15	20	30	35
Speed	5	4	3	3

Mathematical Modeling with Data, Formulas, Rules, Tables, and Graphs (Lesson 10◆5)

In Lesson 10-5, students continue their journey on the American Tour. Using a mathematical formula, students are able to predict when Old Faithful (a geyser in Yellowstone National Park) will erupt next. The formula is then used to solve a variety of problems. Finally, students construct a graph to model the formula.

 See Section 18.3 of the *Teacher's Reference Manual* for additional information about mathematical modeling.

Project Note

Use Project 8, Pendulums, to provide experience collecting, displaying, and analyzing data.

Circumference and Area of Circles
(Lessons 10◆8 and 10◆9)

Students using *Everyday Mathematics* in earlier grades discovered that the circumference of a circle is "about three times as long" as the diameter. In this lesson, students investigate a more precise relationship between the circumference and the diameter of a circle. They find an approximate value for π (pi) by measuring round objects of various sizes and determining the ratio of the circumference to the diameter. They use a similar approach to find the approximate areas of circles and to understand the relationship between the radius of a circle and its area, expressed in the formula $A = \pi r^2$.

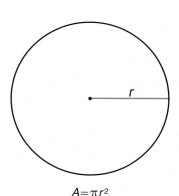

$A = \pi r^2$

 For additional information about circumference and area of circles, refer to Sections 13.4.3 and 14.4.2 of the *Teacher's Reference Manual*.

10·1 Pan-Balance Problems

 Objective To introduce a pan-balance approach for solving simple equations.

Technology Resources www.everydaymathonline.com

 ePresentations

 eToolkit

 Algorithms Practice

 EM Facts Workshop Game™

 Family Letters

 Assessment Management

 Common Core State Standards

 Curriculum Focal Points

 Interactive Teacher's Lesson Guide

1 Teaching the Lesson

Key Concepts and Skills

- Use addition and subtraction to solve pan-balance problems.
  [Operations and Computation Goal 1]

- Use multiplication and division to solve pan-balance problems.
  [Operations and Computation Goal 3]

- Use a pan-balance model to solve linear equations with one unknown.
  [Patterns, Functions, and Algebra Goal 2]

Key Activities

Students find the weight of a given object by adding or removing objects of known weight from both pans of a pan balance. They model pan-balance problems using variables to represent the objects.

 Ongoing Assessment: Informing Instruction See pages 787 and 788.

Key Vocabulary

pan balance

Materials

Math Journal 2, pp. 333 and 334
Student Reference Book Glossary
Class Data Pad (optional) ♦ for demonstration: 100 standard 1" paper clips, 7 identical ballpoint pens, 4 trapezoid pattern blocks (or 4 quarters), pan balance ♦ slate

2 Ongoing Learning & Practice

Finding the Volumes of Solid Figures

Math Journal 2, pp. 334A and 334B
Students measure volumes by counting unit cubes.

 Playing *First to 100*

Student Reference Book, p. 308
Math Masters, pp. 456–458
per partnership: 2 six-sided dice, calculator
Students practice solving open number sentences.

 Math Boxes 10·1

Math Journal 2, p. 335
Students practice and maintain skills through Math Box problems.

 Ongoing Assessment: Recognizing Student Achievement

Use Math Boxes, Problem 5.
[Measurement and Reference Frames Goal 2]

 Study Link 10·1

Math Masters, p. 294
Students practice and maintain skills through Study Link activities.

3 Differentiation Options

READINESS

Exploring Pan Balances

Math Masters, p. 295
per partnership: pan balance, small objects (nickels, pennies, paper clips, centimeter cubes)
Students use a pan balance to explore equivalency.

ENRICHMENT

Solving a Penny Riddle

Students describe how to use a pan balance to determine which penny weighs more than the others.

EXTRA PRACTICE

Weighing Pennies

Math Masters, p. 296
per partnership: pan balance, 30 pennies (10 each from 1981, 1982, and 1983)
Students weigh pennies on a pan balance to identify the year the penny's weight changed.

Advance Preparation

For Part 1, move the fine-tuning adjustment to calibrate your pan balance. You can adjust the balance by taping paper clips to the underside of one pan. For the optional Readiness Activity in Part 3, set up a pan balance and 3 small containers labeled 1981, 1982, and 1983 with 10 pennies from the appropriate year in each container.

 Teacher's Reference Manual, **Grades 4–6** pp. 291–294

Getting Started

Mental Math and Reflexes

FACTS PRACTICE

Students solve extended division facts problems. Write the problems on the board or Class Data Pad. Have students explain the patterns in the number of zeros and placement of the decimal point when a decimal is divided by a power of 10.

- ●○○ $6 \div 3 = 2$
- $60 \div 3 = 20$
- $600 \div 3 = 200$

- ●●○ $81 \div 9 = 9$
- $8.1 \div 9 = 0.9$
- $8.1 \div (9 * 10) = 0.09$

- ●●● $5,600 \div 8 = 700$
- $5.6 \div (8 * 10) = 0.07$
- $5.6 \div (8 * 10^2) = 0.007$

Math Message

Answer the question at the top of page 333 in your journal.

---

1 Teaching the Lesson

▶ Math Message Follow-Up

†††† WHOLE-CLASS DISCUSSION

(*Math Journal 2,* p. 333)

Algebraic Thinking Ask students to share their explanations. If examples are not given, ask volunteers to name and describe something else that operates like a **pan balance.** A playground teeter-totter—the board will balance if the weight on each end is the same.

Emphasize that, unlike a teeter-totter, the pans must balance when they are empty before the balance can be used to weigh objects. Show students the calibrated pan balance with the two pans in balance. Place an object such as a pen or several pattern blocks on one pan. Place the same object(s) on the other pan. Explain that the pans balance because the weight of the objects on each pan is the same; the weight in one pan is equivalent to the weight in the other pan.

▶ Demonstrating How to Solve Pan-Balance Problems

†††† WHOLE-CLASS ACTIVITY

(*Student Reference Book* Glossary)

Demonstrate how to solve pan-balance problems by first using paper clips and either pattern blocks or quarters. Then demonstrate again using ballpoint pens and paper clips.

Interactive whiteboard-ready **ePresentations** are available at www.everydaymathonline.com to help you teach the lesson.

Student Page

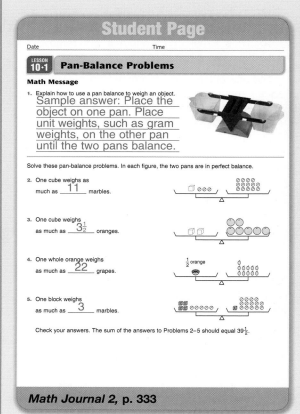

Date _____ Time _____

LESSON 10·1 Pan-Balance Problems

Math Message

1. Explain how to use a pan balance to weigh an object.
   Sample answer: Place the object on one pan. Place unit weights, such as gram weights, on the other pan until the two pans balance.

Solve these pan-balance problems. In each figure, the two pans are in perfect balance.

2. One cube weighs as much as ___11___ marbles.

3. One cube weighs as much as ___$3\frac{1}{2}$___ oranges.

4. One whole orange weighs as much as ___22___ grapes.

5. One block weighs as much as ___3___ marbles.

Check your answers. The sum of the answers to Problems 2–5 should equal $39\frac{1}{2}$.

Math Journal 2, p. 333

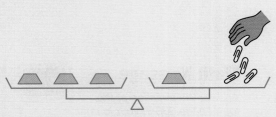

Add clips to balance the pans. This might require 21 clips.

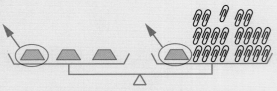

Removing 1 block from each pan will keep the pans balanced.

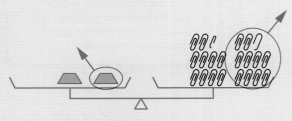

Removing $\frac{1}{2}$ of the objects from each pan will keep the pans balanced.

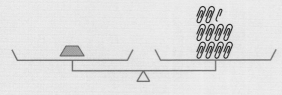

Success!

NOTE In this example, half of 21 clips is $10\frac{1}{2}$ clips. Break one clip in half, and remove 10 clips plus a half clip.

The pan balance is not a precision instrument. For example, two blocks might appear to balance against 21 clips while one block against $10\frac{1}{2}$ clips might show a slight tilt.

Example 1:

Show the trapezoid pattern blocks or quarters and the paper clips. Explain that the goal is to determine the weight of a single pattern block in terms of paper clips.

Place 3 pattern blocks in the left pan and 1 pattern block in the right pan. Add paper clips to the right pan, counting as you go, until the pans balance.

Ask: *How could you change the contents of the pans so 1 pattern block in one pan is balanced with paper clips in the other pan?* Tell students there is one rule to follow: *Whatever you do, the pans must always remain balanced.*

Suppose a student suggests the following incorrect approach: Take the single block from the right pan, and then take two of the three blocks from the left pan. Next remove clips from the right pan until the two pans balance. If you carry out these instructions, the class will observe the rule that the pans must always remain balanced is repeatedly violated.

Have students test their solutions by using the balance.

If necessary, guide students through the manipulations on the pans. (*See margin.*)

Example 2:

Show the ballpoint pens and paper clips. Explain that this time the goal is to determine the weight of a single pen in terms of paper clips.

Place 5 pens and 10 paper clips in the left pan. Place 2 pens in the right pan. Then add clips to the right pan, counting as you go, until the pans balance.

Ask: *How could you change the contents of the pans so 1 pen in one pan is balanced with paper clips in the other pan?* Remind students that the pans must remain balanced after changing the contents of the pans.

Adjusting the Activity ELL

Record the solutions on the board or a transparency by writing the operation used for each change, for example, *subtract 10 C*, or *subtract 2 P*.

AUDITORY ◆ KINESTHETIC ◆ TACTILE ◆ VISUAL

Have volunteers use the pan balance to explain their solutions. Possible approaches:

▷ Add the same number of clips to each pan or remove the same number of clips from each pan. You can also add the same number of pens to each pan or remove the same number of pens from each pan.

▷ Remove the same fraction of objects from each pan. For example, if the left pan contains 3 pens and the right pan contains 30 clips, you can remove $\frac{2}{3}$ of the objects from each pan—2 pens from the left pan and 20 clips from the right pan. (*See margin.*)

Explain that pan-balance problems are also models to help students learn how to solve algebraic equations. Ask students to look up the following terms in the Glossary of the *Student Reference Book*.

▷ **Expression** A group of mathematical symbols that represents a number

▷ **Algebraic expression** An expression that contains a variable

▷ **Equation** A number sentence that contains an equal sign

Ask: *What is an algebraic equation?* A number sentence that contains an equal sign and algebraic expressions

Tell the class that algebraic expressions can be used to represent the weights in pan-balance problems. (*See margin on next page.*) Draw a pan balance on the board or a transparency using variables as shown in the illustration. Let *P* stand for the weight of 1 pen. Let *C* stand for the weight of 1 clip. Note that *P* and *C* do not represent the number of pens and paper clips; they stand for the *weight* of 1 pen and 1 paper clip, respectively.

Explain that in expressions with variables, the multiplication symbol is often omitted. Omitting the symbol avoids confusion between the letter x and the multiplication symbol ×. For example, writing $10C$ has the same meaning as writing $10 * C$, or $10 \times C$.

Draw a new pan balance for each step. If possible, draw each step below the previous step.

Solving Pan-Balance Problems

(*Math Journal 2*, pp. 333 and 334)

PARTNER ACTIVITY

PROBLEM SOLVING

Algebraic Thinking Have partners complete the pan-balance problems on the journal pages. Problems show pictures of objects, squares and triangles, or expressions with variables in the balance pans. Circulate and assist.

⭐ Ongoing Assessment: Informing Instruction

Watch for students who have difficulty keeping track of the changes they make in pan-balance objects. Have them cross out objects that are removed with each change.

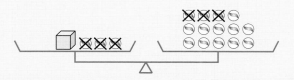

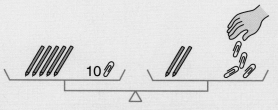

Add clips to balance the pans. This might require 40 clips.

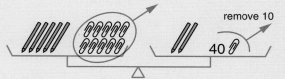

Removing 10 clips from each pan will keep the pans balanced.

Removing 2 pens from each pan will keep the pans balanced.

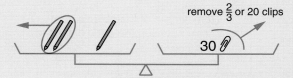

Removing $\frac{2}{3}$ of the objects from each pan will keep the pans balanced.

NOTE You can make a semipermanent set of pan balances on a chalkboard by thoroughly wetting the board and writing heavily with chalk while the board is still wet. After it is dry, draw the specific problems. Erase gently to remove the problems.

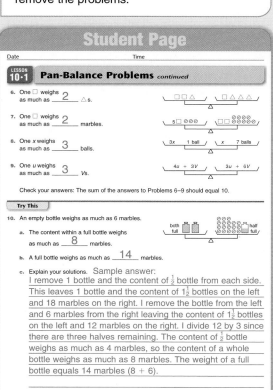

Student Page

Date _____ Time _____

LESSON 10·1 Pan-Balance Problems *continued*

6. One ☐ weighs as much as __2__ △s.

7. One ☐ weighs as much as __2__ marbles.

8. One *x* weighs as much as __3__ balls.

9. One *u* weighs as much as __3__ *V*s.

Check your answers: The sum of the answers to Problems 6–9 should equal 10.

Try This

10. An empty bottle weighs as much as 6 marbles.

a. The content within a full bottle weighs as much as __8__ marbles.

b. A full bottle weighs as much as __14__ marbles.

c. Explain your solutions. Sample answer: I remove 1 bottle and the content of $\frac{1}{2}$ bottle from each side. This leaves 1 bottle and the content of $1\frac{1}{2}$ bottles on the left and 18 marbles on the right. I remove the bottle from the left and 6 marbles from the right leaving the content of $1\frac{1}{2}$ bottles on the left and 12 marbles on the right. I divide 12 by 3 since there are three halves remaining. The content of $\frac{1}{2}$ bottle weighs as much as 4 marbles, so the content of a whole bottle weighs as much as 8 marbles. The weight of a full bottle equals 14 marbles (8 + 6).

Math Journal 2, p. 334

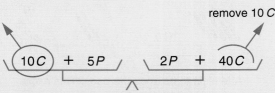
remove 10 C

$10C + 5P$ $2P + 40C$

Removing 10 clips from each pan will keep
the pans balanced.

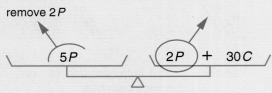
remove 2 P

$5P$ $2P + 30C$

Removing 2 pens from each pan will keep
the pans balanced.

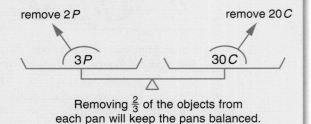
remove 2 P   remove 20 C

$3P$ $30C$

Removing $\frac{2}{3}$ of the objects from
each pan will keep the pans balanced.

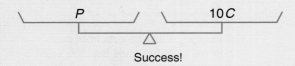
P $10C$

Success!

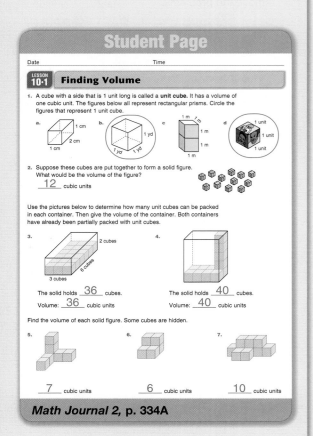

Student Page

Date   Time

LESSON 10·1   Finding Volume

1. A cube with a side that is 1 unit long is called a **unit cube**. It has a volume of one cubic unit. The figures below all represent rectangular prisms. Circle the figures that represent 1 unit cube.

2. Suppose these cubes are put together to form a solid figure. What would be the volume of the figure?
   __12__ cubic units

Use the pictures below to determine how many unit cubes can be packed in each container. Then give the volume of the container. Both containers have already been partially packed with unit cubes.

3.   4.

The solid holds __36__ cubes.   The solid holds __40__ cubes.
Volume: __36__ cubic units   Volume: __40__ cubic units

Find the volume of each solid figure. Some cubes are hidden.

5.   6.   7.

__7__ cubic units   __6__ cubic units   __10__ cubic units

Math Journal 2, p. 334A

Ongoing Assessment: Informing Instruction

Watch for students who have difficulty using the squares and triangles or variables in the journal page problems. Have them write number models for expressions with shapes or variables. *For example:*

- 5 □s can be visualized in the pan balance as □ □ □ □ □. In a number model, 5 □s can be interpreted as □ + □ + □ + □ + □ or 5 ∗ □. (Problem 7)

- $3x$ can be visualized in the pan balance as xxx. In a number model, $3x$ can be interpreted as $x + x + x$ or $3 * x$. (Problem 8)

---

2 ## Ongoing Learning & Practice

▶ ## Finding the Volumes of Solid Figures

PARTNER ACTIVITY

(*Math Journal 2*, pp. 334A and 334B)

Students find volumes by counting unit cubes.

▶ ## Playing *First to 100*

PARTNER ACTIVITY

COMPUTATION PRACTICE

(*Student Reference Book,* p. 308;
Math Masters, pp. 456–458)

Algebraic Thinking Students play *First to 100* to practice a variety of skills involving variables. This game was first introduced in Lesson 4-7. For detailed instructions, see *Student Reference Book,* page 308.

▶ ## Math Boxes 10·1

INDEPENDENT ACTIVITY

(*Math Journal 2*, p. 335)

 Mixed Practice Math Boxes in this lesson are paired with Math Boxes in Lesson 10-3. The skill in Problem 4 previews Unit 11 content.

 Writing/Reasoning Have students write a response to the following: *Explain how you would use a number line to solve Problem 2a, $-7 + (-3) = $ ____.* Sample answer: I would start at -7 and move left 3 spaces to end at -10.

 Writing/Reasoning Have students write a response to the following: *Explain the strategy and reasoning you would use to solve Problem 3b with the standard multiplication algorithm.* Answers vary.

Ongoing Assessment:
Recognizing Student Achievement

Math Boxes Problem 5

Use **Math Boxes, Problem 5** to assess students' ability to find the volume of a rectangular prism. Students are making adequate progress if they are able to calculate the correct volume and record the number model. Some students may be able to record more than one number model for the formulas.

[Measurement and Reference Frames Goal 2]

Study Link 10·1

(*Math Masters*, p. 294)

INDEPENDENT ACTIVITY

Home Connection Students use representations of pan balances to solve problems.

③ Differentiation Options

READINESS

Exploring Pan Balances

(*Math Masters*, p. 295)

PARTNER ACTIVITY

5–15 Min

To provide experience with a pan-balance model of equality, have students explore relationships between the weights of various objects. Have them find combinations of objects that balance the pans. Use small objects such as nickels, pennies, paper clips, and centimeter cubes. Emphasize that the pans must begin in balance. Show students how to adjust the pans if necessary. As they find combinations that balance, have them record the combinations on the master using pictures and words.

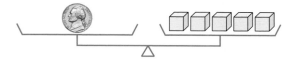

ENRICHMENT

Solving a Penny Riddle

SMALL-GROUP ACTIVITY

5–15 Min

To apply students' understanding of the pan-balance model of equality, pose the following problem: *Suppose you have seven pennies and you know that one penny is heavier than the other six. How can you tell which penny is heavier in two weighings on a pan balance?*

Have students share their strategies. *Possible strategy:*

1. Put 3 pennies on one pan and 3 pennies on the other. If the pans balance, the penny you are not weighing is the heavier penny. If the pans do not balance, you know that the heavy penny is in the heavier pan.

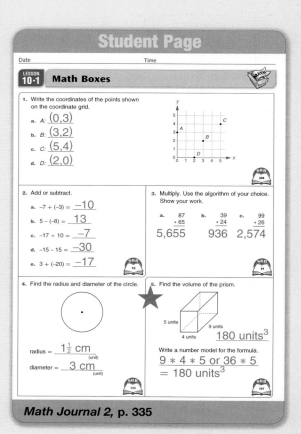

Math Journal 2, p. 335

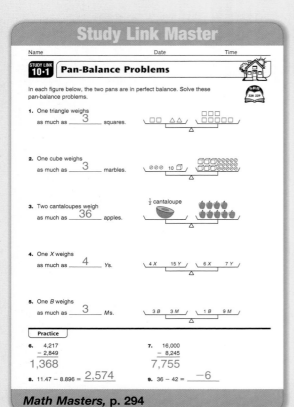
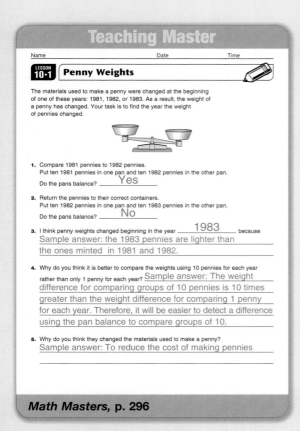
2. Take the 3 pennies from the heavier pan. Put 1 in each pan. If the pans balance, you know that the penny you did not weigh is the heavier penny. If the pans do not balance, you know that the heavy penny is in the heavier pan.

NOTE The weight of the penny changed in 1983. Prior to 1983, a penny weighed about 3.11 grams; it was made up of 95% copper and 5% zinc. Since 1983, a penny has weighed 2.5 grams; it is made up of 97.5% zinc and 2.5% copper.

EXTRA PRACTICE

PARTNER ACTIVITY

30+ Min

▶ # Weighing Pennies

(*Math Masters*, p. 296)

Social Studies Link Students try to determine the year in which the weight of a penny changed. Have students use a pan balance to weigh pennies minted in 1981, 1982, and 1983 and record their results and conclusions on *Math Masters*, page 296.

When partners have finished, discuss their conclusions. If the weight has not changed from one year to the next, 10 pennies from one year should approximately balance 10 pennies from the following year. If the weight has changed, the two sets of 10 pennies will not balance, and it will be clear which year has heavier penny weights.

The U.S. Mint maintains a Web site that contains information about currency and coins: www.usmint.gov.

From the Mint home page, click the photo of a penny to find information specific to pennies.

Planning Ahead

In preparation for working with rates and ratios beginning in Lesson 10-4, assemble a collection of examples for a Rates and Ratios Museum.

10·2 Pan-Balance Problems with Two Balances

 Objective To develop a pan-balance approach for solving sets of two equations with two unknowns.

Technology Resources www.everydaymathonline.com

ePresentations | eToolkit | Algorithms Practice | EM Facts Workshop Game™ | Family Letters | Assessment Management | Common Core State Standards | Curriculum Focal Points | Interactive Teacher's Lesson Guide

① Teaching the Lesson

Key Concepts and Skills

• Use addition and subtraction to solve pan-balance problems.
[Operations and Computation Goal 1]

• Use multiplication and division to solve pan-balance problems.
[Operations and Computation Goal 3]

• Use a pan-balance model to solve linear equations with two unknowns.
[Patterns, Functions, and Algebra Goal 2]

Key Activities

Students solve pan-balance problems involving two balances.

 Ongoing Assessment:
Recognizing Student Achievement
Use the Math Message.
[Patterns, Functions, and Algebra Goal 2]

Materials

Math Journal 2, pp. 336–338
Study Link 10•1
slate ◆ for demonstration purposes:
100 standard 1" paper clips, 3 identical ballpoint pens, 3 identical compasses (pencils removed), 2 identical plastic 6" half-circle protractors, 1 plastic 12" ruler, 1 or 2 pan balances

② Ongoing Learning & Practice

Making and Interpreting Line Plots
Math Journal 2, p. 339
Students construct and interpret a line plot.

 Math Boxes 10·2
Math Journal 2, p. 340
Students practice and maintain skills through Math Box problems.

 Study Link 10·2
Math Masters, p. 297
Students practice and maintain skills through Study Link activities.

③ Differentiation Options

READINESS
Solving Logic Puzzles
Class Data Pad (optional)
Students solve logic puzzles related to pan-balance problems.

ENRICHMENT
Measuring Time
Math Masters, p. 298
Students explore a sandglass model to solve a problem about time intervals.

Advance Preparation

For Part 1, use two pan balances for demonstration purposes. Alternately, the lesson includes instructions for a single pan balance.

 Teacher's Reference Manual, Grades 4–6 pp. 291–294

Getting Started

Mental Math and Reflexes

Write each riddle on the board or prepare a transparency. Students use their slates to write the number and then write the algebraic equation for the riddle: *What number am I?*

- If you double me and add 6, you get 20. 7; $n * 2 + 6 = 20$
- If you add 5 to me, you get 0. -5; $n + 5 = 0$
- If you double me, add 4, subtract 4, and then divide by 2, you get 9. 9; $(n * 2 + 4 - 4) / 2 = 9$
- If you take half of me and triple the result, you get 30. 20; $\frac{n}{2} * 3 = 30$, or $n * \frac{1}{2} * 3 = 30$
- If you double me and double the result, you get 0. 0; $n * 2 * 2 = 0$
- If you multiply me by 100 and add 25, you get 525. 5; $(n * 100) + 25 = 525$
- If you multiply me by 1,000 and add 3, you get a result that is 1,000 times as great as 2.003. 2; $(n * 1,000) + 3 = 2.003 * 1,000$

Math Message ★

Answer Problems 1 and 2 on page 336 of your journal.

Study Link 10·1 Follow-Up

Have partners compare answers and resolve differences. Then have volunteers share their solution strategies.

Ongoing Assessment:
Recognizing Student Achievement

Math Message ★

Use the **Math Message** to assess students' ability to solve equations using a pan-balance model. Students are making adequate progress if they correctly solve both problems.

[Patterns, Functions, and Algebra Goal 2]

---

(1) Teaching the Lesson

▶ Math Message Follow-Up

WHOLE-CLASS DISCUSSION

(*Math Journal 2*, p. 336)

Draw the Math Message pan-balance problems on the board or a transparency. Have volunteers share their answers and solution strategies. Under the pan balances, write: *One block weighs as much as how many marbles?* Ask: *Can you solve this problem using only one of the pan balances?* No Discuss how the information from both pan balances needs to be combined to solve the problem.

▷ One block weighs as much as 2 balls. One ball weighs as much as 5 marbles. Therefore, one block weighs as much as 10 marbles.

▷ Because one ball weighs as much as 5 marbles, 4 balls weigh as much as 20 marbles. Therefore, 2 blocks weigh as much as 20 marbles, and 1 block weighs as much as 10 marbles.

▶ Demonstrating How to Solve More Complex Pan-Balance Problems

WHOLE-CLASS ACTIVITY

Explain that the class will look at two other examples where the information from two pan balances needs to be combined to solve the problems.

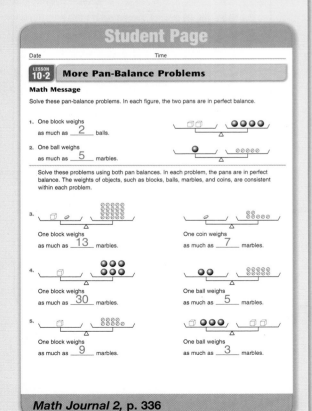

Student Page

Date _____ Time _____

LESSON 10·2 **More Pan-Balance Problems**

Math Message

Solve these pan-balance problems. In each figure, the two pans are in perfect balance.

1. One block weighs as much as __2__ balls.

2. One ball weighs as much as __5__ marbles.

Solve these problems using both pan balances. In each problem, the pans are in perfect balance. The weights of objects, such as blocks, balls, marbles, and coins, are consistent within each problem.

3. One block weighs as much as __13__ marbles.
   One coin weighs as much as __7__ marbles.

4. One block weighs as much as __30__ marbles.
   One ball weighs as much as __5__ marbles.

5. One block weighs as much as __9__ marbles.
   One ball weighs as much as __3__ marbles.

Math Journal 2, p. 336

Example 1:

Show the protractor, ruler, and paper clips. Tell students their goal is to determine the weight of the ruler and the protractor in terms of paper clips. (*See margin.*)

Set up the first pan balance. Place a protractor in one pan. Then add paper clips to the other pan, one at a time, counting as you go, until the pans balance. If you have only one balance available, sketch the results of the first pan-balance situation on the board before setting up the second balance.

Set up the second pan balance. Place a protractor and ruler in one pan. Then add paper clips to the other pan, one at a time, counting as you go, until the pans balance.

Remind students that a protractor weighs 31 paper clips in the first pan balance. All that remains is to find the ruler's weight in paper clips.

Ask: *How can you change the pans to isolate the ruler in one pan, balanced by paper clips in the other pan?* Tell students their solutions must follow one rule: *Whatever you do, the pans must always remain balanced.* Here are two possible approaches:

▷ Remove the protractor and replace it with 31 clips. Because the protractor weighs 31 clips, the pans remain balanced. Now remove 31 clips from each side. The pans remain balanced. So the ruler weighs as much as 39 paper clips.

▷ Remove the protractor from one pan. At the same time, remove 31 clips from the other pan. Because the protractor weighs 31 clips, the pans remain balanced. The ruler is balanced by 39 clips.

Example 2:

Show the ballpoint pens, compasses, and paper clips. Tell students their goal is to find the weight of a pen and the weight of a compass in terms of paper clips.

Set up the first pan balance. Place 2 pens in one pan. Then add clips to the other pan, one at a time, counting as you go, until the pans balance. (*See margin.*) Set up the second pan balance. Place 2 compasses in one pan. Place 1 compass and 1 pen in the other, and add paper clips, one at a time, counting as you go, until the pans balance. (*See margin.*)

Have students use the balances to test their solutions.

▷ Remove $\frac{1}{2}$ of the objects from each pan of the first pan balance. The pans remain balanced. So 1 pen weighs 10 clips.

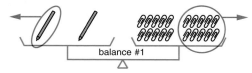

▷ Remove 1 pen from the second pan balance and replace it with 10 clips. The pans remain balanced.

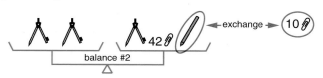

Example 1

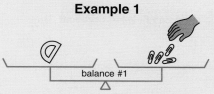

Add clips to balance the pans. For the example here, add 31 clips.

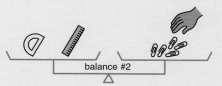

Add clips to balance the pans. This might require 70 clips.

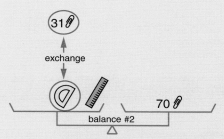

Exchange the protractor for 31 clips.

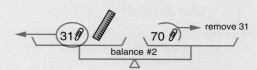

Then remove 31 clips from each pan.

Or remove the protractor from one pan and 31 clips from the other.

Example 2

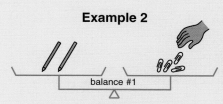

Add clips to balance the pans. This might require 20 clips.

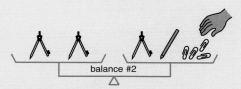

Add clips to balance the pans. This might require 42 clips.

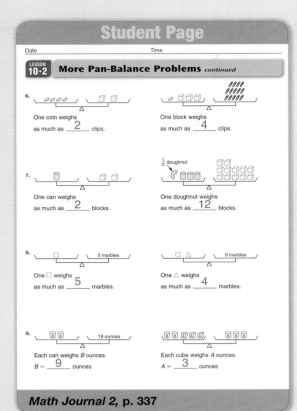

Math Journal 2, p. 337

Adjusting the Activity

Have students write equations with variables to represent each of the pan-balance problems or match the problems to a prepared list of equations. They can record the correct equation above the illustration for each problem.

AUDITORY ◆ KINESTHETIC ◆ TACTILE ◆ VISUAL

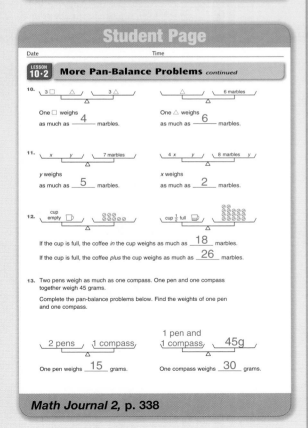

Math Journal 2, p. 338

▷ Remove 1 compass from each pan. The pans remain balanced. So 1 compass weighs 52 clips.

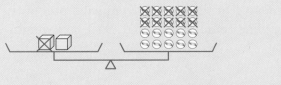

▶ Solving Pan-Balance Problems

PARTNER ACTIVITY

PROBLEM SOLVING

(Math Journal 2, pp. 336–338)

Algebraic Thinking Have partners complete the journal pages. Some of the problems show pictures of objects in the balance pans; some show squares and triangles; and some show expressions with letter variables.

Explain that some problems consist of two related parts and that students need to solve one of the parts before they have enough information to solve the other part. For example, in Problem 3, students need to complete the statement associated with the second pan balance before they can complete the statement associated with the first pan balance.

▷ **Problem 3**

Complete the second statement first. One coin weighs as much as 7 marbles. Since 1 coin weighs as much as 7 marbles and 1 block and 1 coin weigh as much as 20 marbles, 1 block must weigh as much as 13 marbles. Remove the coin and 7 marbles from the pans of the first pan balance.

Adjusting the Activity

ELL

Draw a new pan balance underneath the one on the board to illustrate each step. Refer to the Math Message Follow-Up, and replace each ball with 5 marbles.

Then draw another pan balance underneath to show each side of the balance divided in half. Cross off one half on each side.

AUDITORY ◆ KINESTHETIC ◆ TACTILE ◆ VISUAL

Encourage students to begin by deciding which of the two statements should be completed first. For example, in Problem 3, the second statement needs to be completed first. However, in Problem 5, the first statement should be completed first.

Circulate and assist. A hint for Problem 12 on journal page 338 is to determine the weight of the coffee separate from the cup.

2 Ongoing Learning & Practice

▶ Making and Interpreting Line Plots

INDEPENDENT ACTIVITY

(*Math Journal 2*, p. 339)

Students make and interpret a line plot consisting of a data set of measurements obtained from fraction cards. Students plot fractional units on the number line from 0 through 1. Remind students that they can use benchmarks to place the fractions on the number line. Review fraction operations as needed to find the data landmarks.

▶ Math Boxes 10·2

INDEPENDENT ACTIVITY

(*Math Journal 2*, p. 340)

 Mixed Practice Math Boxes in this lesson are paired with Math Boxes in Lesson 10-4. The skill in Problem 5 previews Unit 11 content.

 Writing/Reasoning Have students write a response to the following: *Explain your solution strategy for Problem 4a.* Sample answer: The area of the rectangle is $3 * 2$ or 6 ft². The area of a triangle is $\frac{1}{2}$ the base times the height. Since the base for both figures is the same, and $\frac{1}{2}$ of the height of the triangle is greater than the height of the rectangle, the triangle's area is greater because $3 * 2.5 = 7.5$ ft².

▶ Study Link 10·2

INDEPENDENT ACTIVITY

(*Math Masters*, p. 297)

 Home Connection Students solve pan-balance problems with one and two balances.

3 Differentiation Options

READINESS

SMALL-GROUP ACTIVITY

🕐 5–15 Min

▶ Solving Logic Puzzles

To provide experience with deductive reasoning required to solve linear equations, have students solve logic puzzles. Write the following statements on the board or the Class Data Pad.

1. All *K* are *M*.
2. All *M* are *B*.

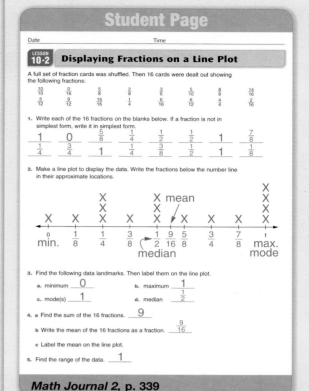

Math Journal 2, p. 339

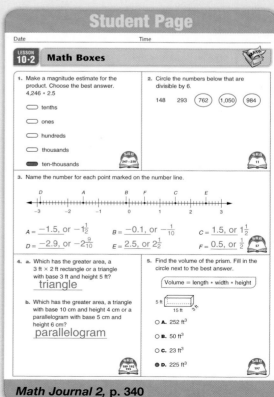

Math Journal 2, p. 340

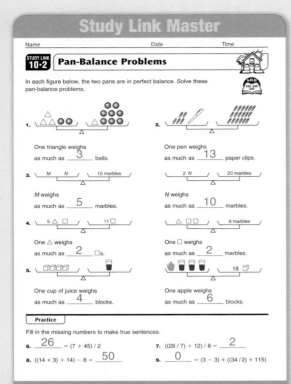

Math Masters, p. 297

Ask students to make a third statement that could be added about K and B. All K are B.

Point out that to make the third statement, students had to put together the information from the first 2 statements. Write the following equations next to the statements on the board or Class Data Pad.

1. $K = M$

2. $M = B$

3. $K = B$

Ask students to substitute numbers for the letters so the sentences are still true, and write these next to the equations.
Sample answers:

1. $18 = 2 * 9$

2. $2 * 9 = 9 + 9$

3. $18 = 9 + 9$

Add the following pair of statements to the board or Class Data Pad.

1. 3 cubes and 1 paper clip weigh as much as 14 marbles.

2. 1 paper clip weighs as much as 2 marbles.

Ask students to make a third statement that could be added about cubes and marbles. 3 cubes weigh as much as 12 marbles, or 1 cube weighs as much as 4 marbles.

Ask students to make another pair of statements that follow this pattern. Use students' responses to clarify their reasoning approaches.

ENRICHMENT

PARTNER ACTIVITY

▶ **Measuring Time**

5–15 Min

(*Math Masters,* p. 298)

To further explore solving a problem with two unknowns, have students use a sandglass model to solve the problem on the *Math Masters* page. Students determine whether a sandglass with a 9-minute interval and one with a 13-minute interval can be used to time a 30-minute period.

When partners have finished, discuss their solution strategies. One approach is to begin by setting the 13-minute sandglass. When it runs out, set the 13-minute and the 9-minute sandglasses at the same time. When the 9-minute sandglass runs out (13 + 9 minutes), start it again. After 4 more minutes, the 13-minute sandglass will run out (13 + 9 + 4), and there will be 4 minutes in the bottom of the 9-minute sandglass. Turn the 9-minute sandglass again so that the 4 minutes of sand on the bottom is now on the top. When this runs out, 30 minutes will have passed (13 + 9 + 4 + 4 = 30 minutes).

Math Masters, p. 298

10·3 Algebraic Expressions

 Objective To introduce the use of algebraic expressions to represent situations and describe rules.

Technology Resources www.everydaymathonline.com

 ePresentations

 eToolkit

 Algorithms Practice

 EM Facts Workshop Game™

 Family Letters

 Assessment Management

 Common Core State Standards

 Curriculum Focal Points

Interactive Teacher's Lesson Guide

1 Teaching the Lesson

Key Concepts and Skills

- Identify and use patterns in tables to solve problems.
  [Patterns, Functions, and Algebra Goal 1]

- Write algebraic expressions to model rules.
  [Patterns, Functions, and Algebra Goal 1]

- Use variables to write number models that describe situations.
  [Patterns, Functions, and Algebra Goal 2]

Key Activities

Students complete statements in which the variable stands for an unknown quantity. They state the rule for "What's My Rule?" tables in words and with an algebraic expression.

 Ongoing Assessment:
Recognizing Student Achievement
Use journal page 341.
[Patterns, Functions, and Algebra Goal 2]

Key Vocabulary

algebraic expression

Materials

Math Journal 2, pp. 341–343
Student Reference Book, p. 218
Study Link 10·2
Class Data Pad ◆ slate

2 Ongoing Learning & Practice

 Playing *Name That Number*
Student Reference Book, p. 325
per partnership: 1 complete deck of number cards (the Everything Math Deck, if available)
Students apply number properties, equivalent names, arithmetic operations, and basic facts.

 Math Boxes 10·3
Math Journal 2, p. 344
compass ◆ Geometry Template or ruler
Students practice and maintain skills through Math Box problems.

 Study Link 10·3
Math Masters, p. 299
Students practice and maintain skills through Study Link activities.

3 Differentiation Options

READINESS
Exploring "What's My Rule?" Tables
Math Masters, p. 300
Students use patterns in tables to solve problems.

EXTRA PRACTICE
Writing Algebraic Expressions
Student Reference Book, p. 218
Students choose variables to write algebraic expressions.

ELL SUPPORT
Building a Math Word Bank
Differentiation Handbook, p. 142
Students define and illustrate the term *algebraic expression.*

ENRICHMENT
Analyzing Patterns and Relationships
Math Masters, p. 300A
Students analyze patterns and relationships.

Advance Preparation

 Teacher's Reference Manual, **Grades 4–6** pp. 278–289

Getting Started

Mental Math and Reflexes

COMPUTATION PRACTICE

Students solve extended multiplication and division facts problems involving powers of 10. Write the problems on the board or Class Data Pad.

●○○ $6 * 10^2 = 600$
$0.254 * 10^3 = 254$
$7.538 * 10^2 = 753.8$

●●○ $4.3 * 10^3 = 4,300$
$7.6 \div 10 = 0.76$
$24 * 10^7 = 240,000,000$

●●● $0.56 \div 10^2 = 0.0056$
$36.5 \div 10^3 = 0.0365$
$8 \div 10^2 = 0.08$

Math Message

Ava, Joe, and Maria are 5th graders. Ava is 1 centimeter taller than Joe, and Joe is 2 centimeters taller than Maria. Make a table of 4 possible heights for Ava, Joe, and Maria.

Heights		
Ava	Joe	Maria

Study Link 10·2 Follow-Up

Have partners compare answers and resolve differences.

---

1 Teaching the Lesson

▶ Math Message Follow-Up

 WHOLE-CLASS DISCUSSION

Algebraic Thinking On the Class Data Pad, draw and label the table for the Math Message. Ask students to share heights listed in their tables. Record them on the Class Data Pad table.

Ask: *How tall is Ava?* Expect that students will respond with one of the heights from the table. Ask them to explain their reasoning. Sample answer: Ava's height is 1 centimeter more than Joe's. *How did you determine Joe's height?* Sample answer: Joe is 2 cm taller than Maria. *How tall is Maria?* Sample answer: Maria's height isn't given, so I picked a likely height for a fifth grader.

Emphasize that Ava's height depends on Joe's height, and Joe's depends on Maria's. We only know that Ava is 1 cm taller than Joe and that Joe is 2 cm taller than Maria. If Maria could be any height, then there would be an infinite number of possibilities for Joe's and Ava's heights. If Maria is 147.5 cm tall, then Joe's height is 149.5 cm, and Ava's height is 150.5 cm. If Maria is 1.48 m tall, then Joe is 1.50 m tall, and Ava is 1.51 m tall.

Ask: *How does Ava's height compare with Maria's height?* Ava is 3 cm taller than Maria. *If Maria is 151.5 cm tall, how tall is Ava?* 154.5 cm *If Ava is 150.2 cm tall, how tall is Maria?* 147.2 cm

▶ Introducing Algebraic Expressions

 WHOLE-CLASS DISCUSSION ELL

(*Student Reference Book,* p. 218)

Algebraic Thinking On the board or Class Data Pad, make a table of just Maria's and Joe's heights. Point out that it is similar to a "What's My Rule?" table. Label Maria's Height *in* and Joe's Height *out.* Ask: *What is the rule for this table?* $out = in + 2$

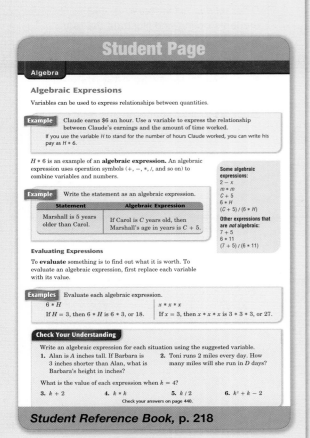

Student Page

Algebra

Algebraic Expressions

Variables can be used to express relationships between quantities.

Example Claude earns $6 an hour. Use a variable to express the relationship between Claude's earnings and the amount of time worked.

If you use the variable *H* to stand for the number of hours Claude worked, you can write his pay as *H* * 6.

H * 6 is an example of an **algebraic expression.** An algebraic expression uses operation symbols (+, −, *, /, and so on) to combine variables and numbers.

Example Write the statement as an algebraic expression.

Statement	Algebraic Expression
Marshall is 5 years older than Carol.	If Carol is *C* years old, then Marshall's age in years is *C* + 5.

Some algebraic expressions:
2 − *x*
m * *m*
C + 5
6 * *H*
(*C* + 5) / (6 * *H*)

Other expressions that are *not* algebraic:
7 + 5
6 * 11
(7 + 5) / (6 * 11)

Evaluating Expressions

To **evaluate** something is to find out what it is worth. To evaluate an algebraic expression, first replace each variable with its value.

Examples Evaluate each algebraic expression.

6 * *H*
If *H* = 3, then 6 * *H* is 6 * 3, or 18.

x * *x* * *x*
If *x* = 3, then *x* * *x* * *x* is 3 * 3 * 3, or 27.

Check Your Understanding

Write an algebraic expression for each situation using the suggested variable.
1. Alan is *A* inches tall. If Barbara is 3 inches shorter than Alan, what is Barbara's height in inches?
2. Toni runs 2 miles every day. How many miles will she run in *D* days?

What is the value of each expression when *k* = 4?
3. *k* + 2 4. *k* * *k* 5. *k* / 2 6. *k*² + *k* − 2

Check your answers on page 440.

Student Reference Book, p. 218

Ask volunteers to represent Joe's height using an algebraic expression. Let M represent Maria's height in inches. Then $M + 2$ represents Joe's height in inches. Add M and $M + 2$ to the column headings in the table on the Class Data Pad.

Review and discuss *Student Reference Book,* page 218. Have students study the examples of expressions that are algebraic and those that are not algebraic. Ask students to explain how the examples are similar and how they are different. Expressions use operation symbols $(+, -, *, \div)$ to combine numbers, but algebraic expressions combine variables and numbers.

Tell students that it is important to remember the following points. To support English language learners, write the statements on the board:

▷ A situation can often be represented in several ways: in words, in a table, or in symbols.

▷ **Algebraic expressions** use variables and other symbols to represent situations.

▷ To evaluate an algebraic expression means to substitute values for the variable(s) and calculate the result.

Ask students to propose algebraic expressions to fit simple situations. To support English language learners, write the situations and respective expressions on the board. *For example:*

▷ Sue weighs 10 pounds less than Jamal. If $J = $ Jamal's weight, then $J - 10$ represents Sue's weight.

▷ Isaac collected twice as many cans as Alex. If $A = $ the number of cans Alex collected, then $2 * A$, or $2A$, represents the number of cans Isaac collected.

▷ There are half as many problems in today's assignment as there were in yesterday's. If $y = $ the number of problems in yesterday's assignment, then there are $\frac{1}{2}y$, $\frac{1}{2} * y$, or $\frac{y}{2}$ problems in today's assignment.

Pose the following problems. Ask students to write an algebraic expression for each problem on their slates.

● Six times the sum of 9 and some number $6\,(9 + n)$

● 10 times the product of a number and 6 $10\,(n * 6)$

● Triple the sum of a number and 20 $3\,(n + 20)$

● 10 less than a number $n - 10$

● 7 less than the product of a number and 6 $n * 6 - 7$

Algebraic expressions can be combined with relation symbols $(=, <, >,$ and so on) to make number sentences. For example, $x + 2 = 15$, or $3y + 7 < 100$. Ask volunteers for the name of number sentences that contain algebraic expressions. Algebraic equations

 Links to the Future

Pictures, diagrams, and graphs are important ways to represent situations, and they are discussed throughout *Everyday Mathematics.* Graphs in an algebra context are discussed in Lesson 10-4.

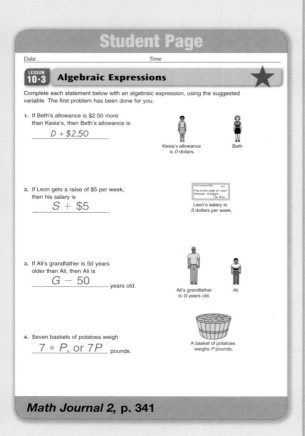

Student Page

Date _____ Time _____

LESSON 10·3 Algebraic Expressions ★

Complete each statement below with an algebraic expression, using the suggested variable. The first problem has been done for you.

1. If Beth's allowance is $2.50 more than Kesia's, then Beth's allowance is
   $D + \$2.50$.

   Kesia's allowance is D dollars.   Beth

2. If Leon gets a raise of $5 per week, then his salary is
   $S + \$5$.

   Leon's salary is S dollars per week.

3. If Ali's grandfather is 50 years older than Ali, then Ali is
   $G - 50$ years old.

   Ali's grandfather is G years old.   Ali

4. Seven baskets of potatoes weigh
   $7 * P$, or $7P$ pounds.

   A basket of potatoes weighs P pounds.

Math Journal 2, p. 341

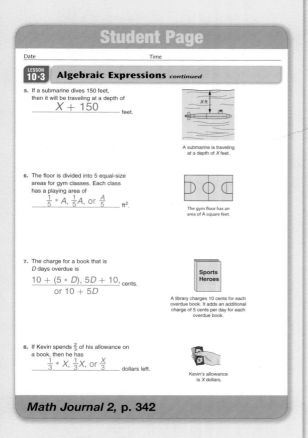

Student Page

Date _____ Time _____

LESSON 10·3 Algebraic Expressions *continued*

5. If a submarine dives 150 feet, then it will be traveling at a depth of
   $X + 150$ feet.

   A submarine is traveling at a depth of X feet.

6. The floor is divided into 5 equal-size areas for gym classes. Each class has a playing area of
   $\frac{1}{5} * A$, $\frac{1}{5}A$, or $\frac{A}{5}$ ft².

   The gym floor has an area of A square feet.

7. The charge for a book that is D days overdue is
   $10 + (5 * D)$, $5D + 10$, or $10 + 5D$ cents.

   A library charges 10 cents for each overdue book. It adds an additional charge of 5 cents per day for each overdue book.

8. If Kevin spends $\frac{2}{3}$ of his allowance on a book, then he has
   $\frac{1}{3} * X$, $\frac{1}{3}X$, or $\frac{X}{3}$ dollars left.

   Kevin's allowance is X dollars.

Math Journal 2, p. 342

▶ **Writing Algebraic Expressions**   PARTNER ACTIVITY

(*Math Journal 2*, pp. 341 and 342)

PROBLEM SOLVING

Algebraic Thinking Go over Problem 1 on journal page 341. Partners then complete the statements on journal pages 341 and 342.

When most students have finished, discuss students' answers, and point out that there are often several ways to write an algebraic expression. The answer to Problem 7 can be written $10 + (5 * D)$, $5D + 10$, or $10 + 5D$. The answer to Problem 8 can be written $\frac{1}{3} * X$, $\frac{1}{3}X$, or $\frac{X}{3}$.

Ask students for the algebraic equation they would write to represent Problem 1. $B = D + \$2.50$ Have students choose and write the algebraic equation for two problems. They should write their equations in the space beneath the problem answer line.

 Ongoing Assessment: Journal Page 341 ★
Recognizing Student Achievement

Use **journal page 341** to assess students' ability to write algebraic expressions that model situations. Students are making adequate progress if they correctly identify and write the expressions for Problems 3 and 4. Some students will correctly write the algebraic equations for the two problems of their choice.

[Patterns, Functions, and Algebra Goal 2]

▶ **Expressing a Rule as an Algebraic Expression**   PARTNER ACTIVITY

(*Math Journal 2*, p. 343)

Algebraic Thinking Have students complete journal page 343. *Everyday Mathematics* students are very familiar with "What's My Rule?" tables because of their experiences with them starting in first grade. Use the Readiness activity in Part 3 with students who do not understand "What's My Rule?" tables.

2 Ongoing Learning & Practice

▶ **Playing *Name That Number***   PARTNER ACTIVITY

(*Student Reference Book*, p. 325)

Students practice applying number properties, equivalent names, arithmetic operations, and basic facts by playing *Name That Number*. Encourage students to find number sentences that use all 5 numbers and to use numbers as exponents or to form fractions.

Math Boxes 10·3

(*Math Journal 2*, p. 344)

Mixed Practice Math Boxes in this lesson are paired with Math Boxes in Lesson 10-1. The skill in Problem 4 previews Unit 11 content.

Writing/Reasoning Have students write a response to the following: *Explain the strategy and reasoning you would use to solve Problem 3b with the standard multiplication algorithm.* Answers vary.

Writing/Reasoning Have students write a response to the following: *Explain how you found the volume for Problem 5.* I knew the base (B) of the prism was 42 cm^2 and the height (h) of the prism was 3 cm. I used the formula $B * h$ to calculate the volume (V): $42 * 3 = 126$ cm^3.

▶ Study Link 10·3

(*Math Masters*, p. 299)

INDEPENDENT ACTIVITY

Home Connection Students complete statements with algebraic expressions. They write the rule and identify the related number sentence for "What's My Rule?" tables.

---

③ Differentiation Options

READINESS

PARTNER ACTIVITY

🕐 5–15 Min

▶ Exploring "What's My Rule?" Tables

(*Math Masters*, p. 300)

Algebraic Thinking To provide experience with using patterns in tables to solve problems, have students make rules and then complete the related table. Partners work together to complete each of their *Math Masters* pages.

When students have finished, discuss the rules and tables they made. Ask partners to share what they think is important to remember when solving "What's My Rule?" tables. Sample answers: If you know the *in* value, follow the rule to find the *out* value. If you know the *out* value, do the opposite of the rule to find the *in* value.

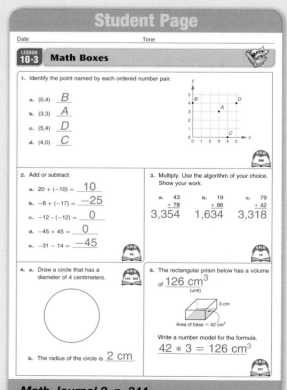

Name   Date   Time

 STUDY LINK 10·3 **Writing Algebraic Expressions**

Complete each statement below with an algebraic expression, using the suggested variable.

1. Lamont, Augusto, and Mario grow carrots in three garden plots. Augusto harvests two times as many carrots as the total number of carrots that Lamont and Mario harvest. So Augusto harvests

   $2 * (L + M)$, or $2(L + M)$ carrots.

   Augusto   Lamont and Mario harvested $L + M$ carrots.

2. Rhasheema and Alexis have a lemonade stand at their school fair. They promise to donate one-fourth of the remaining money (m) after they repay the school for lemons (l) and sugar (s). So the girls donate

   $\frac{1}{4} * (m - (l + s))$, or $\frac{1}{4}(m - (l + s))$ dollars.

3. a. State in words the rule for the "What's My Rule?" table at the right.

   Multiply N by 3 and add 5.

   b. Circle the number sentence that describes the rule.

   $Q = (3 + N) * 5$ $Q = 3 * (N + 5)$ $\boxed{Q = 3N + 5}$

N	Q
2	11
4	17
6	23
8	29
10	35

4. a. State in words the rule for the "What's My Rule?" table at the right.

   Multiply E by 6 and add 15.

   b. Circle the number sentence that describes the rule.

   $R = E * 6 * 15$ $\boxed{R = (E * 6) + 15}$ $R = E * 15 + 6$

E	R
7	57
10	75
31	201
3	33
108	663

Practice

5. $384 * 1.5 =$ ___576___

6. $50.3 * 89 =$ ___4,476.7___

7. $\frac{843}{7} =$ ___$120\frac{3}{7}$___

8. $70.4 / 8 =$ ___8.8___

Math Masters, p. 299

Name   Date   Time

LESSON 10·3 **Patterns and Relationships**

A car is traveling at a given speed over a stretch of highway. You can find the distance the car travels by multiplying its speed by the amount of time it travels.

1. Car A travels at a speed of 30 miles per hour (mph). Car B travels at 60 miles per hour. Complete the tables to find the distance each car travels for the given times.

Car A

Speed: 30 mph	
Time (hr)	Distance (mi)
0	0
1	30
2	60
3	90
4	120

Car B

Speed: 60 mph	
Time (hr)	Distance (mi)
0	0
1	60
2	120
3	180
4	240

2. For each car, write the rule that is used to find the distance.

   Car A: Multiply each hour by 30.

   Car B: Multiply each hour by 60.

3. Use the tables to write a set of ordered pairs in the form (Time, Distance) for each car. Then graph the data and connect the points for each car. Label each graph.

Car A	Car B
(0,0)	(0,0)
(1,30)	(1,60)
(2,60)	(2,120)
(3,90)	(3,180)
(4,120)	(4,240)

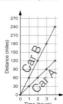

4. As the amount of time increases, explain how the distance Car B travels compares with the distance Car A travels?

   Sample answer: For each hour, Car B travels twice as far as Car A. This is because Car B is traveling twice as fast.

Math Masters, p. 300A

Writing Algebraic Expressions

INDEPENDENT ACTIVITY

5–15 Min

(*Student Reference Book,* p. 218)

Algebraic Thinking Students complete the Check Your Understanding problems on *Student Reference Book,* page 218. Ask students to write algebraic expressions for the first two problems and to describe how they chose the variables to use.

Building a Math Word Bank

SMALL-GROUP ACTIVITY

5–15 Min

(*Differentiation Handbook,* p. 142)

To provide language support for algebra concepts, have students use the Word Bank Template found on *Differentiation Handbook,* page 142. Ask students to write the term *algebraic expression,* draw pictures relating to the term, and write other related words. See the *Differentiation Handbook* for more information.

Analyzing Patterns and Relationships

INDEPENDENT ACTIVITY

5–15 Min

(*Math Masters,* p. 300A)

To extend students' understanding of rules and patterns, students use two sets of rules to generate two tables of values. They form ordered pairs consisting of corresponding terms from two patterns, and graph the ordered pairs on a coordinate plane. Students then use the tables of values, rules, ordered pairs, or graphs to identify a relationship between corresponding terms from each pattern.

10·4 Rules, Tables, and Graphs: Part 1

 Objective To develop representational forms for rates.

Technology Resources www.everydaymathonline.com

| ePresentations | eToolkit | Algorithms Practice | EM Facts Workshop Game™ | Family Letters | Assessment Management | Common Core State Standards | Curriculum Focal Points | Interactive Teacher's Lesson Guide |

1 Teaching the Lesson

Key Concepts and Skills

- Use table data to create line graphs.
  [Data and Chance Goal 1]

- Represent functions with tables, graphs, and formulas.
  [Patterns, Functions, and Algebra Goal 1]

- Extend patterns in graphs and tables to solve problems.
  [Patterns, Functions, and Algebra Goal 1]

Key Activities

Students review the concept of rates and practice representing rates with formulas, tables of values, and graphs.

 **Ongoing Assessment:
Recognizing Student Achievement**
Use journal pages 348 and 349.
[Data and Chance Goal 1]

Key Vocabulary

rate ◆ formula ◆ variable ◆ line graph

Materials

Math Journal 2, pp. 346–349
Student Reference Book, pp. 78 and 225
Study Link 10·3
slate ◆ straightedge

2 Ongoing Learning & Practice

 Math Boxes 10·4
Math Journal 2, p. 345
Students practice and maintain skills through Math Box problems.

 Study Link 10·4
Math Masters, p. 301
Students practice and maintain skills through Study Link activities.

3 Differentiation Options

ENRICHMENT
Solving Rate Problems
Math Masters, p. 302
Students use a formula to solve rate problems in which the rate or the unit is not known.

EXTRA PRACTICE
Graphing "What's My Rule?" Tables
Math Masters, p. 303
Students use rules to generate tables of values and make line graphs from the table data.

EXTRA PRACTICE
Analyzing Two Rates
Math Masters, p. 300B
Students use rules, tables, ordered pairs, and graphs to analyze data.

ELL SUPPORT
Describing Exhibits in the Rates and Ratios Museum
Students describe rate situations and different representations of rates in the Rates and Ratios Museum.

Advance Preparation

Display the rates and ratios you have collected for the Rates and Ratios Museum. Invite students to add to the museum over the next few days.

 Teacher's Reference Manual, Grades 4–6 pp. 64–68, 164, 278–289

Getting Started

Mental Math and Reflexes

Describe number relationships. Have students identify the mystery numbers. *Suggestions:*

● ○ ○ My number times 25 will equal 100. What is my number? 4

● ● ○ 15 divided by my number will equal 6. What is my number? 2.5

● ● ● Let *y* represent my number. 3*y* = 60; *y* = 20

Math Message

Complete the problem at the top of journal page 346.

Study Link 10·3 Follow-Up

Have partners share answers and resolve differences. Discuss students' solution strategies for Problems 3 and 4.

---

1 Teaching the Lesson

▶ **Math Message Follow-Up**

(*Math Journal 2*, p. 346)

WHOLE-CLASS DISCUSSION

ELL

Algebraic Thinking Remind students that a **rate** describes a relationship between two quantities. Point out that the two quantities that make up a rate have different units, for example, miles and hours, dollars and pounds, days and months. A rate tells how many of one type of thing there are for a certain number of another type of thing. To support English language learners, write the important ideas and examples regarding rates on the board.

A basic example for rates is speed. A speed tells how many units of distance there are for a given unit of time. Sixty miles per hour, for example, is a rate that says a distance of 60 miles is traveled for each hour of time.

Rates are often expressed with phrases that include the word *per*, as in 480 miles per hour, \$2 per pound, and 10 rainy days per month. Rates can also be expressed as fractions: $\frac{3 \text{ apples}}{89¢}$, $\frac{12 \text{ inches}}{24 \text{ hours}}$, $\frac{36 \text{ inches}}{1 \text{ yard}}$. Ask students to give other examples of rates they have seen or used.

Have students share their solution strategies to the Math Message problem. Because there are 60 minutes in 1 hour, divide 480 by 60. Thus the distance traveled in 1 minute is 8 miles.

480 miles per hour and *8 miles per minute* are equivalent rates. Ask volunteers to suggest an equivalent rate for 36 inches per 1 yard. 12 inches per foot

---

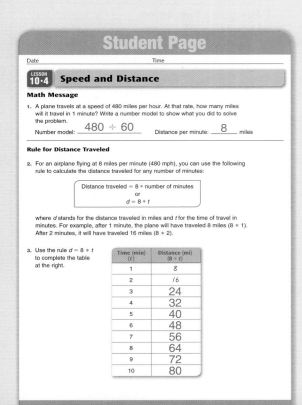

Student Page

Date _____ Time _____

LESSON 10·4 Speed and Distance

Math Message

1. A plane travels at a speed of 480 miles per hour. At that rate, how many miles will it travel in 1 minute? Write a number model to show what you did to solve the problem.

   Number model: __480 ÷ 60__   Distance per minute: __8__ miles

Rule for Distance Traveled

2. For an airplane flying at 8 miles per minute (480 mph), you can use the following rule to calculate the distance traveled for any number of minutes:

   Distance traveled = 8 * number of minutes
   or
   d = 8 * *t*

   where *d* stands for the distance traveled in miles and *t* for the time of travel in minutes. For example, after 1 minute, the plane will have traveled 8 miles (8 * 1). After 2 minutes, it will have traveled 16 miles (8 * 2).

3. Use the rule *d* = 8 * *t* to complete the table at the right.

Time (min) (*t*)	Distance (mi) (8 * *t*)
1	8
2	16
3	24
4	32
5	40
6	48
7	56
8	64
9	72
10	80

Math Journal 2, p. 346

Displaying a Rate of Speed

👫👫 **WHOLE-CLASS ACTIVITY**

(*Math Journal 2*, pp. 346 and 347)

Algebraic Thinking Pose problems based on the rate 8 miles per minute:

● At 8 miles per minute, how far will a plane travel in 10 minutes? 80 miles In $2\frac{1}{2}$ minutes? 20 miles

Ask students to share their solution strategies. To calculate the distance traveled, multiply the number of minutes of travel by 8. Explain that the solution can be expressed by the rule:

Distance traveled = 8 * number of minutes

or, in abbreviated form, by $d = 8 * t$. Remind students that this kind of rule is called a **formula** and the letters d and t are called **variables.** Variables used in formulas describe relationships.

Assign Problems 2–4 on journal pages 346 and 347. Students use the formula $d = 8 * t$ to build a table of values and then display these values on a **line graph.** Circulate and assist.

When students have finished, discuss Problems 5–7 on journal page 347 as a class. Ask volunteers to use these problems to explain how to obtain values from the graph. For example:

▷ **Problem 5**

To find out how far the plane would travel in $1\frac{1}{2}$ minutes, move along the horizontal axis to $1\frac{1}{2}$, which is halfway between 1 and 2 minutes, and mark the point on the line that is directly above $1\frac{1}{2}$. Then move left from there to 12 on the vertical axis. Thus, the plane would travel 12 miles in $1\frac{1}{2}$ minutes.

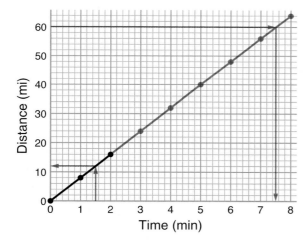

▷ **Problem 7**

To find out how long it would take the plane to travel 60 miles, reverse the procedure. Start at 60 on the vertical axis, move right to the line, and then work down to $7\frac{1}{2}$ on the horizontal axis. It would take the plane $7\frac{1}{2}$ minutes to travel 60 miles.

Point out that the table of values on journal page 346 is an example of a "What's My Rule?" table. Also point out that when the dots on the graph are connected, they form a straight line.

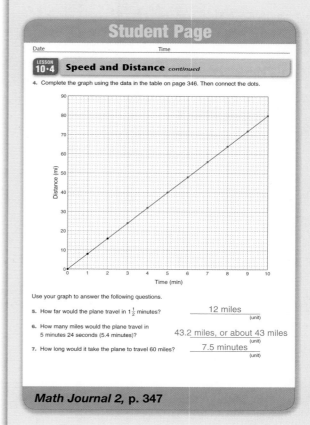

Date _____ Time _____

LESSON 10·4 **Speed and Distance** *continued*

4. Complete the graph using the data in the table on page 346. Then connect the dots.

Use your graph to answer the following questions.

5. How far would the plane travel in $1\frac{1}{2}$ minutes? ___12 miles___ (unit)

6. How many miles would the plane travel in 5 minutes 24 seconds (5.4 minutes)? ___43.2 miles, or about 43 miles___ (unit)

7. How long would it take the plane to travel 60 miles? ___7.5 minutes___ (unit)

Math Journal 2, p. 347

NOTE Continuous quantities can be divided into smaller and smaller amounts. Measures, such as the height or the weight of a student in your class, are continuous quantities. Discrete quantities are countable things that cannot be broken up into smaller amounts. The number of students in your class is a discrete quantity.

The rates in this lesson can be represented by line graphs because most of the variables represent continuous, not discrete, quantities.

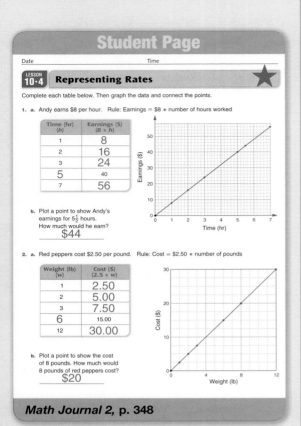

Math Journal 2, p. 348

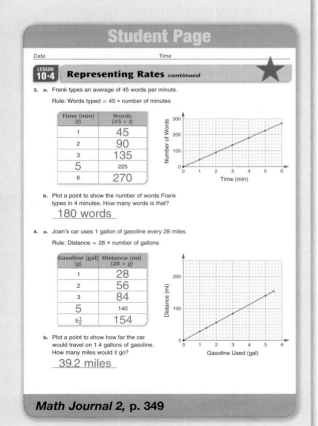

Math Journal 2, p. 349

▶ **Making Line Graphs from Tables of Values**

PARTNER ACTIVITY

(*Math Journal 2,* pp. 348 and 349; *Student Reference Book,* pp. 78 and 225)

Algebraic Thinking Have partners solve problems involving other rate situations on journal pages 348 and 349. Circulate and assist.

When students have finished, ask questions such as the following:

● For Problem 1 on journal page 348, would you use the graph, the rule, or the table to find out how long it took Andy to earn $42? Explain. Sample answer: It is easy to locate $42 on the graph.

● For Problem 4 on journal page 349, would you use the graph, the rule, or the table to find the distance traveled on $4\frac{3}{7}$ gallons? Explain. Sample answer: It is easiest to use the rule and find $28 * 4\frac{3}{7}$.

Ask: *How could you use the Distributive Property to solve the problem $28 * 4\frac{3}{7}$?* Refer students to *Student Reference Book,* pages 78 and 225 as a reminder. $28 * (4 + \frac{3}{7}) = (28 * 4) + (28 * \frac{3}{7})$; $28 * 4 = 112$; $28 * \frac{3}{7} = 12$; $112 + 12 = 124$ Ask students to solve the Check Your Understanding problems on *Student Reference Book,* page 78 using the Distributive Property.

Ongoing Assessment:
Recognizing Student Achievement

Journal Pages 348 and 349

Use **journal pages 348 and 349** to assess students' ability to use table data to plot points on a graph. Students are making adequate progress if their responses to Problems 1 and 3 are correct.

[Data and Chance Goal 1]

▶ **Comparing Three Ways of Representing Rates**

WHOLE-CLASS DISCUSSION

PROBLEM SOLVING

(*Math Journal 2,* pp. 346–349)

Algebraic Thinking Point out that tables, formulas, and graphs are simply different ways of representing the same relationships. There are advantages to each way:

▷ Tables are often the easiest to understand.

▷ Formulas are the shortest forms of representation. They summarize the relationship and can be used to find other values in the table. (Rules expressed in words or by formulas are very much the same. Formulas are more compact, which can make them easier to use.)

▷ Graphs can help you understand the relationship, but are not as useful for finding precise values.

▷ Many relationships do not have formulas and can be reported in tables or graphs only. The sports and financial sections of the newspaper have tables and graphs that are examples of such relationships.

Analyzing Two Rates

 **WHOLE-CLASS DISCUSSION**

(*Math Journal 2*, p. 349)

Remind students that they can also use tables, formulas, and graphs to compare situations in which there are two different rates. Refer students to Problem 4 on journal page 349. Write the following on the Class Data Pad:

Joan's car: $\frac{28 \text{ mi}}{1 \text{ g}}$ Rule: Distance = 28 ∗ number of gallons

Tom's car: $\frac{42 \text{ mi}}{1 \text{ g}}$ Rule: _____

Gasoline (g)	Joan's Car: Distance (mi)	Tom's Car: Distance (mi)
0	0	0
1	28	42
2	56	84
3	84	126
4	112	168
5	140	210

Ask: *What rule describes the distance Tom's car travels for a given number of gallons of gasoline?* Distance = 42 ∗ number of gallons Ask a volunteer to write the rule for Tom's car next to his rate.

Have volunteers complete the table for Joan's and Tom's cars. Then have a volunteer provide the ordered pairs for Tom's car. $(0,0)$, $(1,42)$, $(2,84)$, $(3,126)$, $(4,168)$, $(5,210)$

On journal page 349, Problem 4, ask students to plot the ordered pairs for Tom's car on the grid. Have students label the respective graphs, *Joan's Car* and *Tom's Car.*

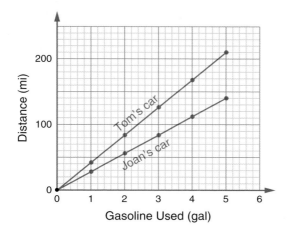

Ask: *For each number of gallons of gasoline greater than 0, how does the distance Tom's car travels compare with the distance Joan's car travels?* Each distance Tom's car travels is $1\frac{1}{2}$ times the distance Joan's car travels. Ask students to explain how they used the rules, table, ordered pairs, and/or graph to help them answer the question. Answers vary.

Student Page

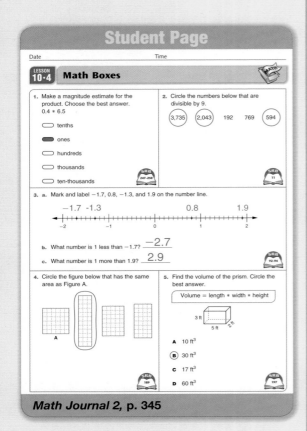

Math Journal 2, p. 345

---

2 Ongoing Learning & Practice

▶ Math Boxes 10·4

(Math Journal 2, p. 345)

 Mixed Practice Math Boxes in this lesson are paired with Math Boxes in Lesson 10-2. The skill in Problem 5 previews Unit 11 content.

Writing/Reasoning Have students write a response to the following: *In Problem 2, explain how to determine whether 3,735 is divisible by 9 without actually dividing.* Sample answer: Add the digits together. If the sum is divisible by 9, then the number is divisible by 9.

▶ Study Link 10·4

(Math Masters, p. 301)

Home Connection Students complete rate tables. They graph the data on line graphs.

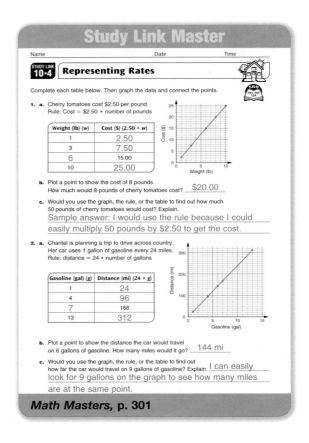

Math Masters, p. 301

3 Differentiation Options

ENRICHMENT

▶ ## Solving Rate Problems

(*Math Masters*, p. 302)

👤 **INDEPENDENT ACTIVITY**

🕐 **5–15 Min**

Algebraic Thinking To apply students' understanding of the basic rate formula, have students solve problems in which the rate or unit is unknown.

When students have finished, ask them to use the variables in the formula $d = r * t$ and to write two division equations. $r = d/t$; $t = d/r$ Emphasize that the relationships in the formula also reflect the relationships between operations.

EXTRA PRACTICE

▶ ## Graphing "What's My Rule?" Tables

(*Math Masters*, p. 303)

👤 **INDEPENDENT ACTIVITY**

🕐 **5–15 Min**

Algebraic Thinking Students use rules to generate tables of values and make line graphs from the table data.

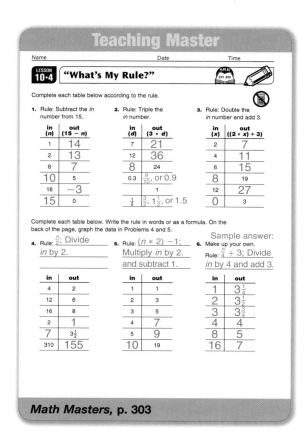

Math Masters, p. 303

Teaching Master

Name _____ Date _____ Time _____

LESSON 10·4 | **Solving Rate Problems**

Rate describes a relationship between two quantities with different units. Rate tells how many of one type of thing there are for a certain number of another type of thing. Rates are often expressed with phrases that include the word *per*. For example, miles per hour, cost per ounce, or books per student.

One example of rate is speed. A basic formula is distance = rate * time. Multiplication can be used for many different problems involving rates. For example, distance = rate * gallons, total cost = rate * ounces, or total books = rate * students.

To solve a problem using a formula, first replace variables with the known values.

Example:

Maribel can travel 5 miles per hour on her skateboard. How far will she travel in 2 hours?

distance = rate * time	d	=	r	*	t
distance = 5 miles per hour * 2 hours	10	=	5	*	2
distance = 10 miles					

Maribel can travel 10 miles.

Use the formula to solve the following problem.

1. Samuel's go-kart can travel 357 miles on 14 gallons of gas. His go-kart travels how many miles per gallon?

distance = rate * gallons of gas	d	=	r	*	g
distance = miles per gallon * 14 gallons of gas	357	=	$25\frac{1}{2}$	*	14
rate = $25\frac{1}{2}$ miles per gallon					

2. Samuel's go-kart can travel ___$25\frac{1}{2}$___ miles per gallon of gas.

Explain your solution.

Sample answer: The rate is the distance for 1 gallon of gas, so I divide 357 by 14 to get $25\frac{1}{2}$ miles per gallon.

Math Masters, p. 302

INDEPENDENT ACTIVITY

5–15 Min

▶ Analyzing Two Rates

(*Math Masters,* p. 300B)

Students use rules, tables, ordered pairs, and a graph to identify a relationship between corresponding terms based on two rates.

ELL SUPPORT

SMALL-GROUP ACTIVITY

15–30 Min

▶ Describing Exhibits in the Rates and Ratios Museum

To provide language support for rates, have students look at the *Rates and Ratios Museum* and describe some of the situations for which rates are used. Have students discuss different representations of rates displayed in the museum. Have them make a list of words associated with the rates in the museum to add to the display.

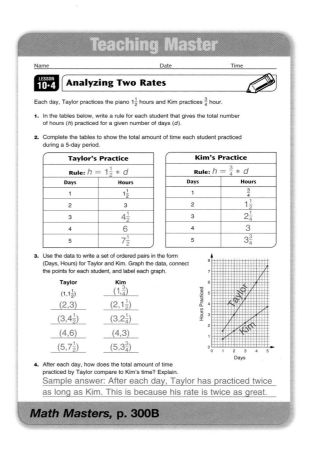

Teaching Master

| Name | | Date | | Time | |

LESSON 10·4 **Analyzing Two Rates**

Each day, Taylor practices the piano $1\frac{1}{2}$ hours and Kim practices $\frac{3}{4}$ hour.

1. In the tables below, write a rule for each student that gives the total number of hours (h) practiced for a given number of days (d).

2. Complete the tables to show the total amount of time each student practiced during a 5-day period.

Taylor's Practice	
Rule: $h = 1\frac{1}{2} * d$	
Days	**Hours**
1	$1\frac{1}{2}$
2	3
3	$4\frac{1}{2}$
4	6
5	$7\frac{1}{2}$

Kim's Practice	
Rule: $h = \frac{3}{4} * d$	
Days	**Hours**
1	$\frac{3}{4}$
2	$1\frac{1}{2}$
3	$2\frac{1}{4}$
4	3
5	$3\frac{3}{4}$

3. Use the data to write a set of ordered pairs in the form (Days, Hours) for Taylor and Kim. Graph the data, connect the points for each student, and label each graph.

Taylor	Kim
$(1,1\frac{1}{2})$	$(1,\frac{3}{4})$
(2,3)	$(2,1\frac{1}{2})$
$(3,4\frac{1}{2})$	$(3,2\frac{1}{4})$
(4,6)	(4,3)
$(5,7\frac{1}{2})$	$(5,3\frac{3}{4})$

4. After each day, how does the total amount of time practiced by Taylor compare to Kim's time? Explain.
Sample answer: After each day, Taylor has practiced twice as long as Kim. This is because his rate is twice as great.

Math Masters, p. 300B

10·5 American Tour: Old Faithful's Next Eruption

 Objective To provide experience with using a formula as a prediction tool.

1 Teaching the Lesson

Key Concepts and Skills

• Construct line graphs that represent single sets of data.
[Data and Chance Goal 1]

• Extend patterns in graphs and tables to solve problems.
[Patterns, Functions, and Algebra Goal 1]

• Represent functions with tables, graphs, and formulas.
[Patterns, Functions, and Algebra Goal 1]

Key Activities

Students read information about Yellowstone National Park and one of its geysers, Old Faithful. They solve problems and generate data for a graph, based on a formula for predicting when Old Faithful will erupt next.

Key Vocabulary

geyser ◆ predict

Materials

Math Journal 2, p. 350
Student Reference Book, pp. 78 and 225
Study Link 10◆4
slate ◆ atlas or map of the United States ◆ straightedge

2 Ongoing Learning & Practice

Solving Pan-Balance Problems

Math Journal 2, p. 351
Students solve pan-balance problems, some of which involve two pan balances.

 ### Math Boxes 10·5

Math Journal 2, p. 352
calculator
Students practice and maintain skills through Math Box problems.

 ### Ongoing Assessment: Recognizing Student Achievement
Use Math Boxes, Problem 3.
[Patterns, Functions, and Algebra Goal 2]

 ### Study Link 10·5

Math Masters, p. 304
Students practice and maintain skills through Study Link activities.

3 Differentiation Options

ENRICHMENT
Graphing Values from a Table

Math Masters, p. 305
straightedge
Students graph values from "What's My Rule?" tables.

EXTRA PRACTICE
5-Minute Math

5-Minute Math™, pp. 114 and 115
Students graph data.

Advance Preparation

 Teacher's Reference Manual, **Grades 4–6** pp. 164, 301–303

Getting Started

Mental Math and Reflexes

Have students practice calculations involving units of time.
Suggestions: Answers vary.

- ●○○ What time will it be in 1 hour?
  What time was it 30 minutes ago?
  How many years ago was 1971?
- ●●○ What time will it be in 55 minutes?
  What day will it be in 48 hours?
  What year was it 7 years ago?

- ●●● How many seconds are in . . .
  2 minutes? 120 sec
  5 minutes? 300 sec
  $2\frac{1}{2}$ minutes? 150 sec
  10 minutes? 600 sec
  $\frac{1}{4}$ hour? 900 sec

Math Message

Read the top of journal page 350.
Explain how a formula and a rule are similar.

Study Link 10·4 Follow-Up

Have partners compare answers and resolve differences.

---

1 Teaching the Lesson

▶ Math Message Follow-Up

WHOLE-CLASS DISCUSSION

(*Math Journal 2,* p. 350)

Ask students to explain how a formula and a rule are similar.
Sample answers: Both a formula and a rule can be described using
numbers and variables. Both a formula and a rule tell how to find
the value of something. Use student responses to emphasize that a
formula is a way to express a rule.

Explain that the formula on journal page 350 can be thought of as
a rule to predict the wait time between Old Faithful eruptions.

▶ Predicting When Old Faithful Will Erupt Next

WHOLE-CLASS ACTIVITY

ELL

PROBLEM SOLVING

(*Math Journal 2,* p. 350; *Student Reference Book,*
pp. 78 and 225)

Algebraic Thinking Use an atlas or a classroom map of the United
States to locate Yellowstone National Park in the northwest corner of
Wyoming. Alternately, refer to The National Park Service Yellowstone
Web site for information about Old Faithful: www.nps.gov/yell.
Select the Photos & Multimedia link and then Webcams to get
more information about Old Faithful and view pictures.

Science Link Some **geysers,** such as Old Faithful in
Yellowstone, erupt at regular intervals. To support English
language learners, discuss the meaning of *geyser, erupt,* and
regular intervals, and use the Web site to provide visual support
for these terms. The park rangers at Yellowstone once used a
formula to **predict** when Old Faithful would erupt next. However,
earthquakes and vandalism have affected Old Faithful, and the
formula is no longer as accurate as it once was. Now park rangers
usually add a few minutes to the time predicted, or they refer to a
table of previous eruption times and intervals.

Student Page

Date _____   Time _____

LESSON 10·5 Predicting When Old Faithful Will Erupt

Old Faithful Geyser in Yellowstone National Park is one of nature's most impressive
sights. Yellowstone has 200 geysers and thousands of hot springs, mud pots, steam vents,
and other "hot spots"—more than any other place on Earth. Old Faithful is not the largest
or tallest geyser in Yellowstone, but it is the most dependable. Using the length
of time for an eruption, park rangers can predict when further eruptions will occur.

Old Faithful erupts at regular intervals that are **predictable.** If you time the length of
one eruption, you can **predict** about how long you must wait until the next eruption.
Use this formula:

Waiting time = (10 * length of eruption) + 30 minutes
$W = (10 * E) + 30$
$W = 10E + 30$

[All times are in minutes.]

1. Use the formula to complete the table below.

Length of Eruption (min) (*E*)	Waiting Time to Next Eruption (min) {(10 * *E*) + 30}
2 min	50 min
3 min	60 min
4 min	70 min
5 min	80 min
1 min	40 min
$2\frac{1}{2}$ min	55 min
3 min 15 sec	62.5, or $62\frac{1}{2}$ min
1.5, or $1\frac{1}{2}$ min	45 min

2. Graph the data from the table. One number pair has been plotted for you.

Waiting Time (min) vs *Length of Eruption (min)*

3. It's 8:30 A.M., and Old Faithful has just finished a 4-minute eruption. About when will it erupt next?

    9:40 A.M.

4. The average time between eruptions of Old Faithful is about 75 minutes. So the average length of an eruption is about how many minutes?

    4.5, or $4\frac{1}{2}$ min

Math Journal 2, p. 350

Read the introduction on the journal page as a class. Write all three versions of the waiting time prediction formula on the board or a transparency.

One version is a description of the formula in words. The second and third versions use variables and represent the formula concisely. Remind students that when one or more of the factors are variables, the multiplication symbol is often omitted.

Working as a class, have students use the formula to complete the table in Problem 1 on the journal page. For example, if the geyser erupted for 5 minutes, multiply 10 by 5 to get 50, and add 30 to that number, for a total of 80. The next eruption would likely occur 80 minutes later.

Ask volunteers to explain how to use the formula when the eruption time is not an exact number of minutes. For example, the table lists eruption times of $2\frac{1}{2}$ minutes and 3 minutes 15 seconds. Expect a variety of solutions such as the following:

▷ Ten times $2\frac{1}{2}$ is like ten 2s, which is 20, and ten halves, which is 5 more. That's 25, and 30 more makes 55.

▷ If the geyser erupts for 2 minutes, the formula says to wait 50 minutes. If it erupts for 3 minutes, the formula says to wait 60 minutes. So if it erupts for $2\frac{1}{2}$ minutes, it's halfway between the two times, or 55 minutes.

▷ Fifteen seconds is $\frac{1}{4}$ of a minute. Ten times $3\frac{1}{4}$ is ten 3s, or 30, and 10 quarters, or $2\frac{1}{2}$ more. That's $32\frac{1}{2}$. Then $32\frac{1}{2}$ plus 30 is $62\frac{1}{2}$.

▷ Ten 3s is 30 minutes. Ten times 15 seconds is 150 seconds, which is $2\frac{1}{2}$ minutes. That's $32\frac{1}{2}$ minutes and 30 more makes $62\frac{1}{2}$ minutes.

You may want to remind students that some of these solutions use an application of the Distributive Property. For example, 10 times $2\frac{1}{2}$ can be written as $(10 * 2) + (10 * \frac{1}{2})$. Refer students to pages 78 and 225 of the *Student Reference Book* as a reminder.

All these solutions are correct and show good reasoning. Students might also suggest changing minutes to seconds. If minutes are converted to seconds, the formula, including all time units, should be written out. *For example:* $2\frac{1}{2}$ minutes = 150 seconds

Waiting time = (10 * 150 seconds) + 30 minutes

$\qquad$ = 1,500 seconds + 30 minutes

$\qquad$ = 25 minutes + 30 minutes

$\qquad$ = 55 minutes

NOTE The journal page formulas include a warning that *all times are in minutes*. If any times are converted to seconds, it is important that all time units be written out to avoid confusion.

Assign the remainder of the journal page. Students plot the ordered pairs onto the graph and then apply the formula to answer specific questions about Old Faithful (Problems 2–4). Allow students to work with a partner. Circulate and assist.

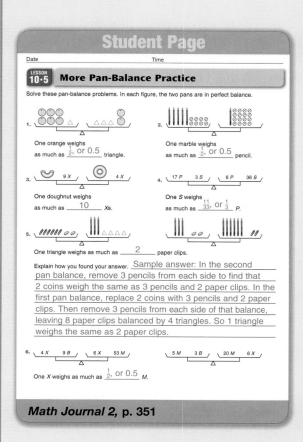

Math Journal 2, p. 351

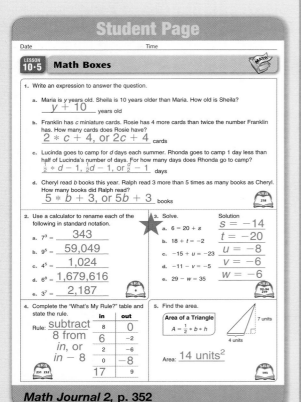

Student Page

Date _____ Time _____

LESSON 10·5 **Math Boxes**

1. Write an expression to answer the question.

a. Maria is y years old. Sheila is 10 years older than Maria. How old is Sheila?
$y + 10$ years old

b. Franklin has c miniature cards. Rosie has 4 more cards than twice the number Franklin has. How many cards does Rosie have?
$2 * c + 4$, or $2c + 4$ cards

c. Lucinda goes to camp for d days each summer. Rhonda goes to camp 1 day less than half of Lucinda's number of days. For how many days does Rhonda go to camp?
$\frac{1}{2} * d - 1$, $\frac{1}{2}d - 1$, or $\frac{d}{2} - 1$ days

d. Cheryl read b books this year. Ralph read 3 more than 5 times as many books as Cheryl. How many books did Ralph read?
$5 * b + 3$, or $5b + 3$ books

2. Use a calculator to rename each of the following in standard notation.

a. $7^3 = $ __343__

b. $9^5 = $ __59,049__

c. $4^5 = $ __1,024__

d. $6^8 = $ __1,679,616__

e. $3^7 = $ __2,187__

3. Solve.

		Solution
a.	$6 = 20 + s$	$s = -14$
b.	$18 + t = -2$	$t = -20$
c.	$-15 + u = -23$	$u = -8$
d.	$-11 - v = -5$	$v = -6$
e.	$29 - w = 35$	$w = -6$

4. Complete the "What's My Rule?" table and state the rule.

Rule: subtract 8 from *in*, or *in* − 8

in	out
8	0
6	−2
2	−6
0	−8
17	9

5. Find the area.

Area of a Triangle
$A = \frac{1}{2} * b * h$

7 units
4 units

Area: __14 units^2__

Math Journal 2, p. 352

Study Link Master

Name _____ Date _____ Time _____

STUDY LINK 10·5 **Cricket Formulas**

In 1897, the physicist, A. E. Dolbear, published an article titled "The Cricket as a Thermometer." In it he claimed that outside temperatures can be estimated by counting the number of chirps made by crickets and then by using that number in the following formula:

Outside temperature (°F) = $\frac{(\text{number of cricket chirps per minute} - 40)}{4} + 50$

1. Write a number model for the formula. $t = \frac{(c - 40)}{4} + 50$

2. According to this formula, what is the estimated outside temperature if you count 80 chirps in a minute? __60°F__

Other cricket formulas exist. The following formula is supposed to work particularly well with field crickets:

Outside temperature (°F) = (number of chirps in 15 seconds) + 37

3. Write a number model for the formula. $t = c + 37$

4. According to this formula, what is the estimated outside temperature if you counted 35 chirps in 15 seconds? __72°F__

5. Compare the two formulas. If you count 30 chirps in 15 seconds, what is the estimated outside temperature for each formula?

a. First formula: __70°F__

b. Second formula: __67°F__

Practice

6. $7 - 2\frac{2}{5} = $ __$4\frac{3}{5}$__

7. $1\frac{1}{2} + 2\frac{2}{3} + 3\frac{3}{4} + \frac{1}{12} = $ __8__

8. $\left(\frac{2}{3} * \frac{2}{3}\right) - \frac{2}{9} = $ __$\frac{2}{9}$__

9. $\frac{12}{9} \div \frac{1}{3} = $ __4__

Math Masters, p. 304

2 Ongoing Learning & Practice

▶ ## Solving Pan-Balance Problems

PARTNER ACTIVITY

(*Math Journal 2*, p. 351)

Algebraic Thinking Students solve pan-balance problems. Some of the problems involve two pan balances.

▶ ## Math Boxes 10·5

INDEPENDENT ACTIVITY

(*Math Journal 2*, p. 352)

Mixed Practice Math Boxes in this lesson are paired with Math Boxes in Lessons 10-7 and 10-9. The skill in Problem 5 previews Unit 11 content.

✔ **Ongoing Assessment:**
Recognizing Student Achievement

Math Boxes Problem 3 ★

Use **Math Boxes, Problem 3** to assess students' ability to solve addition and subtraction open sentences containing negative and positive numbers. Students are making adequate progress if they correctly solve Problems 3a–3c. Some students may correctly solve Problems 3d and 3e.

[Patterns, Functions, and Algebra Goal 2]

▶ ## Study Link 10·5

INDEPENDENT ACTIVITY

(*Math Masters*, p. 304)

Home Connection Students use formulas to predict the outside temperature. Each formula is based on the number of cricket chirps in a given period of time.

3 Differentiation Options

ENRICHMENT

PARTNER ACTIVITY

▶ ## Graphing Values from a Table

5–15 Min

(*Math Masters*, p. 305)

Algebraic Thinking To apply students' understanding of representing functions with graphs, have students complete and graph "What's My Rule?" tables. Suggest that one partner read the values from the table while the other partner finds the pair of numbers on the graph.

5-Minute Math

To offer students more experience with graphing data, see *5-Minute Math*, pages 114 and 115.

Planning Ahead

Throughout Unit 11 you will need an assortment of materials to provide students with concrete models for volume concepts. Consider soliciting the assistance of parents and/or school volunteers. Collect the following items:

▷ prisms, pyramids, cylinders, cones, and spheres (boxes, cans, ice-cream cones, party hats, balls, and so on)

▷ open cans, preferably with the labels removed, or other cylindrical and watertight containers of different sizes

▷ 1-gallon container of water

▷ several measuring cups (marked in milliliters to at least 250 milliliters)

▷ several shallow pans

▷ seven 2-liter, soft-drink bottles, made out of clear or light-colored plastic

▷ seven large-mouthed containers that hold up to 2 liters of water each

▷ 30 to 40 rocks (enough to fill a gallon container), each about half the size of a fist (landscape rocks work well)

▷ several unopened cans of a nondiet soft drink

▷ several baseballs, golf balls, or apples

▷ supply of paper towels

▷ 1 pound of dry fill such as rice or sugar

▷ bucket or clear container

▷ empty margarine tub or yogurt container

▷ empty copy-paper carton, measuring approximately 11 in. by 17 in. by 9 in. with the top removed

▷ empty milk cartons (pint, quart, half-gallon, and gallon)

▷ 1 gallon of water or other pourable substance, such as sand, popcorn, or rice (about 16 cups)

▷ scale, accurate to the nearest ounce

▷ cardboard box with the top taped shut

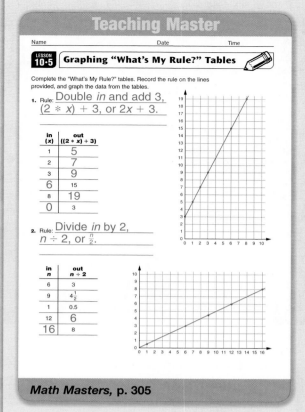

Math Masters, p. 305

10·6 Rules, Tables, and Graphs: Part 2

 Objective To provide experiences with interpreting tables and graphs.

Technology Resources www.everydaymathonline.com

 ePresentations   eToolkit   Algorithms Practice   EM Facts Workshop Game™   Family Letters   Assessment Management   Common Core State Standards Curriculum Focal Points   Interactive Teacher's Lesson Guide

---

1 Teaching the Lesson

Key Concepts and Skills

• Construct line graphs that represent two sets of data.
[Data and Chance Goal 1]

• Extend patterns in graphs and tables to solve problems.
[Patterns, Functions, and Algebra Goal 1]

• Represent rates with formulas, tables, and graphs.
[Patterns, Functions, and Algebra Goal 1]

Key Activities

Students complete a table of values that displays the distance covered by each of two students at various time intervals. They interpret the data in the table, graph the data, and interpret the graph.

 Ongoing Assessment: Informing Instruction See page 817.

 Ongoing Assessment: Recognizing Student Achievement Use an Exit Slip (*Math Masters,* page 414).
[Data and Chance Goal 2]

Key Vocabulary

coordinates ◆ ordered number pairs

Materials

Math Journal 2, pp. 354 and 355
Study Link 10·5
Math Masters, p. 414
Class Data Pad (optional) ◆ slate ◆ calculator ◆ 2 different-colored pencils or markers (optional) ◆ straightedge

2 Ongoing Learning & Practice

 Playing *Mixed-Number Spin* or *Fraction Spin*
Math Journal 2, pp. 255 and 262
Math Masters, pp. 470, 471, 488, and 489
per partnership: large paper clip
Students practice estimating sums and differences of fractions and/or mixed numbers.

 Math Boxes 10·6
Math Journal 2, p. 353
Students practice and maintain skills through Math Box problems.

Study Link 10·6
Math Masters, p. 306
Students practice and maintain skills through Study Link activities.

3 Differentiation Options

READINESS

Interpreting Table Data for Graphs
Math Masters, p. 307
straightedge
Students identify how table data translates to graph elements.

ENRICHMENT

Graphing Race Results
Math Masters, p. 439
per group: stopwatch, 3 or 4 different-colored pencils or markers, straightedge
Students use different movements to cover the same distance, time themselves, and graph the results.

EXTRA PRACTICE

Analyzing Two Rules
Math Masters, pp. 307A and 307B
Students derive data from two rates by making a table and graphing ordered pairs.

Advance Preparation

For the optional Enrichment activity in Part 3, mark off a 5-meter course for a race. Make 1 copy of *Math Masters,* page 439 for each small group.

 Teacher's Reference Manual, Grades 4–6 pp. 64–68, 164

Getting Started

Mental Math and Reflexes

Have students use slates and their calculators to practice converting between units of time. *Suggestions:*

○○○ In 5 years (none are Leap years), there are how many:

months? 60

weeks? 260

days? 1,825

●●○ In 168 hours, there are how many:

weeks? 1

days? 7

minutes? 10,080

●●● In 43,200 minutes, there are how many:

days? 30

hours? 720

seconds? 2,592,000

Math Message

Solve Problem 1 on journal page 354.

Study Link 10·5 Follow-Up

Have partners compare answers and resolve differences.

---

1   Teaching the Lesson

Math Message Follow-Up

(*Math Journal 2*, p. 354)

WHOLE-CLASS ACTIVITY

Algebraic Thinking Draw the table from journal page 354 onto the board or Class Data Pad. Ask volunteers to fill in the *x* and *y* values from the graph. (0,5); (1,4); (2,3); (3,2); (4,1); and (5,0)

Point out that although this table looks different from a "What's My Rule?" table, it still has a rule. In this case, the rule describes the relationship between the **coordinates** of the **ordered number pairs** (*x,y*). Ask students to examine the table data and name a rule that fits. Sample answer: The sum of the coordinates is always 5.

Explain that if *x* and *y* are used as variables, the rule can be written as the equation: $x + y = 5$. Write the equation on the board or Class Data Pad. Ask students to suggest how the rule could be written in a different way. $y = 5 - x$, or $x = 5 - y$ Write the equations on the board or Class Data Pad. Have students select ordered number pairs from the table to verify the equations.

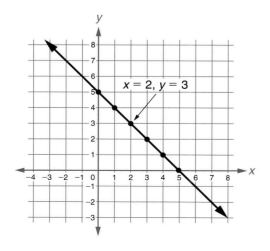

x = 2, y = 3

NOTE For practice solving problems involving numeric patterns, see www.everydaymathonline.com.

Student Page

Date _____   Time _____

LESSON 10·6   Rules, Tables, and Graphs

Math Message

1. Use the graph below. Find the *x*- and *y*-coordinates of each point shown. Then enter the *x* and *y* values in the table.

x	y
0	5
1	4
2	3
3	2
4	1
5	0

x = 2, y = 3

2. Eli is 10 years old and can run an average of 5 yards per second. His sister Lupita is 7 and can run an average of 4 yards per second.

Eli and Lupita have a 60-yard race. Because Lupita is younger, Eli gives her a 10-yard head start.

Complete the table showing the distances Eli and Lupita are from the starting line after 1 second, 2 seconds, 3 seconds, and so on. Use the table to answer the questions below.

Time (sec)	Distance (yd) Eli	Distance (yd) Lupita
start	0	10
1	5	14
2	10	18
3	15	22
4	20	26
5	25	30
6	30	34
7	35	38
8	40	42
9	45	46
10	50	50
11	55	54
12	60	58

a. Who wins the race? __Eli__

b. What is the winning time? __12 seconds__

c. Who was in the lead during most of the race? __Lupita__

Math Journal 2, p. 354

Eli

in/time (sec)	out/distance (yd)
Start 0	0
1	5
2	10
3	15
4	20
5	25
6	30
7	35
8	40
9	45
10	50
11	55
12	60

Lupita

in/time (sec)	out/distance (yd)
Start 0	10
1	14
2	18
3	22
4	26
5	30
6	34
7	38
8	42
9	46
10	50
11	54
12	58

Have students use a straightedge to draw a line that passes through the points marked on the graph. They should extend the line beyond the axes in both directions. (*See page 815.*)

Ask students to name other ordered pairs that are on the line. Then check to see that these pairs satisfy the same $x + y = 5$ rule. Guide students to locate and name ordered number pairs containing fractions or negative numbers.

▷ Fraction pairs: $(\frac{1}{2}, 4\frac{1}{2})$; $(4\frac{1}{2}, \frac{1}{2})$; $(2\frac{1}{3}, 2\frac{2}{3})$; $(4\frac{3}{4}, \frac{1}{4})$; and so on.

▷ Negative numbers: $(6, -1)$; $(7, -2)$; $(8, -3)$; $(-3, 8)$; $(-2\frac{1}{2}, 7\frac{1}{2})$; and so on.

▶ Solving the Footrace Problem   PARTNER ACTIVITY

(*Math Journal 2*, p. 354)

Algebraic Thinking Assign Problem 2 on the journal page. Have students work with partners or in small groups. Point out that they will be completing this table to analyze the results based on two different rules, one rule for Eli and one rule for Lupita. When most students have finished, bring the class together to discuss the answers.

Ask volunteers to explain how they used the table to answer the questions in Problem 2. Look at the distance for Eli and Lupita at each time interval. Lupita leads most of the way, but Eli wins after 12 seconds.

Ask: *After the start of the race, how many yards does Eli gain on Lupita each second?* Eli gains 1 yard each second. Ask: *How did you get your answer?* Sample answers: For 1 second (input), I looked at the difference between the output for Eli and the output for Lupita. Here Lupita is ahead by $14 - 5$, or 9 yards; after 2 seconds, she is ahead by $18 - 10$, or 8 yards; after 3 seconds, she is ahead by $22 - 15$, or 7 yards; and so on. Eli's speed is 1 yard per second faster than Lupita's, so he catches up by 1 yard per second.

▲ Adjusting the Activity

Have students extend the table to answer additional questions such as: *Who is ahead after 8 seconds and by how much?* Lupita, by 2 yards *What if the race had been 50 yards instead of 60?* The race would have ended in a tie, and it would have taken 10 seconds.

AUDITORY ◆ KINESTHETIC ◆ TACTILE ◆ VISUAL

Ask: *What is the rule for the time it takes Eli to cover the distance?* Distance = 5 * number of seconds, or $d = 5t$

Tell students that it might help to think of the table as two "What's My Rule?" tables. In each table, the *in* values are numbers of seconds (time), and the *out* values are numbers of yards (distance). (*See margin.*)

Ask: *What is the rule for the time it takes Lupita to cover the distance?* Distance = 4 * number of seconds + 10, or $d = 4t + 10$

Lupita's rule is less obvious, and students might not discover it on their own. Remind students that Lupita had a 10-yard head start. Her actual running distance is 4 * the number of yards, but her 10-yard head start must be added.

Write the rules on the board or a transparency, and have students verify that the rules are correct for several values from the table.

 Ongoing Assessment: Informing Instruction

Watch for students who do not understand how Lupita's 10-yard head start is part of the rule. Guide them to see the pattern in the computations used to complete Lupita's data in the table. Write the computations in equation form.

0 seconds: $(4 * 0) + 10 = 10$ yards

3 seconds: $(4 * 3) + 10 = 22$ yards

4 seconds: $(4 * 4) + 10 = 26$ yards

10 seconds: $(4 * 10) + 10 = 50$ yards

Graphing the Footrace Data

 **WHOLE-CLASS ACTIVITY**

(*Math Journal 2,* p. 355)

Have students graph the data in their tables, using the grid on the journal page. Students should plot two graphs on the same grid—one for Eli and one for Lupita.

Suggestions:

▷ Students need to plot only a few time and distance results for each runner in order to make the graph. Have them write the ordered pairs for a few results and then plot them. Suggest that students select results whose times are spread out along the interval; for example, 0 seconds (start), 5 seconds, and 10 seconds. Sample answers: For Eli: (0,0), (5,25), (10,50); For Lupita: (0,10), (5,30), and (10,50)

▷ Students should then use a straightedge to connect these points for each runner and label the lines Eli and Lupita.

▷ Have students compare the two lines. *How and why are they different?* Sample answers: Eli's line is steeper because he is running faster. Lupita's line intersects the vertical axis at 10 yards because she had a head start.

▷ Have students verify that all of Eli's and Lupita's times and distances shown in the table are points on the graphs.

▷ The graphs show that Eli and Lupita both cross the 50-yard line in 10 seconds. The lines of the graphs intersect at the point (10 sec, 50 yd).

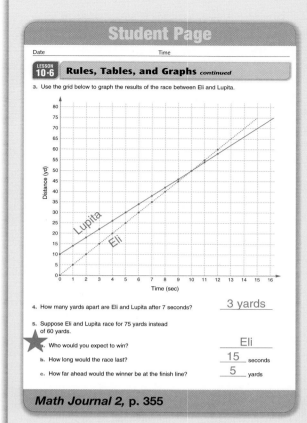

Date _____ Time _____

LESSON 10·6 **Rules, Tables, and Graphs** *continued*

3. Use the grid below to graph the results of the race between Eli and Lupita.

4. How many yards apart are Eli and Lupita after 7 seconds? 3 yards

5. Suppose Eli and Lupita race for 75 yards instead of 60 yards.
   a. Who would you expect to win? Eli
   b. How long would the race last? 15 seconds
   c. How far ahead would the winner be at the finish line? 5 yards

Math Journal 2, p. 355

Ask additional questions that can be answered by referring to the graphs:

- Who was ahead after 4 seconds and by how much? Lupita, by 6 yards

- How far did Eli run in 5 seconds? 25 yards

- If the race had been 70 yards, who would have won and by how much? Eli would have won by 1 second. Use a straightedge to extend the two graphs.

Adjusting the Activity

ELL

Have students use two colors when graphing the footrace data, one color for each data set.

AUDITORY ♦ KINESTHETIC ♦ TACTILE ♦ VISUAL

Have students work with partners or in small groups to complete Problems 4 and 5 on journal page 355. Circulate and assist. Encourage students to answer the questions by using their graphs. They must use a straightedge to extend the graphs before answering the questions about the 75-yard race.

Ongoing Assessment: Recognizing Student Achievement
Exit Slip ★

Use an **Exit Slip** (*Math Masters,* page 414) to assess students' ability to read and interpret graphs. Have students explain their answers for Problem 5a on journal page 355. Sample answer: I drew Eli's and Lupita's lines on the graph so they extended to 75 yards. The lines show that Eli is ahead of Lupita, so I would expect Eli to win. Students are making adequate progress if their writing refers to being able to extend the lines to see an increase in time and distance.

[Data and Chance Goal 2]

2 Ongoing Learning & Practice

Playing *Mixed-Number Spin* or *Fraction Spin*

 PARTNER ACTIVITY

(*Math Journal 2,* pp. 255 and 262; *Math Masters,* pp. 470, 471, 488, and 489)

Students play *Mixed-Number Spin* or *Fraction Spin* to practice estimating sums and differences of fractions and/or mixed numbers. Players use benchmarks to estimate sums and differences as they record number sentences that fit the parameters given on the *Mixed-Number Spin* record sheet, *Math Masters,* page 489. These games were introduced in Lessons 8-3 and 8-5, respectively.

Math Boxes 10·6

 INDEPENDENT ACTIVITY

(*Math Journal 2,* p. 353)

Mixed Practice Math Boxes in this lesson are paired with Math Boxes in Lesson 10-8. The skill in Problem 3 previews Unit 11 content.

Writing/Reasoning Have students write a response to the following: *Explain how you found the answer to Problem 2b. Include the strategies and the reasoning that you used.* Answers vary.

Study Link 10·6

 INDEPENDENT ACTIVITY

(*Math Masters,* p. 306)

Home Connection Students complete a table of values that displays race distance covered in 13 seconds. They interpret the data in the table, graph it, and then interpret the graph.

Date _____ Time _____

LESSON 10·6 Math Boxes

1. Below are the distances (in feet) that a baseball must travel to right field to be a home run in various major league baseball parks.

| 330 | 353 | 330 | 345 | 325 | 330 | 325 | 338 | 318 |
| 302 | 333 | 347 | 325 | 315 | 330 | 327 | 314 | 348 |

a. Make a stem-and-leaf plot for the data. Identify the landmarks.

b. What is the maximum? __353__

c. What is the mode? __330__

d. What is the median? __330__

Stems (100s and 10s)	Leaves (1s)
30	2
31	4 5 8
32	5 5 5 7
33	0 0 0 0 3 8
34	5 7 8
35	3

2. Solve.

a. $3.26 + 504.1 =$ __507.36__

b. __584.035__ $= 793.82 - 209.785$

c. __1,271.15__ $= 987.55 + 283.6$

d. $24.07 - 6.434 =$ __17.636__

e. __9.805__ $= 9.775 + 0.03$

f. $21.574 + 179.48 =$ __201.054__

3. Complete the following equivalents.

a. 1 pint = __2__ cups

b. 1 quart = __2__ pints

c. 1 quart = __4__ cups

d. 1 gallon = __4__ quarts

e. 1 gallon = __16__ cups

Math Journal 2, p. 353

Name _____ Date _____ Time _____

STUDY LINK 10·6 Interpreting Tables and Graphs

Natasha is 12 years old and runs an average of 6 yards per second. Derek is 8 years old and runs about 5 yards per second. Natasha challenged Derek to an 80-yard race and told him she would win even if he had a 10-yard head start.

1. Complete the table showing the distances Natasha and Derek are from the starting line after 1 second, 2 seconds, 3 seconds, and so on.

Time (sec)	Distance (yd) Natasha	Distance (yd) Derek
Start	0	10
1	6	15
2	12	20
3	18	25
4	24	30
9	54	55
10	60	60
11	66	65
12	72	70
13	78	75

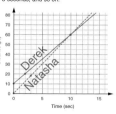

2. Use the table to write rules for the distance covered by Natasha and Derek.

Natasha's Rule: __Multiply time by 6; 6 ∗ t, or 6t.__

Derek's Rule: __Multiply time by 5 and add 10; (5 ∗ t) + 10, 5 ∗ t + 10, or 5t + 10.__

3. Graph the results of the race between Natasha and Derek on the grid above. Label each line.

4. a. Who wins the race? __Natasha__

   b. What is the winning time? __13.$\overline{3}$ or 13$\frac{1}{3}$ seconds__

   c. At what time in the race did Natasha take the lead? __After 10 seconds__

Math Masters, p. 306

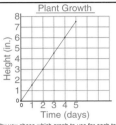

3 Differentiation Options

READINESS

SMALL-GROUP ACTIVITY

5–15 Min

▶ ## Interpreting Table Data for Graphs

(*Math Masters,* p. 307)

Portfolio Ideas

To provide experience with constructing graphs from table data, have students identify the relationship between parts of a table and parts of a graph. Refer students to the tables on *Math Masters,* page 307.

Discuss how students might choose the type of graph to use for each table. Circle graphs show parts of a whole, so Table 2 data could be represented by a circle graph. Line graphs often show change over time, so Table 1 could be represented by a line graph. Discuss how the table organization suggests the title and labels, including line-graph scales, for the graphs.

Have students graph the data from the tables on the *Math Masters* page.

ENRICHMENT

WHOLE-CLASS ACTIVITY

30+ Min

▶ ## Graphing Race Results

(*Math Masters,* p. 439)

To apply students' understanding of constructing graphs from table data, have students explore multiple graphs on a single grid. Divide students into groups of 3 or 4. Each group chooses a different method of movement (for example, hopping on one foot, taking baby steps, or walking backward) for completing the 5-meter course. The groups use a stopwatch to time how long each group member takes to complete the course.

Each group makes a distance-over-time line graph of the results for each group member on the same grid. Plot time on the *x*-axis and distance on the *y*-axis. A student plots his or her starting point at the origin (0,0) and his or her ending point at the number of seconds it takes to cover the distance. The student then connects these two points with a line segment. Draw each group member's line segment in a different color.

Compare the graphs. Discuss similarities and differences.

Analyzing Two Rules

INDEPENDENT ACTIVITY

5–15 Min

(*Math Masters,* pp. 307A and 307B)

Students use two rules to complete a table of values. They list and graph ordered pairs for each rule. They use the table of values and graphs to analyze the data.

Planning Ahead

In Lessons 10-8 and 10-9, you will need a collection of round objects for students to measure, such as rolls of tape, wide markers, food and coffee cans, round clocks, wheels, circular cardboard cutouts, and graduated cylinders. There should be at least one object per student. Ask students to bring these or similar objects from home.

Teaching Master

Name _____ Date _____ Time _____

LESSON 10·6 Analyzing Two Rules

Ivan earns $50 every 2 days. Elise earns $70 every 3 days.

1. Write a rule to describe how much money Ivan earns in a given number of days.

Amount earned = $\frac{\$50}{2}$, or $25 * number of days

2. Write a rule to describe how much money Elise earns in a given number of days.

Amount earned = $\frac{\$70}{3}$ * number of days

3. Complete the table for the outputs in the cells that are not shaded.

4. a. After 6 days, who has earned more money?

___Ivan___

b. After 12 days, who has earned more money?

___Ivan___

c. Who earns more money per day? Explain your answer.

Ivan. Sample answers: The table shows that Ivan earns more after 6 days, and even more after 12 days. Ivan earns $\frac{\$50}{2}$, or $25 per day. Elise earns $\frac{\$70}{3}$, or a bit more than $23 per day.

5. How long does it take each person to make $350?

Ivan: ___14___ days   Elise: ___15___ days

Days	Money Earned	
	Ivan	Elise
0	$0	$0
1		
2	$50	
3		$70
4	$100	
5		
6	$150	$140
7		
8	$200	
9		$210
10	$250	
11		
12	$300	$280
13		
14	$350	
15		$350
16	$400	

***Math Masters,* p. 307A**

Teaching Master

Name _____ Date _____ Time _____

LESSON 10·6 Analyzing Two Rules *continued*

6. Write three ordered pairs to show the relationship between number of days and the amount earned for each person.

Ivan: Sample answer: (0,0), (6,150), (12,300)

Elise: Sample answer: (0,0), (9,210), (15,350)

7. Use the grid to graph your ordered pairs. Use a straightedge to connect the points for each person, and label the lines Ivan and Elise.

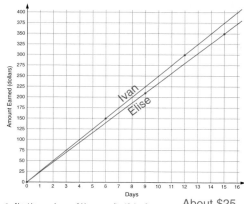

8. About how much more did Ivan earn after 13 days?   About $25

9. Extend the graph to find out about how much Elise earned in 16 days.   About $375

***Math Masters,* p. 307B**

10·7 Reading Graphs

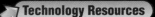

Objective To provide experiences with interpreting line graphs.

Technology Resources www.everydaymathonline.com

ePresentations | eToolkit | Algorithms Practice | EM Facts Workshop Game™ | Family Letters | Assessment Management | Common Core State Standards | Curriculum Focal Points | Interactive Teacher's Lesson Guide

1 Teaching the Lesson

Key Concepts and Skills

• Read and analyze line graphs and answer questions based on the displayed data.
[Data and Chance Goal 2]

• Identify and use patterns in graphs to match graphs with situations.
[Patterns, Functions, and Algebra Goal 1]

Key Activities

Students analyze graphs and answer questions based on the graphs; they match various mystery graphs with descriptions of situations.

 Ongoing Assessment:
Recognizing Student Achievement
Use the Math Message.
[Data and Chance Goal 2]

 Ongoing Assessment:
Informing Instruction See page 822.

Key Vocabulary

mystery graph

Materials

Math Journal 2, pp. 356–358
Study Link 10·6
Class Data Pad (optional) ◆ slate

2 Ongoing Learning & Practice

 **Playing *First to 100***
Student Reference Book, p. 308
Math Masters, pp. 456–458
per partnership: 2 six-sided dice, calculator
Students practice solving open number sentences.

 Math Boxes 10·7
Math Journal 2, p. 359
Students practice and maintain skills through Math Box problems.

 Study Link 10·7
Math Masters, p. 308
Students practice and maintain skills through Study Link activities.

3 Differentiation Options

READINESS
Exploring Silhouettes
Math Masters, p. 309
Students identify objects and situations from their shapes.

READINESS
Finding Graph Errors
Math Masters, p. 311
Students identify and describe errors in graphs.

ENRICHMENT
Making Tables from Graphs
Math Masters, p. 310
Students make data tables and write the rules for line graphs.

EXTRA PRACTICE
5-Minute Math
5-Minute Math™, p. 116
Students identify data landmarks.

Advance Preparation

 Teacher's Reference Manual, **Grades 4–6** pp. 168, 169

Getting Started

Math Message ★

Solve Problems 1–4 on journal page 356.

Study Link 10·6 Follow-Up

Have partners compare answers and resolve differences.

✔ Ongoing Assessment:
Recognizing Student Achievement

Math Message ★

Use the **Math Message** to assess students' ability to interpret line graphs. Students are making adequate progress if they answer Problems 1–4 correctly.

[Data and Chance Goal 2]

---

① Teaching the Lesson

▶ Math Message Follow-Up

WHOLE-CLASS DISCUSSION

(*Math Journal 2*, p. 356)

Discuss the answers. Then ask what else students notice about the graph. Stimulate the discussion with questions such as the following:

- What does the graph show about the distance each person traveled? All the lines seem to end at the same distance, so each person probably traveled the same distance.

- Whose line is steepest? Tamara's **Why?** Because Tamara needed the least time to travel the distance, her line ends nearest to 0 on the time axis.

- Whose line is the least steep? JaDerrick's **Why?** Because JaDerrick needed the most time to travel, his line ends farthest from 0 on the time axis.

▶ Reading Graphs

PARTNER ACTIVITY

(*Math Journal 2*, pp. 356 and 357)

Ask students to look over the graphs and descriptions on journal page 357. Discuss each graph in general terms, but do not delve into the specifics that are covered by the problems.

Student Page

Date _____ Time _____

LESSON 10·7 Running-and-Walking Graph

Math Message

Tamara, William, and Imani timed themselves traveling the same distance in different ways. Tamara ran, William walked, and Imani walked toe-to-heel.

After they timed themselves, they drew a graph.

1. Which line on the graph at the right is for Tamara? **A**

2. Which line is for William? **B**

3. Which line is for Imani? **C**

4. JaDerrick came along later and was the slowest of all. He walked heel-to-toe backward. Draw a line on the graph to show the speed you think JaDerrick walked.

Review: Algebraic Expressions

Complete each statement with an algebraic expression.

5. Alberto is 5 years older than Rick. If Rick is R years old, then Alberto is **$R + 5$** years old.

6. Rebecca's piano lesson is half as long as Kendra's. If Kendra's piano lesson is K minutes long, then Rebecca's is **$\frac{1}{2} * K, \frac{1}{2}K,$ or $\frac{K}{2}$** minutes long.

7. Marlin's dog weighs 3 pounds more than twice the weight of Eddy's dog. If Eddy's dog weighs E pounds, then Marlin's dog weighs **$(2 * E) + 3,$ or $2E + 3$** pounds.

Math Journal 2, p. 356

Date _____ **Time** _____

LESSON 10·7 Reading Graphs

1. Tom and Alisha run a 200-yard race. Tom has a head start.

a. Who wins the race? <u>Alisha</u>

b. By about how much? <u>25 yd</u>

c. Mark the point on the graph where Alisha overtakes Tom.

d. About how many yards does Alisha run before taking the lead? <u>135 yd</u>

e. About how many seconds pass before Alisha takes the lead? <u>16 sec</u>

f. Who is ahead after 9 seconds? <u>Tom</u>

g. By about how much? <u>About 25 yd</u>

2. Ahmed is definitely out of shape, but he runs 100 meters as fast as he can.

a. In the first 10 seconds of his run, Ahmed covers about <u>50</u> meters,

and his speed is about $\dfrac{50 \text{ meters}}{10 \text{ seconds}} = \dfrac{5 \text{ meters}}{1 \text{ second}}$

b. In the final 10 seconds of his run, Ahmed covers about <u>25</u> meters,

and his speed is about $\dfrac{25 \text{ meters}}{10 \text{ seconds}} = \dfrac{2.5 \text{ meters}}{1 \text{ second}}$

Math Journal 2, p. 357

Date _____ **Time** _____

LESSON 10·7 Mystery Graphs

Each of the events described below is represented by one of the following graphs.

Graph A   Graph B   Graph C   Graph D   Graph E

Match each event with its graph.

1. A frozen dinner is removed from the freezer. It is heated in a microwave oven. Then it is placed on the table.

Which graph shows the temperature of the dinner at different times? Graph <u>C</u>

2. Satya runs water into his bathtub. He steps into the tub, sits down, and bathes. He gets out of the tub and drains the water.

Which graph shows the height of water in the tub at different times? Graph <u>A</u>

3. A baseball is thrown straight up into the air.

a. Which graph shows the height of the ball—from the time it is thrown until the time it hits the ground? Graph <u>B</u>

b. Which graph shows the speed of the ball at different times? Graph <u>E</u>

Math Journal 2, p. 358

For example:

▷ Ask what each graph represents, and make sure students notice how the axes are labeled.

▷ Ask why the line for Tom starts at 50 yards and the line for Alisha starts at 0 yards. Tom is given a 50-yard head start in his race with Alisha.

▷ Ask how long it takes to run 100 meters according to the graph in Problem 2. 30 seconds

▷ Mention that Ahmed's graph looks different from other racers' graphs that students have seen. The journal page questions will help students see the reason for the change in the line. Ahmed slows down in the latter $\frac{2}{3}$ of his run.

Have students complete journal pages 356 and 357, working with partners or in small groups.

 Ongoing Assessment: Informing Instruction

Watch for students who have difficulty recognizing a graph as a visual representation of a situation. Draw the graph below onto the board or Class Data Pad. Ask: *What might have happened to a runner if his or her graph looked like this?*

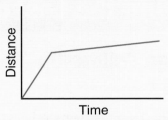

▶ **Interpreting Mystery Graphs** **PROBLEM SOLVING · PARTNER ACTIVITY · ELL**

(*Math Journal 2*, p. 358)

Five **mystery graphs** are shown at the top of the journal page. Students are asked to match each situation described at the bottom of the page with the appropriate graph at the top of the page. Four graphs are used only once. One graph is not used at all.

Ask partners or small groups to complete journal page 358. When most students have finished, bring the class together to discuss students' answers.

On all five graphs, time is represented on the horizontal axis. The quantity represented on the vertical axis depends on the situation:

▷ **Graph A** represents Situation 2, the bath. To support English language learners, ask students to label the different parts of the graph with the meanings. For example, the left-most diagonal line segment shows the height of the water increasing as Satya fills the tub. When he turns off the water, the height is constant for a brief time; then it rises in two increments as he steps into the tub and sits down. The top horizontal segment shows that the height of the water is (approximately) constant while Satya bathes. Then the reverse occurs as he stands up, steps out, and drains the water.

▷ **Graph B** represents the height of the ball in Situation 3. The graph starts above the origin because the ball is being held above the ground. The ball travels up to its maximum height; then it falls to the ground where its height is less than the height at which it began.

▷ **Graph C** represents Situation 1, the frozen dinner. The graph begins below the origin to show that the initial temperature of the dinner is below 0°C. The dinner is taken out of the freezer when the time is 0. As the dinner is heated in the microwave, its temperature increases to a maximum. After the dinner is removed from the microwave, its temperature slowly decreases.

▷ **Graph D** does not match any of the situations.

▷ **Graph E** represents the speed of the ball in Situation 3. As soon as the ball is thrown, its speed begins to decrease under the force of gravity. When the ball reaches its highest point, its speed is 0. The ball then accelerates until it hits the ground.

② Ongoing Learning & Practice

Playing *First to 100*

PARTNER ACTIVITY

COMPUTATION PRACTICE

(*Student Reference Book*, p. 308; *Math Masters*, pp. 456–458)

Algebraic Thinking Students play *First to 100* to practice solving open number sentences. This game was introduced in Lesson 4-7. For detailed instructions, see *Student Reference Book*, page 308.

Math Boxes 10·7

INDEPENDENT ACTIVITY

(*Math Journal 2*, p. 359)

Mixed Practice Math Boxes in this lesson are paired with Math Boxes in Lessons 10-5 and 10-9. The skill in Problem 5 previews Unit 11 content.

Study Link 10·7

INDEPENDENT ACTIVITY

(*Math Masters*, p. 308)

Home Connection Each student creates his or her own mystery graph. Then the student describes the situation that goes with that graph.

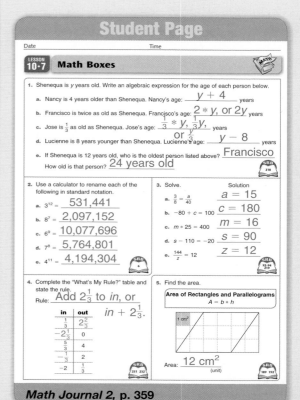
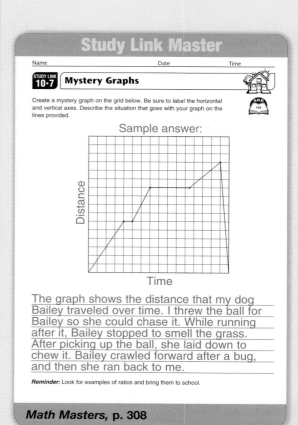

Teaching Master

Name   Date   Time

LESSON 10·7 Analyzing Graph Errors

For each graph below, describe a possible error in the graph.

Favorite Colors

1. The students in Ms. Wyn's fifth-grade class took a favorite color survey. About the same number of people voted for red, blue, and green. Orange and yellow got about the same number of votes, but the votes were a lot less than the other three colors. They made a bar graph of their results.

Describe at least one error in the Favorite Colors graph. Explain how you know this is an error.

<u>Sample answer: The Favorite Colors graph shows four</u>
<u>colors with the same number of votes, but only three colors</u>
<u>should have the same number of votes.</u>

2. There are 26 students in Ms. Wyn's class. They wanted to find the mean number of books that students had read in their class. They found out that half the class had read five or fewer books and the other half had read more than 15 books. The mode for the class was 19 books. They made a line plot of their results.

Books We Have Read

```
 x                        x
 x                        x      x
 x                        x      x x
 x                        x x    x x
 x x   x                  x x    x x
 x x   x          x x x   x x x  x x x
 0 2 4 6 8 10 12 14 16 18 20 22 24 26 28 30
```

Describe at least one error in the Books We Have Read graph. Explain how you know this is an error.

<u>Sample answer: The Books We Have Read graph shows</u>
<u>the mode as 2, but it should be 19.</u>

Math Masters, p. 311

Teaching Master

Name   Date   Time

LESSON 10·7 Making Tables from Graphs

When you plot the values of a table as coordinates on a grid and connect the points, the resulting figure can be called a **line graph**.

For each graph on the grid to the right:

♦ Find the coordinates of four points that lie on the graph.

♦ Write the four points in the "What's My Rule?" table.

♦ Write the rule for the table.

♦ Check that your rule works for all the points on the graph.

1. Rule for Graph A: *y* is 1 more than *x*, or $y = x + 1$.

x	y
−4	−3
−3	−2
0	1
2	3

2. Rule for Graph B: The sum of *y* and *x* is 5, or $y + x = 5$.

x	y
−3	8
2	3
4	1
4.5	0.5

3. Rule for Graph C: *x* is the opposite of *y*, the sum of *y* and *x* is 0, or $y + x = 0$.

x	y
−4	4
−1	1
3	−3
5	−5

Math Masters, p. 310

3 Differentiation Options

READINESS   **SMALL-GROUP ACTIVITY**

▶ Exploring Silhouettes

🕐 5–15 Min

(*Math Masters*, p. 309)

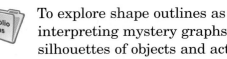

To explore shape outlines as a preparation for interpreting mystery graphs, have students discuss silhouettes of objects and activities. Ask students to write a description of the object or event for each of the silhouettes on the *Math Masters* page.

When students have finished, ask them to share their descriptions and their processes. Tell students that when they interpret mystery graphs, they will use similar processes.

READINESS   **PARTNER ACTIVITY**

▶ Finding Graph Errors

(*Math Masters*, p. 311)

To provide experience with analyzing graphs, have students identify and describe errors in graphs. When students have finished the page, have them share how they found the errors.

ENRICHMENT   **PARTNER ACTIVITY**

▶ Making Tables from Graphs

(*Math Masters*, p. 310)

To apply students' understanding of the relationship between line graphs and data tables, have students construct tables from graph data. Students then write the rule for each table and graph.

When students have finished, discuss any difficulties or curiosities they encountered.

EXTRA PRACTICE   **SMALL-GROUP ACTIVITY**

▶ *5-Minute Math*

🕐 5–15 Min

To offer students more experience with identifying data landmarks, see *5-Minute Math,* page 116.

10·8 Circumference of a Circle

Objectives To provide experience with comparison ratios and the use of the irrational number π.

Technology Resources www.everydaymathonline.com

 ePresentations
 eToolkit
 Algorithms Practice
 EM Facts Workshop Game™
 Family Letters
 Assessment Management
 Common Core State Standards
 Curriculum Focal Points
Interactive Teacher's Lesson Guide

1 Teaching the Lesson

Key Concepts and Skills

- Use ratios to express relationships between dimensions of objects.
  [Operations and Computation Goal 7]
- Find the median of a data set.
  [Data and Chance Goal 2]
- Use ratios to define π and describe the relationship between circumference and diameter.
  [Measurement and Reference Frames Goal 2]

Key Activities

Students find the ratio of the perimeter of squares to the length of their sides. They calculate the ratio of the circumference to the diameter of round objects. They use the π key on their calculators to calculate the circumference of circles.

 **Ongoing Assessment:
Recognizing Student Achievement**
Use journal page 360.
[Measurement and Reference Frames Goal 2]

Key Vocabulary

ratio ◆ ratio comparison ◆ diameter ◆ circumference ◆ radius ◆ pi (π)

Materials

Math Journal 2, pp. 360 and 361
Student Reference Book, Glossary and p. 112
Study Link 10·7 ◆ Class Data Pad (optional) ◆ slate ◆ round objects ◆ calculator ◆ for demonstration: board compass, 1-foot string ◆ per partnership or group: metric tape measure (or meterstick and 4-foot string)

2 Ongoing Learning & Practice

Converting Temperatures

Math Journal 2, p. 362
Students convert between Fahrenheit and Celsius degrees.

 Math Boxes 10·8

Math Journal 2, p. 363
Students practice and maintain skills through Math Box problems.

 Study Link 10·8

Math Masters, p. 312
calculator
Students practice and maintain skills through Study Link activities.

3 Differentiation Options

READINESS

Reading about Circumference

The Librarian Who Measured the Earth
Students read and discuss the book to explore the relationship between circumference and diameter.

ENRICHMENT

Passing Your Body through an Index Card

Math Masters, p. 313
5" by 8" pieces of paper or index cards ◆ scissors
Students explore circumference by reconfiguring a rectangular piece of paper into a circle.

ELL SUPPORT

Building a Math Word Bank

Differentiation Handbook, p. 143
Students define and illustrate the terms *rate, ratio,* and *ratio comparison.*

Advance Preparation

For Part 1, gather the round objects students will measure. Have students mark a 0-point about 2 inches from one end of a 4-foot length of string. When they wrap it around an object, they make another mark where the string meets the 0-point and use the meterstick to measure the length between the marks. For the optional Readiness activity in Part 3, you will need the book ***The Librarian Who Measured the Earth*** by Kathryn Lasky.

 ***Teacher's Reference Manual,* Grades 4–6** pp. 64–68, 185, 186, 219, 221

Getting Started

Mental Math and Reflexes

Use your established slate procedures to dictate problems such as the following:

⬤○○ Write 3.482. Circle the digit in the tenths place. Put an X through the digit in the thousandths place. 3④8ͯ2

⬤⬤○ Write 917.203. Circle the digit in the hundredths place. Put an X through the digit in the tens place. 9ͯ7.2⓪3

⬤⬤⬤ Write 6,000,387,420. Circle the digit in the millions place. Put an X through the digit in the ten thousands place. 6,00⓪,3ͯ87,420

Math Message

Solve the problem at the top of journal page 360.

Study Link 10·7 Follow-Up

Portfolio Ideas — Have students share their mystery graphs and the situations they portray.

Side	Perimeter
10 cm	40 cm
15 cm	60 cm
20 in.	80 in.
5 mi	20 mi

Side	Perimeter	Perimeter / Side
10 cm	40 cm	$\frac{40}{10} = 4$
15 cm	60 cm	$\frac{60}{15} = 4$
20 in.	80 in.	$\frac{80}{20} = 4$
5 mi	20 mi	$\frac{20}{5} = 4$

Student Page

Date _____ Time _____

LESSON 10·8 **A Problem from the National Assessment** ★

The following problem was in the mathematics section of a 1975 national standardized test.

A square has a perimeter of 12 inches. What is the area of the square?

1. Your answer: ___9___ in².

The table below gives the national results for this problem.

Answers	13-Year-Olds	17-Year-Olds	Young Adults
Correct answer	7%	28%	27%
144 sq inches	12%	19%	25%
48 sq inches	20%	10%	10%
24 sq inches	6%	4%	2%
12 sq inches	4%	3%	3%
6 sq inches	4%	2%	1%
3 sq inches	3%	2%	2%
Other incorrect answers	16%	13%	10%
No answer or "I don't know"	28%	19%	20%

Explain why many students might have given the following answers.
Sample answers:
2. 144 square inches Students thought each side of the square measured 12 inches and multiplied 12 ∗ 12 to find the area.

3. 48 square inches Students thought each side of the square measured 12 inches. They confused area with perimeter and added 12 + 12 + 12 + 12 to find the area.

Math Journal 2, p. 360

---

1 Teaching the Lesson

▶ Math Message Follow-Up

WHOLE-CLASS ACTIVITY
ELL

(*Math Journal 2*, p. 360)

Algebraic Thinking Ask students to share their solutions. 9 square inches Have students compare the percent of students in the class with the correct answer with the results from the 1975 National Assessment of Educational Progress. The two most common incorrect responses are 144 square inches and 48 square inches. Ask students to brainstorm in small groups and then complete Problems 2 and 3 on the journal page.

When students have finished, ask volunteers to share their responses with the class.

Ongoing Assessment: Recognizing Student Achievement

Journal Page 360 ★

Use **journal page 360** to assess students' understandings of area and perimeter. Students are making adequate progress if their explanations demonstrate accurate descriptions of area and perimeter.

[Measurement and Reference Frames Goal 2]

Review with students that the perimeter of a closed 2-dimensional figure is the distance around the figure. To support English language learners, use an example and gestures as you discuss the definition. Draw a square on the board, label its side with a measurement, and ask for its perimeter. Repeat for serveral squares. Collect the data in a table on the board. (*See margin.*)

Explain that the relationship between the perimeter of a square and the measure of a side can be expressed as a **ratio.** Add a third column labeled $\frac{\text{Perimeter}}{\text{Side}}$ to the table on the board. Ask students to calculate the perimeter-to-side ratio for each square. (*See margin.*)

This kind of comparison is called a **ratio comparison.** Ask students why the ratio will always be 4. A square consists of 4 sides of equal length. Therefore, the perimeter of a square is 4 times the length of one of its sides.

 Links to the Future

Students had experience with ratio comparisons in Grades 2–4. These experiences will be continued in Unit 12 and will be extended in Grade 6.

► Reviewing the Meanings of Diameter and Radius

 **WHOLE-CLASS DISCUSSION**

ELL

(*Student Reference Book*)

Explain that this lesson is an exploration of a similar ratio for circles that compares the **diameter** of the circle to its **circumference.** Ask students to find the term *circumference* in the *Student Reference Book* Glossary.

Set your board compass for a 6-inch **radius** and draw a circle on the board. Draw a diameter, and label it "1 foot." Ask students to find the terms *diameter* and *radius* in the *Student Reference Book* Glossary.

Draw a radius in the circle on the board, and ask for its length. 6 inches To support English language learners, draw a circle and label it with the terms *circumference, diameter,* and *radius.*

► Introducing the Circumference Investigation

 **WHOLE-CLASS DISCUSSION**

PROBLEM SOLVING

Ask students to estimate the circumference of a 1-foot diameter circle. Use the circle on the board and a 1-foot length of string to guide students to make the following comparisons:

● Is the circumference longer than the diameter? Yes, that's clear from the figure.

● Is the circumference longer than twice the diameter? Yes, the top half of the circle is longer than 1 diameter, so the bottom half must also be longer than 1 diameter.

Draw a square with 1-foot sides around the circle. Ask: *Which path is longer, the one around the square or the one around the circle?* The path around the square, which has a perimeter of 4 feet, or 4 diameters, is longer.

Ask students to give a range for the measure of the circumference of the 1-foot circle. The circumference is more than 2 diameters and less than 4 diameters; the circumference is about 3 times the diameter.

Date _____ Time _____

LESSON 10·8 Ratio of Circumference to Diameter

You are going to explore the relationship between the circumference and the diameter of a circle. **Answers vary.**

1. Using a metric tape measure, carefully measure the circumference and diameter of a variety of round objects. Measure to the nearest millimeter (one-tenth of a centimeter).

2. Record your data in the first three columns of the table below.

3. In the fourth column, write the ratio of the circumference to the diameter as a fraction.

4. In the fifth column, write the ratio as a decimal. Use your calculator to compute the decimal, and round your answer to two decimal places.

Object	Circumference (C)	Diameter (d)	Ratio of Circumference to Diameter	
			as a Fraction ($\frac{C}{d}$)	as a Decimal (from calculator)
Coffee cup	252 mm	80 mm	$\frac{252}{80}$	3.15
	_____ mm	_____ mm		
	_____ mm	_____ mm		
	_____ mm	_____ mm		
	_____ mm	_____ mm		
	_____ mm	_____ mm		

5. What is the median of the circumference-to-diameter ratios in the last column?

_____

6. The students in your class combined their results in a stem-and-leaf plot. Use that plot to find the class median value for the ratio $\frac{C}{d}$.

_____

Math Journal 2, p. 361

Correct   Incorrect

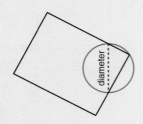

diameter

Ratio of Circumference to Diameter

Stems (1s and 0.1s)	Leaves (0.01s)
2.9	
3.0	
3.1	
3.2	
3.3	
3.4	

Stems (1s and 0.1s)	Leaves (0.01s)
2.9	8
3.0	4 6 9
3.1	2 4 5 6 7 7
3.2	0 4 5 5 6 9
3.3	3 3 4
3.4	6 6

▶ **Investigating Circumference**

 PARTNER ACTIVITY

(*Math Journal 2*, p. 361)

Discuss the journal page. Students work in pairs or groups of three. Each group should have at least as many round objects to measure as there are members in the group. Caution students that, to measure a circumference, they should pull the tape or string straight around the object, not at an angle.

Correct   Incorrect

Measuring the diameter of real objects is difficult because the center is usually not marked. Below are two methods students can use:

1. Position the tape or string so it crosses the widest part of the object. The diameter is the longest line segment, or chord, connecting two points on the circumference.

2. Use a right-angled corner of a book or piece of paper to find a diameter. Position the right angle on the circle. The points where the sides of the angle intersect the circle are the endpoints of a diameter. (*See margin.*)

Have students complete the table on the journal page. Answers should be rounded to hundredths.

▶ **Making a Stem-and-Leaf Plot**

 **WHOLE-CLASS ACTIVITY**

(*Math Journal 2*, p. 361)

Algebraic Thinking Ask students to complete Problem 5 on the journal page. Copy the incomplete stem-and-leaf plot onto the board or a transparency. (*See margin.*) As students finish their calculations, each student finds the median $\frac{C}{d}$ ratio for the objects measured. A partner or group volunteer enters this $\frac{C}{d}$ ratio on the plot.

When students have finished, rewrite the numbers in each leaf in order from least to greatest so finding the median will be easier.

Working together, find the class median ratio. Expect it to be greater than 3 and probably within 0.1 of π (3.14). Students record the class median on Problem 6 of the journal page.

▶ **Discussing Pi**

 **WHOLE-CLASS ACTIVITY**

(*Student Reference Book*, p. 112)

Remind students of the $\frac{\text{perimeter}}{\text{side}}$ ratio for squares from the Math Message Follow-Up. In the circumference investigation, students find that the $\frac{\text{circumference}}{\text{diameter}}$ ratio also appears to be constant, with a value of about 3.1 or 3.2. The exact value of this ratio is an irrational number named for a letter of the Greek alphabet.

Ask whether anyone knows the name of this Greek letter. The letter π, pronounced *pi* Ask students to find the terms *rational number* and *irrational number* in the *Student Reference Book* Glossary.

Read *Student Reference Book*, page 112 as a class. Make sure students understand that the digits in **pi (π),** to the right of the decimal point, continue forever without any discernible pattern. Thus, when calculating with π to find the circumference of a circle, we use an approximation of its exact value. Therefore, the resulting circumference is not an exact value. We can use the symbol ≈, meaning *approximately equal to,* to denote this. Write and label the symbol ≈ on the board or Class Data Pad.

Guide students to find and use the π key on their calculators as in the Check Your Understanding Problems on *Student Reference Book,* page 112.

Note that entering the key sequence `π` `×` `5` `Enter` on the TI-15 will display 5Π, or 5π. On the Casio *fx*-55, it will display a decimal result. To see the answer as a decimal on the TI-15, press `F↔D`. Remind students to round an appropriate number of decimal places.

2 Ongoing Learning & Practice

Converting Temperatures

INDEPENDENT ACTIVITY

(*Math Journal 2,* p. 362)

Students learn a formula and a rule of thumb for converting between Fahrenheit and Celsius degrees.

Math Boxes 10·8

INDEPENDENT ACTIVITY

(*Math Journal 2,* p. 363)

Mixed Practice Math Boxes in this lesson are paired with Math Boxes in Lesson 10-6. The skill in Problem 3 previews Unit 11 content.

Study Link 10·8

INDEPENDENT ACTIVITY

(*Math Masters,* p. 312)

Home Connection Students practice solving problems using the circumference formula. They find the circumference or the diameter.

Remind students to bring examples of ratios that they can add to the Rates and Ratios Museum.

NOTE For practice with unit conversions of metric and customary units of length, see www.everydaymathonline.com.

Date   Time

LESSON 10·8   **Converting Celsius to Fahrenheit**

In the U.S. customary system, temperature is measured in degrees Fahrenheit (°F). The metric system measures temperature in degrees Celsius (°C). Water freezes at 0°C, or 32°F.

1. What temperature is shown on the thermometer at the right? −18°C, or 0°F

The following formula converts temperatures from degrees Celsius to degrees Fahrenheit, where *F* stands for the number of degrees Fahrenheit and *C* stands for the number of degrees Celsius:

    Formula: $F = (1.8 * C) + 32$

A rule of thumb gives a rough estimate of the conversion.

    Rule of thumb: Double the number of degrees Celsius and add the Fahrenheit freezing temperature.

    $F = (2 * C) + 32$

2. Convert Celsius temperatures to Fahrenheit using the formula and the rule of thumb. Compare the results.

°C	−20	−10	0	10	20	30
°F (formula)	−4	14	32	50	68	86
°F (rule of thumb)	−8	12	32	52	72	92

3. Are the results from using the rule of thumb accurate in most situations? Explain. Sample answer: Yes. A difference of about 6 degrees does not matter in non-scientific situations.

4. Name one situation where you would use the formula rather than the rule of thumb to convert to degrees Fahrenheit. Explain. Sample answer: If you were taking your body temperature, you would want as accurate a reading as possible.

5. Normal body temperature is 37°C or 98.6° F.

6. Water boils at 100°C or 212° F.

Math Journal 2, p. 362

Date   Time

LESSON 10·8   **Math Boxes**

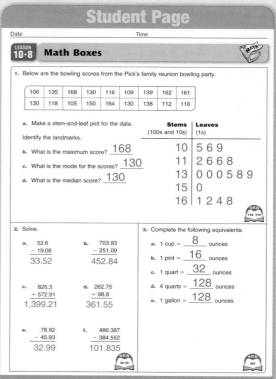

1. Below are the bowling scores from the Pick's family reunion bowling party.

106	135	168	130	116	109	139	162	161
130	118	105	150	164	130	138	112	116

a. Make a stem-and-leaf plot for the data. Identify the landmarks.

Stems (100s and 10s)	Leaves (1s)
10	5 6 9
11	2 6 6 8
13	0 0 0 5 8 9
15	0
16	1 2 4 8

b. What is the maximum score? 168

c. What is the mode for the scores? 130

d. What is the median score? 130

2. Solve.

a. 52.6 − 19.08 = 33.52

b. 703.93 − 251.09 = 452.84

c. 826.3 + 572.91 = 1,399.21

d. 262.75 + 98.8 = 361.55

e. 78.92 − 45.93 = 32.99

f. 486.387 − 384.552 = 101.835

3. Complete the following equivalents.

a. 1 cup = 8 ounces

b. 1 pint = 16 ounces

c. 1 quart = 32 ounces

d. 4 quarts = 128 ounces

e. 1 gallon = 128 ounces

Math Journal 2, p. 363

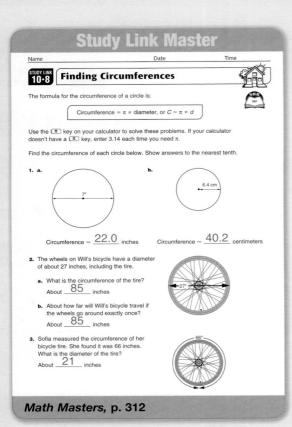
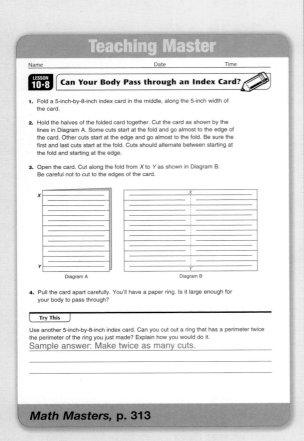

3 Differentiation Options

READINESS

SMALL-GROUP ACTIVITY

5–15 Min

▶ Reading about Circumference

Literature Link To explore the relationship between circumference and diameter, read and discuss the following book with the group. Highlight the measurement techniques and the mathematical concepts.

The Librarian Who Measured the Earth
Summary: The Greek mathematician Eratosthenes (c. 276–194 B.C.E.) calculated the circumference of Earth to within 200 miles of the modern value. This book recounts how Eratosthenes made his calculation and provides multiple opportunities for discussion.

ENRICHMENT

PARTNER ACTIVITY

15–30 Min

▶ Passing Your Body through an Index Card

(*Math Masters*, p. 313)

To further explore students' understanding of circumference, have them reconfigure a rectangular piece of paper into a circle. Explain to students that they are going to figure out a way to pass their entire body through a 5-inch-by-8-inch piece of paper. The only tool they may use is a pair of scissors.

Have partners come up with a plan and implement it. Expect that most students will need to follow the directions on *Math Masters*, page 313.

The circumference of the ring is approximately equal to the sum of the lengths of all the cuts that are made.

ELL SUPPORT

SMALL-GROUP ACTIVITY

5–15 Min

▶ Building a Math Word Bank

(*Differentiation Handbook*, p. 143)

To provide language support for ratios, have students use the Word Bank Template found on *Differentiation Handbook*, page 143. Ask students to write the terms *rate*, *ratio*, and *ratio comparison;* to draw pictures relating to these terms; and to write other related words. See the *Differentiation Handbook* for more information.

Planning Ahead

Store the cylindrical objects you collected for use again in Lesson 10-9.

10·9 Area of a Circle

 Objective To introduce a formula to calculate the area of a circle.

Technology Resources www.everydaymathonline.com

 ePresentations

 eToolkit

 Algorithms Practice

 EM Facts Workshop Game™

 Family Letters

 Assessment Management

CCSS Common Core State Standards

 NCTM Curriculum Focal Points

iTLG Interactive Teacher's Lesson Guide

---

1 Teaching the Lesson

Key Concepts and Skills

- Find the median of a data set.
  [Data and Chance Goal 2]

- Investigate and apply a formula for finding the area of a circle.
  [Measurement and Reference Frames Goal 2]

- Use ratios to describe the relationship between radius and area.
  [Measurement and Reference Frames Goal 2]

- Use patterns in a table to define the relationship between radius and area.
  [Patterns, Functions, and Algebra Goal 1]

Key Activities

Students draw circles by tracing round objects on centimeter grids. They measure the areas and radii and find that the ratio of a circle's area to the square of its radius is close to the value of π. They use the formula to calculate the areas of the circles.

 Ongoing Assessment:
Informing Instruction See page 833.

Materials

Math Journal 2, pp. 364–366B
Study Link 10·8
Math Masters, p. 436
transparencies of *Math Masters,* pp. 314 and 436 ◆ slate ◆ collection of round objects from Lesson 10·8 ◆ calculator ◆ metric ruler

2 Ongoing Learning & Practice

Converting Units of Measure

Math Journal 2, pp. 366A and 366B
Students convert units of measure.

 Playing *First to 100*
Student Reference Book, p. 308
Math Masters, pp. 456–458
per partnership: 2 six-sided dice, calculator
Students practice solving open number sentences.

 Ongoing Assessment:
Recognizing Student Achievement
Use *Math Masters,* page 458.
[Patterns, Functions, and Algebra Goal 2]

 Math Boxes 10·9
Math Journal 2, p. 367
Students practice and maintain skills through Math Box problems.

 Study Link 10·9
Math Masters, p. 315
Students practice and maintain skills through Study Link activities.

3 Differentiation Options

ENRICHMENT
Modeling πr^2

Math Masters, pp. 316 and 317
scissors ◆ colored pencil or marker ◆ construction paper ◆ glue or tape
Students apply their understanding of area formulas to verify the formula for the area of a circle.

EXTRA PRACTICE
Calculating the Circumferences and Areas of Circles

Math Masters, p. 318
Geometry Template ◆ calculator
Students use formulas to solve problems involving circumferences and areas of circles.

Advance Preparation

For Part 1, copy the table on journal page 365 onto the board. Make transparencies of *Math Masters,* pages 314 and 436.

 Teacher's Reference Manual, Grades 4–6 pp. 64–68, 185, 186, 221

Getting Started

Mental Math and Reflexes

Have students record an appropriate unit of measure for given situations.
Suggestions:

- ●○○ Amount of carpet needed to carpet a bedroom ft², yd², or m²

  Distance from where you live to a summer camp on a lake Miles, or kilometers
- ●●○ Length of a dollar bill Inches, or centimeters
- ●●● Amount of juice the average person drinks in a week Cups, gallons, or liters

  Volume of cubes that could be stacked in a desk drawer, filling every space cm³ or in³

Math Message

Solve Problems 1–4 on journal page 364.

Study Link 10·8 Follow-Up

Have partners compare answers and resolve differences.

NOTE All measurement is inexact, but finding the area of a circle by counting square centimeters is especially so. Area, unlike length, volume, or mass, is difficult to measure directly. Area is usually found by measuring lengths and applying a formula. Nevertheless, if students are particularly precise, measuring area by counting square units can be an accurate and practical technique.

Student Page

Date _____ Time _____

LESSON 10·9 **Measuring the Area of a Circle**

Math Message

Use the circle at the right to solve Problems 1–4.

1cm

1. The diameter of the circle is
   about __8__ centimeters.

2. The radius of the circle is
   about __4__ centimeters.

3. a. Write the open number sentence you would use to find the circumference of the circle.
   $C = \pi * 8$, or $C = 3.14 * 8$

   b. The circumference of the circle is
   about __25__ centimeters.

4. Find the area of this circle by counting squares.
   About __50__ cm²

5. What is the median of all the Answers vary.
   area measurements in your class? _____ cm²

6. Pi is the ratio of the circumference to the diameter of a circle. It is also the ratio of the area of a circle to the square of its radius. Write the formulas to find the circumference and the diameter of a circle that use these ratios.

   The formula for the circumference of a circle is $C = \pi * d$, or $C = \pi d$
   The formula for the area of a circle is $A = \pi * r^2$, or $A = \pi r^2$

Math Journal 2, p. 364

---

1 Teaching the Lesson

▶ Math Message Follow-Up

WHOLE-CLASS DISCUSSION

ELL

(*Math Journal 2*, p. 364; *Math Masters*, p. 314)

Verify that students were able to determine the diameter, radius, and circumference of the circle. Then ask students to share their answers to Problem 4. List their measurements in order on the board or a transparency, find the median of the measurements, and have students record the median in Problem 5 on the journal page.

Point out the wide variation in the area measurements. Discuss why it is difficult to measure the area of a circle by counting squares. The pieces are irregular. Then use the transparency of *Math Masters*, page 314 to demonstrate the following method for counting squares.

1. Make a check mark in each whole centimeter square.

2. Mark each centimeter square that is nearly a whole square with an X.

3. Find combinations of partial squares that are about equivalent to a whole square. Number each set, using the same number in each partial square.

4. Count the approximate total number of squares. In the circle in Problem 1, the area of the circle is about 52 square centimeters.

Ask the class to suggest situations in which one might need to find the area of a circle. To support English language learners, list students' suggestions on the board. Explain that students will count squares and use a formula to find the area of circles.

Exploring the Relationship between Radius and Area

WHOLE-CLASS ACTIVITY

PROBLEM SOLVING

(*Math Journal 2*, pp. 364 and 365; *Math Masters*, p. 436)

Algebraic Thinking This exploration requires students to measure the radius of circles where the center is not given and to find the approximate areas of these circles. Demonstrate what students are to do using a round object and the transparency of *Math Masters*, page 436:

1. Make a circle on the transparency by tracing the object.

2. Find the approximate area of the circle by counting squares. Record the name of the object and its approximate area in the first and second columns of the table on the board.

3. Use a right-angled corner of a piece of paper to find a diameter of the circle. Position the right angle on the circle as shown below. Mark the points where the sides of the angle intersect the circle. These are the endpoints of a diameter of the circle. Measure the distance between endpoints.

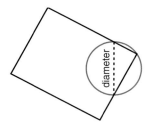

4. Ask students how to find the radius when the diameter is known. Divide by 2. Record the radius in the third column of the table.

 Ongoing Assessment: Informing Instruction

Watch for students who struggle with measuring accurately. Have them trace and measure larger objects. Measurement errors are less significant with longer lengths.

Have partners trace several round objects on a centimeter grid using *Math Masters*, page 436. Then have students measure the radius and the area of each of the tracings using the techniques just demonstrated. Partners use the same objects but measure independently and check each other's work. They record their results in the first three columns of the table on the journal page.

When all groups have traced and measured at least three objects, bring the class together to demonstrate how to complete the last two columns in the table on the journal page. Continue to use the circle you traced on the transparency earlier.

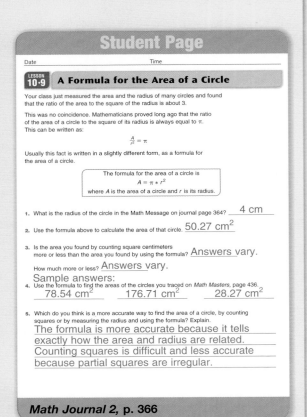

Student Page

Date _____ Time _____

LESSON 10·9 **A Formula for the Area of a Circle**

Your class just measured the area and the radius of many circles and found that the ratio of the area to the square of the radius is about 3.

This was no coincidence. Mathematicians proved long ago that the ratio of the area of a circle to the square of its radius is always equal to π. This can be written as:

$$\frac{A}{r^2} = \pi$$

Usually this fact is written in a slightly different form, as a formula for the area of a circle.

> The formula for the area of a circle is
> $$A = \pi * r^2$$
> where A is the area of a circle and r is its radius.

1. What is the radius of the circle in the Math Message on journal page 364? __4 cm__

2. Use the formula above to calculate the area of that circle. __50.27 cm²__

3. Is the area you found by counting square centimeters more or less than the area you found by using the formula? __Answers vary.__

   How much more or less? __Answers vary.__
   Sample answers:

4. Use the formula to find the areas of the circles you traced on *Math Masters*, page 436.
   __78.54 cm²__   __176.71 cm²__   __28.27 cm²__

5. Which do you think is a more accurate way to find the area of a circle, by counting squares or by measuring the radius and using the formula? Explain.
   __The formula is more accurate because it tells__
   __exactly how the area and radius are related.__
   __Counting squares is difficult and less accurate__
   __because partial squares are irregular.__

Math Journal 2, p. 366

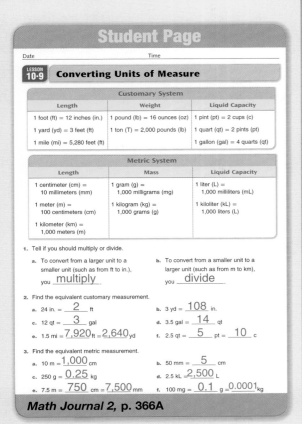

Student Page

Date _____ Time _____

LESSON 10·9 **Converting Units of Measure**

Customary System		
Length	**Weight**	**Liquid Capacity**
1 foot (ft) = 12 inches (in.)	1 pound (lb) = 16 ounces (oz)	1 pint (pt) = 2 cups (c)
1 yard (yd) = 3 feet (ft)	1 ton (T) = 2,000 pounds (lb)	1 quart (qt) = 2 pints (pt)
1 mile (mi) = 5,280 feet (ft)		1 gallon (gal) = 4 quarts (qt)

Metric System		
Length	**Mass**	**Liquid Capacity**
1 centimeter (cm) = 10 millimeters (mm)	1 gram (g) = 1,000 milligrams (mg)	1 liter (L) = 1,000 milliliters (mL)
1 meter (m) = 100 centimeters (cm)	1 kilogram (kg) = 1,000 grams (g)	1 kiloliter (kL) = 1,000 liters (L)
1 kilometer (km) = 1,000 meters (m)		

1. Tell if you should multiply or divide.

   a. To convert from a larger unit to a smaller unit (such as from ft to in.), you __multiply__.

   b. To convert from a smaller unit to a larger unit (such as from m to km), you __divide__.

2. Find the equivalent customary measurement.

   a. 24 in. = __2__ ft
   b. 3 yd = __108__ in.
   c. 12 qt = __3__ gal
   d. 3.5 gal = __14__ qt
   e. 1.5 mi = __7,920__ ft = __2,640__ yd
   f. 2.5 qt = __5__ pt = __10__ c

3. Find the equivalent metric measurement.

   a. 10 m = __1,000__ cm
   b. 50 mm = __5__ cm
   c. 250 g = __0.25__ kg
   d. 2.5 kL = __2,500__ L
   e. 7.5 m = __750__ cm = __7,500__ mm
   f. 100 mg = __0.1__ g = __0.0001__ kg

Math Journal 2, p. 366A

▷ In the fourth column of the table on the board, write the ratio of the circle's area to the radius squared as a fraction. Ask volunteers for another way to express the meaning of *radius squared*. radius * radius

▷ Use a calculator to convert the fraction to a decimal, rounded to two decimal places. Write the resulting decimal in the fifth column of the table.

Have students complete the last two columns of the table on the journal page, find the median of the ratios in the last column, and record it as the answer to Problem 5.

When students have finished, ask them to share the values they found and record them on the board. Most median values should be close to 3, though some might be far off because of various errors—using the diameter instead of the radius, for example, or measuring the radius in inches rather than centimeters.

Ask what number the ratios are close to. π Explain that this is no coincidence: The ratio of the area of a circle to the square of its radius is always equal to π. Help students recognize how remarkable this is—the same number, π, is the ratio of the circumference to the diameter and the ratio of the area to the radius squared. These ratios are the bases for the formulas that can be used to find the circumference and the area of a circle. Have students write the formulas in Problem 6 on journal page 364.

▶ Using a Formula to Find the Area of a Circle

 **WHOLE-CLASS ACTIVITY**

(*Math Journal 2*, pp. 364–366; *Math Masters*, p. 436)

Algebraic Thinking Have students read journal page 366 and use the formula to calculate the areas of the Math Message circle and the circles they traced on *Math Masters*, page 436. They compare the areas they found by counting square centimeters with the areas from the formula.

② Ongoing Learning & Practice

▶ Converting Units of Measure

(*Math Journal 2*, pp. 366A and 366B)

Students convert different-size units of measure, compare units of measure, and solve problems involving measurement conversions.

▶ Playing *First to 100*

(*Student Reference Book*, p. 308; *Math Masters*, pp. 456–458)

Algebraic Thinking Students play *First to 100* to practice solving open number sentences. This game was introduced in Lesson 4-7. For detailed instructions, see *Student Reference Book,* page 308.

Ongoing Assessment: Recognizing Student Achievement

Math Masters Page 458 ★

Use the *First to 100* **Record Sheet** (*Math Masters,* page 458) to assess students' facilities with replacing variables and solving problems. Students are making adequate progress if their number sentences and solutions are correct.

[Patterns, Functions, and Algebra Goal 2]

▶ Math Boxes 10·9

(*Math Journal 2*, p. 367)

 INDEPENDENT ACTIVITY

Mixed Practice Math Boxes in this lesson are paired with Math Boxes in Lessons 10-5 and 10-7. The skill in Problem 5 previews Unit 11 content.

Writing/Reasoning Have students write a response to the following: *Exchange the exponent and base for each of the numbers in Problem 2, for example, $2^{17} \rightarrow 17^2$. Write the standard notation for each new number.* 289; 279,936; 1,000,000; 1,000; 59,049 *Which number is larger than its corresponding original number? Explain why.* Sample answer: The original number 7^6 in standard notation is 117,649; 6^7 or 279,936 is larger than the original number because 6 used as a factor 7 times is greater than 7 used as a factor 6 times.

▶ Study Link 10·9

(*Math Masters*, p. 315)

 INDEPENDENT ACTIVITY

Home Connection Students identify the best measurement to find in specific situations. They solve a set of problems using the formulas for area and circumference of circles.

Student Page

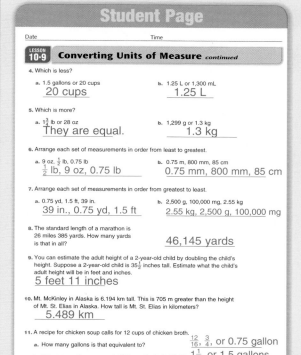

Math Journal 2, p. 366B

Student Page

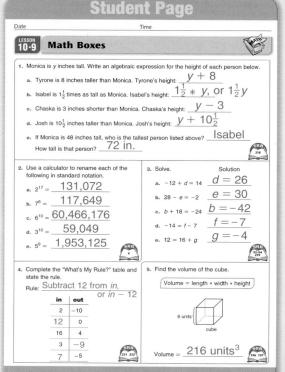

Math Journal 2, p. 367

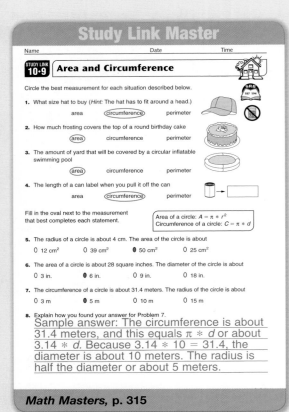
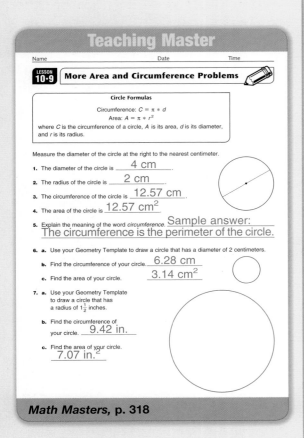
3 Differentiation Options

PARTNER ACTIVITY

 15–30 Min

▶ # Modeling πr^2

(*Math Masters*, pp. 316 and 317)

Algebraic Thinking To apply students' understanding of area formulas, have them cut a circle into pieces and arrange them in the shape of a parallelogram. They draw and label the parts of the parallelogram to compare them to the parts of the circle. Partners follow the directions on *Math Masters*, page 316 to verify the formula for the area of a circle. When students have finished, discuss any difficulties they encountered.

INDEPENDENT ACTIVITY

5–15 Min

▶ # Calculating the Circumferences and Areas of Circles

(*Math Masters*, p. 318)

Algebraic Thinking Students use formulas to solve problems involving the circumferences and areas of circles. They draw the circles before finding the areas and circumferences. Remind students to use the fix function on their calculators to round the calculations to the nearest hundredth.

10·10 Progress Check 10

Objective To assess students' progress on mathematical content through the end of Unit 10.

1 Looking Back: Cumulative Assessment

 Input student data from Progress Check 10 into the **Assessment Management Spreadsheets**.

Materials
- Study Link 10◆9
- *Assessment Handbook,* pp. 126–133, 199–204, 225, and 282–285
- ruler; slate; calculator

CONTENT ASSESSED	LESSON(S)	SELF	ORAL/SLATE	WRITTEN PART A	WRITTEN PART B	OPEN RESPONSE
Interpret mystery line plots and graphs. [Data and Chance Goal 2]	10·7–10·9	3		8		
Measure length to the nearest centimeter. [Measurement and Reference Frames Goal 1]					12, 13	
Use formulas to find the circumference and area of a circle. [Measurement and Reference Frames Goal 2]	10·8, 10·9	5			14, 15	
Distinguish between circumference and area of a circle. [Measurement and Reference Frames Goal 2]	10·9	4	1, 2	9–11		
Represent rate problems using a table, graph and formula; use algebraic expressions to write rules involving the four basic operations. [Patterns, Functions, and Algebra Goal 1]	10·4–10·7, 10·9	7			17, 18	✓
Write and solve algebraic expressions. [Patterns, Functions, and Algebra Goal 2]	10·3–10·7, 10·9	1	3, 4	1–3, 7		✓
Solve pan-balance problems. [Patterns, Functions, and Algebra Goal 2]	10·1, 10·2	2, 6		4–6	16	

2 Looking Ahead: Preparing for Unit 11

 Math Boxes 10◆10

 Study Link 10◆10: Unit 11 Family Letter

Materials
- *Math Journal 2,* p. 368
- *Math Masters,* pp. 319–322

Getting Started

1 Looking Back: Cumulative Assessment

▶ **Math Message Follow-Up**

INDEPENDENT ACTIVITY

(Self Assessment, *Assessment Handbook*, p. 199)

 The Self Assessment offers students the opportunity to reflect upon their progress.

▶ **Oral and Slate Assessments**

 SMALL-GROUP ACTIVITY

Problems 1 and 3 provide summative information and can be used for grading purposes. Problems 2 and 4 provide formative information that can be useful in planning future instruction.

Oral Assessment

1. Show thumbs up if you'd find circumference to solve the problem and thumbs down if you'd find something else. (You might want to ask students to identify what they have to find.)

   Suggestions:

   ● The floor space taken up by a plant in a round pot. down; area

   ● The length of a necklace to fit around a person's neck. up; circumference

   ● The size of the lid of a coffee can. down; area

2. Show thumbs up if the statement is true and thumbs down if the statement is false.

   ● A diameter is a line segment that passes through the center of a circle and has endpoints on the circle. up; true

   ● The circumference of a circle is the space inside the circle. down; false

   ● The radius is a line segment from the center of a circle to any point on the circle. up; true

   ● The formula for finding the circumference of a circle is $C = \pi * d$. up; true

---

Assessment Master

Name		Date		Time

LESSON 10·10 **Self Assessment**

Progress Check 10

Think about each skill listed below. Assess your own progress by checking the most appropriate box.

Skills	I can do this on my own and explain how to do it.	I can do this on my own.	I can do this if I get help or look at an example.
1. Write algebraic expressions to represent situations.			
2. Solve one-step pan-balance problems.			
3. Interpret mystery line plots and graphs.			
4. Distinguish between circumference and area of a circle.			
5. Use formulas to find circumference and area of a circle.			
6. Solve two-step pan-balance problems.			
7. Represent rate problems as formulas.			

Assessment Handbook, p. 199

Slate Assessment

3. Write an algebraic expression to complete each of the following statements:

- Kirsten is 9 years older than Sydney. If Sydney is S years old, Kirsten is <u>$S + 9$</u> years old.

- Peter earns twice as much as Jacob. If Jacob earns J dollars, Peter earns <u>$2 * J$, or $2J$</u> dollars.

- Ryan read five more than half as many books as Lilia. If Lilia read L books, Ryan read <u>$(\frac{1}{2} * L) + 5$, $\frac{1}{2}L + 5$, or $\frac{L}{2} + 5$</u> books.

- Anthony saved \$6 less than 3 times as much money as his younger sister Diana. If Diana saved D dollars, Anthony saved <u>$(3 * D) - 6$, or $3D - 6$</u> dollars.

- One summer, Sarah read one fourth as many books as her cousin Eddie. If Eddie read E books, Sarah read <u>$E \div 4$, $\frac{1}{4} * E$, $\frac{1}{4}E$, or $\frac{E}{4}$</u> books.

4. Write a number sentence to represent each story.

Suggestions:

- Renee bakes 7 trays of a dozen cookies each. She wraps the cookies from 2 trays to take to her neighbors. How many cookies are left? $(7 - 2) * 12 = C$, or $(7 * 12) - (2 * 12) = C$

- There is a sale at the grocery store. Cherie stocks up on 6-packs of soda. She buys four 6-packs for herself and five 6-packs for her friend. How many cans of soda does she buy in all? $(4 + 5) * 6 = S$, or $(4 * 6) + (5 * 6) = S$

- Grant mails 24 invitations to his birthday party. He spends \$1.15 on each card and \$0.37 on each stamp. How much does he spend all together on the invitations? $(24 * \$1.15) + (24 * \$0.37) = I$, or $24 * (\$1.15 + \$0.37) = I$

Written Assessment

👤 **INDEPENDENT ACTIVITY**

(*Assessment Handbook*, pp. 200–203)

Part A Recognizing Student Achievement

Problems 1–11 provide summative information and may be used for grading purposes.

Problem(s)	Description
1–3, 7	Write algebraic expressions to represent situations.
4–6	Solve one-step pan-balance problems.
8	Interpret mystery line plots and graphs.
9–11	Distinguish between circumference and area of a circle.

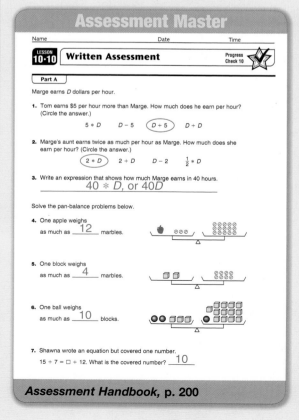

Assessment Master

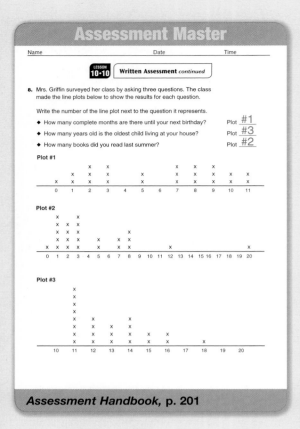

Name _____ Date _____ Time _____

LESSON 10·10 | Written Assessment *continued*

8. Mrs. Griffin surveyed her class by asking three questions. The class made the line plots below to show the results for each question.

Write the number of the line plot next to the question it represents.

◆ How many complete months are there until your next birthday?   Plot **#1**
◆ How many years old is the oldest child living at your house?   Plot **#3**
◆ How many books did you read last summer?   Plot **#2**

Plot #1

```
                    x    x                      x    x    x
          x    x    x         x              x   x    x    x    x
     x    x    x    x         x              x   x    x    x    x
     0    1    2    3    4    5    6    7    8    9   10   11
```

Plot #2

```
          x    x
          x    x    x
          x    x    x                   x
          x    x    x    x         x    x
     x    x    x    x    x         x    x                      x
     0  1  2  3  4  5  6  7  8  9 10 11 12 13 14 15 16 17 18 19 20
```

Plot #3

```
          x
          x
          x
          x
          x    x         x
          x    x    x    x
          x    x    x    x    x    x
          x    x    x    x    x    x              x
         10   11   12   13   14   15   16   17   18   19   20
```

Assessment Handbook, p. 201

Assessment Master

Name _____ Date _____ Time _____

LESSON 10·10 | Written Assessment *continued*

To solve each of the following problems, would you need to find the circumference, perimeter, or area? (Circle the answer.)

9. Mario ran around a circular track 20 times.
How far did he run?   (circumference)   area

10. Mr. Li is planting tomatoes in his garden.
He wants one plant for every 2 square feet.
How many plants should he buy?   perimeter   (area)

11. Jill is building a fence around her swimming pool.
How many feet of fencing should she buy?   (perimeter)   area

Part B

> Circumference of a circle = π * diameter
> Area of a circle = π * radius²

Complete each of the following sentences, rounding each answer to the nearest centimeter. Use the π key on your calculator or use 3.14 as an approximation for π.

12. The diameter is about **6** cm.

13. The radius is about **3** cm.

14. The circumference is about **19** cm.

15. The area is about **28** cm².

Assessment Handbook, p. 202

Part B   Informing Instruction

Problems 12–18 provide formative information that can be useful in planning future instruction.

Problem(s)	Description
12, 13	Measure length to the nearest centimeter.
14, 15	Use formulas to find circumference and area of a circle.
16	Solve two-step pan-balance problems.
17, 18	Represent rate problems as formulas.

 Use the checklists on pages 273 and 275 of the *Assessment Handbook* to record results. Then input the data into the **Assessment Management Spreadsheets** to keep an ongoing record of students' progress toward Grade-Level Goals.

▶ **Open Response**   🧍 INDEPENDENT ACTIVITY

(*Assessment Handbook,* p. 204)

An Age Puzzle

📁 Portfolio Ideas   The open-response item requires students to apply skills and concepts from Unit 10 to solve a multistep problem. See *Assessment Handbook,* pages 129–133 for rubrics and students' work samples for this problem.

Assessment Master

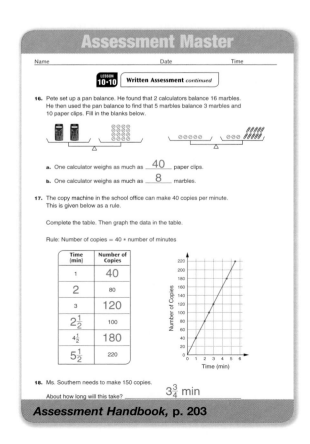

Name _____ Date _____ Time _____

LESSON 10·10 | Written Assessment *continued*

16. Pete set up a pan balance. He found that 2 calculators balance 16 marbles. He then used the pan balance to find that 5 marbles balance 3 marbles and 10 paper clips. Fill in the blanks below.

a. One calculator weighs as much as **40** paper clips.

b. One calculator weighs as much as **8** marbles.

17. The copy machine in the school office can make 40 copies per minute. This is given below as a rule.

Complete the table. Then graph the data in the table.

Rule: Number of copies = 40 * number of minutes

Time (min)	Number of Copies
1	40
2	80
3	120
2½	100
4½	180
5½	220

18. Ms. Southern needs to make 150 copies.

About how long will this take? **3¾** min

Assessment Handbook, p. 203

② Looking Ahead: Preparing for Unit 11

▶ Math Boxes 10·10

(*Math Journal 2*, p. 368)

Mixed Practice This Math Boxes page previews Unit 11 content.

INDEPENDENT ACTIVITY

▶ Study Link 10·10: Unit 11 Family Letter

(*Math Masters*, pp. 319–322)

Home Connection The Unit 11 Family Letter provides parents and guardians with information and activities related to Unit 11 topics.

INDEPENDENT ACTIVITY

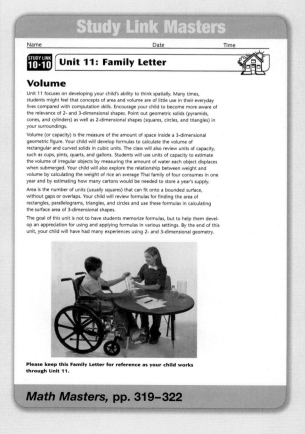

Volume

Overview

In Unit 11, students will review the properties of 3-dimensional shapes and develop formulas for finding volume. They will work with formulas for finding surface area of 3-dimensional figures. Students are introduced to formulas for the volumes of pyramids and cones through hands-on activities and practice finding volume by displacement. Unit 11 has four main areas of focus:

◆ To review properties of common 3-dimensional shapes,

◆ To develop volume formulas for these solids,

◆ To find volume by displacement, and

◆ To find surface area of 3-dimensional shapes.

CCSS Linking to the Common Core State Standards

The content of Unit 11 addresses the Common Core State Standards for Mathematics in *Measurement and Data*. The correlation of the Commom Core State Standards to the *Everyday Mathematics* Grade 5 lessons begins on page CS1.

Contents

Learning In Perspective

	Lesson Objectives	Links to the Past	Links to the Future
11·1	To review the names and properties of geometric solids.	In Grade 4, students describe properties of geometric solids.	In Grade 6, students play *3-D Shape Sort,* sorting geometric solids by their properties.
11·2	To provide experience comparing the properties of geometric solids.	In Grade 4, students classify quadrangles and other polygons based on their properties.	In Grade 6, students explore the properties of similar polygons.
11·3	To introduce the formula for the volume of cylinders.	In Unit 10, students use a formula to find the area of a circle.	In Grade 6, students review and use formulas for perimeter, circumference, and area.
11·4	To provide experiences with investigating the relationships between the volumes of geometric solids.	In Grade 4, students develop and use the formulas for finding the area of a rectangle, a parallelogram, and a triangle.	In Grade 6, students review the volume formulas for rectangular prisms, cylinders, and spheres.
11·5	To introduce finding the volume of irregular objects using a water displacement method.	In Grade 4, students find the volume of rectangular prisms by counting the cubic units.	In Grade 6, students solve volume problems.
11·6	To provide experience with converting measurements among units of weight, capacity, and volume.	In Grade 4, students review equivalencies between units of capacity.	In Grade 6, students solve volume problems.
11·7	To introduce finding the surface area of prisms, cylinders, and pyramids.	In Grade 4 students estimate the area of a surface having a curved boundary.	In Grade 6, students solve area problems.

Key Concepts and Skills	Grade 5 Goals*
11·1 Compare and classify geometric solids.	Geometry Goal 2
Describe and classify polyhedrons according to their faces.	Geometry Goal 2
11·2 Use a Venn diagram to organize data.	Data and Chance Goal 1
Describe and classify geometric solids according to their properties.	Geometry Goal 2
Identify congruent faces on geometric solids.	Geometry Goal 2
11·3 Use tables to collect data.	Data and Chance Goal 1
Apply formulas to calculate the area of a circle and the volume of prisms and cylinders.	Measurement and Reference Frames Goal 2
Compare the volume and the capacity of cylinders.	Measurement and Reference Frames Goal 2
11·4 Use formulas to find the volume of geometric solids.	Measurement and Reference Frames Goal 2
Compare the properties of pyramids, prisms, cones, and cylinders.	Geometry Goal 2
Describe patterns in relationships between the volumes of prisms, pyramids, cones, and cylinders.	Patterns, Functions, and Algebra Goal 1
11·5 Use tables to record data.	Data and Chance Goal 1
Use a displacement method to find the volume of irregular solids.	Measurement and Reference Frames Goal 2
Calibrate and use a metric measuring tool to compare volume and capacity.	Measurement and Reference Frames Goal 2
11·6 Use the formula for the volume of a prism to solve capacity problems.	Measurement and Reference Frames Goal 2
Use capacity calculations to solve problems.	Measurement and Reference Frames Goal 2
Convert between standard units of capacity.	Measurement and Reference Frames Goal 3
11·7 Measure the dimensions of a cylinder in inches and centimeters.	Measurement and Reference Frames Goal 1
Use rectangle and triangle area formulas to find the surface area of prisms and cylinders.	Measurement and Reference Frames Goal 2
Apply a formula to calculate the area of a circle.	Measurement and Reference Frames Goal 2
Identify and use the properties of prisms, pyramids, and cylinders in calculations.	Geometry Goal 2

*See the Appendix for a complete list of Grade 5 Goals.

A Balanced Curriculum

Ongoing Practice

Everyday Mathematics provides numerous opportunities for ongoing practice. These activities are embedded throughout the lessons:

 Mental Math and Reflexes activities promote speed and accuracy in mental computation.

 Math Boxes offer mixed practice and are paired across lessons as shown in the brackets below. This makes them useful as assessment tools. The last one or two boxes on each page preview the next unit's content.

Mixed practice	[11◆1, 11◆3], [11◆2, 11◆4, 11◆6], [11◆5, 11◆7]
Mixed practice with multiple choice	11◆1, 11◆2, 11◆3, 11◆4, 11◆6
Mixed practice with writing/reasoning opportunity	11◆2, 11◆5, 11◆6

 Study Links are daily homework assignments that review the content of the lesson and often contain ongoing facts practice or computation practice.

 5-Minute Math problems are offered for additional practice in Lessons 11◆3 and 11◆4.

 EM Facts Workshop Game provides online practice of basic facts and computation.

EXTRA PRACTICE **Extra Practice** activities are included in Lessons 11◆1, 11◆3, 11◆4, 11◆6, and 11◆7.

Practice through Games

Games are an essential component of practice in the *Everyday Mathematics* program. Games offer skills practice and promote strategic thinking. See the *Differentiation Handbook* for ways to adapt games to meet students' needs.

Lesson	Game	Skill Practiced
11◆2	*3-D Shape Sort*	Matching shapes with property cards [GEO Goal 2]
11◆4	*Rugs and Fences*	Calculating the perimeter and area of polygons [MRF Goal 2]
11◆6	*Name That Number*	Practicing computation skills and order of operations [NN Goal 4 and PFA Goal 3]

[NN] Number and Numeration   [OC] Operations and Computation   [DC] Data and Chance
[MRF] Measurement and Reference Frames   [GEO] Geometry   [PFA] Patterns, Functions, and Algebra

Problem Solving

Experts at problem solving and mathematical modeling generally do these things:

- Identify the problem.
- Decide what information is needed to solve the problem.
- Play with and study the data to find patterns and meaning.

- Identify and use mathematical procedures to solve the problem.
- Decide whether the solution makes sense and whether it can be applied to other problems.

The table below lists some of the opportunities in this unit for students to practice these strategies.

Lesson	Activity
11•1, 11•2	Explore and compare additional characteristics of geometric solids.
11•3	Find the volumes of cylinders and prisms.
11•4	Explore relationships between geometric solids.
11•5	Use the displacement method to find volumes of irregular objects.
11•6	Investigate the capacity of annual rice consumption in Thailand.
11•7	Calculate the surface area of geometric solids.

Lessons that teach through problem solving, not just about problem solving

See Chapter 18: Problem Solving in the *Teacher's Reference Manual* for more information.

The Language of Mathematics

Everyday Mathematics provides lesson-specific suggestions to help all students acquire, process, and express mathematical ideas. Throughout Unit 11, there are lesson-specific language development notes that address the needs of English language learners, indicated by **ELL**.

ELL SUPPORT Activities to support English language learners are in Part 3 of Lessons 11•1, 11•4, and 11•6.

The *English Learners Handbook* and the *Differentiation Handbook* have suggestions for promoting language development and acquisition of mathematics vocabulary. See Unit 11 in each handbook.

Literacy Connection

Flatland, by Edwin Abbott, Perseus Publishing, 2001

Who Sank the Boat? by Pamela Allen, The Putnam and Grosset Group, 1996

The Boy Who Reversed Himself, by William Sleator, Puffin Books, 1998

Sir Cumference and the Sword in the Cone, by Cindy Neuschwander, Charlesbridge Publishing, 2003

For more literacy connections, see the *Home Connection Handbook,* Grades 4–6.

> ## Unit 11 Vocabulary
>
> apex
> base
> calibrate
> cone
> cylinder
> displacement
> edge
> face
> geometric solid
> polyhedron
> prism
> pyramid
> regular polyhedron
> sphere
> surface
> surface area
> vertex (vertices or vertexes)

Cross-Curricular Links

Social Studies – Lesson 11•1
Science – Lesson 11•5

Literature – Lessons 11•2, 11•5

Balanced Assessment

Daily Assessments

- **Recognizing Student Achievement** – A daily assessment that is included in every lesson to evaluate students' progress toward the Grade 5 Grade-Level Goals.

- **Informing Instruction** – Notes that appear throughout the unit to help anticipate students' common errors and suggest appropriate problem-solving strategies.

Lesson	Recognizing Student Achievement	Informing Instruction
11◆1	Understand properties of geometric solids. [GEO Goal 2]	Score fold lines with a ruler and pen before folding.
11◆2	Demonstrate knowledge of the relationship between faces, vertices, and edges of prisms, pyramids, cylinders, and cones. [GEO Goal 2]	Draw one card for all shapes having the first property, then take a second card and put back shapes without the second property.
11◆3	Explain the differences and similarities between finding the volumes of cylinders and prisms. [MRF Goal 2]	
11◆4	Calculate the fraction of a whole and correctly identify each of the five values. [NN Goal 2]	
11◆5	Compare fractions and demonstrate an understanding of the structure of fractions, finding equivalent fractions, and comparing fractions to a reference. [NN Goal 6]	
11◆6	Write number models and demonstrate appropriate use of the order of operations. [NN Goal 4 and PFA Goal 3]	
11◆7	Measure to the nearest $\frac{1}{4}$ inch and centimeter and find the areas of circles, triangles, and rectangles. [MRF Goals 1 and 2]	Use a procedure to cut a sheet of paper as a model for surface area.

[NN] Number and Numeration
[MRF] Measurement and Reference Frames
[OC] Operations and Computation
[GEO] Geometry
[DC] Data and Chance
[PFA] Patterns, Functions, and Algebra

Portfolio Opportunities

The following lessons provide opportunities to gather samples of students' mathematical writings, drawings, and creations to add balance to the assessment process: Lessons 11◆2, 11◆3, 11◆5, 11◆6, and 11◆8.

See pages 16 and 17 in the *Assessment Handbook* for more information about portfolios and how to use them.

Unit Assessment

Progress Check 11 – A cumulative assessment of concepts and skills taught in Unit 11 and in previous units, providing information for evaluating students' progress and planning for future instruction. These assessments include oral/slate, written, and open-response activities, as shown below in the sample Progress Check lesson opener.

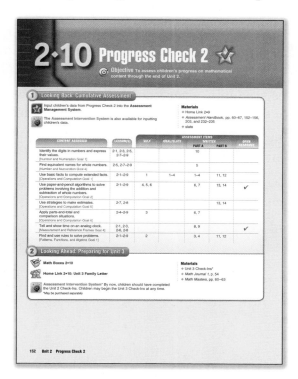

Core Assessment Resources

Assessment Handbook

◆ **Unit 11 Assessment Overview,** pages 134–141

◆ **Unit 11 Assessment Masters,** pages 205–209

◆ **Unit 11 Individual Profiles of Progress,** pages 286, 287, and 302

◆ **Unit 11 Class Checklists,** pages 288, 289, and 303

◆ **Math Logs,** pages 306–308

◆ **Exit Slip,** page 311

◆ **Other Student Assessment Forms,** pages 304, 305, 309, and 310

Assessment Management Spreadsheets

The Assessment Management Spreadsheets consist of the Digital Class Checklists and Individual Profile of Progress Checklists. Use them to monitor, record, and report student progress.

Addressing All Needs

Differentiated Instruction

Adjusting the Activity – suggests adaptations that target advanced learners, English language learners, or learners who need additional instructional support.

ELL SUPPORT / **ELL** – provides lesson-specific suggestions to help English language learners understand and process the mathematical content.

READINESS – accesses students' prior knowledge or previews content that prepares students to engage in the lesson's Part 1 activities.

EXTRA PRACTICE – provides additional opportunities to apply the mathematical content of the lesson.

ENRICHMENT – enables students to apply or further explore the mathematical content of the lesson.

Lesson	Adjusting the Activity	ELL Support/ ELL	Readiness	Extra Practice	Enrichment
11◆1		●		●	●
11◆2		●	●		●
11◆3	●	●	●	●	●
11◆4		●	●	●	●
11◆5		●	●		●
11◆6		●	●	●	●
11◆7				●	●

▶ Additional Resources

Differentiation Handbook
Provides ideas and strategies for differentiating instruction.
Pages 120–126

English Learners Handbook
Contains lesson-specific comprehension strategies.
Pages 101–107

Multilingual Handbook
Previews concepts and vocabulary. It is written in six languages.
Pages 201–214

Planning Tips

Multiage Classroom

Companion Lessons from Grades 4 and 6 can help you meet instructional needs of a multiage classroom. The full Scope and Sequence can be found in the Appendix.

Grade 4	11•2	11•2				11•4	11•7
Grade 5	11•1	11•2	11•3	11•4	11•5	11•6	11•7
Grade 6	10•4	10•4	9•9	9•9		9•9	1•11

Pacing for Success

Pacing depends on a number of factors, such as students' individual needs and how long your school has been using *Everyday Mathematics*. At the beginning of Unit 11, you may want to use tools available at www.everydaymathonline.com to help you set your pace.

Home Support

Unit 11 Family Letter (English/Spanish) provides families with an overview, Do-Anytime Activities, Building Skills through Games, a list of vocabulary, and answers to the daily homework (Study Links). Family Letters in English, Spanish, and seven other languages are also available online.

Study Links are the daily homework assignments. They consist of active projects and ongoing review problems.

▷ Home Support Resources

Home Connection Handbook
Offers ideas and reproducible masters for communicating with families. See Table of Contents for unit information.

Student Reference Book
Provides a resource for students and parents.
Pages 147–152, 196, 197, 325, 332, 338–395, 397

Technology Resources

Algorithms Practice

EM Facts Workshop Game™

Family Letters

Interactive Teacher's Lesson Guide

www.everydaymathonline.com

Unit 11 Organizer

Materials

Technology Resources   www.everydaymathonline.com

ePresentations

eToolkit

Algorithms
Practice

EM Facts
Workshop
Game™

Family
Letters

Assessment
Management

Common
Core State
Standards

Curriculum
Focal Points

Interactive
Teacher's
Lesson Guide

Lesson	Masters	Manipulative Kit	Other Items
11·1	Teaching Masters, pp. 323–326 and 328–330 Study Link Master, p. 327	slate; per group: polyhedral dice; decahedral die	5 index cards; scissors; tape or glue; per group: collection of geometric solids; Geometry Template; Class Data Pad; chart paper
11·2	Game Masters, pp. 505–507 Study Link Master, p. 331 Teaching Masters, pp. 330 (two copies per student) and 332	slate; per group: 1 hexagon pattern block; pattern blocks	Class Data Pad*; per group: set of constructed geometric solids; *Flatland;* scissors; colored pencils or markers; cm ruler; pennies
11·3	Teaching Aid Master, p. 414* Study Link Master, p. 333	base-10 cube	Class Data Pad; open cans or watertight cylindrical containers; ruler; 1-gal container of water; measuring cups (marked in milliliters); Geometry Template; masking tape; per partnership: 4 sheets of $8\frac{1}{2}$ in. by 11 in. construction paper; cylindrical objects; calculator
11·4	Teaching Masters, pp. 334 and 336 Teaching Aid Master, p. 440 Study Link Master, p. 335 Game Masters, pp. 498–501 *Differentiation Handbook,* p. 142	slate	1 piece card stock; food can; dry fill; Class Data Pad; scissors; crayons or colored pencils (yellow, orange, and red); calculator
11·5	Study Link Master, p. 337 Teaching Masters, pp. 338 and 339	slate; per group: measuring cup	Geometry Template or cm ruler; per group: ruler, tape, paper towels, 2-L plastic bottle (top cut off), paper, scissors, rubber bands, large can or jar filled with 2 L of water, rocks and other objects for displacement activities, bucket or clear container (partially filled with water), empty margarine tub or yogurt container, rocks, waterproof marker; dictionaries; *Who Sank the Boat?*
11·6	Study Link Master, p. 340 Game Master, p. 490 *Differentiation Handbook,* p. 143 Teaching Master, p. 347A	slate; per group: 4 each of number cards 0–9, calculator, set of polyhedral dice	Class Data Pad; demonstration materials: containers (cup, pint, quart, half-gallon, and gallon); copy-paper carton; measuring cup; water, sand, popcorn, or rice; scale
11·7	Study Link Master, p. 341 Teaching Masters, pp. 342 and 343	slate; per partnership: 24 centimeter cubes; per group: tape measure	cardboard box; per group: 2 cans, ruler, triangular prism, and square pyramid; calculator
11·8	Assessment Masters, pp. 205–209 Study Link Masters, pp. 344–347	slate	calculator

*Denotes optional materials

Mathematical Background

The discussion below highlights the major content areas presented in Unit 11 and helps establish instructional priorities.

Geometric Solids Review
(Lessons 11◆1 and 11◆2)

Students have worked and played with 3-dimensional shapes in *Everyday Mathematics* since Kindergarten, and with descriptions and definitions of both 2-dimensional and 3-dimensional figures since first grade. The activities in these two lessons are intended partly for enjoyment and partly to prepare students for an exploration of the relationship between the volume of prisms and pyramids and between the volume of cylinders and cones. These concepts will be extended in *Sixth Grade Everyday Mathematics*.

Everyday Mathematics uses the term geometric solid for 3-dimensional shapes. Please be aware that these 3-dimensional shapes are hollow rather than solid—they are made up of their enclosing surfaces and do not include their interiors. In other words, cylinders, cones, prisms, and similar shapes are empty rather than full. The measure of the amount of space they occupy or the amount of "stuff" it would take to fill them is their volume.

Three-dimensional figures that are represented by line drawings or straw constructions may introduce an element of confusion. Only the frames of the surfaces appear, not the surfaces themselves, yet these frames may be referred to as prisms, pyramids, and so on. Such ambiguities are common in the English language. It is useful to remind your students every once in a while that a given "solid" is defined by its surfaces, but don't stress this subtlety. In geometry instruction in sixth grade and beyond, the role of exact definitions in mathematics will be discussed at length.

PROFESSIONAL DEVELOPMENT You can find more information on geometric solids in Section 13.5.1 of the *Teacher's Reference Manual.*

2-D

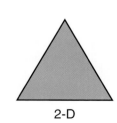
2-D

2-D

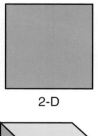
3-D

3-D

3-D

Hands-On Explorations of the Volumes of Pyramids, Cylinders, and Cones (Lessons 11◆3 and 11◆4)

The explorations in Lessons 11-3 and 11-4 reveal that the volume of a pyramid is exactly one-third that of a prism with the same base and height as the pyramid. Similarly, the volume of a cone is exactly one-third that of a cylinder with the same base and height as the cone. Thus, it takes the contents of three pyramids (or cones) to fill a prism (or cylinder) that has the same base and same height.

A useful project to augment the explorations of Lesson 11-4 would be to have the students find, in their everyday environments, cylinder and cone containers that have (or can be modified to have) approximately the same base and height—for example, food cans for cylinders; drinking cups, popcorn containers, or ice-cream cones for cones. By pouring water, sand, or other substances between containers, students can verify the 3-to-1 volume relationship for a variety of containers.

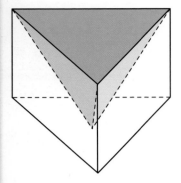

By "fitting" a pyramid inside a prism, students realize that a formula for finding the volume of a pyramid is $V = \frac{1}{3} * B * h$.

PROFESSIONAL DEVELOPMENT For more ways to explore the volume of pyramids, cylinders, and cones, refer to Section 14.5 of the *Teacher's Reference Manual*.

Links of Volume to Density and Displacement (Lesson 11◆5)

This lesson introduces important science concepts with many practical applications. You should not expect that full understanding and mastery will be achieved with these introductory experiences; the concepts will be developed as students study mathematics and science over the next few years.

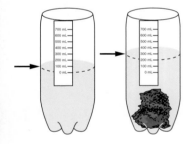

When an object is submerged in water, it pushes aside, or displaces, a volume of water exactly equal to the volume of the object. If an object is submerged in a marked container so that the amount of water displaced can be measured, then the exact volume of the object can be determined, even for objects that are so irregular that calculating the volume with formulas would be difficult or impossible. Lesson 11-5 develops this concept.

PROFESSIONAL DEVELOPMENT For additional ways of linking volume to density and displacement, see Section 14.5 of the *Teacher's Reference Manual*.

Relationships among Units of Capacity, Volume, and Weight
(Lesson 11·6)

So far, students have had quite a bit of experience converting measurements from one unit to another within the same system of measure. For example, they have learned that there are 2 cups in 1 pint, 12 inches in 1 foot, and 100 centimeters in 1 meter. In this lesson, students convert units of capacity to units of weight. For example, they convert gallons to cubic inches.

 For more examples of relationships among units of capacity, volume, and weight, see Sections 14.5 and 14.6 of the *Teacher's Reference Manual.*

Surface Area (Lesson 11·7)

While this lesson introduces the concept of surface area, it does not attempt to develop surface area formulas. Rather, it fosters an understanding of surface area by having students measure the dimensions of concrete models and use previously learned area formulas to calculate the surface area of the model. As in earlier lessons, students learn through hands-on experiences by deconstructing geometric solids into their component surfaces.

 For additional information on surface area, see Section 14.4 of the *Teacher's Reference Manual.*

11·1 Review of Geometric Solids: Part 1

 Objective To review the names and properties of geometric solids.

Technology Resources www.everydaymathonline.com

 ePresentations

 eToolkit

 Algorithms Practice

 EM Facts Workshop Game™

 Family Letters

 Assessment Management

 Common Core State Standards

 Curriculum Focal Points

 Interactive Teacher's Lesson Guide

1 Teaching the Lesson

Key Concepts and Skills

- Compare and classify geometric solids. [Geometry Goal 2]

- Describe and classify polyhedrons according to their faces. [Geometry Goal 2]

Key Activities

Students sort geometric solids into groups: prisms, pyramids, cylinders, cones, and spheres. They build models from paper patterns and use the models and solid-geometry vocabulary to describe and compare solids.

 Ongoing Assessment: Informing Instruction See page 858.

 Ongoing Assessment: Recognizing Student Achievement Use journal page 369. [Geometry Goal 2]

Key Vocabulary

geometric solid ◆ surfaces ◆ faces ◆ edges ◆ vertex ◆ vertices (vertexes) ◆ prisms ◆ pyramids ◆ cylinders ◆ cones ◆ spheres ◆ polyhedrons ◆ regular polyhedrons

Materials

Math Journal 2, pp. 369 and 370; p. 428 (optional)
Student Reference Book, pp. 147–149 and 152
Math Masters, pp. 323–326
slate ◆ 5 index cards or sheets of construction paper ◆ per group: scissors, tape or glue, geometric solids, polyhedral dice

2 Ongoing Learning & Practice

Volume of a Rectangular Prism

Math Journal 2, pp. 371A and 371B
Student Reference Book, pp. 196 and 197
Students find the volumes of rectangular prisms.

Math Boxes 11·1

Math Journal 2, p. 371
Geometry Template
Students practice and maintain skills through Math Box problems.

Study Link 11·1

Math Masters, p. 327
Students practice and maintain skills through Study Link activities.

3 Differentiation Options

ENRICHMENT

Comparing the Faces, Vertices, and Edges of Polyhedrons

Math Masters, p. 328
Class Data Pad ◆ decahedral die
Students compare the number of faces, vertices, and edges of polyhedrons.

EXTRA PRACTICE

Building Models for Geometric Solids

Math Masters, pp. 329 and 330
scissors ◆ tape or glue
Students use patterns to construct a rectangular prism and an octahedron.

ELL SUPPORT

Describing Geometric Solids

chart paper
Students describe the properties of prisms, pyramids, cylinders, cones, and spheres.

Advance Preparation

For Part 1, make and display five labels around the room: Prisms, Pyramids, Cylinders, Cones, and Spheres. Each group of students will need the following: at least one prism, pyramid, cylinder, cone, and sphere (such as boxes, cans, party hats, balls, and so on); a set of polyhedral dice that includes one tetrahedral die (4-sided), one octahedral die (8-sided), one decahedral die (10-sided), one dodecahedral die (12-sided), and one icosahedral die (20-sided); and a set of *Math Masters,* pages 323–326. Make one additional set to construct models. For the optional Extra Practice activity in Part 3, consider copying *Math Masters,* pages 329 and 330 on different-colored construction paper.

 Teacher's Reference Manual, Grades 4–6 pp. 186–192

Getting Started

Mental Math and Reflexes

Have students mentally convert between fractions, decimals, and percents (or refer to the Probability Meter in the reference section of their journals, as needed). *Suggestions:*

●○○ $\frac{3}{4}$ 0.75, 75%   ●●○ 33$\frac{1}{3}$% $\frac{1}{3}$, 0.$\overline{3}$ ●●● 0.6$\overline{6}$ $\frac{2}{3}$, 66$\frac{2}{3}$%

$\frac{1}{5}$ 0.2, 20%   12$\frac{1}{2}$% $\frac{1}{8}$, 0.125   0.375 $\frac{3}{8}$, 37$\frac{1}{2}$%, or 37.5%

$\frac{4}{5}$ 0.8, 80%   87$\frac{1}{2}$% $\frac{7}{8}$, 0.875   1.25 $\frac{5}{4}$, 125%

Math Message

Look at your group's collection of objects and name the geometric solid that each item represents. Use pages 147–149 of the Student Reference Book as a resource.

---

1 Teaching the Lesson

Math Message Follow-Up
(Student Reference Book, pp. 147–149)

WHOLE-CLASS DISCUSSION

Discuss *Student Reference Book,* pages 147 and 148. Emphasize that each **geometric solid** is identified by its **surfaces** (flat and curved), **faces, edges,** and **vertex** or **vertices** (or **vertexes**).

Display the five prepared labels for types of geometric solids around the room. Name one type of geometric solid from the five labeled groups (**prisms, pyramids, cylinders, cones,** and **spheres**). Ask volunteers to show an example of the solid from their group's collection and describe the object in terms of its surfaces, faces, edges, and vertices. Ask students to discuss how it is similar to and different from the other solids. For example, cones and pyramids have one base, but the cone has a curved surface and the pyramid does not have a curved surface. Have a student from each group place the object in the area with the appropriate label. Repeat until all five geometric solids have been identified and sorted and a list of properties has been generated.

Read *Student Reference Book,* page 149 as a class. Ask: *Are all geometric solids also* **polyhedrons?** no *Which solids in the collection are not polyhedrons?* Cylinders, cones, and spheres *Why aren't they polyhedrons?* Because at least one of their surfaces is curved

Exploring Characteristics of Geometric Solids
(Math Journal 2, p. 369; Math Masters, pp. 323–326)

SMALL-GROUP ACTIVITY

Give each group of four a rectangular prism, a cylinder, a cone, and a sphere from the class collection. They will also need one set of *Math Masters,* pages 323–326, scissors, and glue or tape.

NOTE *Math Masters,* pages 323–326 provide patterns (nets) for a cube, a triangular prism, a triangular pyramid, and a square pyramid.

Interactive whiteboard-ready ePresentations are available at www.everydaymathonline.com to help you teach the lesson.

Links to the Future

Students will take a closer look at prisms and pyramids in Lesson 11-2.

Student Page

Date   Time

LESSON 11·1 **Geometric Solids** ★

Each member of your group should cut out one of the patterns from *Math Masters,* pages 323–326. Fold the pattern, and glue or tape it together. Then add this model to your group's collection of geometric solids.

1. Examine your models of geometric solids.

a. Which solids have all flat surfaces? Pyramids and prisms—including cubes

b. Which have no flat surfaces? spheres

c. Which have both flat and curved surfaces? Cylinders and cones

d. If you cut the label of a cylindrical can in a straight line perpendicular to the bottom and then unroll and flatten the label, what is the shape of the label? rectangle

cut line

2. Examine your models of polyhedrons.

a. Which polyhedrons have more faces than vertices? none

b. Which polyhedrons have the same number of faces and vertices? Triangular pyramids and square pyramids

c. Which polyhedrons have fewer faces than vertices? Cubes, triangular prisms, and rectangular prisms

3. Examine your model of a cube.

a. Does the cube have more edges than vertices, the same number of edges as vertices, or fewer edges than vertices? More edges than vertices
Is this true for all polyhedrons? Yes Explain. At least 3 edges are needed to form 1 vertex.

b. How many edges of the cube meet at each vertex? 3 edges
Is this true for all polyhedrons? No Explain. More than 3 edges could meet at the vertex of a pyramid.

Math Journal 2, p. 369

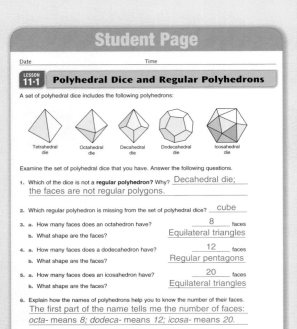

Date _____ Time _____

LESSON
11·1   **Polyhedral Dice and Regular Polyhedrons**

A set of polyhedral dice includes the following polyhedrons:

| Tetrahedral die | Octahedral die | Decahedral die | Dodecahedral die | Icosahedral die |

Examine the set of polyhedral dice that you have. Answer the following questions.

1. Which of the dice is not a **regular polyhedron**? Why? _Decahedral die;_
    the faces are not regular polygons.

2. Which regular polyhedron is missing from the set of polyhedral dice? _cube_

3. a. How many faces does an octahedron have? _8_ faces
    b. What shape are the faces? _Equilateral triangles_

4. a. How many faces does a dodecahedron have? _12_ faces
    b. What shape are the faces? _Regular pentagons_

5. a. How many faces does an icosahedron have? _20_ faces
    b. What shape are the faces? _Equilateral triangles_

6. Explain how the names of polyhedrons help you to know the number of their faces.
    The first part of the name tells me the number of faces:
    octa- means 8; dodeca- means 12; icosa- means 20.

Math Journal 2, p. 370

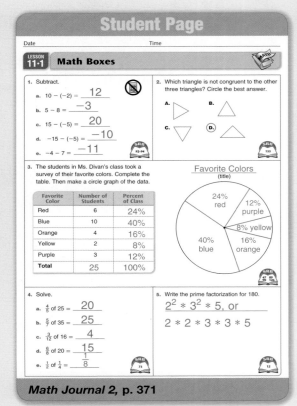

Date _____ Time _____

LESSON
11·1   **Math Boxes**

1. Subtract.
    a. $10 - (-2) =$ _12_
    b. $5 - 8 =$ _-3_
    c. $15 - (-5) =$ _20_
    d. $-15 - (-5) =$ _-10_
    e. $-4 - 7 =$ _-11_

2. Which triangle is not congruent to the other three triangles? Circle the best answer.

    A.   B.

    C.   (D.)

3. The students in Ms. Divan's class took a survey of their favorite colors. Complete the table. Then make a circle graph of the data.

Favorite Color	Number of Students	Percent of Class
Red	6	24%
Blue	10	40%
Orange	4	16%
Yellow	2	8%
Purple	3	12%
Total	25	100%

Favorite Colors
(title)

24% red   12% purple   8% yellow   40% blue   16% orange

4. Solve.
    a. $\frac{4}{5}$ of 25 = _20_
    b. $\frac{5}{7}$ of 35 = _25_
    c. $\frac{3}{12}$ of 16 = _4_
    d. $\frac{6}{8}$ of 20 = _15_
    e. $\frac{1}{2}$ of $\frac{1}{4}$ = _$\frac{1}{8}$_

5. Write the prime factorization for 180.
    $2^2 * 3^2 * 5$, or
    $2 * 2 * 3 * 3 * 5$

Math Journal 2, p. 371

Each student uses a pattern on one of the masters to construct the model of a geometric solid. Each group will then have one constructed model for each of the four solids.

✔ **Ongoing Assessment:**
Informing Instruction   ELL

Watch for students who have difficulty folding the patterns. Suggest that they score the fold lines with a ruler and pen before folding. To support English language learners, model the meaning of *score* in this context.

If students have difficulty adhering the flaps of the patterns, suggest that they tape the flaps to the outside of the models.

Have students use the objects they selected from the labeled groups and the geometric models they constructed to answer the questions on journal page 369. When all groups have completed the journal page, bring the class together to discuss the answers.

✔ **Ongoing Assessment:**   Journal Page 369 ★
Recognizing Student Achievement

Use **journal page 369** to assess students' knowledge of the properties of geometric solids. Students are making adequate progress if they correctly complete Problem 1.

[Geometry Goal 2]

Have students display the objects and constructed models with the appropriate labels. The constructed models will be used in Lesson 11-2.

▶ **Investigating Regular Polyhedrons**    SMALL-GROUP ACTIVITY

(*Math Journal 2*, p. 370; *Student Reference Book*, p. 152)

Distribute one set of polyhedral dice to each group of four and assign students to complete journal page 370. Students examine the dice and use the information on *Student Reference Book*, page 152 to complete the journal page.

When most students have finished, ask volunteers to describe a **regular polyhedron.** Sample answers: Regular polyhedrons are geometric solids with faces that are all the same size and shape. Each face is formed by a regular polygon. Every vertex looks exactly the same as every other vertex. The five kinds of regular polyhedrons are tetrahedrons, cubes, octahedrons, dodecahedrons and icosahedrons.

Ask students to think about the *Everyday Mathematics* games that are played using six-sided dice. Explain that six-sided dice are considered fair because there is an equal chance of any one of the six sides landing on top when the dice are thrown. Discuss whether or not each of the polyhedral dice is fair. Yes, because all of the faces on polyhedral dice have the same size and shape.

2 Ongoing Learning & Practice

▶ Volume of a Rectangular Prism

 INDEPENDENT ACTIVITY

(*Math Journal 2*, pp. 371A and 371B; *Student Reference Book*, pp. 196 and 197)

Students find the volumes of rectangular prisms. Remind students that they can do so by counting unit cubes or applying one of the formulas: $V = B * h$ or $V = l * w * h$.

▶ Math Boxes 11·1

INDEPENDENT ACTIVITY

(*Math Journal 2*, p. 371)

Mixed Practice Math Boxes in this lesson are paired with Math Boxes in Lesson 11-3. The skill in Problem 5 previews Unit 12 content.

▶ Study Link 11·1

INDEPENDENT ACTIVITY

(*Math Masters*, p. 327)

Home Connection Students are given four patterns, three of which can be folded into a cube. Students select which one of the four cannot be folded into a cube and check their selection by cutting out and folding that pattern.

3 Differentiation Options

ENRICHMENT

INDEPENDENT ACTIVITY

▶ Comparing the Faces, Vertices, and Edges of Polyhedrons

5–15 Min

PROBLEM SOLVING

(*Math Masters*, p. 328)

Social Studies Link The Swiss mathematician and physicist Leonard Euler is said to have discovered that the sum of the faces and vertices of any polyhedron is 2 more than the number of edges. Euler's Theorem can be expressed by the formula $F + V - E = 2$, where F stands for the number of faces, V for the number of vertices, and E for the number of edges.

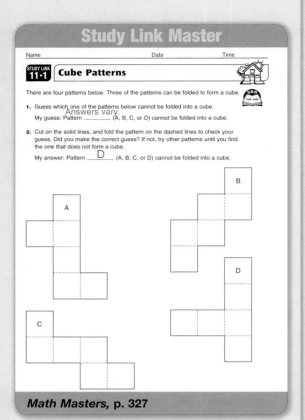
To apply students' understanding of the properties of geometric solids, have students explore relationships between the faces, the vertices, and the edges of polyhedrons. Students list the number of faces, vertices, and edges for the five regular polyhedrons and find the sum of the number of faces and the number of vertices. Then they analyze patterns for a tetrahedron.

When students have finished, discuss their responses to Problem 2. Write *Euler's Theorem* and the formula on the Class Data Pad. Have students use a decahedral die to verify Euler's Theorem by counting the faces, vertices, and edges and by substituting the values in the formula. $10 + 12 - 20 = 2$

Discuss students' solution strategies for Problem 3. Emphasize how faces, vertices, and edges are used to recognize when a pattern will make a tetrahedron.

EXTRA PRACTICE

▶ ## Building Models for Geometric Solids

INDEPENDENT ACTIVITY
15–30 Min

(*Math Masters,* pp. 329 and 330)

Students build models for a rectangular prism and an octahedron from patterns. Display the constructed models with their names and property descriptions.

ELL SUPPORT

▶ ## Describing Geometric Solids

INDEPENDENT ACTIVITY
15–30 Min

To provide language support for geometric solids, have students describe the properties of prisms, pyramids, cylinders, cones, and spheres. They record their observations on chart paper for display as a reference during this and future lessons.

Planning Ahead

Collect open cans, preferably with the labels removed, or other cylindrical and watertight containers of different sizes. In Lesson 11-3, students will need at least 1 can per partnership.

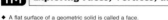

11·2 Review of Geometric Solids: Part 2

 Objective To provide experience comparing the properties of geometric solids.

Technology Resources www.everydaymathonline.com

ePresentations | eToolkit | Algorithms Practice | EM Facts Workshop Game™ | Family Letters | Assessment Management | Common Core State Standards | Curriculum Focal Points | Interactive Teacher's Lesson Guide

1 Teaching the Lesson

Key Concepts and Skills

- Use a Venn diagram to organize data.
  [Data and Chance Goal 1]
- Describe and classify geometric solids according to their properties.
  [Geometry Goal 2]
- Identify congruent faces on geometric solids. [Geometry Goal 2]

Key Activities

Students identify the bases of prisms, pyramids, cylinders, and cones and compare the properties of these solids. Students practice categorizing solids by playing *3-D Shape Sort.*

 Ongoing Assessment:
Recognizing Student Achievement
Use journal page 373.
[Geometry Goal 2]

 Ongoing Assessment:
Informing Instruction See page 864.

Key Vocabulary

base ◆ apex

Materials

Math Journal 2, pp. 372 and 373
Student Reference Book, pp. 150, 151, and 332
Study Link 11·1
Math Masters, pp. 505–507 ◆ Class Data Pad (optional) ◆ slate ◆ per group: 1 hexagon pattern block, 1 set of geometric solids, scissors

2 Ongoing Learning & Practice

 Math Boxes 11·2
Math Journal 2, p. 374
Students practice and maintain skills through Math Box problems.

 Study Link 11·2
Math Masters, p. 331
Students practice and maintain skills through Study Link activities.

3 Differentiation Options

READINESS

Exploring a 2-Dimensional World
Flatland ◆ pennies or pattern blocks
Students investigate ideas of spatial perception and dimension presented in the book.

ENRICHMENT

Exploring Truncated Polyhedrons
Math Masters, p. 330 (2 copies per student) and p. 332
cm ruler ◆ scissors ◆ colored pencils or markers ◆ tape or glue
Students explore patterns of geometric solids by constructing an octahedron and a truncated octahedron.

Advance Preparation

For Part 1, each group of 4 students will need the set of constructed geometric solids and a cylinder and a cone from the class collection used in Lesson 11-1. Copy *Math Masters,* pages 505 and 506 back-to-back to create two-sided property cards for *3-D Shape Sort.* For the optional Readiness activity in Part 3, obtain the book *Flatland* by Edwin Abbott (HarperCollins Publishers, 1983). For an additional mathematics and literacy connection, obtain a copy of *Sir Cumference and the Sword in the Cone* by Cindy Neuschwander (Charlesbridge Publishing, 2003).

 Teacher's Reference Manual, Grades 4–6 pp. 186–192

Getting Started

Mental Math and Reflexes

Have students use place value to write numbers in standard notation.
Suggestions:

- ●○○ I am a 5-digit number with 7 in the thousands place, 6 in the tenths place, and 4 in all other places. What number am I? 7,444.6
- ●●○ I am a 5-digit number with 6 in the 10^2 place, 4 in the 10^4 place, 9 in the 10^3 place, and 5 in all other places. What number am I? 49,655
- ●●● I am a 5-digit number with 6 in the 10^{-2} place, 5 in the 10^2 place, 3 in the 10^{-1} place, and 4 in all other places. What number am I? 544.36

Math Message

Complete journal page 372.

Study Link 11·1 Follow-Up

Pattern D cannot be folded into a cube. Ask volunteers to explain why Pattern D will not make a cube. Two faces will overlap, making an open box but not a cube.

---

① Teaching the Lesson

▶ ## Math Message Follow-Up

 WHOLE-CLASS DISCUSSION

(*Math Journal 2*, p. 372; *Student Reference Book*, pp. 150 and 151)

Draw the Venn diagram circles on the board or Class Data Pad. Complete the diagram by having volunteers share their comparisons. Emphasize that the differences between prisms and pyramids all relate to the base. Discuss the following points:

▷ A **base** of a solid is a face.

▷ Cylinders and prisms have 2 parallel bases.

▷ Rectangular prisms have a special feature: any pair of parallel faces can be chosen as the bases, and the edges connecting these bases are parallel. Have students examine the cube they made in Lesson 11-1 to verify that the edges between any two bases are parallel to each other.

The hexagonal pattern block models a prism that has exactly one pair of parallel bases. Have students examine the hexagonal pattern block to verify that the edges connecting the bases are parallel. Then hold the block with one finger on a rectangular face and the other finger on the opposite, parallel rectangular face. Point out that these two rectangular faces cannot be bases because the edges connecting them are not parallel.

The hexagonal faces are bases. All edges connecting the bases are parallel.

No other faces are bases. Edges connecting these faces are not all parallel.

▷ Prisms and pyramids are named after the shape of their base(s).

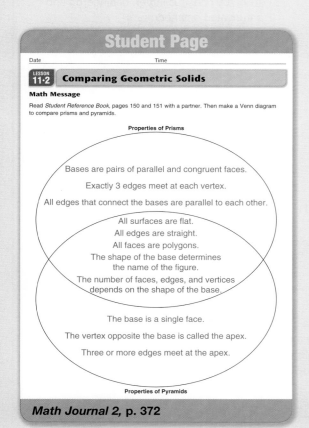

▷ Cones and pyramids have only one base each. In a pyramid, all edges starting at the vertices of the base meet in one point, called the **apex**.

▶ Comparing Geometric Solids

(*Math Journal 2*, p. 373)

SMALL-GROUP ACTIVITY

ELL

PROBLEM SOLVING

Assign groups of four to complete journal page 373. Each group should have the same set of geometric solids used in Lesson 11-1. Circulate and assist.

✓ **Ongoing Assessment:**
Recognizing Student Achievement

Journal Page 373

Use **journal page 373** to assess students' understanding of the properties of prisms, pyramids, cylinders, and cones. Students are making adequate progress if their answers demonstrate knowledge of the relationship between the faces, vertices, and edges of geometric solids.

[Geometry Goal 2]

When all groups have finished, discuss their answers. Summarize the information in a table on the board or Class Data Pad. To support English language learners, draw a prism, a cylinder, a pyramid, and a cone underneath the correct terms in the first row of the table.

	Prisms and Cylinders	Pyramids and Cones
Likenesses	They both have two parallel and congruent bases. The bases are flat surfaces. The name of the base determines the name of the shape.	They both have only one base. The base is a flat surface. Both have a vertex opposite the base. The name of the base determines the name of the shape.
Differences	Cylinders have a curved surface, and prisms have all flat surfaces that are polygons. The bases of cylinders are circles; the bases of prisms are congruent polygons. Cylinders have curved edges; prisms have straight edges. Cylinders don't have vertices; prisms have vertices.	Cones have a curved surface, and pyramids have all flat surfaces that are polygons. The base of a cone is a circle; the base of a pyramid is a polygon. Cones have a curved edge; pyramids have straight edges. Cones have one vertex; pyramids have four or more vertices.

Point out that in a triangular pyramid, any one of the faces can be chosen as the base since the edges from the vertices of any one of the faces meet at one point.

▶ Playing *3-D Shape Sort*

PARTNER ACTIVITY

(*Student Reference Book*, p. 332; *Math Masters*, pp. 505–507)

Have students look over the master for *3-D Shape Sort* shape cards (*Math Masters*, page 507). Ask volunteers why they think

apex

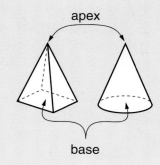

base

Name   Date   Time

3-D Shape Sort Shape Cards

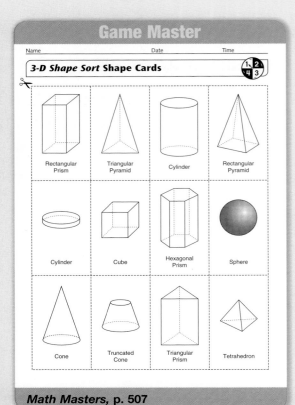

Rectangular Prism	Triangular Pyramid	Cylinder	Rectangular Pyramid
Cylinder	Cube	Hexagonal Prism	Sphere
Cone	Truncated Cone	Triangular Prism	Tetrahedron

Math Masters, p. 507

the one figure is named a truncated cone and how it is different from a cone. The truncated cone looks like the top was cut off; it doesn't have an apex. Explain that the word *truncate* means *to shorten by, or as if by, cutting off.* In this case, the top of the figure seems cut off.

Have students look over the master of *3-D Shape Sort* Property Cards (*Math Masters,* pages 505 and 506). Ask students to identify the two types of property cards. Property cards for vertices and edges; Property cards for surfaces

Tell students that they will cut out the shape and property cards and use them to play *3-D Shape Sort.* This game has the same rules as *Polygon Capture,* but students might want to review the directions on *Student Reference Book,* page 332. Circulate and assist.

 **Ongoing Assessment: Informing Instruction**

Watch for students who have trouble matching shapes with two properties. Have them first draw one card and take all the shapes having this property. Then take a second card and put back all the shapes that do not have the second property.

2 Ongoing Learning & Practice

▶ Math Boxes 11·2
INDEPENDENT ACTIVITY

(*Math Journal 2,* p. 374)

 **Mixed Practice** Math Boxes in this lesson are paired with Math Boxes in Lessons 11-4 and 11-6. The skill in Problem 6 previews Unit 12 content.

Writing/Reasoning Have students write a response to the following: *Explain how to use a factor tree to find the prime factorization for a number. Use your factor tree from Problem 5 as an example.* Sample answer: Find the factor pair with the smallest prime factor such as 2, 3, 5, 7, and so on. Continue to find factor pairs until all of the factors at the bottom of each branch are prime.

▶ Study Link 11·2
INDEPENDENT ACTIVITY

(*Math Masters,* p. 331)

Home Connection Students identify geometric solids. They label the properties (edges, bases, and vertices) of each solid.

Date   Time

LESSON 11·2 Math Boxes

1. Solve.

   a. $\frac{1}{3}$ of 27 = __9__

   b. $\frac{1}{8}$ of 40 = __5__

   c. $\frac{1}{5}$ of 100 = __20__

   d. $\frac{2}{5}$ of 100 = __40__

   e. $\frac{1}{4}$ of 60 = __15__

2. Find the volume of the prism.

   5 units   8 units   5 units

   Volume = $B * h$ where B is the area of the base and h is the height.

   Volume: __100 units^3__

3. To celebrate her birthday, Ms. Chang gives each of the fifth graders 1 piece of licorice. There are 179 fifth graders. The licorice comes in packages of 15 pieces, at a cost of $1.19 per package.

   a. How many packages of licorice does Ms. Chang need to buy? __12__ packages

   b. How much does she spend? __$14.28__

4. Solve.

   a. 2 gal = __8__ qt

   b. __4__ pt = 2 qt

   c. 8 c = __4__ pt

   d. 3 c = __24__ fl oz

   e. 1 qt = __32__ fl oz

5. Make a factor tree to find the prime factorization of 100.

   100
   2 * 50
   2 * 2 * 25
   2 * 2 * 5 * 5

6. Kayin buys 6 envelopes for 14 cents each and 6 stamps for 39 cents each.

   Which expression correctly represents how much money she spends? Circle the best answer.

   A. $(6 + 6) * (14 + 39)$

   B. $(6 * 6) + (14 * 39)$

   C. $6 * (14 + 39)$

Math Journal 2, p. 374

③ Differentiation Options

READINESS

WHOLE-CLASS ACTIVITY
30+ Min

▶ Exploring a 2-Dimensional World

Literature Link To explore the concept of dimension in geometry, have students investigate and discuss ideas from *Flatland*. Read the first section of *Flatland*, entitled "Of the Nature of Flatland," to the class. Have students use pennies or pattern blocks to investigate the idea, as presented in the section, that "Nothing was visible, nor could be visible, to us, except straight lines." Students place the penny or pattern block on a flat surface and view the edge of the surface at eye-level. If your desks have edging, students can stack books to use as the surface.

When all students have tried viewing a penny or pattern block, tell them that females in Flatland are said to be able to disappear. Ask: *What shape would the females have to be so that they could move a certain way and be seen as a point?* A line

Read the section entitled "How the Stranger Vainly Endeavored to Reveal to Me in Words the Mysteries of Spaceland." Discuss the differences in the way that flat versus curved surfaces are perceived in the 2-dimensional world of *Flatland*.

Flatland

Summary: This book describes Flatland, a land that has only two dimensions. The science-fiction elements of the story combine mathematics with satire.

ENRICHMENT

PARTNER ACTIVITY
15–30 Min

▶ Exploring Truncated Polyhedrons

(*Math Masters,* pp. 330 and 332)

To further explore students' understanding of patterns for geometric solids, have students construct an octahedron and a truncated octahedron. Students follow the directions on *Math Masters,* page 332. Then they identify the shapes contained in other truncated polyhedrons.

When students have finished, ask them to solve this riddle: *Which sports teams know the most about truncated icosahedrons?* Soccer teams A soccer ball is shaped like a truncated icosahedron, except that the surfaces of the truncated icosahedrons are flat, not curved as on a soccer ball.

Name   Date   Time

STUDY LINK 11·2 Comparing Geometric Solids

Name the figures, and label their bases, vertices, and edges.

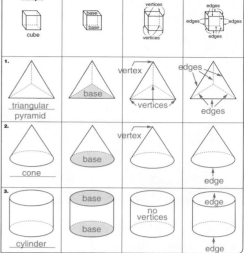

Math Masters, p. 331

Name   Date   Time

LESSON 11·2 Exploring Truncated Polyhedrons

Truncated polyhedrons are formed by shortening the edges of the solid and cutting off the vertices. Follow the steps below to make models of an octahedron and a truncated octahedron.

Part 1: Octahedrons

1. Use a centimeter ruler to mark dots on the lines of the pattern on *Math Masters,* page 330 so that the lines are divided into thirds.

2. Use a colored pencil or marker to connect the dots to form triangles around the vertices of the octahedron.

3. Cut out and assemble the octahedron model.

4. Hold the model so that a vertex is facing you. What shape is formed by the colored lines? A square

Part 2: Truncated Octahedrons

5. Repeat steps 1 and 2 with your second copy of the octahedron pattern.

6. Cut out the pattern. Then cut along the colored lines. You will cut off the vertices and parts of the tabs. Assemble the model.

7. What two shapes are contained in the model? Squares and hexagons

8. What shapes are contained in a truncated hexahedron? Triangles and octagons

9. What shapes are contained in a truncated icosahedron? Pentagons and hexagons

Hexahedron   Truncated Hexahedron   Icosahedron   Truncated Icosahedron

Math Masters, p. 332

11·3 Volume of Cylinders

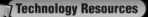

Technology Resources www.everydaymathonline.com

 ePresentations   eToolkit   Algorithms Practice   EM Facts Workshop Game™   Family Letters   Assessment Management   Common Core State Standards   Curriculum Focal Points   Interactive Teacher's Lesson Guide

---

1 Teaching the Lesson

Key Concepts and Skills

• Use tables to collect data.
[Data and Chance Goal 1]

• Apply formulas to calculate the area of a circle and the volume of prisms and cylinders.
[Measurement and Reference Frames Goal 2]

• Compare the volume and the capacity of cylinders.
[Measurement and Reference Frames Goal 2]

Key Activities

Students review the formula for finding the area of a circle. They use the formula for the volume of a cylinder to calculate the volume of open cans and verify the formula by measuring the liquid capacities of the cans.

 Ongoing Assessment:
Recognizing Student Achievement
Use an Exit Slip (*Math Masters*, page 414).
[Measurement and Reference Frames Goal 2]

Materials

Math Journal 2, pp. 375 and 376
Math Masters, p. 414
Study Link 11·2
Class Data Pad ◆ calculator ◆ open cans or watertight cylindrical containers ◆ ruler ◆ 1-gallon container of water ◆ measuring cups (marked in milliliters) ◆ base-10 cube

2 Ongoing Learning & Practice

Finding the Volumes of Rectangular Prisms

Math Journal 2, p. 377
Student Reference Book,
pp. 196 and 197
Students practice finding the volumes of rectangular prisms.

 Math Boxes 11·3
Math Journal 2, p. 378
Geometry Template
Students practice and maintain skills through Math Box problems.

 Study Link 11·3
Math Masters, p. 333
Students practice and maintain skills through Study Link activities.

3 Differentiation Options

READINESS
Comparing Volumes of Cylinders
per partnership: 4 sheets of $8\frac{1}{2}$" by 11" construction paper, ruler, masking tape
Students compare and relate the dimensions of cylinders to the volume of cylinders.

ENRICHMENT
Calculating Volume for Cylinders
per partnership: cylindrical objects, ruler, calculator
Students measure the dimensions and find the volume of cylindrical objects in the classroom.

EXTRA PRACTICE
5-Minute Math
5-Minute Math™, pp. 58 and 229
Students identify geometric solids.

Advance Preparation

For Part 1, collect a set of open cans or other cylindrical and watertight containers of different sizes with the labels removed, if possible. Each partnership will need at least one container. Create a workstation in the classroom for measuring the capacities of containers. Fill a 1-gallon container with water. Provide several measuring cups, each marked to at least 250 mL, and several shallow pans to recover any spilled water.

 Teacher's Reference Manual, Grades 4–6 pp. 185–192, 222–225

Getting Started

Mental Math and Reflexes

Play *Beat the Calculator* to practice rounding numbers. Have students write dictated numbers and then round the numbers to a specified place: pencil-and-paper methods versus calculators (remind students to use the fix function). *Suggestions:*

◐○○ Round to the nearest thousand.

28,152 28,000
65,680 66,000
6,580 7,000

◐◐○ Round to the nearest ten.

4,152 4,150
697 700
285 290

◐◐◐ Round to the nearest tenth.

2.547 2.5
6.785 6.8
3.062 3.1

Math Message

Marble games are often played inside a circle whose diameter is 7 ft. What is the area of the playing surface? Write your solution as a number sentence.

Study Link 11·2 Follow-Up

Have partners compare answers and resolve differences.

---

1 Teaching the Lesson

▶ Math Message Follow-Up

WHOLE-CLASS DISCUSSION

ELL

Algebraic Thinking Ask students what information is needed to solve the Math Message problem. To support English language learners, write the important ideas from the discussion on the board. The properties of a circle; the formula for finding the area of a circle ($A = \pi * r^2$) Ask: *What is the relationship between the diameter and the radius of a circle?* The radius is half of the diameter. *If* **r** *represents radius and* **d** *represents diameter, what open number sentence shows their relationship?* $r = \frac{1}{2} * d$, $r = \frac{d}{2}$, or $d = r * 2$ *If you did not use the pi key on a calculator, what decimal number did you use in the calculations with pi?* 3.14

Have volunteers write their number sentences on the board and explain their solutions. The diameter of the circle is 7 ft, so the radius is 3.5 ft; therefore, the area of the circle is $\pi * 3.5 * 3.5 = 38.48$ ft^2 or about $38\frac{1}{2}$ ft^2.

▶ Introducing and Verifying the Cylinder Volume Formula

SMALL-GROUP ACTIVITY

(*Math Journal 2*, p. 375)

Algebraic Thinking Distribute the open cans, and assign groups of four students to complete Problems 1–3 on journal page 375, using at least two different cans. Remind students that 1 cubic centimeter is equal to 1 milliliter. Use a base-10 cube to show students 1 cubic centimeter. Write the following equivalencies on the Class Data Pad:

1 centimeter (cm) = 10 millimeters (mm)

1 millimeter = 0.1 ($\frac{1}{10}$) centimeter

1 milliliter (mL) = 0.001 ($\frac{1}{1,000}$) liter (L)

1 cubic centimeter (cm^3) = 1 milliliter

NOTE See sample measurements for containers on page 868.

Student Page

Date _____ Time _____

LESSON 11·3 **Volume of Cylinders**

The base of a cylinder is circular. To find the area of the base of a cylinder, use the formula for finding the area of a circle.

Formula for the Area of a Circle

$$A = \pi * r^2$$

where *A* is the area and *r* is the radius of the circle.

The formula for finding the volume of a cylinder is the same as the formula for finding the volume of a prism.

Formula for the Volume of a Cylinder

$$V = B * h$$

where *V* is the volume of the cylinder, *B* is the area of the base, and *h* is the height of the cylinder.

Use the 2 cans you have been given.

1. Measure the height of each can on the inside. Measure the diameter of the base of each can. Record your measurements (to the nearest tenth of a centimeter) in the table below.

2. Calculate the radius of the base of each can. Then use the formula to find the volume. Record the results in the table.

3. Record the capacity of each can in the table, in milliliters. Answers vary.

	Height (cm)	Diameter of Base (cm)	Radius of Base (cm)	Volume (cm³)	Capacity (mL)
Can #1					
Can #2					

4. Measure the liquid capacity of each can by filling the can with water. Then pour the water into a measuring cup. Keep track of the total amount of water you pour into the measuring cup. Answers vary.

Capacity of Can #1: _____ mL   Capacity of Can #2: _____ mL

Math Journal 2, p. 375

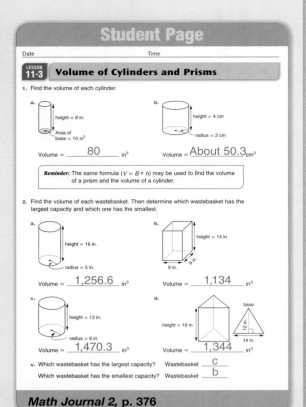

Math Journal 2, p. 376

Student Page

Date _____ Time _____

LESSON 11·3 **Volume of Cylinders and Prisms**

1. Find the volume of each cylinder.

   a. height = 8 in. Area of base = 10 in²
   Volume = __80__ in³

   b. height = 4 cm, radius = 2 cm
   Volume = __About 50.3__ cm³

   Reminder: The same formula (V = B * h) may be used to find the volume of a prism and the volume of a cylinder.

2. Find the volume of each wastebasket. Then determine which wastebasket has the largest capacity and which one has the smallest.

   a. height = 16 in., radius = 5 in.
   Volume = __1,256.6__ in³

   b. height = 14 in., 9 in., 9 in.
   Volume = __1,134__ in³

   c. height = 13 in., radius = 6 in.
   Volume = __1,470.3__ in³

   d. base, height = 16 in., 12 in., 14 in.
   Volume = __1,344__ in³

   e. Which wastebasket has the largest capacity? Wastebasket __c__
   Which wastebasket has the smallest capacity? Wastebasket __b__

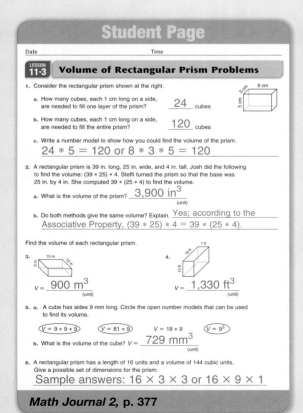

Math Journal 2, p. 377

Student Page

Date _____ Time _____

LESSON 11·3 **Volume of Rectangular Prism Problems**

1. Consider the rectangular prism shown at the right. 3 cm, 8 cm, 5 cm

   a. How many cubes, each 1 cm long on a side, are needed to fill one layer of the prism? __24__ cubes

   b. How many cubes, each 1 cm long on a side, are needed to fill the entire prism? __120__ cubes

   c. Write a number model to show how you could find the volume of the prism.
   24 * 5 = 120 or 8 * 3 * 5 = 120

2. A rectangular prism is 39 in. long, 25 in. wide, and 4 in. tall. Josh did the following to find the volume: (39 * 25) * 4. Steffi turned the prism so that the base was 25 in. by 4 in. She computed 39 * (25 * 4) to find the volume.

   a. What is the volume of the prism? __3,900 in³__ (unit)

   b. Do both methods give the same volume? Explain. Yes; according to the Associative Property, (39 * 25) * 4 = 39 * (25 * 4).

Find the volume of each rectangular prism.

3. 15 m, 5 m, 12 m
   V = __900 m³__ (unit)

4. 7 ft, 19 ft, 10 ft
   V = __1,330 ft³__ (unit)

5. a. A cube has sides 9 mm long. Circle the open number models that can be used to find its volume.
   (V = 9 * 9 * 9)   (V = 81 * 9)   V = 18 * 9   (V = 9³)

   b. What is the volume of the cube? V = __729 mm³__ (unit)

6. A rectangular prism has a length of 16 units and a volume of 144 cubic units. Give a possible set of dimensions for the prism.
   Sample answers: 16 × 3 × 3 or 16 × 9 × 1

Ask: Why do the directions say to measure the height inside the can? Some cans have recessed bottoms, so if you measure the outside of the can, it isn't as accurate as measuring the inside. Circulate and assist.

Adjusting the Activity   ELL

Have students find the diameter of a can by tracing around the base of the can, cutting out the circle, folding it in half, and measuring the length of the fold.

A U D I T O R Y   ◆   K I N E S T H E T I C   ◆   T A C T I L E   ◆   V I S U A L

As students finish, have them verify the capacities recorded in the table by measuring the liquid capacity of each can at the workstation. They record the results in Problem 4.

When all groups have completed the workstation activity, ask students which results they think are more accurate—the volumes obtained by the formula in Problem 3 or the volumes obtained by direct measurement in Problem 4—and why. Point out that inaccuracies might result for any of the following reasons:

▷ The diameter and/or the height of the can might not have been measured accurately.

▷ The can might not be a true cylinder. For example, the bottom of a can often has depressions, so it's not a single flat, circular surface.

▷ Measuring cups are usually marked at 25-mL increments, so readings of liquid capacity are seldom exact.

The following table shows approximate dimensions for a wide range of can sizes. The formula V = B * h has been used to calculate the volume and capacity of each.

Can Size*	Height (cm)	Diameter (cm)	Radius (cm)	Volume (cm³)	Capacity (mL)
6.5 oz (tuna)	3.8	8.6	4.3	221	221
10.5 oz (soup)	9.9	6.6	3.3	339	339
14 oz	8.3	7.5	3.75	367	367
16 oz	10.9	7.3	3.65	456	456
20 oz	11.4	8.4	4.2	632	632
27 oz	11.4	10.2	5.1	932	932
26 oz (salt)	13.3	8.3	4.15	720	720
Small coffee	13.3	10.2	5.1	1,087	1,087
1.5 lb coffee	15.9	12.7	6.35	2,014	2,014
Large coffee	17.8	15.2	7.6	3,230	3,230

*Can Size is listed for identification and not as a measure of capacity or weight. See note on page 885 about ounces and fluid ounces.

▶ Finding the Volumes of Prisms and Cylinders

(*Math Journal 2*, p. 376)

PARTNER ACTIVITY

PROBLEM SOLVING

Algebraic Thinking Remind students that in Lessons 9-8 and 9-9 they found the volume of a prism by multiplying the area of its base by its height. Discuss whether students think it is reasonable that the same formula is used to find the volumes of cylinders (the only difference being the way the area of the base is calculated).

Assign the problems on journal page 376. Circulate and assist.

Ongoing Assessment: Recognizing Student Achievement

Exit Slip ★

Use an **Exit Slip** (*Math Masters*, page 414) to asess students' ability to explain what is similar and what is different between finding the volume of cylinders and finding the volume of prisms. Students are making adequate progress if their explanations refer to using the same formula to find volumes but different formulas to calculate the area of the bases.

[Measurement and Reference Frames Goal 2]

---

② Ongoing Learning & Practice

▶ Finding the Volumes of Rectangular Prisms

INDEPENDENT ACTIVITY

(*Math Journal 2*, p. 377; *Student Reference Book*, pp. 196 and 197)

Students practice finding the volumes of rectangular prisms by packing them with unit cubes, using formulas, and solving real-world problems.

▶ Math Boxes 11·3

INDEPENDENT ACTIVITY

(*Math Journal 2*, p. 378)

Mixed Practice Math Boxes in this lesson are paired with Math Boxes in Lesson 11-1. The skill in Problem 5 previews Unit 12 content.

▶ Study Link 11·3

INDEPENDENT ACTIVITY

(*Math Masters*, p. 333)

Home Connection Students find the volume of two cylindrical objects in their homes. They compare the volume of the larger object to the volume of their toaster and their TV set.

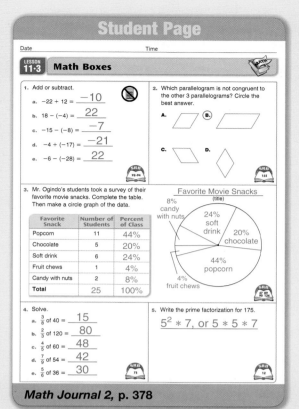

Math Journal 2, p. 378

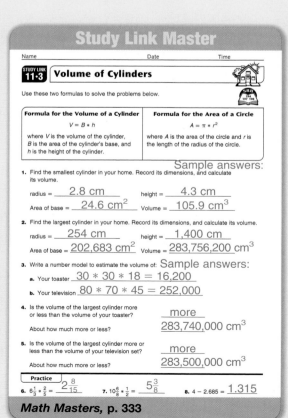

Math Masters, p. 333

**PARTNER
ACTIVITY**

15–30 Min

▶ Comparing Volumes of Cylinders

To explore comparing the volume of cylinders, have students construct and compare paper cylinders. Give partners 4 sheets of construction paper. Explain that, to make a cylinder from the paper, they will first draw a line 1 inch from an edge. Roll the rectangle into a cylinder, and tape the paper along the line. Then they will tape the cylinder to a second piece of paper. Reinforce the concept that the volume of a container is a measure of how much the container will hold.

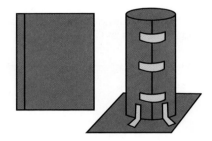

Ask partners to construct two cylinders from the paper. One cylinder should have the largest volume they can make. The other cylinder should have the smallest volume they can make.

When students have finished, have them display their cylinders and explain their solution strategies. Emphasize the relationship between the height and the area of the bases in determining volume. The taller cylinder does not necessarily have a larger volume than a shorter cylinder.

**PARTNER
ACTIVITY**

5–15 Min

▶ Calculating Volume for Cylinders

To apply students' understanding of the formula used to calculate the volume of cylinders, have them work with a partner to find the volume of cylindrical objects in the classroom. They should measure the height and diameter, record the measurements in a table, and calculate the volume.

When students have finished, have partners estimate the volume of the objects from other partnerships and check their estimates against the calculated volumes.

► *5-Minute Math*

 **SMALL-GROUP ACTIVITY**

 5–15 Min

To offer students more experience with identifying geometric solids, see *5-Minute Math,* pages 58 and 229.

Planning Ahead

For Lesson 11-5, you will need the following materials:

Containers

▷ About 7 two-liter soft-drink bottles, made out of clear or light-colored plastic

▷ About 7 large-mouthed containers that hold up to 2 liters of water each, for example, large coffee cans; gallon milk containers that are cut to provide a large opening, while retaining the handle; other large soft-drink bottles with the tops cut off about 9 in. from the bottom

Solid Objects

▷ About 30 to 40 rocks (enough to fill a gallon container), each about half the size of a fist, for example—landscape rocks

▷ A few unopened cans of nondiet soft drink

▷ Other objects for displacement activities, such as baseballs, golf balls, apples, or oranges

▷ A supply of paper towels

11·4 Volume of Pyramids and Cones

Objective To provide experiences with investigating the relationships between the volumes of geometric solids.

Technology Resources www.everydaymathonline.com

 ePresentations   eToolkit   Algorithms Practice   EM Facts Workshop Game™   Family Letters   Assessment Management Common Core State Standards   Curriculum Focal Points iTLG Interactive Teacher's Lesson Guide

---

1 Teaching the Lesson

Key Concepts and Skills

• Use formulas to find the volume of geometric solids.
[Measurement and Reference Frames Goal 2]

• Compare the properties of pyramids, prisms, cones, and cylinders.
[Geometry Goal 2]

• Describe patterns in relationships between the volumes of prisms, pyramids, cones, and cylinders.
[Patterns, Functions, and Algebra Goal 1]

Key Activities

Students observe a demonstration in which models of geometric solids are used to show how to find the volumes of pyramids and cones. Students then calculate the volumes of a pyramid and a cone.

Materials

Math Journal 2, p. 379
Study Link 11·3
Math Masters, pp. 334 and 440
for demonstration: 1 piece card stock, food can, dry fill ◆ slate ◆ calculator

2 Ongoing Learning & Practice

 Playing *Rugs and Fences*
Math Journal 2, p. 380
Math Masters, pp. 498–501
Class Data Pad ◆ scissors
Students practice calculating the perimeters and areas of polygons.

 Math Boxes 11·4
Math Journal 2, p. 381
Students practice and maintain skills through Math Box problems.

Ongoing Assessment:
Recognizing Student Achievement
Use Math Boxes, Problem 1.
[Number and Numeration Goal 2]

 Study Link 11·4
Math Masters, p. 335
Students practice and maintain skills through Study Link activities.

3 Differentiation Options

READINESS
Finding the Areas of Concentric Circles
Math Masters, p. 336
per partnership: crayons or colored pencils (yellow, orange, and red) ◆ Class Data Pad (optional)
Students compare the areas of different circular regions.

ENRICHMENT
Measuring Regions
Math Masters, p. 336
Students investigate the areas of concentric circle regions in relation to their boundaries.

EXTRA PRACTICE
5-Minute Math
5-Minute Math™, pp. 144, 147, and 229
Students identify the properties of geometric solids.

ELL SUPPORT
Building a Math Word Bank
Differentiation Handbook, p. 142
Students define and illustrate the term *volume of a cone*.

Advance Preparation

For Part 1, copy *Math Masters*, page 334 on card stock. Cut out the templates; score the dashed lines; fold them so that the markings are on the inside of the shapes; and tape the sides together completely to seal the seams. If you cannot copy onto card stock, tape the master to card stock, cut along the solid lines for each pattern, and then draw the corresponding dashed lines. Copy *Math Masters*, page 440. Cut out the cone template. Curl it into position by lining up the two heavy black lines and the sets of dotted gray lines. Seal the cone along the seams—inside and out. You will need a 15- or 16-oz food can with the top removed. Place the cone in the can so its tip touches the base of the can. Locate the line on the inside of the cone that touches the can's rim. Cut along the line to remove the excess. You will need about 1 pound of dry fill: rice, sugar, or sand.

 Teacher's Reference Manual, Grades 4–6 pp. 185, 186, 222–225

Getting Started

Mental Math and Reflexes

Have students complete each sentence by using the relationship between multiplication and division.

○○○ $\frac{1}{2} \div 8 = \frac{1}{16}$ because $\frac{1}{16} * \underline{\frac{8}{1}} = \frac{1}{2}$.

$3 \div \frac{1}{2} = 6$ because $6 * \underline{\frac{1}{2}} = 3$.

$9 \div \frac{1}{3} = 27$ because $\underline{27} * \frac{1}{3} = 9$.

●○○ $\frac{1}{4} \div 12 = \frac{1}{48}$ because $\frac{1}{48} * 12 = \underline{\frac{1}{4}}$.

$5 \div \frac{1}{5} = 25$ because $\underline{25} * \frac{1}{5} = 5$.

$7 \div \frac{1}{6} = 42$ because $42 * \underline{\frac{1}{6}} = 7$.

●●○ $\underline{\frac{1}{4}} \div 5 = \frac{1}{20}$ because $\frac{1}{20} * 5 = \underline{\frac{1}{4}}$.

$8 \div \underline{\frac{1}{2}} = 16$ because $16 * \underline{\frac{1}{2}} = 8$.

$\frac{1}{10} \div \underline{10} = \frac{1}{100}$ because $\frac{1}{100} * \underline{10} = \frac{1}{10}$.

Math Message

A rectangular prism and a cylinder each have exactly the same height and exactly the same volume. The base of the prism is an 8 cm × 5 cm rectangle. What is the area of the base of the cylinder?

Study Link 11·3 Follow-Up

Have students share their volume measurements with the class.

---

1 Teaching the Lesson

▶ Math Message Follow-Up

 **WHOLE-CLASS DISCUSSION**

Algebraic Thinking Ask volunteers to share their solution strategies. Since the prism and cylinder each have the same volume and height, the areas of their bases must also be equal. The area of the base of the prism is 40 cm² (8 cm * 5 cm), so the area of the base of the cylinder must also be 40 cm².

▶ Exploring the Relationship between the Volumes of Prisms and Pyramids

 **WHOLE-CLASS ACTIVITY**

PROBLEM SOLVING

(*Math Masters*, p. 334)

Gather the class around a desk or table. Show them the prism and pyramid you have made. Turn the pyramid so that the apex is pointing down and show that, when the pyramid is placed inside the prism, the boundaries of their bases match and the apex of the pyramid will touch a base of the prism. The two solids you made will fit in this way because they have identical bases and heights.

Have students guess how many pyramids filled with material it would take to fill the prism. Select a pair of volunteers to follow the procedure on the next page:

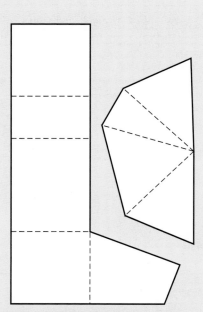

Prism and pyramid patterns from
Math Masters, page 334

1. Fill the pyramid with dry fill so that the material is level with the top. Empty the material into the prism.

2. Fill the pyramid again and empty the material into the prism.

3. Repeat until the prism is full and level at the top. It will take about 3 pyramids of material to fill the prism.

Students need not find the actual volumes of either the prism or the pyramid. It is enough for them to discover that about 3 pyramids of material fill the matching prism. Ask students to state the relationships between the volumes of the two shapes. The volume of the prism is 3 times the volume of the pyramid. The volume of the pyramid is $\frac{1}{3}$ the volume of the prism.

▶ Exploring the Relationship between the Volumes of Cylinders and Cones

WHOLE-CLASS ACTIVITY

PROBLEM SOLVING

(*Math Journal 2*, p. 379; *Math Masters*, p. 440)

Algebraic Thinking Repeat the demonstration using a 15- or 16-oz food can and the cone you have made. Turn the cone upside down and show that, when the cone is placed inside the cylinder, the boundaries of their bases match and the apex of the cone will touch a base of the cylinder. The two solids fit because they have identical bases and heights.

Have students guess how many cones of material will fill the can. Expect that many students will correctly guess 3 because of the previous demonstration.

Select another pair of volunteers to follow the same procedure as before. It takes about 3 cones of material to fill the cylinder.

Ask students to complete Problem 1 on journal page 379: *How would you calculate the volume of a pyramid or a cone?* Then have students share their solution strategies. Emphasize the following points:

▷ Since the volume of a pyramid (cone) is $\frac{1}{3}$ the volume of a prism (cylinder) with an identical base and height, you can calculate the volume of a pyramid (cone) by multiplying the area of the base of the pyramid (cone) by its height and then dividing the result by 3.

▷ A formula for finding the volume of a pyramid or cone is $V = \frac{1}{3} * B * h$.

▶ Solving Volume Problems

INDEPENDENT ACTIVITY

(*Math Journal 2*, p. 379)

Algebraic Thinking Assign the rest of journal page 379. Circulate and assist. When students have completed the page, ask them to share their solution strategies. Emphasize the following points:

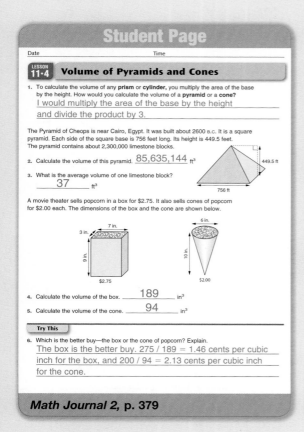

Cone pattern from *Math Masters*, page 440

Student Page

Date _____ Time _____

LESSON 11·4 Volume of Pyramids and Cones

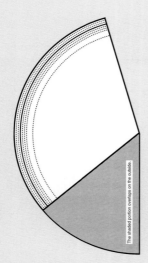

1. To calculate the volume of any **prism** or **cylinder**, you multiply the area of the base by the height. How would you calculate the volume of a **pyramid** or a **cone**?
   I would multiply the area of the base by the height and divide the product by 3.

The Pyramid of Cheops is near Cairo, Egypt. It was built about 2600 B.C. It is a square pyramid. Each side of the square base is 756 feet long. Its height is 449.5 feet. The pyramid contains about 2,300,000 limestone blocks.

2. Calculate the volume of this pyramid. 85,635,144 ft³

3. What is the average volume of one limestone block? 37 ft³

A movie theater sells popcorn in a box for $2.75. It also sells cones of popcorn for $2.00 each. The dimensions of the box and the cone are shown below.

4. Calculate the volume of the box. 189 in³

5. Calculate the volume of the cone. 94 in³

Try This

6. Which is the better buy—the box or the cone of popcorn? Explain.
   The box is the better buy. 275 / 189 = 1.46 cents per cubic inch for the box, and 200 / 94 = 2.13 cents per cubic inch for the cone.

Math Journal 2, p. 379

Problem 2

A rectangular prism with the same base and height as the Pyramid of Cheops would have a volume of

$$B * h = 756^2 * 449.5 = 256{,}905{,}432 \text{ ft}^3.$$

The pyramid's volume is $\frac{1}{3}$ as much, or $85{,}635{,}144 \text{ ft}^3$.

Problem 3

To find the average volume of a block, divide the total volume by the number of blocks: $\frac{85{,}635{,}144}{2{,}300{,}00} =$ slightly more than 37 cubic feet per block.

Problem 4

The popcorn box is a rectangular prism whose volume equals 189 in^3.

Problem 5

A cylinder with the same base and height as the popcorn cone would have a volume of $B * h = (\pi * 3^2) * 10 = 283 \text{ in}^3$. The cone's volume is $\frac{1}{3}$ as much, or 94 in^3.

Problem 6

The box is the better buy. Ask students to calculate a cost-volume ratio for each container: $\frac{200}{94} = 2.13$ cents per cubic inch for the cone, and $\frac{275}{189} = 1.46$ cents per cubic inch for the box.

2 Ongoing Learning & Practice

Playing *Rugs and Fences*

PARTNER ACTIVITY

(*Math Journal 2*, p. 380; *Math Masters*, pp. 498–501)

Algebraic Thinking Students practice calculating the perimeter and area of polygons by playing *Rugs and Fences*. Write "P = perimeter," "A = area," "b = length of base," and "h = height" on the Class Data Pad. Ask students to define *perimeter*. The distance around a closed, 2-dimensional shape Then have volunteers write the formulas for the area of a rectangle, $A = b * h$, or $A = bh$ a parallelogram, $A = b * h$, or $A = bh$ and a triangle $A = \frac{1}{2} * (b * h)$, or $A = \frac{1}{2}bh$ on the board or Class Data Pad. Read the game directions on journal page 380 as a class. Partners cut out the cards on the *Math Masters* pages and play eight rounds, recording their score on *Math Masters*, page 501. See the margin for the area and perimeter of each figure.

Student Page

Date _____ Time _____

LESSON 11·4 **Rugs and Fences: An Area and Perimeter Game**

Materials
- ☐ 1 *Rugs and Fences* Area and Perimeter Deck (*Math Masters*, p. 498)
- ☐ 1 *Rugs and Fences* Polygon Deck (*Math Masters*, pp. 499 and 500)
- ☐ 1 *Rugs and Fences* Record Sheet (*Math Masters*, p. 501)

Players 2

Object of the game To score the highest number of points by finding the area and perimeter of polygons.

Directions

1. Shuffle the Area and Perimeter Deck, and place it facedown.

2. Shuffle the Polygon Deck, and place it facedown next to the Area and Perimeter Deck.

3. Players take turns. At each turn, a player draws one card from each deck and places it faceup. The player finds the perimeter or area of the figure on the Polygon card as directed by the Area and Perimeter card.

   ◆ If a Player's Choice card is drawn, the player may choose to find either the area or the perimeter of the figure.

   ◆ If an Opponent's Choice card is drawn, the other player chooses whether the area or the perimeter of the figure will be found.

4. Players record their turns on the record sheet by writing the Polygon card number, by circling A (area) or P (perimeter), and then by writing the number model used to calculate the area or perimeter. The solution is the player's score for the round.

5. The player with the highest total score at the end of 8 rounds is the winner.

Math Journal 2, p. 380

Polygon Deck B			Polygon Deck C		
Card	A	P	Card	A	P
1	35	24	17	48	28
2	36	26	18	22	20
3	14	18	19	48	36
4	60	32	20	17	20
5	64	32	21	28	28
6	8	18	22	40	36
7	36	24	23	28	32
8	54	30	24	24	24
9	48	32	25	23	26
10	6	12	26	28	32
11	54	36	27	86	54
12	192	64	28	48	32
13	32	26	29	22	30
14	64	36	30	48	52
15	20	25	31	60	32
16	216	66	32	160	70

The area (A) and perimeter (P) of the polygons in *Rugs and Fences*

Student Page

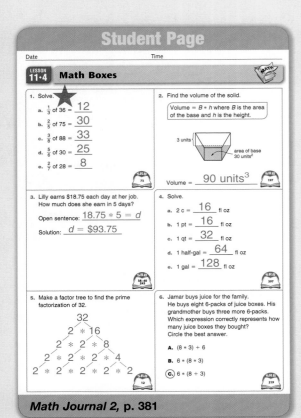

Math Journal 2, p. 381

Math Boxes 11·4

INDEPENDENT ACTIVITY

(*Math Journal 2*, p. 381)

Mixed Practice Math Boxes in this lesson are paired with Math Boxes in Lessons 11-2 and 11-6. The skill in Problem 5 previews Unit 12 content.

Ongoing Assessment:
Recognizing Student Achievement

Math Boxes Problem 1

Use **Math Boxes, Problem 1** to assess students' ability to calculate a fraction of a whole. Students are making adequate progress if they correctly identify each of the five values.

[Number and Numeration Goal 2]

Study Link 11·4

INDEPENDENT ACTIVITY

(*Math Masters*, p. 335)

Home Connection Students compare the volumes of geometric solids.

3 Differentiation Options

READINESS

PARTNER ACTIVITY

Finding the Areas of Concentric Circles

5–15 Min

(*Math Masters*, p. 336)

Algebraic Thinking To explore the relationship between radius and the area of circles, have students compare the areas of different circular regions. Read the introduction to *Math Masters*, page 336. Write the formula for finding the area of a circle: $A = \pi * r * r$ or $A = \pi * r^2$ on the board or the Class Data Pad, and then make the table shown below. Ask students to use the formula to find the area for each circle.

Radius	Area
1 in.	3.14 in^2
2 in.	12.56 in^2
3 in.	28.26 in^2
4 in.	50.24 in^2
5 in.	78.50 in^2

Have partners solve Problem 1. Suggest that they discuss their strategy before they begin. Circulate and assist.

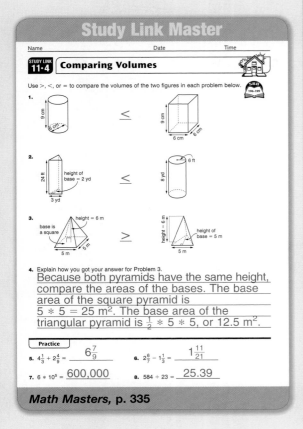

Study Link Master

Name ___ **Date** ___ **Time** ___

STUDY LINK 11·4 Comparing Volumes

Use >, <, or = to compare the volumes of the two figures in each problem below.

1. $\leq$

2. $\leq$

3. $\geq$

4. Explain how you got your answer for Problem 3.
Because both pyramids have the same height, compare the areas of the bases. The base area of the square pyramid is $5 * 5 = 25 \text{ m}^2$. The base area of the triangular pyramid is $\frac{1}{2} * 5 * 5$, or 12.5 m^2.

Practice

5. $4\frac{1}{3} + 2\frac{4}{9} =$ $6\frac{7}{9}$

6. $2\frac{6}{7} - 1\frac{1}{3} =$ $1\frac{11}{21}$

7. $6 * 10^5 =$ $600,000$

8. $584 \div 23 =$ 25.39

Math Masters, p. 335

When students have finished, have volunteers explain their solution strategies. Sample answers: In Problem 1, we know that the area for the red region is the same as the area of the third circle. The area for the orange region is the same as the area for the fifth circle minus the area for the fourth circle. The area for the red region is the same as the area for the orange region.

ENRICHMENT

PARTNER ACTIVITY

Measuring Regions

15–30 Min

(*Math Masters*, p. 336)

To apply students' understanding of area, have them modify the distance between concentric circles to enlarge or shrink regions. Have partners complete Problem 2 on *Math Masters*, page 336.

When students have finished, have them share and discuss their solution strategies.

For Problem 2a, I would make a table to record region areas and the distance between the circles. Then I would use guess-and-check to increase the radius of the circle for the yellow region until it is about twice the area of the red region.

For Problem 2b, I would decrease the red region to make the areas of the yellow and orange regions equal.

EXTRA PRACTICE

SMALL-GROUP ACTIVITY

5-Minute Math

5–15 Min

To offer students more experience with identifying the properties of geometric solids, see *5-Minute Math,* pages 144, 147, and 229.

ELL SUPPORT

PARTNER ACTIVITY

Building a Math Word Bank

15–30 Min

(*Differentiation Handbook*, p. 142)

To provide language support for *volume*, have students use the Word Bank Template found on *Differentiation Handbook*, page 142. Ask students to write the phrase *volume of a cone* and write words, numbers, symbols, or draw pictures that are related to the term. See the *Differentiation Handbook* for more information.

Planning Ahead

Be sure to collect the materials listed at the end of Lesson 11-3 before the start of the next lesson.

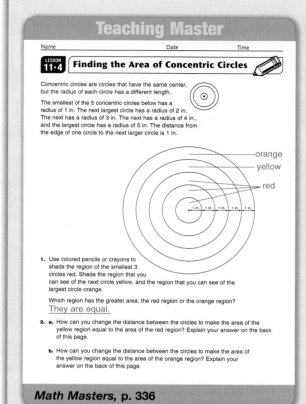

Teaching Master

Name   Date   Time

LESSON 11·4 | **Finding the Area of Concentric Circles**

Concentric circles are circles that have the same center, but the radius of each circle has a different length.

The smallest of the 5 concentric circles below has a radius of 1 in. The next largest circle has a radius of 2 in. The next has a radius of 3 in. The next has a radius of 4 in., and the largest circle has a radius of 5 in. The distance from the edge of one circle to the next larger circle is 1 in.

orange
yellow
red

1 in. 1 in. 1 in. 1 in. 1 in.

1. Use colored pencils or crayons to shade the region of the smallest 3 circles red. Shade the region that you can see of the next circle yellow, and the region that you can see of the largest circle orange.

   Which region has the greater area, the red region or the orange region?
   They are equal.

2. **a.** How can you change the distance between the circles to make the area of the yellow region equal to the area of the red region? Explain your answer on the back of this page.

   b. How can you change the distance between the circles to make the area of the yellow region equal to the area of the orange region? Explain your answer on the back of this page.

Math Masters, p. 336

11·5 Finding Volume by a Displacement Method

 Objective To introduce finding the volume of irregular objects using a water displacement method.

Technology Resources www.everydaymathonline.com

ePresentations | eToolkit | Algorithms Practice | EM Facts Workshop Game™ | Family Letters | Assessment Management | Common Core State Standards | Curriculum Focal Points | Interactive Teacher's Lesson Guide

---

1 Teaching the Lesson

Key Concepts and Skills

- Use tables to record data.
  [Data and Chance Goal 1]

- Use a displacement method to find the volume of irregular solids.
  [Measurement and Reference Frames Goal 2]

- Calibrate and use a metric measuring tool to compare volume and capacity.
  [Measurement and Reference Frames Goal 2]

Key Activities

Students calibrate a bottle and use it to measure the volume of various objects by a displacement method.

 Ongoing Assessment:
Recognizing Student Achievement
Use Mental Math and Reflexes.
[Number and Numeration Goal 6]

Key Vocabulary

displacement ◆ calibrate

Materials

Math Journal 2, pp. 382 and 383
Study Link 11·4
slate ◆ dictionary ◆ per workstation: ruler, measuring cup, tape, paper towels, 2-L plastic bottle (top cut off), paper, scissors, rubber bands, large can or jar filled with 2 L of water, rocks and other objects for displacement activities

2 Ongoing Learning & Practice

Solving American Tour Problems

Math Journal 2, p. 384
Student Reference Book, pp. 338–395
Students solve problems using American Tour data.

Solving Additive Volume Problems

Math Journal 2, pp. 384A and 384B
Students solve real-world problems involving the volumes of two adjacent rectangular prisms.

 Math Boxes 11·5

Math Journal 2, p. 385
cm ruler or Geometry Template
Students practice and maintain skills through Math Box problems.

 Study Link 11·5

Math Masters, p. 337
Students practice and maintain skills through Study Link activities.

3 Differentiation Options

READINESS

Reading about Displacement

Who Sank the Boat?
Students read the book and discuss the principle of displacement illustrated in the story.

ENRICHMENT

Finding Volume by Displacement

Math Masters, pp. 338 and 339
per workstation: bucket or clear container (partially filled with water), empty margarine tub or yogurt container, rocks, waterproof marker
Students explore the principle of displacement by solving a thought experiment about a boat and a stone.

Advance Preparation

For Part 1, make a model of a calibrated bottle (journal page 382). Organize workstations for groups of four students. Furnish each workstation with the materials listed on journal page 382. Cut off the top part of each 2-L bottle, about 9 in. from the bottom. Each station requires an unopened can of a nondiet soft drink (diet drinks will float), rubber bands, several rocks, and about 4 other objects whose volume can be measured. You will also need a supply of paper towels. If you do not have easy access to a sink, use a bucket of water. For the optional Readiness activity in Part 3, obtain a copy of the book ***Who Sank the Boat?*** by Pamela Allen (Paperstar, 1996). Equip a workstation with a bucket or clear container half-filled with water, an empty margarine tub or yogurt container, and several rocks.

 Teacher's Reference Manual, Grades 4–6 pp. 222–225

Getting Started

Mental Math and Reflexes

Have students compare two fractions by writing >, <, or =. Ask volunteers to share their strategies. *Suggestions:*

●○○ $\frac{29}{30}$ and $\frac{29}{31}$ >; The numerators are the same, and $\frac{1}{30}$ is greater than $\frac{1}{31}$.

●●○ $\frac{18}{45}$ and $\frac{30}{75}$ =; The simplest form of both fractions is $\frac{2}{5}$.

●●● $\frac{18}{23}$ and $\frac{9}{12}$ >; $\frac{18}{23}$ is a little more than $\frac{18}{24}$, which is equal to $\frac{9}{12}$, or $\frac{3}{4}$.

Math Message

Use a dictionary to find the meanings of displacement *and* calibrate.

Study Link 11·4 Follow-Up

Have partners compare answers and resolve differences. Ask volunteers to explain their solution strategies for Problem 3. Since the square pyramid base area is twice that of the tetrahedron and both have the same height, the square pyramid volume is twice that of the tetrahedron.

✔ Ongoing Assessment: Recognizing Student Achievement

Mental Math and Reflexes

Use the **Mental Math and Reflexes** problems to assess students' ability to compare fractions. Students are making adequate progress if they demonstrate an understanding of the structure of fractions, finding equivalent fractions, and comparing fractions to a reference.

[Number and Numeration Goal 6]

---

1 Teaching the Lesson

▶ Math Message Follow-Up

WHOLE-CLASS DISCUSSION
ELL

Have students share their definitions of the words *displacement* and *calibrate.* To displace something is to move it out of its proper place; to calibrate is to divide or mark with gradations, such as on a thermometer. To support English language learners, model the meanings of the words.

NOTE It is important for students to have at least a vague understanding of these words at the beginning of the lesson. As the lesson progresses, the meanings of the words will become clearer.

▶ Calibrating a Bottle

SMALL-GROUP ACTIVITY
ELL

(*Math Journal 2,* p. 382)

Show the class a rock, and ask students to suggest how they might go about finding its volume. Ask: *Can we use a volume formula to find the volume of the rock?* No *Why not?* The rock has an irregular shape, so there isn't a base or a consistent height. Tell students that in this lesson they will explore a method for measuring the volumes of irregular objects.

Assign groups of four students to work at the workstations. Show your model of a calibrated bottle, and go over the directions on

---

Student Page

Date _____ Time _____

LESSON 11·5 How to Calibrate a Bottle

Materials
☐ 2-L plastic soft-drink bottle with the top cut off
☐ can or jar filled with about 2 L of water
☐ measuring cup   ☐ ruler
☐ scissors   ☐ paper
☐ tape

1. Fill the bottle with about 5 inches of water.

2. Cut a 1 in. by 6 in. strip of paper. Tape the strip to the outside of the bottle with one end at the bottle top and the other end below the water level.

3. Mark the paper strip at the water level. Write "0 mL" next to the mark.

4. Pour 100 milliliters of water into a measuring cup. Pour the water into the bottle. Mark the paper strip at the new water level, and write "100 mL."

5. Pour another 100 milliliters of water into the measuring cup. Pour it into the bottle, and mark the new water level "200 mL."

6. Repeat, adding 100 milliliters at a time until the bottle is filled to within an inch of the top.

7. Pour out the water until the water level in the bottle falls to the 0 mL mark.

How would you use your calibrated bottle to find the volume of a rock?
Fill the bottle with water to the 0 mL level. Drop the rock into the bottle. The amount that the water rises shows the volume of the rock in milliliters.

Math Journal 2, p. 382

journal page 382. To support English language learners, ask students to give examples of situations where the term *calibrate* might be used. Have each group then calibrate a bottle. Circulate and assist.

Ask students to answer the question at the bottom of journal page 382. When students have finished, bring the class together to share students' suggestions for measuring the volume of a rock. Discuss other related methods of finding the volume of an object:

▷ Start with the object already submerged, and read the water level. Remove the object, and read the new, lower water level. Subtract it from the starting level—this gives the volume of the object.

▷ Place a container inside another container. Fill the inside container with water to the very top. Drop the object into the inside container. Water will overflow into the outside container. The volume of the water in the outside container is the volume of the object.

▶ Demonstrating a Displacement Method for Finding the Volume of an Irregular Object

WHOLE-CLASS ACTIVITY
ELL
PROBLEM SOLVING

Science Link Use your calibrated bottle to demonstrate a displacement method. Fill the bottle with water to the 0-mL level, and drop a rock into the bottle. The water will rise to a higher level. This shows the volume of the rock in milliliters. (*See margin.*) To support English language learners, explain the meaning of *displacement* in this context, and use the vocabulary to describe what is happening with the water.

Remind students that 1 cubic centimeter is equal to 1 milliliter. Ask the following questions:

● How many cubic centimeters are equal to 200 mL? 200 cm^3

● How many milliliters are equal to 1 L? $1{,}000 \text{ mL}$

● How many cubic centimeters are equal to $\frac{1}{2}$L? 500 cm^3, or $\frac{1}{2} \text{ L} = 500 \text{ mL} = 500 \text{ cm}^3$

● What is the volume of the demonstration rock in cubic centimeters? It is the same as the volume in milliliters.

NOTE The volumes of most solids, such as rocks, are usually reported in cubic units. The volumes of liquids are usually reported in units such as liters, milliliters, gallons, quarts, and pints.

Make sure students understand why this method can be used to find the volume of an object. Discuss the following points:

▷ Water has volume. When an object is added to the water, it takes up (displaces) space that was previously occupied by water. This pushes the water level higher than it was. The volume of water between the original level mark and the new

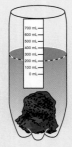

Water level at 0 mL

Water level at 200 mL

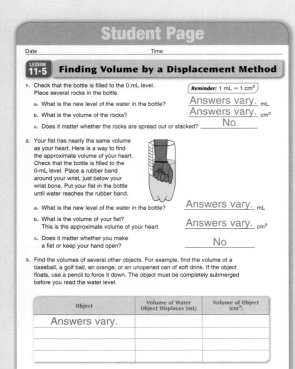

Student Page

Date   Time

LESSON 11·5 **Finding Volume by a Displacement Method**

1. Check that the bottle is filled to the 0 mL level. Place several rocks in the bottle.

Reminder: 1 mL = 1 cm³

a. What is the new level of the water in the bottle? Answers vary. mL

b. What is the volume of the rocks? Answers vary. cm³

c. Does it matter whether the rocks are spread out or stacked? No

2. Your fist has nearly the same volume as your heart. Here is a way to find the approximate volume of your heart. Check that the bottle is filled to the 0-mL level. Place a rubber band around your wrist, just below your wrist bone. Put your fist in the bottle until water reaches the rubber band.

a. What is the new level of the water in the bottle? Answers vary. mL

b. What is the volume of your fist? This is the approximate volume of your heart. Answers vary. cm³

c. Does it matter whether you make a fist or keep your hand open? No

3. Find the volumes of several other objects. For example, find the volume of a baseball, a golf ball, an orange, or an unopened can of soft drink. If the object floats, use a pencil to force it down. The object must be completely submerged before you read the water level.

Object	Volume of Water Object Displaces (mL)	Volume of Object (cm³)
Answers vary.		

Math Journal 2, p. 383

level mark must be equal to the volume of the added object. (If the object floats, it must be forced down so it is completely submerged.)

▷ You don't need to know the volume of the water in the container before the object is added—only the change in water level. The paper scale on the calibrated bottle allows you to read the change in water level directly.

Using a Calibrated Bottle to Measure the Volumes of Various Objects

SMALL-GROUP ACTIVITY

(*Math Journal 2*, p. 383)

Each group will need several rocks and about four other objects. If the number of objects is limited, groups should trade objects. Have students use the 100-mL intervals on the paper scale to estimate the water level to the nearest 10 mL or at least to the nearest 25 mL after adding an object to the bottle. Assign groups to complete Problems 1 and 2 on journal page 383. Circulate and assist.

When groups have finished, discuss the last question in each of the problems. Explain that volume is conserved—that is, it remains unchanged under different arrangements of the material.

Assign Problem 3. Have students begin with an unopened can of a nondiet soft drink. They can check their volume estimates (in milliliters) against the can label.

NOTE A 12-oz can of regular cola contains about 10 tsp of sugar. Because the molecules of sugar spread evenly in the empty spaces between the water molecules, the sugar dissolves in the liquid without increasing its volume. Therefore, the additional molecules of sugar in the cola make it more dense. Diet colas are usually sweetened with aspartame, which is 160 times sweeter than sugar. Considerably less aspartame is needed to sweeten diet cola; therefore, a can of diet cola weighs less than a can of regular cola, is less dense, and is more likely to float.

If any groups work with the same kind of small objects, such as golf balls, they should estimate the combined volume for 4 or 5 balls and then divide the result by the number of balls. (One golf ball has a volume of about 41 cm^3.) This will yield more accurate results than estimating the volume of a single ball because the measurement error for a small object is likely to be a larger percent of the measurement than the measurement error for a larger object.

2 Ongoing Learning & Practice

Solving American Tour Problems

INDEPENDENT ACTIVITY

(*Math Journal 2*, p. 384; *Student Reference Book*, pp. 338–395)

Students solve problems using data from the American Tour section of the *Student Reference Book*.

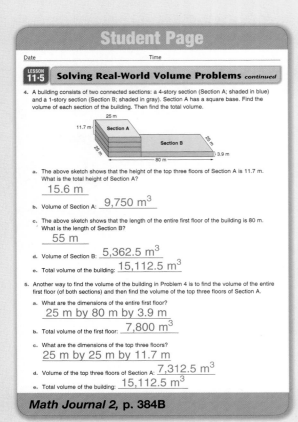

Student Page

Date _____ Time _____

LESSON 11·5 Solving Real-World Volume Problems *continued*

4. A building consists of two connected sections: a 4-story section (Section A; shaded in blue) and a 1-story section (Section B; shaded in gray). Section A has a square base. Find the volume of each section of the building. Then find the total volume.

a. The above sketch shows that the height of the top three floors of Section A is 11.7 m. What is the total height of Section A?
   15.6 m

b. Volume of Section A: **9,750 m³**

c. The above sketch shows that the length of the entire first floor of the building is 80 m. What is the length of Section B?
   55 m

d. Volume of Section B: **5,362.5 m³**

e. Total volume of the building: **15,112.5 m³**

5. Another way to find the volume of the building in Problem 4 is to find the volume of the entire first floor (of both sections) and then find the volume of the top three floors of Section A.

a. What are the dimensions of the entire first floor?
   25 m by 80 m by 3.9 m

b. Total volume of the first floor: **7,800 m³**

c. What are the dimensions of the top three floors?
   25 m by 25 m by 11.7 m

d. Volume of the top three floors of Section A: **7,312.5 m³**

e. Total volume of the building: **15,112.5 m³**

Math Journal 2, p. 384B

Student Page

Date _____ Time _____

LESSON 11·5 Math Boxes

1. Write each fraction in simplest form.
   a. $\frac{29}{3}$ = **$9\frac{2}{3}$**
   b. $\frac{43}{5}$ = **$8\frac{3}{5}$**
   c. $26\frac{34}{60}$ = **$26\frac{17}{30}$**
   d. $15\frac{9}{8}$ = **$16\frac{1}{8}$**

2. Find the volume of the prism.

   Volume of a Triangular Box
   Volume = Area of the base * height
   Volume = **108** cm³

3. Find the volume of the cylinder.
   Volume of a Cylinder
   Volume = Area of the base * height
   7 in.
   2 in.
   Volume = **87.96** in³

4. Measure the base and the height of the triangle to the nearest centimeter.
   a. The base is about **7** cm.
   b. The height is about **1** cm.

   c. Find the area of the triangle to the nearest square centimeter.
      Area = $\frac{1}{2} * b * h$
      Area: about **$3\frac{1}{2}$** cm²

5. Solve.
   a. One △ weighs as much as **2** Xs.
      One ▱ weighs as much as **12** Xs.
   b. One ▱ weighs as much as **10** marbles.
      One △ weighs as much as **4** marbles.

Math Journal 2, p. 385

▶ **Solving Additive Volume Problems**   **INDEPENDENT ACTIVITY**

(*Math Journal 2*, pp. 384A and 384B)

Students solve real-world problems involving the volumes of two adjacent rectangular prisms. Then they add the two volumes to find the volume of the entire solid. Review the two formulas used to find the volume of prisms: $V = B * h$ and $V = l * w * h$. When most students have finished, ask volunteers to share their solutions.

▶ **Math Boxes 11·5**   **INDEPENDENT ACTIVITY**

(*Math Journal 2*, p. 385)

Mixed Practice Math Boxes in this lesson are paired with Math Boxes in Lesson 11-7. The skill in Problem 5 previews Unit 12 content.

Writing/Reasoning Have students write a response to the following: *Explain how you found the simplest form of $\frac{29}{3}$ in Problem 1.* First I renamed $\frac{29}{3}$ as a mixed number by dividing 29 by 3. $\frac{29}{3} = 9\frac{2}{3}$. A mixed number is in simplest form if the fraction part is in simplest form. In $9\frac{2}{3}$, the fraction $\frac{2}{3}$ is in simplest form because the numerator and the denominator cannot be divided by a common factor greater than 1.

▶ **Study Link 11·5**   **INDEPENDENT ACTIVITY**

(*Math Masters*, p. 337)

Home Connection Students perform a displacement experiment. You may choose to have them do this during class time or offer it as an optional home assignment.

3 Differentiation Options

READINESS   **WHOLE-CLASS ACTIVITY**

▶ **Reading about Displacement**    15–30 Min

Literature Link To explore the concept of displacement, have students tell which character they think is responsible for the mishap in the book *Who Sank the Boat?* Read the book and have students predict which character displaced so much water that the boat finally sank. Share the illustrations and discuss how characters balanced each other in the boat. Then discuss the results of the story.

Who Sank the Boat?

Summary: As each character gets into the boat, the waterline approaches the rim of the boat. Surprisingly, the smallest creature of all is the one who causes the boat to sink.

ENRICHMENT

Finding Volume by Displacement

(*Math Masters,* pp. 338 and 339)

To apply students' understanding of displacement, have them solve a thought experiment about a boat and a stone. Ask partners to read the introduction and solve Problem 1 on *Math Masters,* page 338. When students have finished, discuss their solution strategies. Then have partners check their solutions by following the directions on *Math Masters,* page 339 to make a model of the problem.

Study Link Master

Name   Date   Time

STUDY LINK 11·5 A Displacement Experiment

Try this experiment at home.

Materials
☐ drinking glass
☐ water
☐ 2 large handfuls of cotton
   (Be sure to use real cotton. Synthetic materials will not work.)

Directions
◆ Fill the drinking glass almost to the top with water.
◆ Put the cotton, bit by bit, into the glass. Fluff it as you go.

If you are careful, you should be able to fit all of the cotton into the glass without spilling a drop of water.

Think about what you know about displacement and volume. Why do you think you were able to fit the cotton into the glass without the water overflowing?

Most of the space taken up by a handful of cotton is air between the fibers, so it did not displace too much water.

Math Masters, p. 337

Teaching Master

Name   Date   Time

LESSON 11·5 A Boat and a Stone

A thought experiment uses the imagination to solve a problem. Mathematicians, physicists, philosophers, and others use thought experiments to investigate ideas about nature and the universe.

One early example of a thought experiment attempts to show that space is infinite. Use your imagination to picture what is being described in the experiment below.

If there is a boundary to the universe, we can toss a spear at it. If the spear flies through, it isn't a boundary after all. If the spear bounces back, then there must be something beyond the supposed edge of space—a cosmic wall which is itself in space that stopped the spear. Either way, there is no edge of the universe; space is infinite.

Often it is impossible to investigate the situation in a thought experiment directly. This might be because of physical or technological limitations. But the thought experiment in Problem 1 can be modeled directly. Solve Problem 1, and then follow the directions in Problem 2 to model the experiment.

1. Imagine that you are in a small boat. There is a large stone in the bottom of the boat. The boat is floating in a swimming pool. If you throw the stone overboard, does the level of the boat on the water go up, down, or stay the same? Does the level of the water in the pool go up, down, or stay the same?

   The boat will go up. The water level of the pool will remain the same.

Math Masters, p. 338

Teaching Master

Name   Date   Time

LESSON 11·5 A Boat and a Stone *continued*

2. Model the thought experiment, "A Boat and a Stone."

Materials

☐ bucket or clear container
☐ small container that floats and fits in the bucket or clear container with plenty of space all around
☐ several rocks   ☐ water
☐ waterproof marker

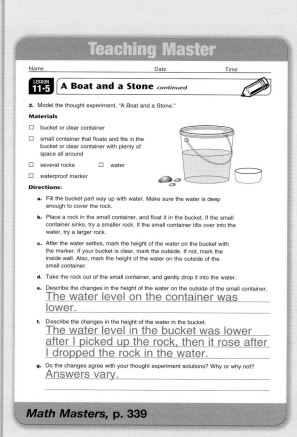

Directions:

a. Fill the bucket part way up with water. Make sure the water is deep enough to cover the rock.

b. Place a rock in the small container, and float it in the bucket. If the small container sinks, try a smaller rock. If the small container tilts over into the water, try a larger rock.

c. After the water settles, mark the height of the water on the bucket with the marker. If your bucket is clear, mark the outside. If not, mark the inside wall. Also, mark the height of the water on the outside of the small container.

d. Take the rock out of the small container, and gently drop it into the water.

e. Describe the changes in the height of the water on the outside of the small container.
   The water level on the container was lower.

f. Describe the changes in the height of the water in the bucket.
   The water level in the bucket was lower after I picked up the rock, then it rose after I dropped the rock in the water.

g. Do the changes agree with your thought experiment solutions? Why or why not?
   Answers vary.

Math Masters, p. 339

11·6 Capacity and Weight

◎ Objective To provide experience with converting measurements among units of weight, capacity, and volume.

Technology Resources www.everydaymathonline.com

| ePresentations | eToolkit | Algorithms Practice | EM Facts Workshop Game™ | Family Letters | Assessment Management | Common Core State Standards | Curriculum Focal Points | Interactive Teacher's Lesson Guide |

① Teaching the Lesson

Key Concepts and Skills

• Use the formula for the volume of a prism to solve capacity problems.
[Measurement and Reference Frames Goal 2]

• Use capacity calculations to solve problems.
[Measurement and Reference Frames Goal 2]

• Convert between standard units of capacity.
[Measurement and Reference Frames Goal 3]

Key Activities

Students review the equivalencies among cups, pints, quarts, half-gallons, and gallons. They find the weight of 1 cup of rice and use it to convert between weight and volume for other amounts of rice. Students solve a capacity problem by converting a unit of liquid capacity (gallon) to a volume in cubic units.

Materials

Math Journal 2, pp. 386 and 387
Student Reference Book, p. 397
Study Link 11•5
Class Data Pad ◆ slate ◆ for demonstration: containers (cup, pint, quart, half-gallon, and gallon), empty copy-paper carton

② Ongoing Learning & Practice

 Playing *Name That Number*
Student Reference Book, p. 325
Math Masters, p. 490
per group: 4 each of number cards 0–9 (from the Everything Math Deck, if available), calculator, set of polyhedral dice
Students practice computation skills and order of operations.

 Ongoing Assessment:
Recognizing Student Achievement
Use the Record Sheet (*Math Masters,* page 490).
[Number and Numeration Goal 4; Patterns, Functions, and Algebra Goal 3]

 Math Boxes 11•6
Math Journal 2, p. 388
Students practice and maintain skills through Math Box problems.

 Study Link 11•6
Math Masters, p. 340
Students practice and maintain skills through Study Link activities.

③ Differentiation Options

READINESS

Exploring Capacity and Weight Equivalencies

for demonstration: measuring cup; water, sand, popcorn, or rice; scale
Students convert between standard units of capacity using a concrete model.

EXTRA PRACTICE

Finding Equivalent Measures

Student Reference Book, p. 397
slate
Students practice converting among units of capacity and units of weight.

ELL SUPPORT

Building a Math Word Bank

Differentiation Handbook, p. 143
Students define and illustrate the terms *volume, weight,* and *capacity.*

ENRICHMENT

Adding and Subtracting Measurements

Math Masters, p. 347A
Students apply their knowledge of measurement conversions to add and subtract measurements.

Advance Preparation

For Part 1, obtain an empty copy-paper carton, measuring approximately 11 in. by 17 in. by 9 in. with the top removed, and empty milk cartons or other containers to model a cup, a pint, a quart, a half-gallon, and a gallon. For the optional Readiness activity in Part 3, obtain the following materials: a measuring cup; at least 1 gallon of water or other pourable substance, such as sand, popcorn, or rice (about 16 cups); and a scale that measures to the nearest ounce.

 Teacher's Reference Manual, Grades 4–6 pp. 217–218, 222–225

Getting Started

Mental Math and Reflexes

Have students mentally solve extended multiplication and division facts problems and write the answers on their slates. Ask students to explain the patterns in the products and quotients.
Suggestions:

●○○	$8.9 * 10 = 89$
	$8.9 * 10^2 = 890$
	$0.4 * 10 = 4$

●●○	$350 \div 10 = 35$
	$350 \div 10^2 = 3.5$
	$275 \div 10 = 27.5$

●●●	$68 \div 10^1 = 6.8$
	$68 \div 10^2 = 0.68$
	$9.4 \div 10^2 = 0.094$

Math Message

Complete the Math Message problem on journal page 386.

Study Link 11·5 Follow-Up

Have students share their experiment results with the class. Cotton fibers are made up of hollow plant cells filled with air. The water fills these cells, displacing the air that was present. Because the cotton is made up of so little solid mass, it will fit in the glass.

---

1 Teaching the Lesson

Math Message Follow-Up

†∔†∔†∔ WHOLE-CLASS DISCUSSION

Ask volunteers to share their descriptions of the meaning of the Math Message picture. The picture shows the equivalencies among cups, pints, quarts, and gallons. The frame is in the shape of the letter G; it represents the word *gallon*. Inside the G, there are four Q's, each one representing the word *quart*. Inside each Q, there are two P's, each one representing the word *pint*. Inside each P, there are two C's, each one representing the word *cup*.

Display the cup, pint, quart, half-gallon, and gallon containers. Ask students to identify each. Write the equivalencies from the picture on the Class Data Pad.

$$1 \text{ pint} = 2 \text{ cups}$$
$$1 \text{ quart} = 2 \text{ pints}$$
$$1 \text{ half-gallon} = 2 \text{ quarts}$$
$$1 \text{ gallon} = 4 \text{ quarts}$$

Solving Problems Involving Units of Weight and Capacity

†† PARTNER ACTIVITY

(*Math Journal 2*, p. 386; *Student Reference Book*, p. 397)

Ask: *How many fluid ounces are in 1 cup of water?* 8 ounces Write *1 cup = 8 fluid ounces* on the Class Data Pad. Explain that fluid ounces are measures of volume or capacity, not weight. Knowing the weight of a given volume of a substance can be useful. For example, rice is sold by weight, but is often measured by volume. If you know how much a cup of rice weighs, you know about how many cups are in a 1-pound package. A cup of uncooked white rice weighs, on average, between $6\frac{1}{2}$ and 8 oz. Ask students to use 8 oz as the average in solving problems on journal page 386.

Student Page

Date _____ Time _____

LESSON 11·6 **Capacity and Weight**

Math Message

1. Describe the meaning of the picture, and explain how it can help you to convert among units of capacity (cups, pints, quarts, gallons, and so on).
   <u>The picture models the relationship between units of capacity. It helps to convert among these units because it shows how many cups are in a pint, how many pints are in a quart, and how many quarts are in a gallon.</u>

Students weighed dry, uncooked rice and found that 1 cup weighed, on average, 8 ounces.

2. 2 cups of dry (uncooked) rice weigh about <u>16</u> ounces.

3. Use the answer in Problem 2 and *Student Reference Book*, page 397 to complete the following:
   a. 1 pint of rice weighs about <u>16</u> ounces.
   b. 1 quart of rice weighs about <u>32</u> ounces.
   c. 1 gallon of rice weighs about <u>128</u> ounces.
   d. 1 gallon of rice weighs about <u>8</u> pounds. (1 pound = 16 ounces)

4. On average, a family of 4 in Nepal eats about 110 pounds of rice per month.
   a. That's how many pounds in a year? <u>1,320 lbs</u>
   b. How many gallons in a year? <u>165 gal</u>

5. On average, a family of 4 in the United States eats about 120 pounds of rice per year. That's about how many gallons per year? <u>15 gal</u>

6. On average, a family of 4 in Thailand eats about 3.5 gallons of rice in a week.
   a. That's about how many gallons per year? <u>182 gal</u>
   b. How many pounds per year? <u>1,456 lb</u>

Math Journal 2, p. 386

NOTE U.S. customary measures use the word *ounce* as both a measure of capacity or volume and of weight. It is easy to confuse the two units. You may want to explain that the fluid ounce was originally defined as the volume of 1 ounce of water (at normal pressure and temperature). Over time, the definition has changed slightly, but a fluid ounce of water still weighs almost exactly 1 ounce. One way to remember this is the saying, "A pint's a pound the world around." That is, a pint of water (16 fluid ounces) weighs almost exactly 1 pound (16 ounces of weight). Note that this is only true in the United States: most other English-speaking countries use the Imperial pint, which is 20 ounces. Note also that 16 fluid ounces of another liquid or pourable substance may weigh much more or less than a pound.

Assign partners to complete journal page 386. Circulate and assist.

When students have finished, bring the class together to go over the answers. The answer to Problem 6 will be used as data in the follow-up activity below:

● **Problems 2 and 3**

Assuming that 1 cup of uncooked rice weighs about 8 ounces, then 1 pint weighs about 16 ounces, 1 quart about 32 ounces, and 1 gallon about 128 ounces. Because there are 16 ounces in 1 pound, 128 ounces is equivalent to 8 pounds ($\frac{128}{16} = 8$).

● **Problem 4**

A family of four in Nepal eats about 1,320 pounds of rice per year. To find the number of gallons, divide the total weight by 8 ($\frac{1,320}{8} = 165$ gallons).

● **Problem 5**

$\frac{120}{8} = 15$ gallons

● **Problem 6**

A family of four in Thailand eats about 3.5 gallons of rice per week. That's equivalent to 182 gallons per year ($3.5 * 52 = 182$). To find the weight of the rice consumed, multiply ($182 * 8 = 1,456$ pounds).

▶ **Investigating the Capacity of the Annual Rice Consumption for a Thai Family of Four**

 PARTNER ACTIVITY

PROBLEM SOLVING

(*Math Journal 2,* pp. 386 and 387)

On the board, write the number of gallons and the number of pounds of rice a typical Thai family of four eats in a year. In Thailand, a family of four eats about 182 gallons, or 1,456 pounds (uncooked weight) of rice per year, assuming that 1 gallon of rice weighs about 8 pounds.

Display an empty copy-paper carton, without the top. Ask students to guess about how many cartons would be needed to store all the rice a Thai family of four eats in a year.

Draw a number line on the board and make a line plot of students' guesses as they report them. Have students identify the minimum, maximum, median, and modal (most frequent) guesses.

Read the problems on journal page 387 as a class. Remind students that often the answer to one problem can be used to solve other problems. Then have partners complete the page. Circulate and assist.

When students have finished, ask volunteers to share their solution strategies.

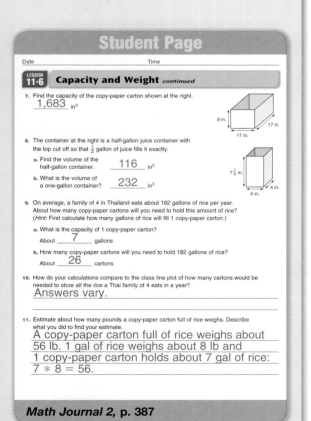

Student Page

Date _____ Time _____

LESSON 11·6 **Capacity and Weight** *continued*

7. Find the capacity of the copy-paper carton shown at the right.
   1,683 in³
   9 in. 17 in. 11 in.

8. The container at the right is a half-gallon juice container with the top cut off so that ½ gallon of juice fills it exactly.
   a. Find the volume of the half-gallon container. **116** in³
   b. What is the volume of a one-gallon container? **232** in³
   7¼ in. 4 in. 4 in.

9. On average, a family of 4 in Thailand eats about 182 gallons of rice per year. About how many copy-paper cartons will you need to hold this amount of rice? (*Hint:* First calculate how many gallons of rice will fill 1 copy-paper carton.)
   a. What is the capacity of 1 copy-paper carton?
   About **7** gallons
   b. How many copy-paper cartons will you need to hold 182 gallons of rice?
   About **26** cartons

10. How do your calculations compare to the class line plot of how many cartons would be needed to store all the rice a Thai family of 4 eats in a year?
    Answers vary.

11. Estimate about how many pounds a copy-paper carton full of rice weighs. Describe what you did to find your estimate.
    A copy-paper carton full of rice weighs about 56 lb. 1 gal of rice weighs about 8 lb and 1 copy-paper carton holds about 7 gal of rice: 7 * 8 = 56.

Math Journal 2, p. 387

● Problem 7

The copy-paper carton is a rectangular prism. Use the formula to find the volume (capacity) of the carton in cubic-inch units. The volume of the carton is $11 * 17 * 9 = 1{,}683$ in^3.

● Problem 8

The gallon is a unit of capacity that is used to measure the volume of liquids or pourable materials, but we don't know how many cubic-inch units are in 1 gallon. The half-gallon container is also a rectangular prism. Its dimensions can be used to calculate the number of cubic inches in $\frac{1}{2}$ gallon and then in 1 gallon. The volume of the half-gallon container is $4 * 4 * 7.25 = 116$ in^3. So 1 gallon $= 232$ in^3.

● Problem 9

Once the capacities of the carton and 1 gallon have been determined, students estimate the number of cartons needed to hold the total yearly consumption of rice. A possible estimation strategy: The capacity of a copy-paper carton is about 7 gallons. $\frac{1{,}683}{232} = 7.25 \rightarrow 7$, rounded to the nearest gallon. This means that 2 cartons hold about 14 gallons, 20 cartons hold about 140 gallons, 25 cartons hold about 175 gallons, and 26 cartons hold about 182 gallons.

Discuss how students' calculations compare to the line plot of their guesses.

2 Ongoing Learning & Practice

Playing *Name That Number*

 SMALL-GROUP ACTIVITY

(*Student Reference Book*, p. 325; *Math Masters*, p. 490)

Students practice computation skills and order of operations by playing *Name That Number*. For detailed instructions, see page 325 in the *Student Reference Book*. For this variation, have students use polyhedral dice instead of the number cards and play in groups of four.

✔ Ongoing Assessment:
Recognizing Student Achievement

Math Masters
Page 490 ★

Use the *Name That Number* **Record Sheet** (*Math Masters*, page 490) to assess students' skill with calculating larger numbers and understanding order of operations. Have students record their best number models for Rounds 1 and 2 on the game record sheet. Students are making adequate progress if their number models are correct and if they demonstrate appropriate use of the order of operations. Some of the students might use nested parentheses.

[Number and Numeration Goal 4; Patterns, Functions, and Algebra Goal 3]

Game Master

Name _____ Date _____ Time _____

| **Name That Number Record Sheet** | |

Round 1

Target number: _____ My cards: _____ _____ _____ _____ _____

My best solution (number model): _____

Number of cards used: _____

Round 2

Target number: _____ My cards: _____ _____ _____ _____ _____

My best solution (number model): _____

Number of cards used: _____

- ✂

Name _____ Date _____ Time _____

| **Name That Number Record Sheet** | |

Round 1

Target number: _____ My cards: _____ _____ _____ _____ _____

My best solution (number model): _____

Number of cards used: _____

Round 2

Target number: _____ My cards: _____ _____ _____ _____ _____

My best solution (number model): _____

Number of cards used: _____

Math Masters, p. 490

Student Page

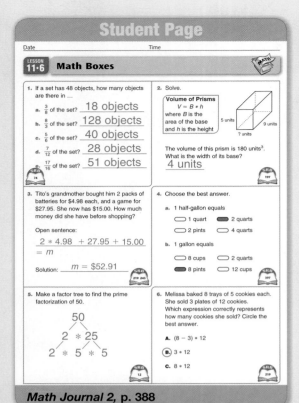

Math Journal 2, p. 388

▶ **Math Boxes 11·6**

(Math Journal 2, p. 388)

Mixed Practice Math Boxes in this lesson are paired with Math Boxes in Lessons 11-2 and 11-4. The skill in Problem 6 previews Unit 12 content.

Writing/Reasoning Have students write a response to the following: *Explain how you found the value for the width of the base of the rectangular prism in Problem 2.* I know that I get the volume of a rectangular prism by multiplying the area of the base by the height. I divided the volume by the height, $180 \div 5 = 36$. This quotient is the area of the base. Then I divided that quotient by the length of the base to get the value for the width, $36 \div 9 = 4$.

▶ **Study Link 11·6**

(Math Masters, p. 340)

INDEPENDENT ACTIVITY

Home Connection Students review, compare, and convert between units of volume and units of capacity.

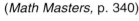

3 Differentiation Options

READINESS

SMALL-GROUP ACTIVITY

15–30 Min

▶ **Exploring Capacity and Weight Equivalencies**

To explore converting between standard units of capacity using a concrete model, have students measure, weigh, and compare cups, ounces, and pounds. Ask: *How would you measure amounts of rice to be used in a recipe?* Most likely by using a measuring cup Explain that a measuring cup may be used to find the volumes of both liquids and pourable solids.

Ask students how they would find the weight of 1 cup of uncooked rice. *Possible methods:*

▷ Use a diet or postal scale to weigh an empty measuring cup. Fill it with rice to the one-cup level. Weigh the filled cup. Subtract the weight of the empty cup from the weight of the cup containing rice.

▷ Fill the measuring cup with rice to the one-cup level. Pour the rice into a plastic bag, hang the bag on a spring scale, and read the weight of the rice directly.

Have students weigh 1 cup of rice as accurately as they can. Expect a range of $6\frac{1}{2}$ to 8 ounces for 1 cup.

Study Link Master

Name   Date   Time

STUDY LINK 11·6   Units of Volume and Capacity

Write >, <, or = to compare the measurements below.

1. 5 cups $>$ 1 quart   2. 30 mL $=$ 30 cm³   3. 1 quart $<$ 1 liter

4. 15 pints $<$ 8 quarts   5. 100 cm³ $<$ 1 gallon   6. 10 cups $=$ 5 pints

Circle the unit you would use to measure each of the following.

7. The volume of a square pyramid

gallons   (cubic inches)   ounces   meters

8. The amount of milk a fifth grader drinks in a week

(gallons)   milliliters   ounces   meters

9. The amount of water used to fill a swimming pool

(gallons)   milliliters   ounces   meters

10. The amount of penicillin given in a shot

gallons   (milliliters)   liters   meters

11. The volume of a rectangular prism

gallons   (cubic centimeters)   liters   meters

12. Would you think of volume or capacity if you wanted to know how much juice a jug holds?   capacity

13. Would you think of volume or capacity if you wanted to know how much closet space a stack of boxes would take up?   volume

Practice

14. $-200 + (-50) =$ ____ -250

15. $685 * 201 =$ ____ $137,685$

16. $13\frac{1}{5} - 2\frac{4}{5} =$ ____ $10\frac{2}{5}$

17. $3.84 \div 8 =$ ____ 0.48

Math Masters, p. 340

Ask: *How can we use this weight and the empty containers to find the weight of pints, quarts, half-gallons, and gallons of rice?* Expect students to suggest counting how many cups of rice each container will hold. Have them work together to use their method to find the weights for a pint, a quart, a half-gallon, and a gallon of rice. Then ask students to make a poster showing in pounds and ounces the weight of a pint, a quart, a half-gallon, and a gallon of rice.

EXTRA PRACTICE

▶ ## Finding Equivalent Measures

(Student Reference Book, p. 397)

WHOLE-CLASS ACTIVITY

15–30 Min

COMPUTATION PRACTICE

Use your established slate procedure to have students convert measurements given in one unit to equivalent measurements in another unit. *Suggestions:*

- 8 pints = ? quarts 4
  8 pints = ? fluid ounces 128

- 24 cups = ? pints 12
  24 cups = ? quarts 6

- 30 quarts = ? cups 120
  30 quarts = ? gallons 7.5

- 2 gallons = ? cups 32
  2 gallons = ? pints 16
  2 gallons = ? fluid ounces 256

ELL SUPPORT

▶ ## Building a Math Word Bank

(Differentiation Handbook, p. 143)

SMALL-GROUP ACTIVITY

15–30 Min

To provide language support for measurement terms, have students use the Word Bank Template found on *Differentiation Handbook,* page 143. Ask students to write the terms *volume, weight,* and *capacity;* draw pictures relating to each term; and write other related words. See the *Differentiation Handbook* for more information.

ENRICHMENT

▶ ## Adding and Subtracting Measurements

(Math Masters, p. 347A)

INDEPENDENT ACTIVITY

5–15 Min

To apply their understanding of measurement conversions, students add and subtract measurements and make appropriate conversions as needed.

Teaching Master

Name   Date   Time

LESSON 11·6 | **Adding and Subtracting Measurements**

Example 1: Add.

| 6 lb   7 oz |
| + 3 lb   11 oz |
| 9 lb   18 oz = 10 lb 2 oz |

Because 18 oz > 1 lb, rename 18 oz as 1 lb 2 oz. So the sum in simplest form is 9 lb + 1 lb + 2 oz, or 10 lb 2 oz.

Example 2: Subtract.

| 9 ft   5 in. |
| − 6 ft   8 in. |

Because 8 in. > 5 in., rename 9 ft 5 in. as 8 ft 17 in. so that you can subtract the inches.

| 8   17 |
| 9̸ ft 5̸ in. |
| − 6 ft   8 in. |
| 2 ft   9 in. |

Add or subtract. When you add, be sure your answer is in simplest form. When you subtract, you may have to rename in order to have enough of a given unit to subtract.

1. 10 ft 9 in.	**2.** 6 gal 3 qt	**3.** 8 yd 1 ft
+ 10 ft 7 in.	+ 5 gal 3 qt	− 3 yd 2 ft
21 ft. 4 in.	12 gal 2 qt	4 yd 2 ft

4. 7 ft 0 in.	**5.** 89 lb 10 oz	**6.** 20 qt 1 pt
− 1 ft 9 in.	+ 76 lb 15 oz	− 19 qt 2 pt
5 ft. 3 in.	166 lb 9 oz	1 pt

Convert the measurements so that their units match the unit given in the answer. Then add or subtract.

7. 10 m + 15 cm = __1,015__ cm   **8.** 8 m + 8 cm + 8 mm = __8,088__ mm

9. 50 kg − 50 g = __49,950__ g   **10.** 10,000 L − 2 kL = __8__ kL

Math Masters, p. 347A

11·7 Surface Area

Objective To introduce finding the surface area of prisms, cylinders, and pyramids.

Technology Resources www.everydaymathonline.com

ePresentations | eToolkit | Algorithms Practice | EM Facts Workshop Game™ | Family Letters | Assessment Management | Common Core State Standards | Curriculum Focal Points | Interactive Teacher's Lesson Guide

---

1 Teaching the Lesson

Key Concepts and Skills

• Measure the dimensions of a cylinder in inches and centimeters.
[Measurement and Reference Frames Goal 1]

• Use rectangle and triangle area formulas to find the surface area of prisms and cylinders. Apply a formula to calculate the area of a circle.
[Measurement and Reference Frames Goal 2]

• Identify and use the properties of prisms, pyramids, and cylinders in calculations.
[Geometry Goal 2]

Key Activities

Students find the surface areas of prisms, cylinders, and pyramids by calculating the area of each surface of a solid and then finding the sum.

 Ongoing Assessment:
Informing Instruction See page 892.

 Ongoing Assessment:
Recognizing Student Achievement
Use journal pages 389 and 390.
[Measurement and Reference Frames Goals 1 and 2]

Key Vocabulary

surface area

Materials

Math Journal 2, pp. 389 and 390
Study Link 11·6
slate ◆ calculator ◆ cardboard box ◆
per workstation: 2 cans, tape measure, ruler, triangular prism, square pyramid

2 Ongoing Learning & Practice

Plotting and Analyzing Insect Data

Math Journal 2, pp. 390A and 390B
Students plot insect lengths in fractional units on a line plot. They use the line plot to analyze the data.

 ### Math Boxes 11·7

Math Journal 2, p. 391
Students practice and maintain skills through Math Box problems.

 ### Study Link 11·7

Math Masters, p. 341
Students practice and maintain skills through Study Link activities.

3 Differentiation Options

ENRICHMENT

Finding the Smallest Surface Area for a Given Volume

Math Masters, p. 342
per partnership: 24 cm cubes
Students find the rectangular prism with the smallest surface area for a given volume.

EXTRA PRACTICE

Finding Area, Surface Area, and Volume

Math Masters, p. 343
Student Reference Book, pp. 196 and 197
Students practice calculating area, surface area, and volume.

Advance Preparation

For Part 1, organize workstations for groups of 4 students (2 partnerships each). Each group will need 2 cans (see Lesson 11-3) and 1 each of the triangular prism and square pyramid models (*Math Masters,* pages 324 and 326) constructed in Lesson 11-1. Place a cardboard box with the top taped shut near the Math Message.

 Teacher's Reference Manual, Grades 4–6 pp. 220–222

Getting Started

Mental Math and Reflexes

Have students write numbers from dictation and mark the indicated digits. *Suggestions:*

◉○○ 5,024,039 Circle the digit in the thousands place, and put an X through the digit in the hundred-thousands place.

28,794,052 Circle the digit in the ten-thousands place, and put an X through the digit in the hundreds place.

◉◉○ 31.005 Circle the digit in the thousandths place, and put an X through the digit in the hundredths place.

150,247.653 Circle the digit in the thousandths place, and put an X through the digit in the thousands place.

◉◉◉ 587.624 Circle the digit in the tens place, and put an X through the digit in the hundredths place.

94,679,424 Circle each digit in the millions period, and put an X through each digit in the ones period.

Math Message

If you were to wrap this box as a gift, how would you calculate the least amount of wrapping paper needed?

Study Link 11·6 Follow-Up

Briefly review the answers. Ask: *How would you explain the difference between capacity and volume?* Volume is the measure of how much space a solid object occupies. Capacity is the measure of how much a container can hold.

---

1 Teaching the Lesson

▶ Math Message Follow-Up

WHOLE-CLASS ACTIVITY

(*Math Journal 2,* p. 389)

Ask volunteers to use geometry vocabulary to describe the box. The box is a rectangular prism that has six rectangular faces. Then have students explain their solution strategies. If wrapping paper covers each face of the box exactly, the least amount of wrapping paper needed is the sum of the area of each of the six faces. Tell students that the sum of the areas of the faces or the curved surface of a geometric solid is called **surface area.** If wrapping paper covers each face of the box exactly, the area of paper required is the surface area of the box. If the area of the available wrapping paper is less than the surface area of the box, the paper will not completely cover the box.

Ask a pair of students to measure the length, width, and height of the box to the nearest inch. Have students record these dimensions on the figure in Problem 1 on journal page 389, find and record the areas of the six sides of the box, and add these to find the total surface area. Remind students that opposite sides (top and bottom, left and right, front and back) of the box have the same area. This means that students need to calculate only three different areas.

▶ Finding the Surface Area of a Can

PARTNER ACTIVITY

PROBLEM SOLVING

(*Math Journal 2,* p. 389)

Algebraic Thinking Distribute one can to each partnership. Ask students to imagine that the top lids of their cans have *not* been removed. Ask: *How would you find the surface area of your can?*

 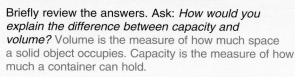

Student Page

Date _____ Time _____

LESSON 11·7 **Surface Area** *continued* ⭐

Formula for the Area of a Triangle
$$A = \frac{1}{2} * b * h$$
where A is the area of the triangle, b is the length of its base, and h is its height.

3. Use your model of a triangular prism.

a. Find the dimensions of the triangular and rectangular faces. Then find the areas of these faces. Measure lengths to the nearest $\frac{1}{4}$ inch.

base = __2__ in.   length = __$4\frac{1}{2}$__ in.

height = __$1\frac{3}{4}$__ in.   width = __2__ in.

Area = __$1\frac{3}{4}$__ in²   Area = __9__ in²

b. Add the areas of the faces to find the total surface area.

Area of 2 triangular bases = __$3\frac{1}{2}$__ in²

Area of 3 rectangular sides = __27__ in²

Total surface area = __$30\frac{1}{2}$__ in²

4. Use your model of a square pyramid.

a. Find the dimensions of the square and triangular faces. Then find the areas of these faces. Measure lengths to the nearest tenth of a centimeter.

length = __6.3__ cm   base = __6.3__ cm

width = __6.3__ cm   height = __5.5__ cm

Area = __39.69__ cm²   Area = __17.325__ cm²

b. Add the areas of the faces to find the total surface area.

Area of square base = __39.69__ cm²

Area of 4 triangular sides = __69.3__ cm²

Total surface area = __108.99__ cm²

Math Journal 2, p. 390

Student Page

Date _____ Time _____

LESSON 11·7 **Analyzing Fraction Data**

Kerry measured life-size photos of 15 common insects to the nearest $\frac{1}{8}$ of an inch. His measurements are given in the table below.

Insect	Length (nearest $\frac{1}{8}$ in.)	Insect	Length (nearest $\frac{1}{8}$ in.)
American Cockroach	$1\frac{3}{8}$	Heelfly	$\frac{3}{8}$
Ant	$\frac{1}{4}$	Honeybee	$\frac{3}{4}$
Aphid	$\frac{1}{8}$	House Centipede	$1\frac{3}{8}$
Bumblebee	$1\frac{1}{2}$	Housefly	$\frac{1}{4}$
Cabbage Butterfly	$1\frac{1}{4}$	June Bug	1
Cutworm	$1\frac{1}{2}$	Ladybug	$\frac{5}{8}$
Deerfly	$\frac{3}{8}$	Silverfish	$\frac{3}{8}$
Field Cricket	$\frac{7}{8}$		

1. Make a line plot of the insect lengths on the number line below. Be sure to label the axes and provide a title for the graph.

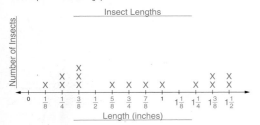

Math Journal 2, p. 390A

Remind students that in this problem they are finding the area of the surface of their can, not the volume. Give students plenty of time to explore solution strategies among themselves, without your help. Add the areas of the top, bottom, and curved surface to find the total surface area. Ask a volunteer to explain how to find the area of the circular top and bottom. Use the formula $A = \pi * r^2$. Ask another volunteer to explain how to find the area of the curved surface between the top and bottom of the can. Calculate the circumference of the base using the formula $c = \pi * d$, and then multiply the circumference by the height of the can.

If students are unable to suggest an approach for finding this area, remind or show them that the label on a food can is shaped like a rectangle if it is cut off and unrolled.

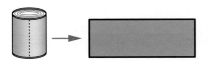

If you cut a can label in a straight line perpendicular to the bottom, it will have a rectangular shape when it is unrolled and flattened.

Draw a rectangle on the board:

● How would you measure the can to find the length of the base of the rectangle? Guide students to recognize the following two possibilities:

  1. Measure the circumference of the base of the can with a tape measure.

  2. Measure the diameter of the base of the can. Calculate the circumference of the base, using the formula $c = \pi * d$.

● How would you find the other dimension (the width) of the rectangle? Measure the height of the can.

Have partners measure the dimensions of their cans and complete Part 2 on journal page 389. Circulate and assist.

⭐ **Ongoing Assessment: Informing Instruction**

Watch for students who seem to have difficulty with visualizing the cutting and unrolling of the can label. Have them use the following procedure to cut a sheet of paper to use as a label for the side of the can:

1. Mark the top and bottom rims of the can at the can's seam.

2. Lay the can on the sheet of paper with the marks touching the paper. Mark these points on the paper.

3. Roll the can one complete revolution, until the marks touch the paper again. Mark these points on the paper.

4. Connect the four marks on the paper to form a rectangle. Cut out the rectangle.

Finding the Surface Area of a Prism and a Pyramid

 PARTNER ACTIVITY

(*Math Journal 2*, p. 390)

Algebraic Thinking Have partners measure each solid constructed in Lesson 11-1 from *Math Masters*, pages 324 and 326 and record the dimensions on journal page 390. Then have them calculate and record the face areas and total surface area for each solid. Circulate and assist.

 Ongoing Assessment:
Recognizing Student Achievement

Journal pages 389 and 390

Use **journal pages 389 and 390** to assess students' ability to measure to the nearest $\frac{1}{4}$ inch and 0.1 cm and to find the area of circles, triangles, and rectangles. Students are making adequate progress if they correctly answer Problems 2 and 3 and use rectangle, circle, and triangle area formulas to find the surface area of prisms and cylinders.

[*Measurement and Reference Frames Goals 1 and 2*]

2 Ongoing Learning & Practice

Plotting and Analyzing Insect Data

INDEPENDENT ACTIVITY

(*Math Journal 2*, pp. 390A and 390B)

Students plot insect lengths in fractional units on a line plot. They use the line plot to analyze data and solve problems involving addition, subtraction, multiplication, and division with fractions. As needed, review how to make a line plot based on fractional units and how to perform operations with fractions.

Math Boxes 11·7

INDEPENDENT ACTIVITY

(*Math Journal 2*, p. 391)

 Mixed Practice Math Boxes in this lesson are paired with Math Boxes in Lesson 11-5. The skill in Problem 5 previews Unit 12 content.

Study Link 11·7

INDEPENDENT ACTIVITY

(*Math Masters*, p. 341)

 Home Connection Students practice using formulas to calculate volume and surface area. If students use calculators, remind them to enter 3.14 for π if necessary.

Date _____ Time _____

LESSON 11·7 **Analyzing Fraction Data** *continued*

Use the data and the line plot you made on journal page 390A to solve these problems. Give all answers in simplest form.

2. What is the maximum length of the insects measured? $1\frac{1}{2}$ in.

3. What is the minimum length? $\frac{1}{8}$ in.

4. What is the range of insect lengths? $1\frac{3}{8}$ in.

5. What is (are) the mode length(s) of the insects? $\frac{3}{8}$ in.

6. What is the median length of the insects? $\frac{3}{4}$ in.

7. How much longer is the American cockroach that Kerry measured than the field cricket? $\frac{1}{2}$ in.

8. Suppose 5 ladybugs were placed end to end. How long would they be? $3\frac{1}{8}$ in.

9. How many times as long is the bumblebee than the housefly? 6 times as long

10. a. Suppose all of the insects less than $\frac{3}{4}$ inch long were placed end-to-end. How long would they be? $2\frac{3}{8}$ in.

b. Suppose all of the insects greater than $\frac{5}{8}$ inch long were placed end-to-end. How long would they be? $9\frac{5}{8}$ in.

c. What is the total length of all 15 insects placed end to end? 12 in.

11. What is the mean length of the 15 insects that were measured? $\frac{4}{5}$ in.

Math Journal 2, p. 390B

Date _____ Time _____

LESSON 11·7 **Math Boxes**

1. Write each number in simplest form.
   a. $\frac{80}{5} =$ 16
   b. $\frac{53}{6} =$ $8\frac{5}{6}$
   c. $8\frac{24}{48} =$ $8\frac{1}{2}$
   d. $11\frac{38}{54} =$ $11\frac{19}{27}$

2. How are cylinders and cones alike? Both have a circular base and one curved surface.

3. Find the volume of the rectangular prism.

   Volume of rectangular prism
   $V = B \cdot h$

   $V =$ 12 cm³

4. Find the area and perimeter of the rectangle.

   7 cm
   $3\frac{1}{2}$ cm

   Area = 24.5 cm² (unit)
   Perimeter = 21 cm (unit)

5. Solve the pan-balance problems below.
   a. One ⊘ weighs as much as 3 Xs.
   One ⬚ weighs as much as 6 Xs.
   b. One △ weighs as much as 5 paper clips.
   One ⊘ weighs as much as 5 paper clips.

Math Journal 2, p. 391

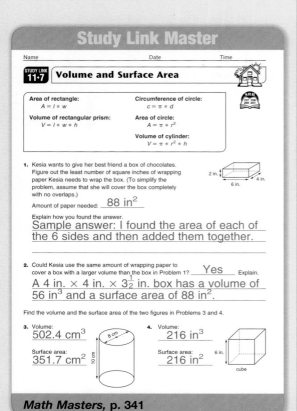
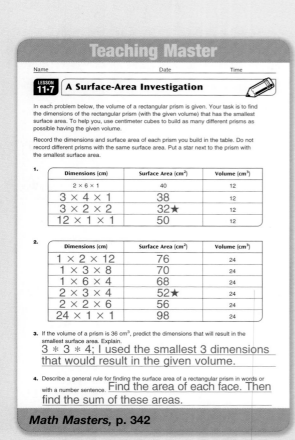
3 Differentiation Options

ENRICHMENT

PARTNER ACTIVITY
15–30 Min

▶ **Finding the Smallest Surface Area for a Given Volume**

(*Math Masters*, p. 342)

Algebraic Thinking To apply students' understanding of volume and surface area, have them use given volumes to find the dimensions of rectangular prisms. Partners use the patterns in the dimensions to identify the dimensions of a prism that would have the smallest surface area.

When students have finished, discuss any difficulties or curiosities they encountered.

EXTRA PRACTICE

INDEPENDENT ACTIVITY
5–15 Min

▶ **Finding Area, Surface Area, and Volume**

(*Math Masters*, p. 343; *Student Reference Book*, pp. 196 and 197)

Students practice calculating area, surface area, and volume of various geometric figures.

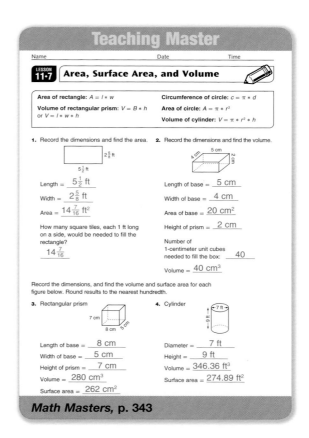

11·8 Progress Check 11

Objective To assess students' progress on mathematical content through the end of Unit 11.

1 Looking Back: Cumulative Assessment

Input student data from Progress Check 11 into the **Assessment Management Spreadsheets**.

Materials
◆ Study Link 11◆7
◆ *Assessment Handbook,* pp. 134–141, 205–209, 226, and 276–279
◆ slate; calculator

CONTENT ASSESSED	LESSON(S)	SELF	ORAL/SLATE	WRITTEN PART A	WRITTEN PART B	OPEN RESPONSE
Use algorithms to solve problems involving multiplication. [Operations and Computation Goal 3]						✔
Use formulas to find the volume of geometric solids. [Measurement and Reference Frames Goal 2]	11·3, 11·4, 11·6	1	4	5, 6, 11, 14–16	19, 20	✔
Use formulas to find the area of polygons and circles. [Measurement and Reference Frames Goal 2]	11·3, 11·4, 11·7	2	3	7–10, 12		
Find the surface area of prisms. [Measurement and Reference Frames Goal 2]	11·7	3			17	
Understand how to find the surface area of cylinders. [Measurement and Reference Frames Goal 2]	11·7	4			18	
Understand the concept of capacity and how to calculate it. [Measurement and Reference Frames Goal 2]	11·3, 11·5, 11·6	6	2		21, 22	
Understand the properties of geometric figures. [Geometry Goal 2]	11·1, 11·2, 11·4, 11·7	1–6	1	1–4, 7–9, 13		
Write number sentences to represent finding volume and relationships between volumes of solids. [Patterns, Functions, and Algebra Goal 2]	11·4	5		16	19, 20	✔

2 Looking Ahead: Preparing for Unit 12

Math Boxes 11◆8

Study Link 11◆8: Unit 12 Family Letter

Materials
◆ *Math Journal 2,* p. 392
◆ *Math Masters,* pp. 344–347
◆ calculator

Getting Started

1 Looking Back: Cumulative Assessment

▶ Math Message Follow-Up

INDEPENDENT ACTIVITY

(Self Assessment, *Assessment Handbook,* p. 205)

 The Self Assessment offers students the opportunity to reflect upon their progress.

▶ Oral and Slate Assessments

SMALL-GROUP ACTIVITY

Problems 1 and 3 provide summative information and can be used for grading purposes. Problems 2 and 4 provide formative information that can be useful in planning future instruction.

Oral Assessment

1. Students show thumbs up if the statement is true and thumbs down if the statement is false. If the statement is false, you might want to have students name the correct shape. *Suggestions:*

   ● A pear is shaped like a sphere. down

   ● A baseball cap is shaped like a cone. down

   ● A penny is shaped like a cylinder. up

   ● Pattern blocks are prisms. up

   ● A door is shaped like a rectangular prism. up

2. Students show thumbs up if they would find the capacity and thumbs down if they would find something else to solve the problems. If students would find something else, you might want to ask students what information they would need to solve the problem. *Suggestions:*

   ● The amount of space a large box will take up in the closet. down; volume

   ● The amount of juice a container will hold. up

   ● The size of the floor of your classroom. down; area

   ● The amount of rice a carton will hold. up

   ● The amount of cabinet space needed for a can of peas. down; volume

   ● The amount of paper needed to make a label for a can of peas. down; area

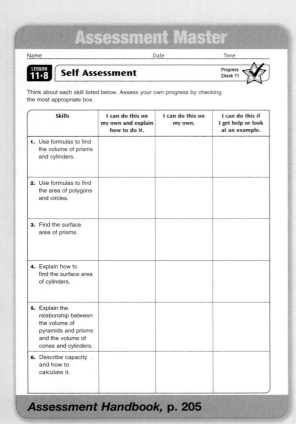

Assessment Master

Name _____ Date _____ Time _____

LESSON 11·8 | **Self Assessment** | Progress Check 11

Think about each skill listed below. Assess your own progress by checking the most appropriate box.

Skills	I can do this on my own and explain how to do it.	I can do this on my own.	I can do this if I get help or look at an example.
1. Use formulas to find the volume of prisms and cylinders.			
2. Use formulas to find the area of polygons and circles.			
3. Find the surface area of prisms.			
4. Explain how to find the surface area of cylinders.			
5. Explain the relationship between the volume of pyramids and prisms and the volume of cones and cylinders.			
6. Describe capacity and how to calculate it.			

Assessment Handbook, p. 205

Slate Assessment

3. Students find the area for each figure. *Suggestions:*

- Parallelogram with a base of $8\frac{1}{2}$ in. and a height of 11 in. 93.5 in^2

- Triangle with a base of 6 m and a height of 9 m 27 m^2

- Square with a perimeter of 48 in. 144 in^2

- Rectangle with a base of $7\frac{1}{2}$ in. and a height of 3 in. 22.5 in^2

- Right triangle with one side forming the right angle measuring 7 cm and the other side forming the right angle measuring 4 cm (*See margin.*) 14 cm^2

4. Students use a calculator to find the following:

The volume for . . .

- a rectangular prism whose base has an area of 6 units^2 and a height of 10 units 60 units^3

- a cylinder whose base is a circle with a radius of 2 cm and a height of 10 cm 125.6 cm^3

The height for . . .

- a rectangular prism whose base has an area of 250 in^2 and a volume of 2,500 in^3 10 in.

- a cube whose base has an area of 25 ft^2 and a volume of 125 ft^3 5 ft

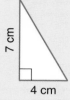

7 cm

4 cm

▶ Written Assessment

INDEPENDENT ACTIVITY

(*Assessment Handbook,* pp. 206–208)

Part A Recognizing Student Achievement

Problems 1–16 provide summative information and may be used for grading purposes.

Problem(s)	Description
1–4, 7–9, 13	Know the properties of geometric figures.
5, 6, 11, 14–16	Use formulas to find the volume of prisms and cylinders.
7–10, 12	Use formulas to find the area of polygons and circles.

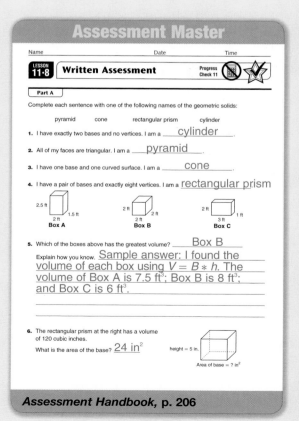

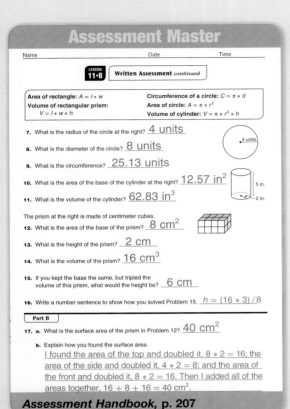

Assessment Master

LESSON 11·8   Written Assessment *continued*

Area of rectangle: $A = l * w$	Circumference of a circle: $C = \pi * d$
Volume of rectangular prism: $V = l * w * h$	Area of circle: $A = \pi * r^2$
	Volume of cylinder: $V = \pi * r^2 * h$

7. What is the radius of the circle at the right? **4 units**

8. What is the diameter of the circle? **8 units**

9. What is the circumference? **25.13 units**

4 units

10. What is the area of the base of the cylinder at the right? **12.57 in²**

11. What is the volume of the cylinder? **62.83 in³**

5 in.
2 in.

The prism at the right is made of centimeter cubes.

12. What is the area of the base of the prism? **8 cm²**

13. What is the height of the prism? **2 cm**

14. What is the volume of the prism? **16 cm³**

15. If you kept the base the same, but tripled the volume of this prism, what would the height be? **6 cm**

16. Write a number sentence to show how you solved Problem 15. **$h = (16 * 3)/8$**

Part B

17. a. What is the surface area of the prism in Problem 12? **40 cm²**

    b. Explain how you found the surface area.
    I found the area of the top and doubled it, $8 * 2 = 16$; the area of the side and doubled it, $4 * 2 = 8$; and the area of the front and doubled it, $8 * 2 = 16$. Then I added all of the areas together, $16 + 8 + 16 = 40$ cm².

Assessment Handbook, p. 207

Use the checklists on pages 277 and 279 of the *Assessment Handbook* to record results. Then input the data into the **Assessment Management Spreadsheets** to keep an ongoing record of students' progress toward Grade-Level Goals.

Part B   Informing Instruction

Problems 17 and 18–22 provide formative information that can be useful in planning future instruction.

Problem(s)	Description
17	Find the surface area of prisms.
18	Understand how to find the surface area of cylinders.
19, 20	Understand and write number sentences to represent the relationship between the volume of pyramids and prisms and the volume of cones and cylinders.
21, 22	Understand the concept of capacity and how to calculate it.

▶ Open Response

👤 **INDEPENDENT ACTIVITY**

(*Assessment Handbook,* p. 209)

A Treasure Hunt

📁 Portfolio Ideas

The open-response item requires students to apply skills and concepts from Unit 11 to solve a multistep problem. See *Assessment Handbook,* pages 137–141 for rubrics and students' work samples for this problem.

Assessment Master

LESSON 11·8   Written Assessment *continued*

18. What information do you need to figure out how many square inches of paint you would use if you painted the entire cylinder on page 207 (top, bottom, and sides)?
The area of the base, the circumference of the base, and the height

19. If you place a cone inside of the cylinder in Problem 11 on page 207, and the cone is an exact fit (that is, the apex of the cone touches the bottom of the cylinder, and the base of the cone fits exactly at the top of the cylinder), what would the volume of the cone be? **20.94 in³**

Write a number sentence to show how you found your answer.
$\frac{1}{3} * 62.83 = 20.94$ in³, or $62.83 \div 3 = 20.94$ in³

20. The pyramid at the right has the same height as the prism in Problem 6 on page 206.
What is the volume of the pyramid? **40 in³**

Area of base = 24 in²

Write a number sentence to show how you found your answer.
$V = \frac{1}{3} * 24 * 5$, or $V = \frac{120}{3}$

Min's fish are sick, and she wants to add medicine to the tank. The instructions suggest adding one drop of medicine for every 4 L of water. The base of the fish tank measures 40 cm by 25 cm. The tank is filled with water to a height of about 20 cm.

Reminder: 1 L = 1,000 cm³

20 cm
25 cm
40 cm

21. How many drops of medicine should Min add to her tank? **5 drops**

22. Explain what you did to find the answer.
The volume of the water is 20,000 cm³ ($40 * 25 * 20$), which is 20 L. $20 \div 4 = 5$ drops.

Assessment Handbook, p. 208

Assessment Master

LESSON 11·8   Open Response   Progress Check 11 ⭐

A Treasure Hunt

The intrepid explorer Cindy Rella went to the Amazon basin in search of the lost treasure of the Waorani Indians.

Traps had been set to guard the treasure. Cindy fell through a trap door into a 9-foot high rectangular room that measured 4 feet wide by 6 feet long.

Suddenly, the room began to fill with water but stopped when it was 3 feet deep. Cindy sighed with relief, but her relief didn't last long.

The two 4-foot wide walls of the room began to move, making the room smaller and causing the water level to rise. Every 10 minutes, the walls were 1 foot closer together.

1. Label the rectangular prism with the dimensions of the original room.

2. Figure out how much time will pass before the water lifts Cindy to the trapdoor exit in the ceiling of the room.

    Show your work and explain how you found your answer.

Assessment Handbook, p. 209

2 Looking Ahead: Preparing for Unit 12

► **Math Boxes 11·8**

(*Math Journal 2*, p. 392)

INDEPENDENT ACTIVITY

Mixed Practice This Math Boxes page previews Unit 12 content.

► **Study Link 11·8:**
Unit 12 Family Letter

(*Math Masters*, pp. 344–347)

INDEPENDENT ACTIVITY

Home Connection The Unit 12 Family Letter provides parents and guardians with information and activities related to Unit 12 topics.

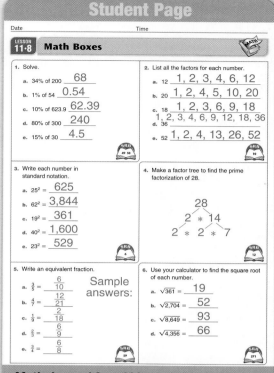

Student Page

Date _____ Time _____

LESSON 11·8 **Math Boxes**

1. Solve.
a. 34% of 200 __68__
b. 1% of 54 __0.54__
c. 10% of 623.9 __62.39__
d. 80% of 300 __240__
e. 15% of 30 __4.5__

2. List all the factors for each number.
a. 12 __1, 2, 3, 4, 6, 12__
b. 20 __1, 2, 4, 5, 10, 20__
c. 18 __1, 2, 3, 6, 9, 18__
d. 36 __1, 2, 3, 4, 6, 9, 12, 18, 36__
e. 52 __1, 2, 4, 13, 26, 52__

3. Write each number in standard notation.
a. 25^2 __625__
b. 62^2 __3,844__
c. 19^2 __361__
d. 40^2 __1,600__
e. 23^2 __529__

4. Make a factor tree to find the prime factorization of 28.

28
2 * 14
2 * 2 * 7

5. Write an equivalent fraction.
a. $\frac{3}{5} = \frac{6}{10}$
b. $\frac{4}{7} = \frac{12}{21}$
c. $\frac{1}{9} = \frac{2}{18}$
d. $\frac{2}{3} = \frac{6}{9}$
e. $\frac{3}{4} = \frac{6}{8}$

Sample answers:

6. Use your calculator to find the square root of each number.
a. $\sqrt{361} =$ __19__
b. $\sqrt{2,704} =$ __52__
c. $\sqrt{8,649} =$ __93__
d. $\sqrt{4,356} =$ __66__

Math Journal 2, p. 392

Study Link Master

Name _____ Date _____ Time _____

STUDY LINK 11·8 **Unit 12: Family Letter**

Probability, Ratios, and Rates

A **ratio** is a comparison of two quantities with the same unit. For example, if one house has a floor area of 2,000 ft², and a second house has a floor area of 3,000 ft², the ratio of the areas is 2,000 to 3,000, or 2 to 3, simplified.

To prepare students for working with ratios in algebra, the class will review the meanings and forms of ratios and will solve number stories involving ratios of part of a set to the whole set. Your child will find, write, and solve many number models (equations) for ratio problems.

Your child will continue to use the American Tour section of the *Student Reference Book* as part of the discussion of ratios. We will also be doing projects based on information in the American Tour.

A **rate** is a comparison of two quantities with different units. For example, speed is expressed in miles per hour. In our study of rates, students will determine their own heart rates (heartbeats per minute). Then they will observe the effect of exercise on heart rate and represent the class results graphically.

We will continue our study of probability by looking at situations in which a sequence of choices is made. For example, if a menu offers you 2 choices of appetizer, 4 choices of entrée, and 3 choices of dessert, and you choose one of each kind, there are 2 * 4 * 3 or 24 different possible combinations for your meal. If all the choices were equally appealing (which is unlikely), and you chose at random, the probability of any one combination would be $\frac{1}{24}$.

Your child will play *Frac-Tac-Toe*, which was introduced in Unit 5, as well as a new game, *Spoon Scramble*, to practice operations and equivalencies with fractions, decimals, and percents.

You can help your child by asking questions about homework problems; by pointing out fractions, percents, and ratios that you encounter in everyday life; and by playing *Frac-Tac-Toe* and *Spoon Scramble* to sharpen his or her skills.

Please keep this Family Letter for reference as your child works through Unit 12.

Math Masters, pp. 344–347

Probability, Ratios, and Rates

> Overview

In Unit 12, students use factor trees to find prime factorizations, greatest common factors, and least common multiples. They also use tree diagrams to represent combinations of choices and to find probabilities in situations where the combinations are equally likely. The unit concludes with reviewing and practicing ratio and rates problems, including a series of lessons involving heart rate and exercise. Unit 12 has five main areas of focus:

- ◆ To find the greatest common factor and least common multiple of two numbers,
- ◆ To use the Multiplication Counting Principle and tree diagrams,
- ◆ To use ratios and ratio comparisons,
- ◆ To write number models for ratio number stories, and
- ◆ To calculate rates from data.

CCSS Linking to the Common Core State Standards

The content of Unit 12 addresses the Common Core Standards for Mathematics in *Measurement and Data*. The correlation of the Common Core State Standards to the *Everyday Mathematics* Grade 5 lessons begins on page CS1.

Contents

Learning In Perspective

	Lesson Objectives	Links to the Past	Links to the Future
12·1	To provide experiences with finding the greatest common factor and the least common multiple of two numbers.	In fourth grade, students apply multiplication facts.	In sixth grade, students use the greatest common factor and the least common multiple of two numbers in operations with fractions and mixed numbers.
12·2	To introduce the Multiplication Counting Principle and tree diagrams.	In fourth grade, students use tables and graphical representations of data.	In sixth grade, students use tree diagrams to solve problems.
12·3	To provide experiences with the uses of ratios and ratio comparisons.	In fourth grade, students evaluate rate data for reasonableness.	In sixth grade, students solve ratio number stories.
12·4	To provide experience with ratios of part of a set to the whole set.	In fourth grade, students identify fractional parts of a collection of objects.	In sixth grade, students write open proportions to model and solve problems.
12·5	To introduce writing number models for ratio number stories.	In fourth grade, students solve open number sentences.	In sixth grade, students write algebraic expressions to represent solutions.
12·6	To provide experience calculating rates from data.	In fourth grade, students calculate unit rates.	In sixth grade, students use rate tables to solve problems.
12·7	To provide experience with using graphs to represent, compare, and interpret data.	In fourth grade, students use graphs to display and analyze data.	In sixth grade, students represent rates with formulas, tables, and graphs.
12·8	To provide experience with calculating rates and using rates to compare data.	In fourth grade, students collect and compare rate data.	In sixth grade, students solve rate number stories.

Key Concepts and Skills	Grade 5 Goals*
12·1 Identify the prime factorization for a number.	Number and Numeration Goal 3
Find greatest common factors and least common multiples using factor strings.	Number and Numeration Goal 3
Use greatest common factors and least common multiples to rename fractions.	Number and Numeration Goal 5
Use multiplication facts to find factor strings.	Operations and Computation Goal 2
12·2 Describe events using basic probability terms.	Data and Chance Goal 3
Use the Multiplication Counting Principle and tree diagrams to solve probability problems.	Data and Chance Goal 4
Express the probability of an event as a fraction.	Data and Chance Goal 4
12·3 Write ratios in equivalent forms.	Number and Numeration Goal 5
Compare numbers that are 10 times more or 10 times less than each other.	Number and Numeration Goal 6
Express ratios in a variety of ways.	Operations and Computation Goal 7
12·4 Use equivalent fractions and ratio models to solve fraction-of problems.	Number and Numeration Goal 2
Model and solve ratio problems.	Operations and Computation Goal 7
12·5 Use equivalent fractions and ratio models to solve ratio number stories.	Number and Numeration Goal 5
Model and solve ratio problems.	Operations and Computation Goal 7
12·6 Identify equivalent expressions for whole numbers.	Number and Numeration Goal 4
Use multiplication to make estimates.	Operations and Computation Goal 6
Solve rate problems.	Operations and Computation Goal 7
Measure to the nearest inch.	Measurement and Reference Frames Goal 1
12·7 Solve rate problems.	Operations and Computation Goal 7
Construct line graphs and side-by-side line plots of collected data.	Data and Chance Goal 1
Find and interpret the landmarks for collected data.	Data and Chance Goal 2
Make predictions based on simple experiments.	Data and Chance Goal 4
12·8 Solve rate problems using multiplication.	Operations and Computation Goal 3
Compare rates and solve rate problems.	Operations and Computation Goal 7
Solve ratio problems.	Operations and Computation Goal 7

*See the Appendix for a complete list of Grade 5 Goals.

A Balanced Curriculum

Ongoing Practice

Everyday Mathematics provides numerous opportunities for ongoing practice. These activities are embedded throughout the lessons:

 Mental Math and Reflexes activities promote speed and accuracy in mental computation.

 Math Boxes offer mixed practice and are paired across lessons as shown in the brackets below. This makes them useful as assessment tools.

Mixed practice   [12◆1, 12◆3], [12◆2, 12◆4], [12◆5, 12◆7], [12◆6, 12◆8]
Mixed practice with multiple choice   12◆6, 12◆8
Mixed practice with writing/reasoning opportunity   12◆1, 12◆4, 12◆6, 12◆7

 Study Links are daily homework assignments that review the content of the lesson and often contain ongoing facts practice or computation practice.

 5-Minute Math problems are offered for additional practice in Lessons 12◆2 and 12◆7.

 EM Facts Workshop Game provides online practice of basic facts and computation.

EXTRA PRACTICE **Extra Practice** activities are included in Lessons 12◆1, 12◆2, 12◆3, 12◆4, 12◆5, 12◆7, and 12◆8.

Practice through Games

Games are an essential component of practice in the *Everyday Mathematics* program. Games offer skills practice and promote strategic thinking. See the *Differentiation Handbook* for ways to adapt games to meet students' needs.

Lesson	Game	Skill Practiced
12◆1	*Factor Captor*	Finding factors and recognizing multiples [NN Goal 3 and OC Goal 2]
12◆3	*First to 100*	Solving open number sentences [PFA Goal 2]
12◆6	*Spoon Scramble*	Identifying equivalent expressions for whole numbers [NN Goal 4]
12◆8	*Coordinate Search*	Plotting points on a grid [MRF Goal 4]

[NN] Number and Numeration   [OC] Operations and Computation   [DC] Data and Chance
[MRF] Measurement and Reference Frames   [GEO] Geometry   [PFA] Patterns, Functions, and Algebra

Problem Solving

Experts at problem solving and mathematical modeling generally do these things:

- Identify the problem.
- Decide what information is needed to solve the problem.
- Play with and study the data to find patterns and meaning.

- Identify and use mathematical procedures to solve the problem.
- Decide whether the solution makes sense and whether it can be applied to other problems.

The table below lists some of the opportunities in this unit for students to practice these strategies.

Lesson	Activity
12◆1	Find the greatest common factor and least common multiple.
12◆3	Use ratios to examine trends in data about types of workers.
12◆4, 12◆5	Use models to solve ratio problems.
12◆7	Make a personal and whole-class heart-rate profile.
12◆8	Solve problems involving cardiac output and heart rate.

Lessons that teach through problem solving, not just about problem solving

See Chapter 18: Problem Solving in the *Teacher's Reference Manual* for more information.

The Language of Mathematics

Everyday Mathematics provides lesson-specific suggestions to help all students acquire, process, and express mathematical ideas. Throughout Unit 12, there are lesson-specific language development notes that address the needs of English language learners, indicated by **ELL**.

ELL SUPPORT Activities to support English language learners are in Part 3 of Lessons 12◆1, 12◆2, and 12◆8.

The *English Learners Handbook* and the *Differentiation Handbook* have suggestions for promoting language development and acquisition of mathematics vocabulary. See Unit 12 in each handbook.

Literacy Connection

Jumanji, by Chris Van Allsburg, Houghton Mifflin, 1981
If You Hopped Like a Frog, by David M. Schwartz, Scholastic Inc., 1999
Do You Wanna Bet? Your Chance to Find Out About Probability, by Jean Cushman, Houghton Mifflin, 2007

For more literacy connections, see the *Home Connection Handbook,* Grades 4–6.

Cross-Curricular Links

Language Arts – Lesson 12◆3
Literature – Lessons 12◆2, 12◆8
Social Studies – Lesson 12◆3

Health – Lessons 12◆6, 12◆7
Science – Lesson 12◆8

Unit 12 Vocabulary

carbon dioxide
cardiac output
common factor
equally likely
factor tree
greatest common factor
heart rate
least common multiple
magnitude
Multiplication Counting
  Principle
nutrients
oxygen
prime factorization
probability
profile
pulse
pulse rate
rate
ratio
ratio comparison
target heart rate
tree diagram

Balanced Assessment

Daily Assessments

- **Recognizing Student Achievement** – A daily assessment that is included in every lesson to evaluate students' progress toward the Grade 5 Grade-Level Goals.

- **Informing Instruction** – Notes that appear throughout the unit to help anticipate students' common errors and suggest appropriate problem-solving strategies.

Lesson	Recognizing Student Achievement	Informing Instruction
12◆1	Use factor trees to factor numbers and identify prime factorization. [NN Goal 3]	
12◆2	Solve and rephrase probability problems using fractions and basic probability terms. [DC Goal 4]	Circle and count ordered pairs as a single choice.
12◆3	Solve fraction division problems. [OC Goal 5]	
12◆4	Solve ratio problems. [OC Goal 7]	Model ratios by first placing the total number of tiles and then turning over the indicated number of shaded tiles.
12◆5	Estimate and solve multidigit multiplication problems. [OC Goal 6]	Read the parts of a problem while working to identify the unknown. Model number stories with square tiles before writing the number models.
12◆6	Identify equivalent expressions. [NN Goal 4]	
12◆7	Round numbers to a specified place-value digit. [NN Goal 1]	
12◆8	Plot and label ordered number pairs on a coordinate grid. [MRF Goal 4]	

[NN] Number and Numeration   [OC] Operations and Computation   [DC] Data and Chance
[MRF] Measurement and Reference Frames   [GEO] Geometry   [PFA] Patterns, Functions, and Algebra

Portfolio Opportunities

The following lessons provide opportunities to gather samples of students' mathematical writings, drawings, and creations to add balance to the assessment process: Lessons 12◆1, 12◆3, 12◆6, and 12◆9.

See pages 16 and 17 in the *Assessment Handbook* for more information about portfolios and how to use them.

⭐ Unit Assessment

Progress Check 12 – A cumulative assessment of concepts and skills taught in Unit 12 and in previous units, providing information for evaluating students' progress and planning for future instruction. These assessments include oral/slate, written, and open-response activities, as shown below in the sample Progress Check lesson opener.

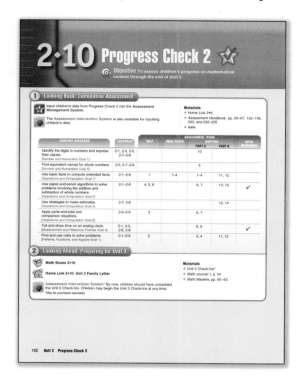

Core Assessment Resources

Assessment Handbook

- ◆ **Unit 12 Assessment Overview,** pages 142–151

- ◆ **Unit 12 Assessment Masters,** pages 210–215

- ◆ **Unit 12 Individual Profiles of Progress,** pages 290, 291, and 302

- ◆ **Unit 12 Class Checklists,** pages 292, 293, and 303

- ◆ **End-of-Year Assessment,** pages 234–241

- ◆ **Quarterly Checklist: Quarter 4,** pages 300 and 301

- ◆ **Math Logs,** pages 306–308

- ◆ **Exit Slip,** page 311

- ◆ **Other Student Assessment Forms,** pages 304, 305, 309, and 310

Assessment Management Spreadsheets

The Assessment Management Spreadsheets consist of the Digital Class Checklists and Individual Profile of Progress Checklists. Use them to monitor, record, and report student progress.

Addressing All Needs

Differentiated Instruction

 Adjusting the Activity – suggests adaptations that target advanced learners, English language learners, or learners who need additional instructional support.

ELL SUPPORT / **ELL** – provides lesson-specific suggestions to help English language learners understand and process the mathematical content.

READINESS – accesses students' prior knowledge or previews content that prepares students to engage in the lesson's Part 1 activities.

EXTRA PRACTICE – provides additional opportunities to apply the mathematical content of the lesson.

ENRICHMENT – enables students to apply or further explore the mathematical content of the lesson.

Lesson	Adjusting the Activity	ELL Support/ ELL	Readiness	Extra Practice	Enrichment
12◆1		●	●	●	●
12◆2	●	●	●	●	●
12◆3		●	●	●	●
12◆4		●	●	●	
12◆5		●		●	●
12◆6	●		●	●	●
12◆7	●		●	●	●
12◆8	●	●		●	●

▷ Additional Resources

Differentiation Handbook
Provides ideas and strategies for differentiating instruction.
Pages 127–133

English Learners Handbook
Contains lesson-specific comprehension strategies.
Pages 108–115

Multilingual Handbook
Previews concepts and vocabulary. It is written in six languages.
Pages 215–230

Planning Tips

Multiage Classroom

Companion Lessons from Grades 4 and 6 can help you meet instructional needs of a multiage classroom. The full Scope and Sequence can be found in the Appendix.

Grade 4		7•11		12•5	3•8, 6•1, 12•2	12•3	2•5	12•3
Grade 5	12•1	12•2	12•3	12•4	12•5	12•6	12•7	12•8
Grade 6	7•1	7•4	8•6	8•6	8•6			

Pacing for Success

Pacing depends on a number of factors, such as students' individual needs and how long your school has been using *Everyday Mathematics*. At the beginning of Unit 12, you may want to use tools available at www.everydaymathonline.com to help you set your pace.

Home Support

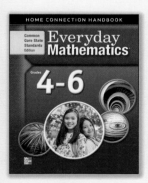

Unit 12 Family Letter (English/Spanish)
provides families with an overview, Do-Anytime Activities, Building Skills through Games, a list of vocabulary, and answers to the daily homework (Study Links). Family Letters in English, Spanish, and seven other languages are also available online.

Study Links are the daily homework assignments. They consist of active projects and ongoing review problems.

▷ **Home Support Resources**

Home Connection Handbook
Offers ideas and reproducible masters for communicating with families. See Table of Contents for unit information.

Student Reference Book
Provides a resource for students and parents.
Pages 80A, 80B, 306, 308, 330, 356, 357, 359, and Glossary

Technology Resources

Algorithms Practice

EM Facts Workshop Game™

Family Letters

Interactive Teacher's Lesson Guide

www.everydaymathonline.com

Unit 12 Organizer

Materials

Lesson	Masters	Manipulative Kit	Other Items
12•1	Study Link Master, p. 348 Game Master, p. 455 Teaching Masters, pp. 349 and 350		Class Data Pad; coin-size counters; chart paper; markers; calculator
12•2	Study Link Master, p. 351 Teaching Master, p. 352 Teaching Aid Master, p. 436 *Differentiation Handbook*, p. 142	per partnership: 2 dice	*Jumanji*
12•3	Study Link Master, p. 353 Game Masters, pp. 456–458 Teaching Masters, pp. 354–356	slate; per partnership: 2 six-sided dice	per partnership: calculator
12•4	Study Link Master, p. 357 Teaching Masters, pp. 358, 359, and 360* Teaching Aid Master, p. 431		scissors and envelope
12•5	Study Link Master, p. 361 Teaching Masters, pp. 362 and 363 Teaching Aid Master, p. 431	slate	
12•6	Game Masters, pp. 503 and 512 Teaching Master, p. 360 Study Link Master, p. 364	slate	per partnership: watch or classroom clock that displays seconds, calculator, inch ruler; Class Data Pad; unlined paper; reference sources about animals; per group: 3 spoons, index cards*
12•7	Teaching Master, p. 360 Study Link Master, p. 365		per group: watch or classroom clock that displays seconds, sturdy chair; stick-on notes, colored pencil or crayon, ruler or straightedge
12•8	Study Link Master, p. 366 Game Masters, pp. 448 and 449 Teaching Master, p. 367		empty 1-gallon container; *If You Hopped Like a Frog;* calculator
12•9	Assessment Masters, pp. 210–215 Study Link Masters, pp. 368–371	slate	

*Denotes optional materials

Mathematical Background

The discussion below highlights the major content areas presented in Unit 12 and helps establish instructional priorities.

Factor Trees (Lesson 12•1)

Finding prime factors with "factor trees" revisits and reinforces some number theory ideas of Unit 1. Prime factorizations are then applied to finding common factors and multiples.

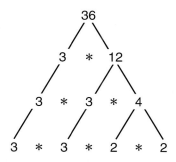

Use factor trees to review prime numbers and factors, and to help in finding common denominators, greatest common factors, and least common multiples.

 For more information about factor trees, see Section 9.8 of the *Teacher's Reference Manual.*

Choices, Tree Diagrams, and Probability (Lesson 12•2)

Lesson 12-2 presents the Multiplication Counting Principle, a method of counting combinations of choices, and tree diagrams, a method of representing combinations of choices graphically. These are introduced through an example of a stadium that can be entered by any of three gates (A, B, and C) and exited through any of four other gates (W, X, Y, and Z).

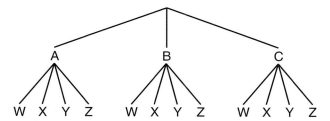

There are 3 * 4 = 12 ways to enter through gate A, B, or C, and exit through gate W, X, Y, or Z.

Multiplication Counting Principle: Suppose you can make a first choice in m ways, and a second choice in n ways. Then there are $m * n$ ways of making the first choice followed by the second choice. Three or more choices can be counted in the same way, by multiplication.

Students solve problems about combinations of choices, and in those cases where each choice is between equally likely alternatives, they calculate the probabilities of various outcomes.

 More about choices, tree diagrams, and probability can be found in Sections 12.1 and 12.4.3 of the *Teacher's Reference Manual.*

Ratios (Lessons 12◆3–12◆5)

Ratios, rates, and proportional thinking, while often used in the everyday world, are poorly understood. Ratios are used to compare quantities that have the same unit, often to indicate relative size. Rates are used to compare quantities that have different units—for example, miles per gallon or heartbeats per minute.

Ratios are usually set up initially as fractions in which the numerator and the denominator are measures or counts with the same unit. The units cancel, leaving a pure number with no unit—often converted by division to a decimal or percent. In Lesson 12-3, students are introduced to many forms and uses of ratios through a series of explorations based on the American Tour. In Lesson 12-4, students cut out paper tiles that are white on one side and shaded on the other side. They use the tiles to model the solutions to ratio problems.

Writing number models for ratio number stories (Lesson 12-5) is a procedure that prepares students for success in algebra. In number stories involving ratios, one of the four numbers needed to express equal ratios is not known.

What is the chance that a diamond card will be drawn?

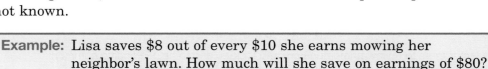

Example: Lisa saves $8 out of every $10 she earns mowing her neighbor's lawn. How much will she save on earnings of $80?

8/10 = _____/80

If equivalent ratios are written with the place for the "unknown" number left blank, it is frequently obvious what that number must be. An important part of algebra is work with equations in which variables are used to represent numbers not yet known; Lesson 12-5 anticipates this later work.

 PROFESSIONAL DEVELOPMENT See Section 9.3.3 of the *Teacher's Reference Manual* for more information about ratios.

Heart Rate and Exercise Project

(Lessons 12◆6–12◆8)

This project furthers important objectives of *Fifth Grade Everyday Mathematics* and provides links to science and health concepts. Students gather and use rate data, deriving the rate for heartbeats per minute from data on heartbeats for 15 seconds (Lesson 12-6). They establish some cause-and-effect relationships, display the data in line graphs and line plots, and interpret the data (Lesson 12-7). They use formulas and other calculations with existing data to create new data—in this case, data on cardiac output (Lesson 12-8).

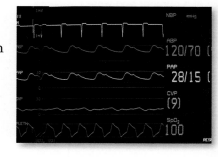

 Learn more about the Heart Rate and Exercise Project in Section 1.2.7 of the *Teacher's Reference Manual.*

12·1 Factor Trees

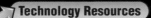

Objective To provide experiences with finding the greatest common factor and the least common multiple of two numbers.

Technology Resources www.everydaymathonline.com

 ePresentations
 eToolkit
 Algorithms Practice
 EM Facts Workshop Game™
 Family Letters
 Assessment Management
 Common Core State Standards
 Curriculum Focal Points
 Interactive Teacher's Lesson Guide

---

1 Teaching the Lesson

Key Concepts and Skills

- Identify the prime factorization for a number.
  [Number and Numeration Goal 3]

- Use greatest common factors and least common multiples to rename fractions.
  [Number and Numeration Goal 5]

- Use multiplication facts to find factor strings.
  [Operations and Computation Goal 2]

- Find greatest common factors and least common multiples using factor strings.
  [Number and Numeration Goal 3]

Key Activities

Students use factor trees to find all the prime factors of a number and write the prime factorization. They use prime factorizations to simplify fractions.

 Ongoing Assessment:
Recognizing Student Achievement
Use journal page 394.
[Number and Numeration Goal 3]

Key Vocabulary

prime factorization ◆ factor tree ◆ common factor ◆ greatest common factor ◆ least common multiple

Materials

Math Journal 2, pp. 393–396
Student Reference Book Glossary
Class Data Pad

2 Ongoing Learning & Practice

 Playing *Factor Captor*
Student Reference Book, p. 306
Math Masters, p. 455
calculator ◆ paper and pencil ◆ per partnership: 70 counters
Students practice finding factors of larger numbers and recognizing prime factors.

 Math Boxes 12·1
Math Journal 2, p. 397
Students practice and maintain skills through Math Box problems.

 Study Link 12·1
Math Masters, p. 348
Students practice and maintain skills through Study Link activities.

3 Differentiation Options

READINESS
Making Factor Rainbows
Students factor numbers by making factor rainbows.

ENRICHMENT
Using a Division Method for Prime Factorizations
Math Masters, p. 349
Students use division to find prime factorizations.

EXTRA PRACTICE
Using Factor Trees to Find Common Denominators
Math Masters, p. 350
Students identify common denominators by using factor trees.

ELL SUPPORT
Making a Factor Tree Poster
per group: chart paper, markers
Students make a display to reference concepts related to factor trees.

Advance Preparation

 Teacher's Reference Manual, **Grades 4–6** pp. 79–82

Getting Started

Mental Math and Reflexes

Have students compute each quotient and explain their answer using the relationship between multiplication and division.

●○○ $5 \div (\frac{1}{2}) = 10$ because $10 * (\frac{1}{2}) = 5$.
$(\frac{1}{4}) \div 2 = \frac{1}{8}$ because $(\frac{1}{8}) * 2 = \frac{1}{4}$.

●●○ $(\frac{1}{2}) \div 4 = \frac{1}{8}$ because $(\frac{1}{8}) * 4 = \frac{1}{2}$.
$6 \div (\frac{1}{4}) = 24$ because $24 * (\frac{1}{4}) = 6$.

●●● $5 \div (\frac{1}{3}) = 15$ because $15 * (\frac{1}{3}) = 5$.
$(\frac{1}{5}) \div 3 = \frac{1}{15}$ because $(\frac{1}{15}) * 3 = \frac{1}{5}$.

Math Message

Solve Problems 1 and 2 on journal page 393.

---

1 Teaching the Lesson

Math Message Follow-Up

WHOLE-CLASS DISCUSSION

(*Math Journal 2*, p. 393; *Student Reference Book* Glossary)

Have students read the definitions for *factor, factor pair, composite number, prime number,* and *factor string* in the *Student Reference Book* Glossary. Read and discuss how the terms relate. Discussion should include the following points:

▷ A factor of a number can be any type of number, but the other terms only refer to whole numbers.

▷ Numbers can be defined by their factors. For example, a prime number has only two whole-number factors, 1 and itself. A composite number has more than two whole-number factors. A square number has an odd number of factors.

▷ Each factor in the longest factor string of a number is prime. The longest factor string is called its **prime factorization.**

Ask: *What device can be used to find all the factor pairs for a number?* Factor rainbow Have students make factor rainbows for 48 and share their solutions using the Class Data Pad. A **factor tree** is a device that can be used to find the prime factorization of a number. Draw one for 48 on the Class Data Pad. Ask: *What is the prime factorization for 48?* $2 * 2 * 2 * 2 * 3$ Have students refer to the factor tree examples for 45 on *Math Journal 2*, page 393. Note that each factor tree begins with two different factors for 45 but the prime factorizations are the same. Ask students to make factor trees for 36. Ask: *What do you notice about the longest factor string you recorded for Problem 2 and the result of your factor tree for 36?* They are the same: $2 * 2 * 3 * 3$.

Finding Greatest Common Factors

WHOLE-CLASS ACTIVITY

(*Math Journal 2*, pp. 393–395)

Write the numbers 18 and 30 on the board. Ask students to name all the factors of each number while you list them.

Student Page

Date _____ Time _____

LESSON 12·1 **Factors**

Math Message

1. Write all the pairs of factors whose product is 48. One pair has been done for you.

    $48 = \underline{6 * 8}; 1 * 48; 2 * 24; 3 * 16; 4 * 12$

2. One way to write 36 as a product of factors is $2 * 18$. Another way is $2 * 2 * 9$. Write 36 as the product of the longest possible string of factors. Do not include 1 as a factor.

    $\underline{2 * 2 * 3 * 3}$

Factor Trees and Greatest Common Factors

One way to find the prime factors of a number is to make a **factor tree.** First write the number. Underneath the number write any two factors whose product is that number. Then write factors of each of these factors. Continue until all the factors are prime numbers. Below are two factor trees for 45.

```
    45              45
   3 * 15          9 * 5
  3 * 3 * 5      3 * 3 * 5
```

The **greatest common factor** of two whole numbers is the largest number that is a factor of both numbers.

Example: Find the greatest common factor of 24 and 60.

Step 1 List all the factors of 24: 1, 2, 3, 4, 6, 8, 12, and 24.

Step 2 List all the factors of 60: 1, 2, 3, 4, 5, 6, 10, 12, 15, 20, 30, and 60.

Step 3 1, 2, 3, 4, 6, and 12 are on both lists. They are **common factors.** 12 is the largest number, so it is the greatest common factor of 24 and 60.

3. Find the greatest common factor of 18 and 27.

    Factors of 18: $\underline{1, 2, 3, 6, 9, 18}$

    Factors of 27: $\underline{1, 3, 9, 27}$

    Greatest common factor: $\underline{9}$

Math Journal 2, p. 393

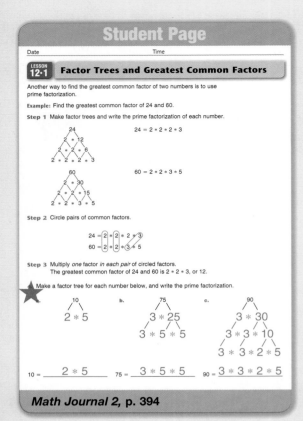

Math Journal 2, p. 394

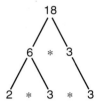

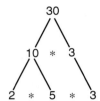

Math Journal 2, p. 395

Factors of 18: 1, 2, 3, 6, 9, and 18
Factors of 30: 1, 2, 3, 5, 6, 10, 15, and 30

Circle 1, 2, 3, and 6 on both lists. Explain that because 1, 2, 3, and 6 are factors of both 18 and 30, they are called **common factors.**

The largest of these common factors is called the **greatest common factor.** The greatest common factor of 18 and 30 is 6.

There are two ways to find the greatest common factor of two numbers:

▷ List all the factors of each number and identify the largest common factor.

▷ Use factor trees to write the prime factorization of each number. Identify the prime factors that these two numbers have in common, and multiply them.

Ask students to make factor trees for 18 and 30, and have volunteers draw these two factor trees on the board.

Write the prime factorizations for 18 and 30 as shown below (one above the other) on the board or a transparency. Ask: *What prime factors do these two numbers have in common?* 2 and 3 Circle the pairs of common factors in the prime factorizations for 18 and 30. Explain that since 2 * 3 = 6, the greatest common factor is 6. It is the greatest number by which both 18 and 30 are divisible.

$$18 = \boxed{2} * \boxed{3} * 3$$
$$30 = \boxed{2} * \boxed{3} * 5$$
GCF = 2 * 3
Greatest Common Factor = 6

Have students make factor trees for 24 and 50, and have volunteers add these two trees to the display on the board. Ask: *What is the greatest common factor of 24 and 50?* 2 *How do the factor trees confirm that 2 is the greatest common factor of 24 and 50?* They show that 2 is the only common prime factor.

Have students refer back to the factor trees for 24 and 36. Ask: *What is the greatest common factor of 24 and 36?* 2 * 2 * 3, or 12 Write the prime factorizations for 24 and 36, circling the pairs of common factors. Point out that 2, 2, and 3 are the common prime factors. Therefore, the greatest common factor is 2 * 2 * 3, or 12.

Tell students that the greatest common factor can be used to simplify fractions. Ask students how they might use the greatest common factor and the division rule to simplify the fraction $\frac{24}{36}$. The factor trees for 24 and 36 show their greatest common factor to be 12. Divide the numerator and the denominator by the greatest common factor, $\frac{24 \div 12}{36 \div 12} = \frac{2}{3}$. The simplified fraction is $\frac{2}{3}$.

Have students complete journal pages 393–395.

Finding Least Common Multiples

PARTNER ACTIVITY

(*Math Journal 2*, p. 396; *Student Reference Book* Glossary)

PROBLEM SOLVING

Have students locate the term *least common multiple* in the *Student Reference Book* Glossary and read the entry. Ask: *What is a common multiple?* A number that is a multiple of two or more given numbers The quick common denominator is an example of a common multiple. The smallest number that is a multiple of two or more numbers is the **least common multiple.**

Have students list the first seven multiples of 6 and 9. Ask: *What numbers are in both lists?* The common multiples are 18 and 36. *What is the least common multiple of 6 and 9?* 18

Tell students that factor trees also can be used to find the least common multiple of two numbers. This procedure is similar to finding the greatest common factor.

Step 1: Refer to the prime factorizations for 18 and 30 from the previous activity, circling the pairs of common factors.

Step 2: Draw a line through one factor in each of the pairs of common factors.

$$18 = 2 * 3 * 3$$
$$30 = 2 * 3 * 5$$
Least common multiple: $2 * 3 * 3 * 5 = 90$

Step 3: Write the remaining factors in a multiplication expression, $2 * 3 * 3 * 5 = 90$. The least common multiple of 18 and 30 is 90.

Have partners complete journal page 396. Circulate and assist.

2 Ongoing Learning & Practice

Playing *Factor Captor*

PARTNER ACTIVITY

(*Student Reference Book*, p. 306;
Math Masters, p. 455)

COMPUTATION PRACTICE

Students practice finding factors of larger numbers and recognizing prime factors by playing *Factor Captor* on the 1–110 Grid.

Date _____ Time _____

LESSON 12·1 **Factor Trees and Least Common Multiples**

The **least common multiple** of two numbers is the smallest number that is a multiple of both numbers.

Example: Find the least common multiple of 8 and 12.

Step 1 List the multiples of 8: 8, 16, 24, 32, 40, 48, 56, and so on.

Step 2 List the multiples of 12: 12, 24, 36, 48, 60, and so on.

Step 3 24 and 48 are in both lists. They are common multiples.
24 is the smallest number. It is the least common multiple for 8 and 12.
24 is also the smallest number that can be divided by both 8 and 12.

Another way to find the least common multiple for two numbers is to use prime factorization.

Example: Find the least common multiple of 8 and 12.

Step 1 Write the prime factorization of each number:

$$8 = 2 * 2 * 2 \qquad 12 = 2 * 2 * 3$$

Step 2 Circle pairs of common factors. Then cross out one factor in each pair as shown below.

Step 3 Multiply the factors that are not crossed out. The least common multiple of 8 and 12 is $2 * 2 * 2 * 3$, or 24.

1. Make factor trees and write the prime factorizations for each number.

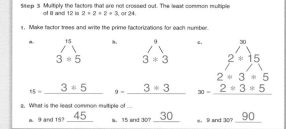

  a.   15 = ___3 * 5___   b.   9 = ___3 * 3___   c.   30 = ___2 * 3 * 5___

2. What is the least common multiple of …

  a. 9 and 15? __45__   b. 15 and 30? __30__   c. 9 and 30? __90__

Math Journal 2, p. 396

Name _____ Date _____ Time _____

Factor Captor 1–110 Grid

1	2	3	4	5	6	7	8	9	10
11	12	13	14	15	16	17	18	19	20
21	22	23	24	25	26	27	28	29	30
31	32	33	34	35	36	37	38	39	40
41	42	43	44	45	46	47	48	49	50
51	52	53	54	55	56	57	58	59	60
61	62	63	64	65	66	67	68	69	70
71	72	73	74	75	76	77	78	79	80
81	82	83	84	85	86	87	88	89	90
91	92	93	94	95	96	97	98	99	100
101	102	103	104	105	106	107	108	109	110

Math Masters, p. 455

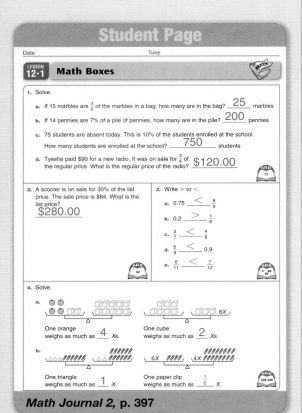

▶ Math Boxes 12·1

(*Math Journal 2,* p. 397)

 Mixed Practice Math Boxes in this lesson are paired with Math Boxes in Lesson 12-3.

Writing/Reasoning Have students write a response to the following: *Explain your solution strategy for Math Boxes, Problem 2.* Since $84.00 represents 30%, I divided 84 by 3 to find 10% of the list price. Then I multiplied that result by 10 to find the total list price; $84 \div 3 * 10 = \$280.00$.

▶ Study Link 12·1

(*Math Masters,* p. 348)

Home Connection Students work with factor trees. They use these to write prime factorizations and to write fractions in simplest form.

(3) Differentiation Options

READINESS

▶ Making Factor Rainbows

5–15 Min

To provide experience finding all the factors of a number, have students make factor rainbows. For example, to make a factor rainbow for the number 48, list all the factors of 48 in ascending order. Then connect factor pairs. Every factor should be paired with another factor. If there is an odd number of factors, the middle factor is paired with itself. The product of each pair of factors should be 48.

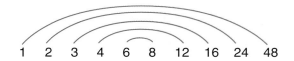

1   2   3   4   6   8   12   16   24   48

Have students make factor rainbows for given numbers. *Suggestions:* 25, 32, 40, 49, 80, 100

ENRICHMENT

▶ Using a Division Method for Prime Factorizations

5–15 Min

(*Math Masters,* p. 349)

 To apply students' understanding of factors, have them use a division method to find prime factorizations. When students have finished, discuss any questions or curiosities they encountered.

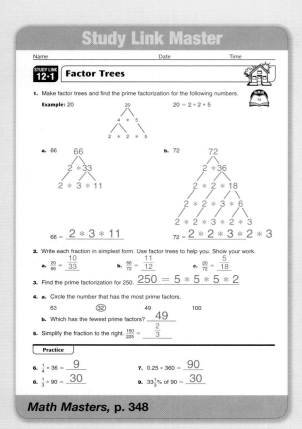

INDEPENDENT ACTIVITY

5–15 Min

Using Factor Trees to Find Common Denominators

(*Math Masters*, p. 350)

Students practice making factor trees to find prime factorizations. They use factor trees to find common denominators, identify the least common multiple of the denominators, and use the least common multiple as a common denominator.

ELL SUPPORT

SMALL-GROUP ACTIVITY

15–30 Min

Making a Factor Tree Poster

To provide language support for factors, guide students to make a poster showing important vocabulary words related to factor trees. Display the poster during lessons in this unit.

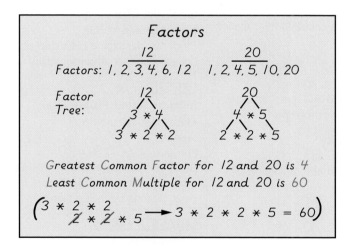

Teaching Master

Name   Date   Time

LESSON 12·1   The Division Method for Prime Factorization

Use the method below to find the prime factorization of the following numbers.

Example: Find the prime factorization for 732.

Step 1 Divide, using the smallest prime factor of the number as the divisor.

Step 2 The quotient becomes the dividend. Use the smallest prime factor as the divisor, and continue dividing until the quotient is a prime number.

2 | 732   Divide: 732 ÷ 2 = 366

2 | 366   Divide: 366 ÷ 2 = 183
                   2 is not a factor of 183.
                   The next smallest prime factor is 3.

3 | 183   Divide: 183 ÷ 3 = 61

| 61   61 is a prime number.

The prime factorization of 732 is
2 * 2 * 3 * 61

Step 3 Write the divisors as a multiplication expression.

732 = 2 * 2 * 3 * 61

This is the prime factorization of 732.

Use the division method to find the prime factorizations. Show your work.

1. 1,056   **2.** 3,190   **3.** 24,598

$2^5 * 3 * 11$ $2 * 5 * 11 * 29$ $2 * 7^2 * 251$

2 | 1,056   2 | 3,190   2 | 24,598
2 | 528   5 | 1,595   7 | 12,299
2 | 264   29 | 319   7 | 1,757
2 | 132 | 11 | 251
2 | 66
3 | 33
| 11

Math Masters, p. 349

Teaching Master

Name   Date   Time

LESSON 12·1   Factor Trees and Adding Fractions

1. Make factor trees and write the prime factorization for each number below.

a. 12

6 * 2
2 * 3 * 2

b. 42

7 * 6
7 * 2 * 3

c. 32

2 * 16
2 * 2 * 8
2 * 2 * 2 * 4
2 * 2 * 2 * 2 * 2

12 = 2 * 3 * 2   42 = 7 * 2 * 3   32 = 2 * 2 * 2 * 2 * 2

2. Add the following fractions. Use the factor trees above to help you find the least common multiple of the denominators. Use this least common multiple as a common denominator.

a. $\frac{5}{12} = \frac{40}{96}$

$+ \frac{7}{32} = \frac{21}{96}$

$\frac{61}{96}$

b. $\frac{41}{42} = \frac{82}{84}$

$+ \frac{1}{12} = \frac{7}{84}$

$\frac{89}{84}$, or $1\frac{5}{84}$

3. Use factor trees or some other method to find a common denominator for the fraction pairs below. If you do not use factor trees, explain how you found the least common denominators.

a. $\frac{5}{14}$ and $\frac{2}{21}$ 42

b. $\frac{7}{18}$ and $\frac{16}{36}$ 36

c. $\frac{9}{24}$ and $\frac{21}{64}$ 192

Math Masters, p. 350

12·2 Choices, Tree Diagrams, and Probability

 Objective To introduce the Multiplication Counting Principle and tree diagrams.

1 Teaching the Lesson

Key Concepts and Skills

• Describe events using basic probability terms.
[Data and Chance Goal 3]

• Use the Multiplication Counting Principle and tree diagrams to solve probability problems.
[Data and Chance Goal 4]

• Express the probability of an event as a fraction.
[Data and Chance Goal 4]

Key Activities

Students find the number of ways in which a sequence of choices can be made using the Multiplication Counting Principle and tree diagrams to represent and count combinations of choices. They find probabilities in equally likely situations.

 Ongoing Assessment:
Recognizing Student Achievement
Use journal page 398.
[Data and Chance Goal 4]

 Ongoing Assessment:
Informing Instruction See page 922.

Key Vocabulary

probability ◆ Multiplication Counting Principle ◆ tree diagram ◆ equally likely

Materials

Math Journal 2, pp. 398–401
Study Link 12•1

2 Ongoing Learning & Practice

Solving Number Stories

Math Journal 2, p. 402
Students solve a set of number stories involving rates.

 Math Boxes 12·2

Math Journal 2, p. 403
Students practice and maintain skills through Math Box problems.

 Study Link 12·2

Math Masters, p. 351
Students practice and maintain skills through Study Link activities.

3 Differentiation Options

READINESS
Exploring Chance and Probability

Math Masters, p. 352
Students investigate the difference between chance and probability.

ENRICHMENT
Reading about Probability

Math Masters, p. 436
Jumanji
per partnership: 2 dice
Students read the book and discuss the probability of obtaining different number combinations by rolling dice.

EXTRA PRACTICE
5-Minute Math

5-Minute Math™, pp. 129 and 210
Students draw tree diagrams.

ELL SUPPORT
Building a Math Word Bank

Differentiation Handbook, p. 142
Students define and illustrate the term *equally likely.*

Advance Preparation

For Part 1, make 2 transparencies: draw the rectangular array column and row headings from page 922 onto one, and draw the tree diagram for the stadium example onto the other. For the optional Enrichment activity in Part 3, obtain the book *Jumanji* by Chris Van Allsburg (Houghton Mifflin, 1981).

 Teacher's Reference Manual, **Grades 4–6** pp. 155–158, 172, 173

Getting Started

Mental Math and Reflexes `ELL`

Have students calculate the probability of simple events and explain their answers. To support English language learners who are unfamiliar with the language of cards, model the meaning of *suits, face cards,* and *colors.* Suggestions:

If you draw a card from a regular deck of 52 cards, what is the probability that the card will be . . .

- a red card? $\frac{1}{2}$; half of the cards in a deck are black and half are red.

- a heart? $\frac{13}{52}$, or $\frac{1}{4}$; there are four suits (spades, hearts, diamonds, clubs), each with 13 cards.

- a 5? $\frac{4}{52}$, or $\frac{1}{13}$; there are four 5s, one in each suit.

- a face card? $\frac{12}{52}$, or $\frac{3}{13}$; each suit has a jack, a queen, and a king.

- the king of clubs? $\frac{1}{52}$; there is only 1 king of clubs.

Math Message

Work with a partner. Read journal page 398 and solve the problems.

Study Link 12·1 Follow-Up

Have partners compare answers and resolve differences. Ask students whether they recognized 150 and 225 as having common factors (5, 15, 25, and 75) or as being multiples of 75 before they made factor trees. Remind students that they will often be able to find a problem's solution by using what they know about number relationships. Then devices such as factor trees can be used to check their answers.

---

1 Teaching the Lesson

▶ Math Message Follow-Up 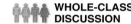 WHOLE-CLASS DISCUSSION

(*Math Journal 2,* p. 398)

Remind students of their work with the Probability Meter and the use of terms such as *certain, likely, 50–50 chance, unlikely,* and *impossible* to describe the likelihood of events. Ask them to use probability descriptions to rephrase some of the problems and answers on the journal page. For example, in Problem 1 the spinner lands on an odd number, and its answer, $\frac{5}{10}$, can be rephrased in a variety of ways:

▷ The **probability** that the spinner will land on an odd number is $\frac{5}{10}$.

▷ If I spin the spinner many times, I expect it to land on an odd number about 5 out of 10 times.

▷ The fraction of times the spinner will land on an odd number is about $\frac{5}{10}$.

▷ The spinner will land on an odd number about half of the time.

★ Ongoing Assessment: Recognizing Student Achievement

Journal Page 398

Use **journal page 398** and the Math Message discussion to assess students' ability to express probability using fractions and basic probability terms. Students are making adequate progress if they are able to correctly solve and rephrase the problems.

[Data and Chance Goal 4]

Student Page

Date _____ Time _____

LESSON 12·2 Probability ★

When a fair 6-sided die is rolled, each number from 1 to 6 has an equal chance of coming up. The numbers 1, 2, 3, 4, 5, and 6 are **equally likely**.

The spinner below is divided into 10 equal sections, so the chance of spinning the numbers 1–10 is **equally likely**. This does not mean that if you spin 10 times, each number from 1 to 10 will come up exactly once—2 might come up four times, and 10 might not come up at all. But if you spin many times (for example—1,000 times), each number is likely to come up about $\frac{1}{10}$ of the time. The **probability** of landing on 1 is $\frac{1}{10}$. The probability of landing on 2 is also $\frac{1}{10}$, and so on.

Example: What is the probability that the spinner at the right will land on an even number?

The spinner will land on an even number if it lands on 2, 4, 6, 8, or 10. Each of these even numbers is likely to come up $\frac{1}{10}$ of the time. The total probability that one of these even numbers will come up is found by adding:

$$\frac{1}{10} + \frac{1}{10} + \frac{1}{10} + \frac{1}{10} + \frac{1}{10} = \frac{5}{10}$$

Lands on: 2   4   6   8   10

The probability of landing on an even number is $\frac{5}{10}$.

Find the probability of each of the following for this spinner.

1. The spinner lands on an odd number. $\frac{5}{10}$

2. The spinner lands on a number less than 7. $\frac{6}{10}$

3. The spinner lands on a multiple of 3. $\frac{3}{10}$

4. The spinner lands on a number that is a factor of 12. $\frac{5}{10}$

5. The spinner lands on the greatest common factor of 4 and 6. $\frac{1}{10}$

6. The spinner lands on a prime number. $\frac{4}{10}$

7. The spinner lands on a number that is *not* a prime number. $\frac{6}{10}$

Math Journal 2, p. 398

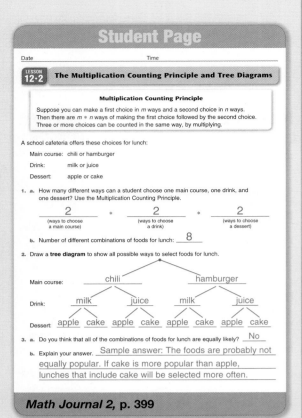

Math Journal 2, p. 399

▶  **Introducing the Multiplication Counting Principle and Tree Diagrams**

(*Math Journal 2*, p. 399)

Pose the following situation: A stadium has three gates on its West side—A, B, and C. It has four gates on its East side—W, X, Y, and Z. People can enter the stadium through any of the three West gates. They can exit the stadium through any of the four East gates. To support English language learners, draw a sketch of the stadium on the board.

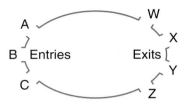

Ask: *How many different combinations of entering and leaving the stadium are possible?* 12 different combinations

Suggest that one way to organize the entrance and exit possibilities is with a rectangular array in which each row represents an entry gate and each column represents an exit gate. Display the prepared transparency of the row and column headings. Explain that each cell in the array contains an ordered pair of letters. The first letter names the entry gate; the second letter names the exit gate. Complete the array as shown below.

		Exit Gate (East)			
		W	X	Y	Z
	A	(A,W)	(A,X)	(A,Y)	(A,Z)
Entry Gate (West)	B	(B,W)	(B,X)	(B,Y)	(B,Z)
	C	(C,W)	(C,X)	(C,Y)	(C,Z)

Point out that the array has 3 rows and 4 columns, so there is a total of 3 * 4, or 12 ordered pairs. There are 12 different ways of entering through a West gate and exiting through an East gate.

 Ongoing Assessment: Informing Instruction

Watch for students who do not count the ordered pairs as a single choice. Circle the ordered pair in each cell and have students count the choices in the first column and in the first row.

Read the Multiplication Counting Principle at the top of journal page 399 as a class. Explain that just as it is possible to use multiplication to find the total number of objects in an array, the **Multiplication Counting Principle** uses multiplication to count the total number of possible combinations of choices in a given situation. Combinations of two, three, or more choices can be counted in the same way, by multiplying.

Verify with the class that the Multiplication Counting Principle works for the stadium example—that is,

$$\underbrace{\dfrac{3}{\text{(Ways to Enter)}}}\ *\ \underbrace{\dfrac{4}{\text{(Ways to Exit)}}}\ =\ \underbrace{\dfrac{12}{\text{(Total Ways to Enter and Exit)}}}$$

Read the introduction to the problems on journal page 399. Then have students solve Problem 1. Circulate and assist. When students have finished, have a volunteer explain the solution.

Tell students that another way to count the total number of possible combinations in a given situation is to use a **tree diagram.** Explain that with a tree diagram each possible combination of choices can be found by following a path from the top to the bottom of the diagram. The total possible combination of choices can be found by counting the paths.

Use the stadium example to demonstrate a tree diagram. Draw a tree diagram like the one shown below on the board or a transparency. Point out the choices and the lines that connect them. There are 12 paths in all.

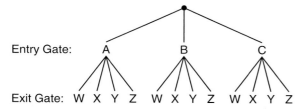

Ask: *Are all 12 paths equally likely?* Guide students to see that some entry gates will probably be used more than others, as will some exit gates. However, there is not enough information to be certain. This is *not* an **equally likely** situation.

Have students complete Problem 2 on the journal page. Circulate and assist.

Ask: *Is this an equally likely situation?* Have students respond by completing Problem 3. When students have finished, discuss their responses.

NOTE The Multiplication Counting Principle does *not* make any assumptions about whether or not the choices are equally likely. In the stadium example and the situation about school lunches, the choices and therefore, the combinations are not equally likely. But in the problems on journal pages 400 and 401, the combination paths are equally likely, and students can calculate probabilities.

▶ Solving Probability Problems

👤 INDEPENDENT ACTIVITY

(*Math Journal 2,* pp. 400 and 401)

Read the problem at the top of each of the two journal pages as a class. Emphasize that with these two situations each choice is a choice between equally likely alternatives (shirt, pants; train to work, train from work). Have students complete the journal pages.

When most students have finished, bring the class together to discuss their solutions and the relationship between the Multiplication Counting Principle and tree diagrams.

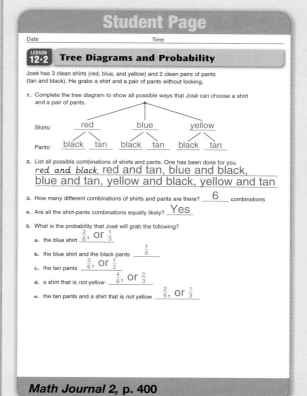

Math Journal 2, p. 400

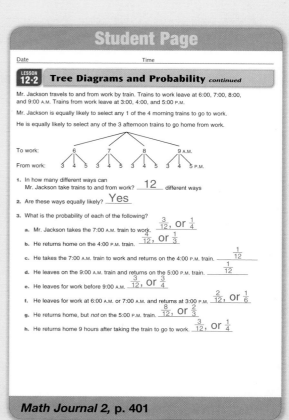

Math Journal 2, p. 401

Student Page

Date _____ Time _____

LESSON 12·2 **Rate Number Stories**

1. Mica reads about 44 pages in an hour.
   About how many pages will she read in $2\frac{3}{4}$ hour? __121__ pages

   Explain how you found your answer. Sample answer: I know that in two hours, she read 88 pages, and $\frac{1}{4}$ of 44 is 11 pages, so $\frac{3}{4}$ is 33 pages. 88 + 33 = 121.

   If Mica starts reading a 230-page book at 3:30 P.M., and she reads straight through the book without stopping, about what time will Mica finish the book? __8:45 P.M.__

   Explain how you found your answer. Sample answer: I calculated the number of pages read for different times: 220 pages in 5 hours and 11 pages in $\frac{1}{4}$ hour. 220 + 11 = 231 pages in $5\frac{1}{4}$ hours, and 3:30 P.M. + 5 hours 15 minutes = 8:45 P.M.

2. Tyree and Jake built a tower of centimeter cubes. The bottom floor of the tower is rectangular. It is 5 cubes wide and 10 cubes long. The completed tower is the shape of a rectangular prism. They began building at 2 P.M. They built for about 1 hour. They used approximately 200 cubes every 10 minutes.

   How tall was the final tower? __24 floors__
                                        (unit)

   Explain how you found your answer. Sample answer: Each floor is the same shape. Since the bottom floor is 5 cubes wide and 10 cubes long, each floor is made up of 50 centimeter cubes. Since Tyree and Jake used about 200 cubes every 10 minutes, they built about 4 floors in 10 minutes. In 60 minutes they built about 6 ∗ 4, or 24 floors.

Math Journal 2, p. 402

Student Page

Date _____ Time _____

LESSON 12·2 **Math Boxes**

1. Divide mentally.
   a. 382 / 7 → __54 R4__
   b. 796 / 5 → __159 R1__
   c. 499 / 4 → __124 R3__
   d. 283 ÷ 6 → __47 R1__
   e. 1,625 ÷ 8 → __203 R1__

2. Draw a rectangle whose perimeter is the same as the perimeter of the rectangle shown, but whose sides are not the same length as those shown.
   Sample answers:

   3.5 cm · 2.5 cm · 2 cm · 4 cm

   What is the area of the figure you've drawn?
   __8 cm²__

3. Multiply. Show your work.
   a. 5.5
      ∗ 3.7
      20.35
   b. 3.18 ∗ 6.4 =
      20.352
   c. Explain your strategy for solving Problem A.
      Answers vary.

4. a. Measure the radius of the circle in centimeters. __2 cm__

   b. Find the area to the nearest cm² and the circumference to the nearest cm.

   Area = π ∗ radius²

   Circumference = π ∗ diameter
   The area is about __13 cm²__
   The circumference is about __13 cm__

Math Journal 2, p. 403

Adjusting the Activity

Ask students to explain why it is not possible to use the tree diagrams to find the probability of an event if the choices are not equally likely.

AUDITORY ◆ KINESTHETIC ◆ TACTILE ◆ VISUAL

2 Ongoing Learning & Practice

▶ Solving Number Stories
INDEPENDENT ACTIVITY

(*Math Journal 2*, p. 402)

Students solve a set of number stories involving rates and elapsed time.

NOTE You may want to pose additional problems involving elapsed time. *For example:* Tyler got on his school bus at 7:50 A.M. He arrived at school at 8:12 A.M. How long was his bus ride?

▶ Math Boxes 12·2
INDEPENDENT ACTIVITY

(*Math Journal 2*, p. 403)

Mixed Practice Math Boxes in this lesson are paired with Math Boxes in Lesson 12-4.

▶ Study Link 12·2
INDEPENDENT ACTIVITY

(*Math Masters*, p. 351)

Home Connection Students use tree diagrams to count possible outcomes and to solve a probability problem.

3 Differentiation Options

READINESS
PARTNER ACTIVITY

▶ Exploring Chance and Probability
 5–15 Min

(*Math Masters*, p. 352)

To provide experience with the language of probability, have students distinguish between events that can be described as chance events and events that can be described using probability. Read and discuss the introduction on *Math Masters*, page 352. Then have students answer the questions.

When students have finished, discuss their solutions. Consider having students suggest events for the group to describe using *C* for *chance* or *P* for *probability*.

12·3 American Tour: Ratio Exploration

Objective To provide experiences with the uses of ratios and ratio comparisons.

Technology Resources www.everydaymathonline.com

ePresentations | eToolkit | Algorithms Practice | EM Facts Workshop Game™ | Family Letters | Assessment Management | Common Core State Standards | Curriculum Focal Points | Interactive Teacher's Lesson Guide

---

1 Teaching the Lesson

Key Concepts and Skills

• Write ratios in equivalent forms.
[Number and Numeration Goal 5]

• Compare numbers that are 10 times more or 10 times less than each other.
[Number and Numeration Goal 6]

• Express ratios in a variety of ways.
[Operations and Computation Goal 7]

Key Activities

Students use data from the American Tour to read ratios and write them in equivalent forms. They use ratios to examine trends in data and make ratio comparisons expressed as 10 times more and $\frac{1}{10}$ of.

 Ongoing Assessment:
Recognizing Student Achievement
Use Mental Math and Reflexes.
[Operations and Computation Goal 5]

Key Vocabulary

ratio ◆ ratio comparison ◆ magnitude

Materials

Math Journal 2, pp. 404–406
Student Reference Book, pp. 356, 357, and 359
Study Link 12·2
slate

2 Ongoing Learning & Practice

 Playing *First to 100*
Student Reference Book, p. 308
Math Masters, pp. 456–458
per partnership: 2 six-sided dice, calculator
Students practice solving open number sentences.

Math Boxes 12·3
Math Journal 2, p. 407
Students practice and maintain skills through Math Box problems.

Study Link 12·3
Math Masters, p. 353
Students practice and maintain skills through Study Link activities.

3 Differentiation Options

READINESS
Reading a Pictograph
Math Masters, p. 354
Students analyze a pictograph to solve ratio problems.

ENRICHMENT
Imagining 10 Times More or 10 Times Less
Math Masters, p. 355
Students explore magnitude by describing what life would be like if select things were 10 times more or 10 times less.

EXTRA PRACTICE
Reading and Writing Ratios
Math Masters, p. 356
Students write ratios in equivalent forms.

Advance Preparation

 Teacher's Reference Manual, Grades 4–6 pp. 64–68, 168, 169

Getting Started

Mental Math and Reflexes

Have students compute each quotient and explain their answer using the relationship between multiplication and division.

●○○ $9 \div (\frac{1}{2}) = 18$ because $18 * (\frac{1}{2}) = 9$. ●●● $8 \div (\frac{1}{6}) = 48$ because $48 * (\frac{1}{6}) = 8$.

$(\frac{1}{3}) \div 2 = \frac{1}{6}$ because $(\frac{1}{6}) * 2 = \frac{1}{3}$. $(\frac{1}{9}) \div 3 = \frac{1}{27}$ because $(\frac{1}{27}) * 3 = \frac{1}{9}$.

●●○ $(\frac{1}{4}) \div 3 = \frac{1}{12}$ because $(\frac{1}{12}) * 3 = \frac{1}{4}$.

$7 \div (\frac{1}{3}) = 21$ because $21 * (\frac{1}{3}) = 7$.

Math Message

Study the example on journal page 404. Then solve the Math Message problems.

Study Link 12·2 Follow-Up

Have partners compare answers and resolve differences. Ask volunteers to explain their solution strategies for Problem 5.

✓ Ongoing Assessment: Recognizing Student Achievement

Mental Math and Reflexes

Use the **Mental Math and Reflexes** problems to assess students' ability to solve fraction division problems. Students are making adequate progress if they correctly calculate the quotient for the ●○○, the ●●○, and the ●●● problems. Some students may be able to write the related multiplication problem for each fraction division problem.

[Operations and Computation Goal 5]

---

1 Teaching the Lesson

▶ Math Message Follow-Up

👥👥 WHOLE-CLASS DISCUSSION

(*Math Journal 2*, p. 404)

Briefly discuss the **ratio** essay on the journal page. Then have volunteers explain their solution strategies. Encourage students to express the meaning of ratio in their own words.

▶ Reading Ratios and Writing Them in Equivalent Forms

👥👥 WHOLE-CLASS ACTIVITY

(*Student Reference Book*, p. 359)

As a class, read the information at the top of *Student Reference Book*, page 359 and examine the Participation in Selected Activities during a Year table. Ask questions such as the following:

● What information does the table display? It tells how popular various activities are among different categories of people.

● How is the information reported? It is given with percents.

● Where did the data come from? The data came from a sample of 15,000 households.

Student Page

Date _____ Time _____

LESSON 12·3 Ratios

Ratios can be expressed in many ways. All of the following are statements of ratios:

◆ It is estimated that by the year 2020 there will be 5 times as many people 100 years old or older than there were in 1990.

◆ Elementary school students make up about 14% of the U.S. population.

◆ On an average evening, about $\frac{1}{3}$ of the U.S. population watches TV.

◆ The chances of winning a lottery can be less than 1 in 1,000,000.

◆ A common scale for dollhouses is 1 inch to 12 inches.

A **ratio** uses division to compare two counts or measures having the same unit. Ratios can be stated or written in a variety of ways. Sometimes a ratio is easier to understand or will make more sense if it is rewritten in another form.

Example: In a group of ten students, eight students are right-handed and two are left-handed. The ratio of left-handed students to all students can be expressed in the following ways:

◆ With words: Two out of the ten students are left-handed.
Two in ten students are left-handed.
The ratio of left-handed students to all students is two to ten.

◆ With a fraction: $\frac{2}{10}$, or $\frac{1}{5}$ of the students are left-handed.

◆ With a percent: 20% of the students are left-handed.

◆ With a colon between the two numbers being compared:
The ratio of left-handed students to all students is 2:10 (two to ten).

Math Message

Express the ratio of right-handed students to all students in the example above.

1. With words: <u>Eight out of ten</u> students are right-handed.

2. With a fraction: <u>$\frac{8}{10}$, or $\frac{4}{5}$</u> of the students are right-handed.

3. With a percent: <u>80%</u> of the students are right-handed.

4. With a colon: The ratio of right-handed students to all students is <u>8:10</u>

Math Journal 2, p. 404

Student Page

LESSON 12·3 Using Ratios to Examine a Trend

1. **a.** According to the table on page 356 of the *Student Reference Book*, has the ratio of farmers to all working people increased or decreased since 1900?

   decreased

   b. Why do you think this has happened? **Sample answer: Fewer people are living in rural areas, and technology makes it possible for fewer people to do the same amount of work.**

2. **a.** Has the ratio of engineers to all working people increased or decreased since 1900?

   increased

   b. Why do you think this has happened? **Sample answer: With the increase in technology, more engineers are needed.**

3. **a.** How has the ratio of photographers to all working people changed since 1900?

   increased

   b. Why do you think this has happened? **Sample answer: Photography was not available to many people in 1900. Today, it is very popular.**

4. About how many farmers were there …

   a. in 1900? **9,700,000**

   b. in 2000? **3,400,000**

5. About how many photographers were there …

   a. in 1900? **29,000**

   b. in 2000? **137,000**

Math Journal 2, p. 405

Student Page

LESSON 12·3 10 Times

Have you ever heard or used expressions such as "10 times more," "10 times as many," "10 times less," or "$\frac{1}{10}$ as many?" These are **ratio comparisons**. Be sure to use expressions like these with caution. Increasing or reducing something by a factor of 10 makes a big difference!

Scientists call a difference of 10 times a **magnitude**, and they believe that the world as we know it changes drastically when something is increased or decreased by a magnitude.

Example: A person can jog about 5 miles per hour. A car can travel 10 times faster than that, or 50 miles per hour. A plane can travel 10 times faster than that, or 500 miles per hour. Each magnitude increase in travel speed has had a great effect on our lives.

Complete the following table. Then add two of your own events or items to the table.

Event or Item	Current Measure or Count	10 Times More	10 Times Less ($\frac{1}{10}$ as much)
Length of math class	Answers vary.		
Number of students in math class			
Length of your stride			

Math Journal 2, p. 406

Briefly discuss students' observations. Remind students that sometimes thinking of an alternative way to express a ratio can be helpful. The percents in the table can be restated with fractions or decimals, or with words such as "*x* out of 100 people participated in the activity."

Use your established slate procedures for the following questions:

- In which activities do more than 40% of 11-year-olds participate? swimming

- About how many 11-year-olds out of 100 go swimming? 41 About how many go bicycle riding? 39

- What is the third most popular activity among 11-year-olds? roller or in-line skating

- According to the survey, how many 11-year-olds out of 100 play basketball? About 32 What percent is this? 32% What simple fraction is this percent close to? $\frac{1}{3}$

- What percent of 11-year-olds go camping? About 28% Express this ratio as a fraction. $\frac{28}{100}$

- Is it true that baseball is played by 20 out of 100 11-year-olds, but by only 3 out of 100 people ages 35 to 44? Yes What fraction of 11-year-olds play baseball? $\frac{20}{100}$, or $\frac{1}{5}$

- What is an activity more popular among males than among females? Sample answer: golf What is an activity more popular among females than among males? Sample answer: Aerobic exercising Use ratios to support your answers. 17% of males, but only 4% of females play golf; 18% of females, but only 6% of males do aerobic exercising.

▶ Using Ratios to Examine Trends

PARTNER ACTIVITY

PROBLEM SOLVING

(*Math Journal 2*, p. 405; *Student Reference Book*, pp. 356 and 357)

 Social Studies Link Have partners read the information about work on *Student Reference Book*, page 356 and answer the questions on journal page 405.

Bring the class together to share answers and students' reasoning. Problems 4 and 5 can both be answered by referring to the ratios at the top of the *Student Reference Book* page and the bar graph at the bottom of the page showing the total number of workers.

- 1900: There was a total of 29 million workers. $\frac{1}{3}$ of these were farm workers. About 1 in 1,000 were photographers. 29 million divided by 3 = 9.7 million farm workers 29 million divided by 1,000 = 29,000 photographers

- 2000: There was a total of 137 million workers. $\frac{1}{40}$ of these were farm workers. About 1 in 1,000 were photographers. 137 million divided by 40 = 3.4 million farm workers 137 million divided by 1,000 = 137,000 photographers

Refer students to the icon graphs on *Student Reference Book*, page 357. Farm-worker populations are printed below the farmer icons (about 10 million in 1900, and about 3.5 million in 2000). Ask: *What does each individual icon represent?* Each individual icon represents 5 million people. *Why does the icon for the year 2000 show only $\frac{3}{5}$ of a farmer icon?* In the year 2000, there were 3 million farm-workers. This is $\frac{3}{5}$ of 5 million.

Based on trends, predict the ratios for various jobs in the year 2030 (when today's fifth graders will be in the workforce). Ask: *Will the fraction or percent of people in various jobs—farmers, engineers, clergy, and so on—increase, decrease, or stay about the same, compared with the current levels?*

▶ Considering What "10 Times" Means

(*Math Journal 2*, p. 406)

INDEPENDENT ACTIVITY
ELL

Read the introduction on journal page 406 as a class. Emphasize that a difference of 10 times, or $\frac{1}{10}$ of, is much larger than is commonly assumed. Have students complete the table of "10 times" and "$\frac{1}{10}$ of" for everyday events and items.

When most students have finished, discuss the table. Ask students to share any questions or insights they have about **ratio comparisons** and **magnitudes.** To support English language learners, write the key ideas on the board.

NOTE A difference of 10 times is often called a magnitude.

② Ongoing Learning & Practice

▶ Playing *First to 100*

(*Student Reference Book*, p. 308; *Math Masters*, pp. 456–458)

PARTNER ACTIVITY
COMPUTATION PRACTICE

Algebraic Thinking Students practice solving open number sentences by playing *First to 100*. This game was introduced in Lesson 4-7. For detailed instructions, see *Student Reference Book*, page 308.

▶ Math Boxes 12·3

(*Math Journal 2*, p. 407)

INDEPENDENT ACTIVITY

Mixed Practice Math Boxes in this lesson are paired with Math Boxes in Lesson 12-1.

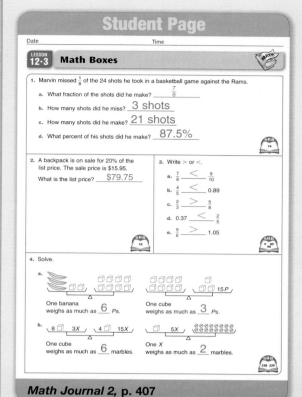

Date _____ Time _____

LESSON 12·3 **Math Boxes**

1. Marvin missed $\frac{1}{8}$ of the 24 shots he took in a basketball game against the Rams.
   a. What fraction of the shots did he make? $\frac{7}{8}$
   b. How many shots did he miss? **3 shots**
   c. How many shots did he make? **21 shots**
   d. What percent of his shots did he make? **87.5%**

2. A backpack is on sale for 20% of the list price. The sale price is $15.95.
   What is the list price? **$79.75**

3. Write > or <.
   a. $\frac{7}{8}$ < $\frac{9}{10}$
   b. $\frac{4}{5}$ < 0.89
   c. $\frac{2}{3}$ > $\frac{5}{8}$
   d. 0.37 < $\frac{2}{5}$
   e. $\frac{9}{6}$ > 1.05

4. Solve.
   a. One banana weighs as much as **6** *P*s. One cube weighs as much as **3** *P*s.
   b. One cube weighs as much as **6** marbles. One *X* weighs as much as **2** marbles.

Math Journal 2, p. 407

Name _____ Date _____ Time _____

STUDY LINK 12·3 **Ratios**

Ratios can be stated or written in a variety of ways. Sometimes a ratio is easier to understand or will make more sense if it is rewritten in another form.

Example: In a group of 25 students, 16 students walk to school and 9 take a bus. The ratio of students who take a bus compared to all students in the group can be expressed in the following ways:

◆ With words: Nine out of twenty-five students take a bus.
◆ With a fraction: $\frac{9}{25}$ of the students take a bus.
◆ With a percent: 36% of the students take a bus.
◆ With a colon between the two numbers being compared: The ratio of students who take a bus to all students in the group is 9:25 (nine out of twenty-five).

Revise the above statements to express the ratio of students who walk to school to all students.

1. With words: <u>Sixteen out of twenty-five</u> students walk to school.
2. With a fraction: <u>$\frac{16}{25}$</u> of the students walk to school.
3. With a percent: <u>64%</u> of the students walk to school.
4. With a colon: The ratio of students who walk to school to all students is <u>16:25</u>

In each problem, fill in the ovals next to each correct ratio.

5. Fifty cars drove past in 10 minutes. Twenty-three cars were blue.
   ○ 23:50 of the cars were blue. ○ 23% of the cars were blue. ● 0.46 of the cars were blue.

6. In a group of 9 people, 6 were swimmers.
   ● $\frac{2}{3}$ of the people were swimmers. ● 6:9 of the people were swimmers. ● 66$\frac{2}{3}$% of the people were swimmers.

7. In a sports shop, 35 of the 40 caps sold the day before the World Series were baseball caps.
   ● 7 out of 8 caps sold were baseball caps. ○ 35% of the caps sold were baseball caps. ● 35:40 of the caps sold were baseball caps.

Math Masters, p. 353

Teaching Master

Name _____ Date _____ Time _____

LESSON 12·3 Picturing Ratios

The following pictograph shows how the 785 students at Windward Academy responded to a survey about the activities they thought were the most summer fun.

Pictograph of Summer Fun Data

Swimming	☀☀☀☀☀☀☀☀
Traveling	☀☀☀☀☀☀☀☀☀☀☀☀
Organized Sports	☀☀☀☀☀☀☀⁑
Bike Riding	☀☀☀⁑
Reading	☀⁑
Other	☀☀☀

Each ☀ represents 20 students.

Use the pictograph to answer the questions.

1. How many ☀ would represent 100 students? __5 suns__

2. Which activity is the most popular for students at Windward Academy? __traveling__

3. Which activity is about $\frac{1}{2}$ as popular as traveling? __swimming__

4. Which activity is five times more popular than reading? __Organized sports__

5. Explain how using a pictograph to solve simple ratio problems is different from using only numbers. Use an example to support your explanation.
__Sample answer: In one way, it is easier because you can__
__see the differences. In another way, it is harder because__
__you have to convert the symbols into numbers to find exact__
__amounts of differences. For example, to find out how many__
__students like bike riding, you have to figure out how much__
__$\frac{1}{4}$ of a sun is worth.__

Math Masters, p. 354

Teaching Master

Name _____ Date _____ Time _____

LESSON 12·3 More Ratios

1. There are 12 children on a bus. In all, 50 people are on the bus. Express the ratio of children to all people on the bus.

   a. With words: __Twelve out of fifty__ people on the bus are children.

   b. With a fraction: __$\frac{12}{50}$, or $\frac{6}{25}$__ of the people on the bus are children.

   c. With a percent: __24%__ of the people on the bus are children.

   d. With a colon: The ratio of children to all people on the bus is __12:50, or 6:25__

2. In Mrs. Horton's fifth-grade class, 6 students own a cat. In all, 20 students own pets. Express the ratio of cat owners to all pet owners in the class.

   a. With words: __Six out of twenty__ pet owners are cat owners.

   b. With a fraction: __$\frac{6}{20}$, or $\frac{3}{10}$__ of all pet owners are cat owners.

   c. With a percent: __30%__ of all pet owners are cat owners.

   d. With a colon: The ratio of cat owners to all pet owners is __6:20, or 3:10__

3. In a survey about favorite flavors of ice cream, 8 people said they liked chocolate ice cream best. A total of 24 people were surveyed. Express the ratio of people who chose chocolate ice cream as their favorite to all the people surveyed.

   a. With words: __Eight out of twenty-four__ people surveyed prefer chocolate.

   b. With a fraction: __$\frac{8}{24}$, or $\frac{1}{3}$__ of the people surveyed prefer chocolate.

   c. With a percent: __$33\frac{1}{3}$%__ of the people surveyed prefer chocolate.

   d. With a colon: The ratio of people who prefer chocolate to all the people surveyed is __8:24, or 1:3__

Math Masters, p. 356

▶ **Study Link 12·3**

(*Math Masters,* p. 353)

INDEPENDENT ACTIVITY

 Home Connection Students write ratios in various forms and answer questions about ratios.

3 Differentiation Options

READINESS

PARTNER ACTIVITY

5–15 Min

▶ **Reading a Pictograph**

(*Math Masters,* p. 354)

To provide experience with representing ratios in a variety of ways, have students answer questions based on a pictograph. When students have finished the page, have them compare representing ratios in pictographs with using numbers (fractions, decimals, or percents) to represent ratios.

ENRICHMENT

INDEPENDENT ACTIVITY

15–30 Min

▶ **Imagining 10 Times More or 10 Times Less**

(*Math Masters,* p. 355)

 Language Arts Link To apply students' understanding of ratio comparisons and magnitude, have students write a story about what life would be like if select things were suddenly 10 times more/greater or 10 times less/smaller.

EXTRA PRACTICE

INDEPENDENT ACTIVITY

5–15 Min

▶ **Reading and Writing Ratios**

(*Math Masters,* p. 356)

Students read ratios in three different word problem situations. They rewrite the ratios in words, as fractions, as percents, and in colon notation.

930 Unit 12 Probability, Ratios, and Rates

12·4 Ratios of Parts to Wholes

 Objective To provide experience with ratios of part of a set to the whole set.

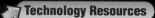 **Technology Resources** www.everydaymathonline.com

 Presentations

 eToolkit

 Algorithms Practice

 EM Facts Workshop Game™

 Family Letters

 Assessment Management

 Common Core State Standards

Curriculum Focal Points

 Interactive Teacher's Lesson Guide

1 Teaching the Lesson

Key Concepts and Skills

- Use equivalent fractions and ratio models to solve fraction-of problems.
  [Number and Numeration Goal 2]

- Model and solve ratio problems.
  [Operations and Computation Goal 7]

Key Activities

Students use tiles to model and solve ratio problems that compare part of a set to the whole set.

 Ongoing Assessment:
Informing Instruction See page 933.

 Ongoing Assessment:
Recognizing Student Achievement
Use journal page 408.
[Operations and Computation Goal 7]

Materials

Math Journal 2, pp. 408 and 409
Math Masters, p. 431
Study Link 12·3
scissors ◆ envelope

2 Ongoing Learning & Practice

Calculating Choices

Math Journal 2, p. 410
Students use the Multiplication Counting Principle to solve problems.

 Math Boxes 12·4

Math Journal 2, p. 411
Students practice and maintain skills through Math Box problems.

 Study Link 12·4

Math Masters, p. 357
Students practice and maintain skills through Study Link activities.

3 Differentiation Options

READINESS

Writing Ratios in Simplest Form

Math Masters, p. 358
Students write ratios as fractions in simplest form.

EXTRA PRACTICE

Using Ratios to Compare

Math Masters, p. 359
Square Tiles (*Math Masters,* p. 431; optional)
Students solve a set of ratio problems.

Advance Preparation

For Part 1, each student will need a small envelope in which to store the tiles cut from *Math Masters,* page 431.

 Teacher's Reference Manual, Grades 4–6 pp. 64–68

Getting Started

Mental Math and Reflexes

Have students solve fraction-of problems.
Ask volunteers to share their solution strategies.
Suggestions:

- If the whole set is 15, $\frac{2}{3}$ of the set is how many? 10
- If the whole set is 20, $\frac{3}{5}$ of the set is how many? 12
- If the whole set is 36, $\frac{7}{9}$ of the set is how many? 28
- If the whole set is 24, $\frac{7}{8}$ of the set is how many? 21
- If the whole set is 42, $\frac{4}{7}$ of the set is how many? 24

Math Message

Cut out the 48 square tiles on Math Masters, *page 431. Store them in an envelope.*

Study Link 12·3 Follow-Up

Have students compare answers and resolve differences.

---

1 Teaching the Lesson

▶ Math Message Follow-Up

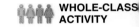 **WHOLE-CLASS ACTIVITY**

(*Math Masters*, p. 431)

Write the following problem on the board or a transparency:

▷ There are 20 students in Mr. Wyatt's class. Three out of 5 students are girls. How many students are girls?

Ask: *How would you solve this problem?* There are 4 groups of 5 in the class. 3 students in every group are girls: $3 * 4 = 12$. There are 12 girls in Mr. Wyatt's class. Explain that the square tiles they cut out from *Math Masters*, page 431 can be used to model this type of ratio problem. Have students use their cutout tiles to complete the following:

▷ Take out 20 tiles. Let each tile stand for 1 student. Separate the 20 tiles into 4 groups of 5 tiles. Turn the tiles in each group so that the shaded side is up on 3 of them and the white side is up on the rest. Count the number of shaded tiles. These represent the total number of girls.

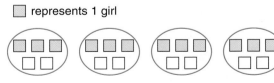

12 girls out of 20 students

▶ Solving Ratio Problems

 WHOLE-CLASS ACTIVITY ELL

Have students use their tiles to model the solutions to the following ratio problems. To support English language learners, make a sketch of the tiles for each problem and the resulting number sentence.

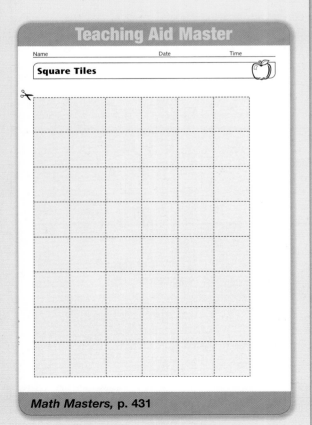

1. Place 15 tiles on your desk so that the white side is up on 1 out of every 3 tiles. How many tiles are white? 5 How many are shaded? 10

2. Place 24 tiles on your desk so that 3 out of every 4 tiles are white. How many are white? 18 How many are shaded? 6

3. Place 4 white tiles on your desk. Add some shaded tiles so that 1 out of 7 tiles is white. How many tiles are there in all? 28

4. Place 16 white tiles on your desk. Add some shaded tiles so that 2 out of 3 tiles are white. How many tiles are there in all? 24

5. Place 36 tiles on your desk so that 15 out of 18 are white. How many are white? 30 How many are shaded? 6

6. Place 35 tiles on your desk so that 4 out of 10 are white. How many are white? 14 How many are shaded? 21

Emphasize that these examples represent three types of problems:

▷ In Problems 1 and 2, the total number of tiles and a ratio in its simplest form are given. Students are to find the numbers of white and shaded tiles.

▷ In Problems 3 and 4, the number of white tiles and a ratio in its simplest form are given. Students are supposed to find the total number of tiles.

▷ Problems 5 and 6 are similar to Problems 1 and 2, except that the given ratio is not in simplest form. One way to solve Problem 5 is to double the given ratio—a ratio of 15 out of 18 is the same as a ratio of 30 out of 36. You can solve Problem 6 by dividing the ratio by 2—a ratio of 4 out of 10 is the same as a ratio of 2 out of 5.

✔ Ongoing Assessment: Informing Instruction

Watch for students who use the wrong total number of tiles. *For example:*

"1 out of 4 is shaded" might incorrectly be modeled as

"3 out of 5 are shaded" might incorrectly be modeled as

Have students place the total number of tiles in front of them, and then turn over the indicated number of shaded tiles.

▶ Solving Ratio Problems

(*Math Journal 2*, pp. 408 and 409)

INDEPENDENT ACTIVITY

Read the instructions on journal page 408 as a class. Then have students use their tiles to model and solve the number stories involving ratios on journal pages 408 and 409.

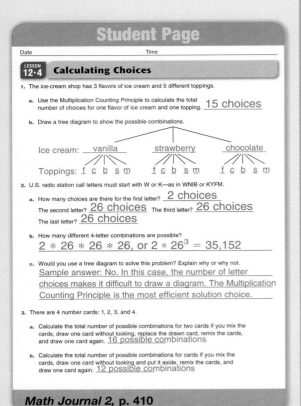

Student Page

Date _____ Time _____

LESSON 12·4 Calculating Choices

1. The ice-cream shop has 3 flavors of ice cream and 5 different toppings.

   a. Use the Multiplication Counting Principle to calculate the total number of choices for one flavor of ice cream and one topping. __15 choices__

   b. Draw a tree diagram to show the possible combinations.

   Ice cream: vanilla   strawberry   chocolate
   Toppings: f c b s m   f c b s m   f c b s m

2. U.S. radio station call letters must start with W or K—as in WNIB or KYFM.

   a. How many choices are there for the first letter? __2 choices__
   The second letter? __26 choices__ The third letter? __26 choices__
   The last letter? __26 choices__

   b. How many different 4-letter combinations are possible?
   __2 * 26 * 26 * 26, or 2 * 26³ = 35,152__

   c. Would you use a tree diagram to solve this problem? Explain why or why not.
   __Sample answer: No. In this case, the number of letter__
   __choices makes it difficult to draw a diagram. The Multiplication__
   __Counting Principle is the most efficient solution choice.__

3. There are 4 number cards: 1, 2, 3, and 4.

   a. Calculate the total number of possible combinations for two cards if you mix the cards, draw one card without looking, replace the drawn card, remix the cards, and draw one card again. __16 possible combinations__

   b. Calculate the total number of possible combinations for cards if you mix the cards, draw one card without looking and put it aside, remix the cards, and draw one card again. __12 possible combinations__

Math Journal 2, p. 410

When most students have finished, discuss their solution strategies. Point out that for Problem 2 on journal page 409, one approach is to rename the ratio in simplest form—6 out of 9 is equal to $\frac{2}{3}$ of the total number of tiles. So x out of 15 will also have to equal $\frac{2}{3}$. Therefore, 10 out of the 15 tiles are white.

Ongoing Assessment:
Recognizing Student Achievement   Journal Page 408 ★

Use **journal page 408** to assess students' ability to solve ratio problems. Students are making adequate progress if their solutions and drawings for Problems 1 and 3 are correct.

[Operations and Computation Goal 7]

---

2 Ongoing Learning & Practice

▶ **Calculating Choices**   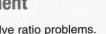 PARTNER ACTIVITY
(*Math Journal 2,* p. 410)

Students use the Multiplication Counting Principle to solve problems.

▶ **Math Boxes 12·4**   INDEPENDENT ACTIVITY
(*Math Journal 2,* p. 411)

 Mixed Practice Math Boxes in this lesson are paired with Math Boxes in Lesson 12-2.

Writing/Reasoning Have students write a response to the following: *If you did not have a calculator available for Problem 4, what value would you use for π?* I would use 3.14 to represent π.

▶ **Study Link 12·4**   INDEPENDENT ACTIVITY
(*Math Masters,* p. 357)

 **Home Connection** Students practice solving ratio problems similar to the ones done in class.

Student Page

Date _____ Time _____

LESSON 12·4 Math Boxes

1. Divide mentally.
   a. 472 ÷ 5 → __94 R2__
   b. 389 / 6 → __64 R5__
   c. 729 / 8 → __91 R1__
   d. 543 ÷ 4 → __135 R3__
   e. 580 ÷ 9 → __64 R4__

2. a. A rectangle has an area of 8 cm². Draw and label the sides of the rectangle.
   Sample answers:
   4 cm
   2 cm

   b. What is the perimeter of the rectangle you've drawn? __12 cm__

3. Multiply. Show your work.
   a. 2.6
      * 3.2
      8.32

   b. 7.1 * 0.58 =
      4.118

   c. Explain your strategy for solving Problem 3b.
   __Answers vary.__

4. a. Draw a circle with a radius of 2.5 centimeters.

   2.5 cm

   b. What is the area of this circle to the nearest square centimeter?
   Area = π * radius²
   About __20 cm²__
   (unit)

Math Journal 2, p. 411

---

③ Differentiation Options

READINESS

SMALL-GROUP ACTIVITY

▶ **Writing Ratios in Simplest Form**

5–15 Min

(*Math Masters,* p. 358)

To explore the relationship between ratios and equivalent fractions, have students write ratios as fractions in simplest form. When students have finished, discuss their solution strategies.

EXTRA PRACTICE

INDEPENDENT ACTIVITY

▶ **Using Ratios to Compare**

5–15 Min

(*Math Masters,* p. 359)

Students solve a set of ratio problems. They may use the Square Tiles from *Math Masters,* page 431 to help them.

Planning Ahead

In Lesson 12-7, students collect heart-rate data after increasingly strenuous activity, in which they step up on and down from a chair. If necessary, prepare a permission slip, and send it home for parents or guardians to sign. Sample forms are provided on *Math Masters,* page 360.

Study Link Master

Name _____ Date _____ Time _____

STUDY LINK 12·4 Ratios Problems

1. Draw 20 tiles so that 2 out of 10 tiles are white and the rest are shaded.

   a. How many tiles are white? __4__ tiles

   b. How many tiles are shaded? __16__ tiles

2. Draw 9 shaded tiles.

   Add white tiles until 2 out of 5 tiles are white.

   How many tiles are there in all? __15__ tiles

3. Imagine 48 tiles. If 4 out of 12 tiles are white, how many tiles are white? __16__ tiles

4. There are 24 players on the soccer team. Two out of every 3 players have not scored a goal yet this year. How many players have scored a goal this year? __8__ players

5. For every 8 spelling tests Justine took, she earned 3 perfect scores. If Justine earned 12 perfect scores this year, how many spelling tests did she take? __32__ tests

Practice

6. $92\overline{)9{,}054}$ → __98 R38__

7. 98 * 92 = __9,016__

8. 90.16 + 0.38 = __90.54__

9. 90.54 * 10² = __9,054__

Math Masters, p. 357

Teaching Master

Name _____ Date _____ Time _____

LESSON 12·4 Writing Ratios

Some **ratios** compare part of a collection of things to the total number of things in the collection. The statement *6 out of 24 fifth graders have a pet* compares the number of fifth graders who have pets to the total number of fifth graders. This ratio can be expressed in several ways.

In *words:* For every 24 fifth graders, 6 have a pet. Six in 24 fifth graders have a pet. The ratio of fifth graders who have pets to the total number of fifth graders is 6 to 24.

With a *fraction:* $\frac{6}{24}$ of fifth graders have a pet.

A ratio is in simplest form if, when expressed as a fraction, the fraction is in simplest form. For example, the ratio *9 out of 36 fifth graders wear braces on his or her teeth* can be expressed in simplest form as $\frac{1}{4}$ of fifth graders wear braces.

Express each ratio below with a fraction, using the simplest form.

1. Eighteen out of 24 fifth graders do not have a pet.
   $\frac{3}{4}$ of fifth graders do not have a pet.

2. There are 18 water birds in the pond and 3 are swans.
   $\frac{1}{6}$ of the water birds are swans.

3. Of the 54 tropical fish in the school aquarium, 27 are tiger fish.
   $\frac{1}{2}$ of the fish are tiger fish.

4. For every 6 hot dogs sold at the ballpark, 4 are chili dogs.
   $\frac{2}{3}$ of the hot dogs sold are chili dogs.

Math Masters, p. 358

Teaching Master

Name _____ Date _____ Time _____

LESSON 12·4 Ratios

Solve the following ratio problems. Use the Square Tiles from *Math Journal 2,* Activity Sheet 7 to help you.

1. Place 20 tiles on your desk so that 3 out of 4 tiles are white and the rest are shaded.
   How many tiles are white? __15__
   How many tiles are shaded? __5__

2. Place 25 tiles on your desk so that 3 out of 5 tiles are white and the rest are shaded.
   How many tiles are white? __15__
   How many tiles are shaded? __10__

3. Place 4 white tiles on your desk. Add some tiles until 1 out of 5 tiles is white and the rest are shaded. How many tiles are there in all? __20__

4. Place 9 white tiles on your desk. Add some tiles until 3 out of 8 tiles are white and the rest are shaded. How many tiles are there in all? __24__

5. Imagine 28 tiles. If 4 out of 7 are white, how many are white? __16__

6. Imagine 24 tiles. If 5 out of 6 are white, how many are white? __20__

7. Place 18 tiles on your desk so that 6 are white and the rest are shaded.
   One out of __3__ tiles is white.

8. Place 30 tiles on your desk so that 20 are white and the rest are shaded.
   Out of 3 tiles, __2__ are white.

9. Make up a ratio number story for a partner to solve.

   _____

   Answer: _____

Math Masters, p. 359

12·5 Number Models for Ratio Number Stories

◎ **Objective** To introduce writing number models for ratio number stories.

▶ **Technology Resources** www.everydaymathonline.com

| ePresentations | eToolkit | Algorithms Practice | EM Facts Workshop Game™ | Family Letters | Assessment Management | Common Core State Standards | Curriculum Focal Points | Interactive Teacher's Lesson Guide |

---

1 Teaching the Lesson

Key Concepts and Skills
- Use equivalent fractions and ratio models to solve ratio number stories.
  [Number and Numeration Goal 5]
- Model and solve ratio problems.
  [Operations and Computation Goal 7]

Key Activities
Students use tiles to model and solve number stories involving ratios of part of a set to the whole set. They write and solve number models that represent ratio number stories.

 Ongoing Assessment:
Informing Instruction See page 938.

 Ongoing Assessment:
Informing Instruction See page 939.

Materials
Math Journal 2, pp. 412 and 413
Study Link 12·4
Square Tiles ◆ slate

2 Ongoing Learning & Practice

Dividing with Unit Fractions
Math Journal 2, p. 414; *Student Reference Book,* pp. 80A and 80B
Students practice dividing with unit fractions and whole numbers.

 Math Boxes 12·5
Math Journal 2, p. 415
Students practice and maintain skills through Math Box problems.

 Ongoing Assessment:
Recognizing Student Achievement
Use Math Boxes, Problem 3.
[Operations and Computation Goal 6]

 Study Link 12·5
Math Masters, p. 361
Students practice and maintain skills through Study Link activities.

3 Differentiation Options

ENRICHMENT
Introducing Cross Multiplication for Solving Ratio Problems
Math Masters, p. 362
Students use cross multiplication to solve ratio number stories.

EXTRA PRACTICE
Solving Ratio Number Stories
Math Masters, p. 363
Students write and solve ratio number stories.

Advance Preparation

 Teacher's Reference Manual, Grades 4–6 pp. 64–68

Getting Started

Mental Math and Reflexes

Have students find equivalent fractions. Ask volunteers to explain how they used the multiplication rule or the division rule in their solutions. *Suggestions:*

○○○ Find equivalent fractions with a denominator of 4.

$$\frac{3}{2} \quad \frac{6}{4} \qquad \frac{4}{1} \quad \frac{16}{4} \qquad \frac{12}{8} \quad \frac{6}{4}$$

●○○ Find equivalent fractions with a denominator of 12.

$$\frac{6}{36} \quad \frac{2}{12} \qquad \frac{24}{6} \quad \frac{48}{12} \qquad 3 \quad \frac{36}{12}$$

●●○ Find equivalent fractions with a numerator of 8.

$$\frac{2}{7} \quad \frac{8}{28} \qquad \frac{16}{20} \quad \frac{8}{10} \qquad \frac{88}{121} \quad \frac{8}{11}$$

Math Message

Model this problem using your tiles. Then write the solution as a faction to express the ratio. Josie tosses a penny 32 times. It lands heads up 5 out of 8 times. How many times does the penny land heads up? $\frac{20}{32}$

Study Link 12·4 Follow-Up

Have partners share their answers and resolve differences.

---

1 Teaching the Lesson

▶ Math Message Follow-Up

👥👥 **WHOLE-CLASS DISCUSSION**

Ask volunteers to draw their tile models on the board and explain their solution strategies. Encourage students to use ratio language when sharing their solutions. *For example:*

▷ If the penny landed heads up 5 out of 8 tosses, it must have landed heads up on 20 out of 32 tosses.

▷ For every 8 tosses, the penny landed heads up 5 times. So it landed heads up 20 times in 32 tosses.

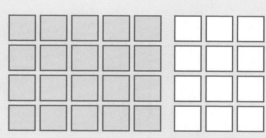

HEADS: 20   TAILS: 12

Square Tiles from *Math Journal 2,* Activity Sheet 7

▶ Introducing Number Models for Ratio Number Stories

👥👥 **WHOLE-CLASS ACTIVITY**

ELL

Algebraic Thinking Show students how to represent the Math Message problem with a number model. *Josie tossed a penny 32 times. It landed heads up 5 out of 8 times. How many times did the penny land heads up?*

Ask a volunteer to express the ratio *5 out of 8 times* as a fraction. $\frac{5}{8}$ Write the fraction on the board or a transparency. This ratio is equivalent to an unknown number of times the penny landed heads up out of 32 tosses. To support English language learners, discuss the meaning of *unknown* in this context, and explain that it can be represented by using a symbol as shown in the display. Add this information to the display on the board or transparency.

Explain that when writing a number model for a ratio number story, it is important to keep in mind what the numerator and denominator of the fraction represent. One approach is to write key words next to the numerator and denominator. Add the words *heads* and *tosses* to the display. (*See margin.*)

$$\text{(heads)} \ \frac{5}{8} = \frac{\square}{32} \ \text{(tosses)}$$

Student Page

Date _____ Time _____

LESSON 12·5 **More Ratio Number Stories**

Student Page (left top)

Date _____ Time _____

LESSON 12·5 More Ratio Number Stories

You can solve ratio number stories by first writing a number model for the story.

> **Example:** Sidney missed 2 out of 9 problems on the math test. There were 36 problems on the test. How many problems did he miss?
>
> ◆ Write a number model. $\frac{\text{(missed)}}{\text{(total)}} \frac{2}{9} = \frac{\square}{36}$
>
> ◆ Find the missing number.
>
> Think: 9 times what number equals 36? $9 * 4 = 36$
>
> Multiply the numerator, 2, by this number: $2 * 4 = 8$
>
> $\frac{\text{(missed)}}{\text{(total)}} \frac{2 * 4}{9 * 4} = \frac{8}{36}$
>
> ◆ Answer: Sidney missed 8 out of 36 problems.

Write a number model for each problem. Then solve the problem.

1. Of the 42 animals in the Children's Zoo, 3 out of 7 are mammals. How many mammals are in the Children's Zoo?

Number model: $\frac{\text{(mammals)}}{\text{(animals)}} \frac{3}{7} = \frac{\square}{42}$ or x Answer: __18 mammals__ (unit)

2. Five out of 8 students at Kenwood School play an instrument. There are 224 students at the school. How many students play an instrument?

Number model: $\frac{\text{(play instrument)}}{\text{(students)}} \frac{5}{8} = \frac{\square}{224}$ or x Answer: __140 students__ (unit)

3. Mr. Lopez sells subscriptions to a magazine. Each subscription costs $18. For each subscription he sells, he earns $8. One week, he sold $198 worth of subscriptions. How much did he earn?

Number model: $\frac{\text{(earnings)}}{\text{(subscriptions)}} \frac{8}{18} = \frac{\square}{198}$ or x Answer: __$88__

Math Journal 2, p. 412

Student Page (left bottom)

Date _____ Time _____

LESSON 12·5 More Ratio Number Stories *continued*

4. Make up a ratio number story. Ask your partner to solve it.

_____

_____

_____

Number model: _____

Answer: _____

Find the missing number.

5. $\frac{1}{3} = \frac{x}{39}$
   $x =$ __13__

6. $\frac{3}{4} = \frac{21}{y}$
   $y =$ __28__

7. $\frac{7}{8} = \frac{f}{56}$
   $f =$ __49__

8. $\frac{1}{5} = \frac{13}{n}$
   $n =$ __65__

9. $\frac{5}{6} = \frac{m}{42}$
   $m =$ __35__

10. $\frac{9}{25} = \frac{s}{100}$
    $s =$ __36__

11. There are 48 students in the fifth grade at Robert's school. Three out of 8 fifth graders read two books last month. One out of 3 students read just one book. The rest of the students read no books at all.

How many books in all did the fifth graders read last month? __52 books__ (unit)

Explain what you did to find the answer.

$\frac{3}{8} = \frac{\square}{48} \rightarrow \frac{3*6}{8*6} = \frac{18}{48}$. So 18 students read two books each.

That is 36 books in all. $\frac{1}{3} = \frac{\square}{48} \rightarrow \frac{1*16}{3*16} = \frac{16}{48}$. So 16 students

read 1 book each. The total number of books read was

$36 + 16 = 52$.

Math Journal 2, p. 413

Tell students that to find the missing number in the number model, they need to find a fraction that has 32 as its denominator and is equivalent to $\frac{5}{8}$. Ask: *Would you use the multiplication rule or the division rule to find the equivalent fraction?* The multiplication rule *Why?* 8 is less than 32, so multiply. Think: *8 times what number equals 32?* Since $8 * 4 = 32$, multiply the denominator, 8, and the numerator, 5, by 4. **Modify the display on the board or transparency:**

$$\frac{\text{(heads)}}{\text{(tosses)}} \frac{5 * 4}{8 * 4} = \frac{20}{32}$$

The penny landed heads up 20 times.

Give another example:

● Marcus received 3 votes for every 5 votes cast. If he received 18 votes, how many votes were cast?

Ask students to write a number model for the problem. When most students have finished, ask a volunteer to express the ratio *3 votes for every 5 votes cast* as a fraction. $\frac{3}{5}$ Write the fraction on the board or a transparency. Ask volunteers to explain how to complete writing the number model for the problem.

$$\frac{\text{(Marcus's votes)}}{\text{(total votes)}} \frac{3}{5} = \frac{18}{\square}$$

Ask: *How would you find the missing number?* Think: *3 times what number equals 18?* Since $3 * 6 = 18$, multiply the numerator, 3, and the denominator, 5, by 6. **Modify the display on the board or transparency:**

$$\frac{\text{(Marcus's votes)}}{\text{(total votes)}} \frac{3 * 6}{5 * 6} = \frac{18}{30}$$

In all, 30 votes were cast.

 Ongoing Assessment: Informing Instruction

Watch for students who write 18 in the denominator instead of the numerator. Have them read the parts of the problem as they work. For example, Marcus received 3 of every 5 votes. Marcus received 18 votes, so 18 is the numerator. The denominator is the unknown.

▶ Solving Ratio Number Stories

 WHOLE-CLASS ACTIVITY

PROBLEM SOLVING

(Math Journal 2, pp. 412 and 413)

Algebraic Thinking Pose ratio number stories for students to solve. Have them write number models for the number stories on their slates and then solve the number models. Discuss solutions after each problem.

Suggestions:

▷ Maria saved \$2 out of every \$5 she earned delivering newspapers. How much did she save from earnings of \$45? $18

▷ Two out of 3 pieces of candy in a bag are lemon flavored. The bag contains 24 lemon-flavored pieces of candy. How many pieces of candy are in the bag? 36 pieces

▷ A parking garage reserves 1 out of 11 parking spaces for cars with handicapped permits. If the garage has 99 parking spaces in all, how many are reserved for handicapped spaces? 9 parking spaces

▷ A choir has 50 members. Twenty members are sopranos. How many sopranos are there for every 5 members of the choir? 2 sopranos

 Ongoing Assessment: Informing Instruction

Watch for students who have difficulty writing the number models. Have them work with a partner to model the number stories with their square tiles.

Have students complete journal pages 412 and 413. Remind students to label their number models for the ratio problems with key words next to the numerators and denominators.

2 Ongoing Learning & Practice

Dividing with Unit Fractions
👤 **INDEPENDENT ACTIVITY**

(*Math Journal 2,* p. 414; *Student Reference Book,* pp. 80A and 80B)

Students practice dividing a whole number by a unit fraction, and a unit fraction by a whole number. Students use the relationship of multiplication and division to solve problems. Remind students to review *Student Reference Book,* pages 80A and 80B as needed.

Math Boxes 12·5
👤 **INDEPENDENT ACTIVITY**

(*Math Journal 2,* p. 415)

 Mixed Practice Math Boxes in this lesson are paired with Math Boxes in Lesson 12-7.

 Ongoing Assessment: Recognizing Student Achievement
Math Boxes Problem 3 ★

Use **Math Boxes, Problem 3** to assess students' ability to estimate and solve multidigit multiplication problems. Students are making adequate progress if their estimates demonstrate the use of magnitude and their solutions are correct.

[Operations and Computation Goal 6]

Date _____ Time _____

LESSON 12·5   Dividing with Unit Fractions

1. Five pizzas will each be sliced into fourths. Use the circles to show how the pizzas will be cut. Find how many slices there will be in all.

The pizzas will be cut into __20__ slices.

$5 \div \frac{1}{4} = $ __20__

2. The blueberries in $\frac{1}{5}$ of a farmer's field need to be picked. Four workers will share the work equally. Divide the rectangle to show how much of the field each worker will pick.

Each worker will pick __$\frac{1}{20}$__ of the field.

$\frac{1}{5} \div 4 = $ __$\frac{1}{20}$__

3. Each division number sentence on the left can be solved by using a related multiplication number sentence on the right. Write the letter for the multiplication sentence next to its related division sentence.

Division		Multiplication
$8 \div \frac{1}{3} = n$	__d__	a. $n * 10 = \frac{1}{8}$
$\frac{1}{8} \div 10 = n$	__a__	b. $n * 8 = \frac{1}{3}$
$8 \div \frac{1}{10} = n$	__c__	c. $n * \frac{1}{10} = 8$
$\frac{1}{3} \div 8 = n$	__b__	d. $n * \frac{1}{3} = 8$

4. Solve the following division number sentences (from above). Use the related multiplication number sentences to help you find each quotient.

a. $8 \div \frac{1}{3} = $ __24__   b. $\frac{1}{8} \div 10 = $ __$\frac{1}{80}$__

c. $8 \div \frac{1}{10} = $ __80__   d. $\frac{1}{3} \div 8 = $ __$\frac{1}{24}$__

Math Journal 2, p. 414

Date _____ Time _____

LESSON 12·5   Math Boxes

1. Rewrite each fraction pair with common denominators.

a. $\frac{1}{3}$ and $\frac{1}{2}$ __$\frac{2}{6}$ and $\frac{3}{6}$__

b. $\frac{3}{4}$ and $\frac{2}{5}$ __$\frac{15}{20}$ and $\frac{8}{20}$__

c. $\frac{2}{8}$ and $\frac{9}{12}$ __$\frac{6}{24}$ and $\frac{18}{24}$__

2. List the factors of 142.

__1, 2, 71, 142__

3. Estimate the answer for each problem. Then solve the problem.

	Estimate	Solution
a. $302 * 57$	15,000	17,214
b. $599 * 9$	5,400	5,391
c. $701 * 97$	70,000	67,997
d. $498 * 501$	250,000	249,498

4. There are 270 students in the soccer league. Two out of three students are boys. How many students are boys? __180 students__

5. Complete the table. Graph the data and connect the points with line segments.

Maryanne earns \$12 per hour.

Rule:
Earnings = 12 * number of hours

Hours	Earnings
2	\$24.00
4	\$48.00
5	60
7	84
9	\$108.00

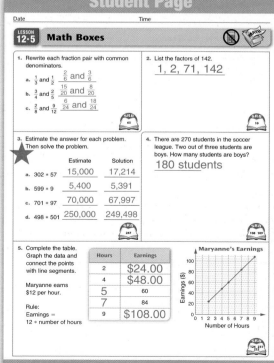

Maryanne's Earnings

Math Journal 2, p. 415

Study Link Master

Study Link 12·5 ▶ **INDEPENDENT ACTIVITY**

(Math Masters, p. 361)

 **Home Connection** Students write and solve number models for ratio problems.

Name   **Date**   **Time**

STUDY LINK 12·5 | **Ratio Problems**

Find the missing number.

1. $\frac{1}{5} = \frac{x}{40}$ $x = $ __8__

2. $\frac{2}{3} = \frac{16}{y}$ $y = $ __24__

3. $\frac{5}{6} = \frac{m}{54}$ $m = $ __45__

4. $\frac{1}{4} = \frac{15}{n}$ $n = $ __60__

5. $\frac{5}{8} = \frac{f}{32}$ $f = $ __20__

6. $\frac{13}{50} = \frac{g}{100}$ $g = $ __26__

Write a number model for each problem. Then solve the problem.

7. Of the 115 students in the sixth grade, 2 out of 5 belong to the Drama Club. How many students are members of the Drama Club?

Number model: $\frac{2}{5} = \frac{\square}{115}$ Answer: __46 students__ (unit)

8. Three out of 4 students at Highland School ordered a hot lunch today. There are 156 students at the school. How many students ordered a hot lunch?

Number model: $\frac{3}{4} = \frac{\square}{156}$ Answer: __117 students__ (unit)

9. Gina and the other members of her troop sell cookies for $3 a box. For each box they sell, the troop earns $1.50. One week, Gina's troop sold $90 worth of cookies. How much did the troop earn?

Number model: $\frac{1.50}{3} = \frac{\square}{90}$ Answer: __$45.00__

10. 30% of the tickets sold by a movie theater for the Friday night show were children's tickets at $4 each. The rest of the tickets were sold at the full price of $8.50. The movie theater collected $360 just for the children's tickets. How many tickets did they sell in all?

Number model: $360 \div 4 = 90;$ $\frac{30}{100} = \frac{90}{x}$ Answer: __300 tickets__ (unit)

Practice

11. $6^3 = $ __216__   12. $3^6 = $ __729__   13. $6^3 * 10^2 = $ __21,600__

Math Masters, p. 361

---

3 Differentiation Options

ENRICHMENT ▶ **SMALL-GROUP ACTIVITY**

Introducing Cross Multiplication for Solving Ratio Problems 🕐 15–30 Min

(Math Masters, p. 362)

Algebraic Thinking To explore using cross multiplication to solve ratio problems, have students solve ratio number stories. Ask students to write the number model for the problem from this lesson's Math Message and use the variable x for the missing number.

$$\text{(HEADS)} \atop \text{(tosses)} \quad \frac{5}{8} = \frac{x}{32}$$

When this problem was solved earlier in the lesson, $\frac{5}{8}$ was changed to the equivalent fraction $\frac{5*4}{8*4}$.

Another strategy is based on the idea of the quick common denominator. Remind students that a quick common denominator of two fractions is the product of their denominators.

$$\text{(HEADS)} \atop \text{(tosses)} \quad \frac{5*32}{8*32} = \frac{x*8}{32*8}$$

Since the two fractions are equivalent, the renamed numerators must be equal.

$$5 * 32 = x * 8$$
$$\text{So } 160 = x * 8$$

Ask: *What number times 8 equals 160?* 20

The missing number is 20. The penny lands on HEADS 20 times.

Compare the number model to the equation obtained from the quick common denominator. *(See following page.)* Point out that the equation can be obtained by multiplying the numerator of the second fraction by the denominator of the first fraction, and multiplying the denominator of the second fraction by the numerator of the first fraction. This process, called cross multiplication, is a convenient way to solve equations in which two fractions are equal.

Teaching Master

Name   **Date**   **Time**

LESSON 12·5 | **Solving Ratio Problems with Cross Multiplication**

Cross multiplication is a strategy for solving ratio problems that is based on the quick common denominator.

Example:

Josie tosses a penny 32 times. It lands heads up 5 out of 8 times. How many times does the penny land heads up?

Number Model: $\frac{5}{8} = \frac{x}{32}$

Cross multiply: $\frac{5}{8} \diagdown\diagup \frac{x}{32}$

$8 * x = 5 * 32$

Solution: $8 * x = 160$
$x = 20$

Answer: __20 times__ (unit)

Use cross multiplication to solve the following problems. Let the variable x represent the missing number in each problem.

1. Jeremy received 3 votes for every 5 votes cast. If he received 18 votes, how many votes were cast?

Number model: $\frac{3}{5} = \frac{18}{x}$ Solution: $3 * x = 90; x = 30$

Cross multiply: $3 * x = 5 * 18$ Answer: __30 votes__ (unit)

2. The restaurant at the mall sold 324 lunches. For every 9 lunches served, 3 were fish plates. How many fish plates were served?

Number model: $\frac{3}{9} = \frac{x}{324}$ Solution: $9 * x = 972; x = 108$

Cross multiply: $9 * x = 3 * 324$ Answer: __108 fish lunches__ (unit)

3. The Nature Center has a total of 87 amphibians on display. For every 6 amphibians, 2 are types of salamanders. How many salamanders are there?

Number model: $\frac{2}{6} = \frac{x}{87}$ Solution: $6 * x = 174; x = 29$

Cross multiply: $6 * x = 2 * 87$ Answer: __29 salamanders__ (unit)

4. Write a ratio number story for your partner to solve using cross multiplication.

Math Masters, p. 362

Have students complete the master. Remind students that the strategy of cross multiplication is not a trick. It is based on the use of multiplication to find a common denominator for equivalent fractions. Circulate and assist.

quick common denominator equation:

$$\frac{5 * 32}{8 * 32} = \frac{x * 8}{32 * 8}$$

(HEADS)
(tosses)

$$\frac{5}{8} = \frac{x}{32}$$

cross-multiplication number model:

$$8 * x = 5 * 32$$

EXTRA PRACTICE

Solving Ratio Number Stories

(*Math Masters*, p. 363)

 PARTNER ACTIVITY

15–30 Min

Algebraic Thinking Students solve ratio number stories. Then they write a ratio number story for partners to solve.

12·6 Finding Your Heart Rate

◎ **Objective** To provide experience calculating rates from data.

Technology Resources www.everydaymathonline.com

| ePresentations | eToolkit | Algorithms Practice | EM Facts Workshop Game™ | Family Letters | Assessment Management | Common Core State Standards | Curriculum Focal Points | Interactive Teacher's Lesson Guide |

---

① Teaching the Lesson

Key Concepts and Skills

- Identify equivalent expressions for whole numbers. [Number and Numeration Goal 4]

- Use multiplication to make estimates. [Operations and Computation Goal 6]

- Solve rate problems. [Operations and Computation Goal 7]

- Measure to the nearest inch. [Measurement and Reference Frames Goal 1]

Key Activities

Students discuss the heart and find their heart rates. They practice recognizing equivalent expressions by playing *Spoon Scramble*.

 Ongoing Assessment: Recognizing Student Achievement Use *Math Masters,* page 503. [Number and Numeration Goal 4]

Key Vocabulary

pulse ◆ pulse rate ◆ heart rate

Materials

Math Journal 2, p. 416
Student Reference Book, p. 330
Math Masters, pp. 360, 503, and 512
Study Link 12·5
slate ◆ per partnership: watch or classroom clock that displays seconds ◆ calculator ◆ inch ruler ◆ per group of 4 students: 3 spoons, index cards (optional)

② Ongoing Learning & Practice

 Math Boxes 12·6
Math Journal 2, p. 417
Students practice and maintain skills through Math Box problems.

 Study Link 12·6
Math Masters, p. 364
Students practice and maintain skills through Study Link activities.

③ Differentiation Options

READINESS

Expressing Ratios

Class Data Pad
Students identify equivalent expressions for ratios.

ENRICHMENT

Calculating Heartbeats

unlined paper ◆ reference sources about animals
Students research the average heart rate for a variety of animals and compare their own heart rates to those of the animals.

Advance Preparation

For Part 1, each partnership will need a timer with a second hand. This can be the classroom clock, a watch, or a stopwatch. If students play *Spoon Scramble* in groups of 4, each group will need 3 spoons.

For the optional Enrichment activity in Part 3, students will need access to reference sources about animals, such as encyclopedias, animal books, magazines, and Internet sites. Designate a classroom area for a Rates and Ratios Museum. If you distributed permission slips (*Math Masters,* page 360), remind students who have not returned a signed slip to do so by the next math class.

 Teacher's Reference Manual, **Grades 4–6** pp. 64–68

Getting Started

Math Message

Brainstorm with a partner.
Make a list of everything that you know about your heart.

Study Link 12·5 Follow-Up

Have partners share answers and resolve differences.

---

① Teaching the Lesson

▶ Math Message Follow-Up

WHOLE-CLASS DISCUSSION
ELL

Ask partners to share their list of information about the human heart. To support English language learners, write the important ideas on the board. *For example:*

▷ The heart contracts and expands, usually at a steady rate.

▷ The heart pumps blood, which carries oxygen and nutrients to various parts of the body.

▷ With each contraction of the heart, the arteries stretch and then return to their original shape.

▷ The throbbing of the arteries is called the **pulse.** The **pulse rate** is the same as the **heart rate**—the number of heartbeats per minute.

▶ Finding Heart Rates

PARTNER ACTIVITY

(*Math Journal 2,* p. 416)

Health Link Read "The Heart," at the top of the journal page as a class. Then have students complete the section, My Heart Rate, on the journal page. Explain that each student will count the number of times their heart beats while their partner times them for 15 seconds. Partners should do this several times, until they are sure their count is fairly accurate, and then record it on the journal page.

Remind the class that the heart rate is usually given as a number of heartbeats per minute. Students calculate their heart rates, and then the number of times their hearts beat in 1 hour, 1 day, and 1 year. (The number of heartbeats in 1 year should be around 40 million.) Circulate and assist.

Student Page

Date _____ Time _____

LESSON 12·6 The Heart

The heart is an organ in your body that pumps blood through your blood vessels. **Heart rate** is the rate at which your heart pumps blood. It is usually expressed as the number of heartbeats per minute. With each heartbeat, the arteries stretch and then return to their original size. This throbbing of the arteries is called the **pulse.** The **pulse rate** is the same as the heart rate.

You can feel your pulse along your wrist, near the bone and below the thumb. You can also feel it in your neck. Run your index and middle fingers from your ear, past the curve of your jaw, and press them into the soft part of your neck just below your jaw.

My Heart Rate

Feel your pulse and count the number of heartbeats in 15 seconds. Your partner can time you with a watch or the classroom clock. Do this several times, until you are sure that your count is accurate. Sample answers:

1. About how many times does your heart beat in 15 seconds? About 17 times

2. Use this rate to complete the table.

About how many times your heart beats . . .	
in 1 minute	About 68 times
in 1 hour	About 4,080 times
in 1 day	About 97,920 times
in 1 year	About 35,740,800 times

3. Your fist and your heart are about the same size. Measure your fist with your ruler. Record the results.

My heart is about __4__ inches wide and __3__ inches long.

4. A person's heart weighs about 1 ounce per 12 pounds of body weight.

Circle how much your heart weighs.

Less than 15 ounces   About 15 ounces   More than 15 ounces

Math Journal 2, p. 416

Game Master

Name _____ Date _____ Time _____

Spoon Scramble Record Sheet

Player Name:

Record your letters on the lines below.

_____ _____ _____ _____

Winning Combinations

In each row, record the four cards that are of equal value from two of the rounds that you won.

✂ -

Name _____ Date _____ Time _____

Spoon Scramble Record Sheet

Player Name:

Record your letters on the lines below.

_____ _____ _____ _____

Winning Combinations

In each row, record the four cards that are of equal value from two of the rounds that you won.

Math Masters, p. 503

Student Page

Date _____ Time _____

LESSON 12·6 Math Boxes

1. Plot and label the ordered number pairs on the grid.

   M: (2,5)

   N: (−2,1)

   O: (−3,−4)

   P: (−4,3)

   Q: (6,−2)

2. Find the fraction equivalent to $\frac{35}{84}$.

   Circle the best answer.

   A. $\frac{3}{5}$

   B. $\frac{3}{4}$

   C. $\frac{5}{6}$

   D. $\frac{5}{12}$

3. What is the measure of angle *A*? Do *not* use a protractor.

   ∠A = ___45°___

4. Name two equivalent fractions for each fraction below.

   Sample answers:

   a. $\frac{7}{8} = \frac{14}{16}, \frac{21}{24}$

   b. $\frac{3}{10} = \frac{9}{30}, \frac{12}{40}$

   c. $\frac{6}{7} = \frac{12}{14}, \frac{30}{35}$

   d. $\frac{1}{6} = \frac{2}{12}, \frac{5}{30}$

   e. $\frac{12}{5} = \frac{24}{10}, \frac{36}{15}$

5. Write > or <.

   a. 50% ___<___ $\frac{2}{3}$

   b. 620 − 80 ___<___ 30 * 40

   c. $\frac{7}{8}$ ___>___ $\frac{1}{4} + \frac{2}{4}$

   d. 20 * 19 ___<___ 20^2

   e. 0.35 + 0.25 ___>___ $\frac{1}{8} + \frac{1}{8}$

Math Journal 2, p. 417

When most students have finished, bring the class together and discuss answers.

▶ **Playing *Spoon Scramble***  SMALL-GROUP ACTIVITY

(*Student Reference Book*, p. 330; *Math Masters*, pp. 503 and 512)

This game is specified for groups of 4. The number of players can be changed, provided that each group has 4 *Spoon Scramble* cards of equivalent value per player and one fewer spoon than the number of players.

Adjusting the Activity

Have students play a variation of the game by using index cards to make their own Spoon Scramble cards.

AUDITORY ◆ KINESTHETIC ◆ TACTILE ◆ VISUAL

Have each group cut out the cards from *Math Masters*, page 512. Go through the directions for *Spoon Scramble* on *Student Reference Book*, page 330 with the class. Play a few fishbowl rounds—you and 3 students play while the class watches. Then students play *Spoon Scramble* in groups. Circulate and assist.

Ongoing Assessment: Recognizing Student Achievement

Math Masters Page 503 ★

Use **Math Masters, page 503** to assess students' ability to identify equivalent expressions in a variety of ways. Have students record two of their winning combinations from *Spoon Scramble*. Students are making adequate progress if their recorded combinations accurately show equal values.

[Number and Numeration Goal 4]

2 Ongoing Learning & Practice

▶ **Math Boxes 12·6**   INDEPENDENT ACTIVITY

(*Math Journal 2*, p. 417)

Mixed Practice Math Boxes in this lesson are paired with Math Boxes in Lesson 12-8.

Writing/Reasoning Have students write a response to the following: *Explain your solution strategy for Problem 4.*

Sample answer: I multiplied each numerator and denominator by the same nonzero number to get an equivalent fraction. Then I picked another nonzero number and multiplied each numerator and denominator again to get the second equivalent fraction.

INDEPENDENT
ACTIVITY

Home Connection Students fill in rate tables and solve rate word problems.

3 Differentiation Options

READINESS

SMALL-GROUP
ACTIVITY

5–15 Min

▶ **Expressing Ratios**

To provide experience with identifying equivalent expressions for ratios, have students write ratios using fractions, decimals, and percents. Make a large 4-by-4 grid on the Class Data Pad. (*See margin.*) Guide students through the following steps:

1. Ask a volunteer to choose a number between 1 and 10. Write this number on the board.

2. Ask students to rename the chosen number as the fraction of a whole number. For example, $8 = \frac{1}{4}$ of 32. Select one student's suggestion, and write the expression in the grid.

3. Ask students to rename the chosen number as a multiplication expression with fractions. For example, $8 = \frac{1}{5} * 40$. Select one suggestion, and write the expression in the grid.

4. Ask students to rename the chosen number as a multiplication expression with decimals. For example, $8 = 0.2 * 40$. Select one suggestion, and write the expression in the grid.

5. Ask students to rename the chosen number as the percent of a whole number. For example, $8 = 50\%$ of 16. Select one suggestion, and write the expression in the grid.

Repeat steps 1–5 until the grid is filled.

ENRICHMENT

INDEPENDENT
ACTIVITY

30+ Min

▶ **Calculating Heartbeats**

To further explore solving rate problems, have students research the number of heartbeats per minute for a variety of animals. Then they calculate the number of heartbeats in an hour, in a day, and in a year. They can compare their heart rate with those of the animals they've researched.

If a number of students participate in the above activity, they should gather data on large animals, small animals, cold-blooded animals, and warm-blooded animals.

Have students make posters of their findings for display in the Rates and Ratios Museum.

Study Link Master

Name	Date	Time

STUDY LINK 12·6 Rates

Complete each table using the given information. Then answer the question below each table.

1. It would take 27,000 spiders, each spinning a single web, to produce a pound of spider webs.

   a.
Number of Spiders	27,000	54,000	81,000	108,000	135,000
Pounds of Spider Webs	1	2	3	4	5

   b. At this rate, how many spiders, each spinning a single web, would be needed to produce 10 pounds of spider webs? __270,000__ spiders

2. It used to be thought that the deer botfly flies so fast that it is almost invisible to the human eye. It has since been tested, and scientists found that it actually flies about 25 miles per hour.

   a.
Miles	25	50	75	100	125
Hours	1	2	3	4	5

   b. At this rate, about how far could a deer botfly travel in 1 minute? __0.42__ mile(s)

Solve the following rate problems. Make a table if it will help you.

3. About 50 gallons of maple sap are needed to make 1 gallon of maple syrup. How many gallons of maple sap are needed to make 20 gallons of maple syrup?

   About __1,000__ gallons

4. For 186 days a year, the sun is not visible at the North Pole. During a 5-year period, about how many days is the sun not visible?

   About __930__ days

5. In a beehive, about $1\frac{1}{2}$ ounces of beeswax are used to build a honeycomb that holds 4 pounds of honey. How much beeswax is needed to build a honeycomb that could hold 20 pounds of honey?

   About $7\frac{1}{2}$, or 7.5 ounces

Source: *2201 Fascinating Facts*

Math Masters, p. 364

Fraction of a Whole Number	Multiplication Expressions		Percent of a Whole Number
	With Fractions	With Decimals	
$\frac{1}{4}$ of 32	$\frac{1}{5} * 40$	$0.2 * 40$	50% of 16

12·7 Collecting, Graphing, and Interpreting Data

Objective To provide experience with using graphs to represent, compare, and interpret data.

1 Teaching the Lesson

Key Concepts and Skills

- Solve rate problems.
  [Operations and Computation Goal 7]
- Construct line graphs and side-by-side line plots of collected data.
  [Data and Chance Goal 1]
- Find and interpret the landmarks for collected data. [Data and Chance Goal 2]
- Make predictions based on simple experiments. [Data and Chance Goal 4]

Key Activities

Students discuss the meaning of *rate* and uses of rates. They collect and graph personal and class data about their heart rates after physical exercise. Then students compare the class data landmarks with their personal data.

 Ongoing Assessment:
Recognizing Student Achievement
Use Mental Math and Reflexes.
[Number and Numeration Goal 1]

Key Vocabulary

rate ◆ profile ◆ target heart rate

Materials

Math Masters, p. 360
Math Journal 2, pp. 418–420
Student Reference Book Glossary
Study Link 12·6
per partnership: watch or classroom clock that displays seconds, sturdy chair ◆ colored pencil or crayon ◆ ruler or straightedge ◆ 6 stick-on notes

2 Ongoing Learning & Practice

Solving Pan-Balance Problems

Math Journal 2, p. 421
Students solve pan-balance problems with two balances.

 ### Math Boxes 12·7

Math Journal 2, p. 422
Students practice and maintain skills through Math Box problems.

Study Link 12·7

Math Masters, p. 365
Students practice and maintain skills through Study Link activities.

3 Differentiation Options

READINESS

Making Line Plots

stick-on notes
Students make line plots with stick-on notes and identify data landmarks.

ENRICHMENT

Collecting Exercise Data

Students find their heart rates after different kinds of exercise and compare these rates to the number of calories the activities use.

EXTRA PRACTICE

5-Minute Math

5-Minute Math™, pp. 40, 116, and 198
Students solve data landmark problems.

Advance Preparation

For Part 1, collect permission slips before the activity. Each partnership will need one sturdy chair. The seats of all of the chairs must be the same height above the floor. The smallest child in the class must be able to step up on the seat. Each student will need 6 small stick-on notes. On the board, draw the six vertical number lines shown at the right. Make each about 3 feet long.

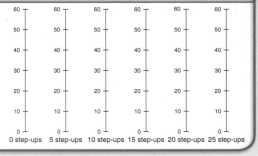

 Teacher's Reference Manual, Grades 4–6 pp. 64–68, 160–169, 260, 261

Getting Started

Mental Math and Reflexes

Have students round numbers. *Suggestions:*

Round to the nearest tenth.

●○○ 3.689 3.7
    14.27 14.3
    6.89 6.9

Round to the nearest ten.

●●○ 287.5 290
    207.5 210
    201.5 200

Round to the nearest whole number.
Then multiply by 8.

●●● 6.74 7; 56
    19.87 20; 160
    31.476 31; 248

Math Message

Without looking in your journal or Student Reference Book, explain what a rate is and describe situations that involve rates. Be ready to share your answer.

Study Link 12·6 Follow-Up

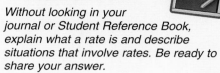

Have partners share answers and resolve differences.

 Ongoing Assessment:
Recognizing Student Achievement

Mental Math and Reflexes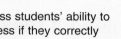

Use the **Mental Math and Reflexes** problems to assess students' ability to round numbers. Students are making adequate progress if they correctly identify and round to the specified place-value digit.

[Number and Numeration Goal 1]

---

1   Teaching the Lesson

▶ Math Message Follow-Up

🧍🧍🧍🧍 **WHOLE-CLASS DISCUSSION**

(*Student Reference Book* Glossary)

Have volunteers share their explanations of **rates** and their descriptions of situations in which rates are used.

After several students share their answers, have a volunteer read the glossary entry for *rate* in the *Student Reference Book*. Ask: *What units are being compared in heart rates?* Heartbeats and time

▶ Recording Heart Rates after Exercise

🧍🧍 **PARTNER ACTIVITY**

(*Math Journal 2*, p. 418)

Read through the procedure on the journal page with the class. Ask the class to decide on a comfortable rate for doing step-ups, that is, stepping up and down from a chair. The chosen step-up rate should not be overly strenuous, for example, once every 3 seconds. Ask a volunteer to demonstrate.

Student Page

Date   Time

LESSON 12·7   **Exercise Your Heart**

Exercise increases the rate at which a person's heart beats. Very strenuous exercise can double the heart rate.

Work with a partner to find out how exercise affects your heart rate.

1. Sit quietly for a minute. Then have your partner time you for 15 seconds while you take your pulse. Record the number of heartbeats in the first row of the table at the right.

2. Step up onto and down from a chair 5 times without stopping. Maintain your balance each time you step up or down. As soon as you finish, take your pulse for 15 seconds while your partner times you. Record the number of heartbeats in the second row of the table.

3. Sit quietly. While you are resting, your partner can do 5 step-ups, and you can time your partner.

4. When your pulse is almost back to normal, step up onto and down from the chair 10 times. Record the number of heartbeats in 15 seconds in the third row of the table. Then rest while your partner does 10 step-ups.

5. Repeat the procedure for 15, 20, and 25 step-ups.

6. Why is it important that all students step up at the same rate?
   <u>It is important so students can compare data from similar experiences.</u>

Step-ups	Heartbeats per 15 Seconds
0	
5	
10	
15	
20	
25	

Math Journal 2, p. 418

Students begin the activity by taking their resting (normal) pulse for 15 seconds and recording it in the journal. Then partners take turns doing 5 step-ups each. They take their pulse and record it.

Partners repeat this procedure for 10, 15, 20, and 25 step-ups.

Emphasize the following points:

▷ All students must step up and down in the same way and at the same rate. A comparison of two students' heart rates is not useful if one student steps up and down as fast as possible and the other student moves very slowly.

▷ Students should take their pulse immediately after each set of step-ups. Their partners time them for 15 seconds, signaling when to start counting heartbeats and when to stop. They record the number of heartbeats in the table on the journal page.

▷ Students should sit quietly after each set of step-ups and not start the next set until their heart rate is almost back to normal.

Have students complete journal page 418. Circulate and assist.

▶ Making a Personal Heart-Rate Profile

WHOLE-CLASS ACTIVITY

PROBLEM SOLVING

(*Math Journal 2*, pp. 418 and 419)

Health Link Students use the grid in Problem 1 on journal page 419 to make a line graph of the data they recorded on journal page 418. Show students how to plot their resting heart rate by making a dot on the vertical axis. Then they plot the result of each exercise period and use a ruler or straightedge to connect the dots. This graph is a **profile** that shows the changes in a student's heart rate as the exercise becomes more strenuous.

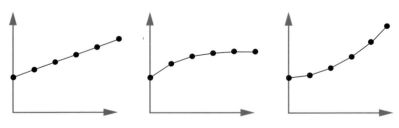

Heart-rate profiles for 3 students

Have students compare their profiles. Ask: *Are all profiles the same shape, or are there several shapes?*

Ask students to use their profiles to predict their heart rate for 30 step-ups and record their predictions in Problem 2 on journal page 419. Ask: *How did you decide on a predicted rate?* Sample answer: I looked for a pattern in the graph and extended the segment that connects the last two points to a predicted point for 30 step-ups.

Finally, point out to students that they must be careful not to exercise too strenuously to avoid straining their hearts. Problem 3, on journal page 419, describes a method for computing a target heart rate when exercising.

Have students compute their **target heart rate** and record it in Problem 3. Ask whether anyone's heart rate after exercise exceeded his or her target heart rate.

▶ Constructing Side-by-Side Line Plots

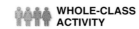 **WHOLE-CLASS ACTIVITY**

(*Math Journal 2,* p. 418)

Distribute 6 stick-on notes to each student. (*See Advance Preparation.*) Direct the class as follows:

1. Copy the data from each line in the table on journal page 418 onto your stick-on notes. Write the number of step-ups (0, 5, 10, ...) in the upper right-hand corner of the stick-on note. (Write it small.) Write the corresponding heart rate for 15 seconds on the rest of the note. (Write it large.)

    Example: On the note with 0 in the corner, write the resting heart rate; on the note with 5 in the corner, write the rate after 5 step-ups, and so on. (*See margin.*)

2. Stick all 6 of your stick-on notes onto a sheet of paper so they are easier to handle.

3. Line up at the board. Attach one stick-on note to each of the six vertical number lines. Remember that the number in the corner of the note shows which number line to use. Attach that note next to the corresponding number of heartbeats.

    Example: Attach the note with 15 in the corner to the 15 step-ups number line.

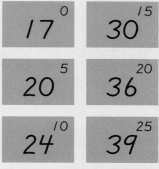

Each student marks 6 stick-on notes to show their personal heart-rate data.

▶ Comparing Line Plots

 **WHOLE-CLASS ACTIVITY**

Ask students to find the following landmarks for each line plot: minimum, maximum, range, and median. Record them on the board beneath the line plots.

Encourage students to share their observations about the line plots. These observations should include the following facts:

▷ The minimum, maximum, and median all increase as the number of step-ups increase.

▷ The normal, resting heart rates are not as spread out as are the rates after strenuous exercise. (Expect the range of pulse counts for 25 step-ups to be about twice as great as the range for pulse counts at rest.)

Ask: *If there are unusual counts that do not fit into a pattern, what might account for them?* Sample answer: Incorrect counting of pulse or illness

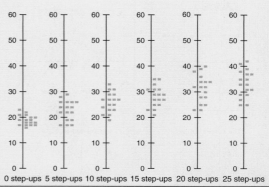

NOTE You may want to have students make a double bar graph comparing their individual heart rates with the class medians.

▶ Making a Class Profile

WHOLE-CLASS ACTIVITY

PROBLEM SOLVING

(*Math Journal 2*, pp. 419 and 420)

Have students do the following:

1. Record the landmarks for the class data in the table on journal page 420.

2. Graph the medians of the class data on the same grid as the graph of the individual data on journal page 419. Use a colored pencil or crayon to distinguish between the two graphs. Label the line graphs My Own Profile and Class Profile.

3. Compare the personal profile with the class profile.

⬆ Adjusting the Activity

Tell students that long-distance runners usually have slower heart rates than people who do not exercise much. By exercising regularly, a person might reduce his or her resting heart rate by 10 beats or more per minute. Ask students to figure out how many heartbeats per hour and per day they might save at that rate.

AUDITORY ◆ KINESTHETIC ◆ TACTILE ◆ VISUAL

② Ongoing Learning & Practice

▶ Solving Pan-Balance Problems

INDEPENDENT ACTIVITY

(*Math Journal 2*, p. 421)

Algebraic Thinking Students solve pan-balance problems with two balances. When most students have finished, discuss their solution strategies.

▶ Math Boxes 12·7

INDEPENDENT ACTIVITY

(*Math Journal 2*, p. 422)

Mixed Practice Math Boxes in this lesson are paired with Math Boxes in Lesson 12-5.

Writing/Reasoning Have students write a response to the following: *Explain how your answer to Problem 4 could be expressed as a fraction and a percent.* Sample answer: It could be written as $\frac{1}{4}$ or 25%.

▶ Study Link 12·7

INDEPENDENT ACTIVITY

(*Math Masters*, p. 365)

Home Connection Students solve problems involving operations with fractions.

3 Differentiation Options

WHOLE-CLASS ACTIVITY

▶ ## Making Line Plots

15–30 Min

To provide experience with line plots and statistical landmarks, have students collect data and make a line plot of the results with stick-on notes. After students make the line plot, have them identify the following data landmarks: minimum, maximum, range, and median. *Possible topics:*

▷ height of students

▷ age of parent (mother or father)

▷ number of people in family

ENRICHMENT

SMALL-GROUP ACTIVITY

▶ ## Collecting Exercise Data

15–30 Min

To apply students' understanding of making predictions from data, have them find their heart rates after different kinds of exercise and compare the various heart rates to the number of calories the activities use. Ask: *Is there a relationship between heart rate and the number of calories used?*

Have students create a display of their findings. Suggest that they make graphs and/or tables. Post the displays in the Rates and Ratios Museum. Provide students with the data below, or have them research the caloric rate for other activities.

Activity	Calories Used per Hour
Walking slowly (about 2 mph)	130
Walking quickly (about 3.5 mph)	180
Bicycling (6 mph)	170
Bicycling (20 mph)	500
Running (5 mph)	360
Swimming (20 yds/min)	200
Playing basketball or soccer (vigorously)	580

EXTRA PRACTICE

▶ ## 5-Minute Math

SMALL-GROUP ACTIVITY

To offer students more experience with data landmarks, see *5-Minute Math* pages 40, 116, and 198.

Student Page

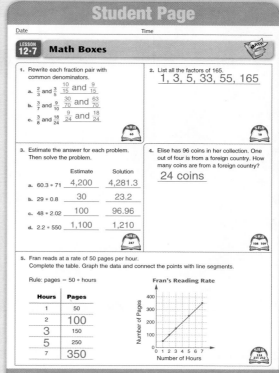

Date | Time

LESSON 12·7 Math Boxes

1. Rewrite each fraction pair with common denominators.
   a. $\frac{2}{3}$ and $\frac{3}{5}$ $\frac{10}{15}$ and $\frac{9}{15}$
   b. $\frac{3}{7}$ and $\frac{9}{10}$ $\frac{30}{70}$ and $\frac{63}{70}$
   c. $\frac{3}{8}$ and $\frac{18}{24}$ $\frac{9}{24}$ and $\frac{18}{24}$

2. List all the factors of 165.
   1, 3, 5, 33, 55, 165

3. Estimate the answer for each problem. Then solve the problem.

	Estimate	Solution
a. 60.3 * 71	4,200	4,281.3
b. 29 * 0.8	30	23.2
c. 48 * 2.02	100	96.96
d. 2.2 * 550	1,100	1,210

4. Elise has 96 coins in her collection. One out of four is from a foreign country. How many coins are from a foreign country?
   24 coins

5. Fran reads at a rate of 50 pages per hour. Complete the table. Graph the data and connect the points with line segments.

Rule: pages = 50 * hours

Hours	Pages
1	50
2	100
3	150
5	250
7	350

Fran's Reading Rate

Math Journal 2, p. 422

Study Link Master

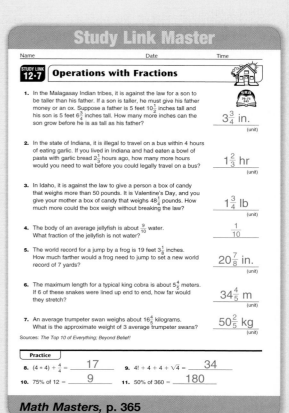

Name | Date | Time

STUDY LINK 12·7 **Operations with Fractions**

1. In the Malagasay Indian tribes, it is against the law for a son to be taller than his father. If a son is taller, he must give his father money or an ox. Suppose a father is 5 feet $10\frac{1}{2}$ inches tall and his son is 5 feet $6\frac{3}{4}$ inches tall. How many more inches can the son grow before he is as tall as his father?
   $3\frac{3}{4}$ in. (unit)

2. In the state of Indiana, it is illegal to travel on a bus within 4 hours of eating garlic. If you lived in Indiana and had eaten a bowl of pasta with garlic bread $2\frac{1}{3}$ hours ago, how many more hours would you need to wait before you could legally travel on a bus?
   $1\frac{2}{3}$ hr (unit)

3. In Idaho, it is against the law to give a person a box of candy that weighs more than 50 pounds. It is Valentine's Day, and you give your mother a box of candy that weighs $48\frac{1}{4}$ pounds. How much more could the box weigh without breaking the law?
   $1\frac{3}{4}$ lb (unit)

4. The body of an average jellyfish is about $\frac{9}{10}$ water. What fraction of the jellyfish is not water?
   $\frac{1}{10}$

5. The world record for a jump by a frog is 19 feet $3\frac{1}{8}$ inches. How much farther would a frog need to jump to set a new world record of 7 yards?
   $20\frac{7}{8}$ in. (unit)

6. The maximum length for a typical king cobra is about $5\frac{4}{5}$ meters. If 6 of these snakes were lined up end to end, how far would they stretch?
   $34\frac{4}{5}$ m (unit)

7. An average trumpeter swan weighs about $16\frac{4}{5}$ kilograms. What is the approximate weight of 3 average trumpeter swans?
   $50\frac{2}{5}$ kg (unit)

Sources: *The Top 10 of Everything; Beyond Belief!*

Practice

8. (4 * 4) + $\frac{4}{4}$ = ___17___

9. 4! + 4 + 4 + $\sqrt{4}$ = ___34___

10. 75% of 12 = ___9___

11. 50% of 360 = ___180___

Math Masters, p. 365

12·8

Finding Your Cardiac Output

Objective To provide experience with calculating rates and using rates to compare data.

Technology Resources www.everydaymathonline.com

 ePresentations

 eToolkit

 Algorithms Practice

 EM Facts Workshop Game™

 Family Letters

 Assessment Management

 Common Core State Standards

 Curriculum Focal Points

Interactive Teacher's Lesson Guide

---

1 Teaching the Lesson

Key Concepts and Skills

• Solve rate problems using multiplication.
[Operations and Computation Goal 3]

• Compare rates and solve rate problems.
[Operations and Computation Goal 7]

• Solve ratio problems.
[Operations and Computation Goal 7]

Key Activities

Students read about the heart and cardiac output. They calculate and compare their cardiac outputs at rest and after exercise.

Key Vocabulary

oxygen ◆ nutrients ◆ carbon dioxide ◆ cardiac output

Materials

Math Journal 2, pp. 418, 419, and 423–425
Study Link 12•7
calculator ◆ an empty 1-gallon container

2 Ongoing Learning & Practice

Playing *Coordinate Search*

Math Masters, pp. 448 and 449
Students practice plotting positions on a grid.

Math Boxes 12·8

Math Journal 2, p. 426
Students practice and maintain skills through Math Box problems.

Ongoing Assessment:
Recognizing Student Achievement
Use Math Boxes, Problem 1.
[Measurement and Reference Frames Goal 4]

Study Link 12·8

Math Masters, p. 366
Students practice and maintain skills through Study Link activities.

3 Differentiation Options

ENRICHMENT

Reading about Ratios

If You Hopped Like a Frog
Students read the book and discuss ratios that compare human and animal abilities.

EXTRA PRACTICE

Solving Ratio Problems

Math Masters, p. 367
Students use data about musical instruments to solve ratio problems.

ELL SUPPORT

Comparing Ratios and Rates

Students make a Venn diagram to compare ratios and rates.

Advance Preparation

For the optional Enrichment activity in Part 3, obtain the book *If You Hopped Like a Frog* by David M. Schwartz (Scholastic Inc., 1999).

Getting Started

Mental Math and Reflexes

Have students write and solve open sentences. Pose problems like the following:

● ○ ○ What number times 2 is equal to 1? $n * 2 = 1$; $n = \frac{1}{2}$

What number times 93 is equal to 1? $n * 93 = 1$; $n = \frac{1}{93}$

● ● ○ What number times 2 is equal to $1\frac{1}{2}$? $n * 2 = 1\frac{1}{2}$; $n = \frac{3}{4}$

What number minus 2 times 6 is equal to 54? $n - 2 * 6 = 54$; $n = 66$

● ● ● What number times $\frac{1}{3}$ is equal to $2\frac{2}{3}$? $n * \frac{1}{3} = 2\frac{2}{3}$; $n = 8$

What number divided by 12 times 3 is equal to 13.5? $n \div (12 * 3) = 13.5$; $n = 486$

Math Message

Complete journal page 423.

Study Link 12·7 Follow-Up

Have partners compare answers and resolve differences.

---

1 Teaching the Lesson

▶ ## Math Message Follow-Up

(*Math Journal 2*, p. 423)

WHOLE-CLASS DISCUSSION

Review students' answers on the journal page. Have volunteers explain their solution strategies.

▶ ## Calculating Cardiac Output

(*Math Journal 2*, pp. 424 and 425)

WHOLE-CLASS ACTIVITY

ELL

PROBLEM SOLVING

Science Link Read the essay on journal page 424 as a class. Discuss the essay and have students ask any questions they might have. You might want to expand on the information in this essay. However, it is not necessary for students to fully understand how blood circulates through the body. It is enough for them to have an idea of the function of blood: to supply the tissues with **oxygen** and **nutrients** and to remove **carbon dioxide** and other waste.

Be sure students understand that **cardiac output** is a rate—the amount of blood the heart pumps per minute—and that this rate depends on how many times the heart beats per minute.

If the amount of blood pumped with each heartbeat and the number of heartbeats per minute are known, the cardiac output can be calculated by multiplying the average amount of blood pumped per heartbeat by the heart rate. To support English language learners, write the following on the board:

Cardiac output =
(amount of blood pumped per heartbeat) * (heart rate)

Display the 1-gallon container to help students visualize the amount of blood their hearts pump in 1 minute.

Student Page

Date _____ Time _____

LESSON 12·8 Review of Ratios

1. What is the ratio of the length of line segment *AB* to the length of line segment *CD*?
   1 to 2
   A _____ B _____ C _____ D
   $1\frac{1}{2}$ in.   3 in.

2. Circle the pair of line segments whose lengths have the same ratio as *AB* to *CD* in Problem 1.
   a. E F _____ G _____ H
      1 cm   5 cm
   b.  J K _____ L
      $\frac{3}{4}$ in. $1\frac{1}{2}$ in.
   c. M _____ N O _____ P
      10 cm   6 cm

3. There are 13 boys and 15 girls in a group. What fractional part of the group is boys? $\frac{13}{28}$

4. Problem 3 was given to groups of 13-year-olds, 17-year-olds, and adults. The answers and the percent of each group that gave those particular answers are shown in the table below.

Answers	13-Year-Olds	17-Year-Olds	Adults
$\frac{13}{28}$	20%	36%	25%
$\frac{13}{28}$ written as a decimal	0%	0%	1%
$\frac{13}{15}$ or 0.86	17%	17%	15%
$\frac{15}{28}$	2%	2%	3%
Other incorrect answers	44%	29%	35%
Don't know	12%	13%	20%
No answer	5%	3%	1%

a. What mistake was made by the people who gave the answer $\frac{15}{28}$?
   They used the number of girls instead of boys.

b. What mistake was made by the people who gave the answer $\frac{13}{15}$?
   They compared the number of boys to girls, not to the entire group.

Math Journal 2, p. 423

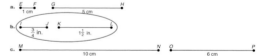

Student Page

Date _____ Time _____

**LESSON
12·8**   **The Heart Pump**

Your heart is the strongest muscle in your body. It needs to be because it never rests.
Every day of your life, 24 hours a day, your heart pumps blood throughout your body.
The blood carries the **nutrients** and **oxygen** your body needs to function.

You breathe oxygen into your lungs. The oxygen passes from your lungs into your
bloodstream. As your heart pumps blood throughout your body, the oxygen is
deposited in the cells of your body and is replaced by waste products (mainly **carbon
dioxide**). The blood carries the carbon dioxide back to your lungs, which get rid of the
carbon dioxide when you exhale. The carbon dioxide is replaced by oxygen, and the
cycle begins again.

The amount of blood the heart pumps in 1 minute is called the **cardiac output.**
To find your cardiac output, you need to know your **heart rate** and the average amount
of blood your heart pumps with each heartbeat. Cardiac output is calculated as follows:

Cardiac output = (amount of blood pumped per heartbeat) * (heart rate)

On average, the heart of a fifth grader pumps about 1.6 fluid ounces of blood with each
heartbeat. If your heart beats about 90 times per minute, then your heart pumps about
1.6 * 90, or 144 fluid ounces of blood per minute. Your cardiac output would be about
144 fluid ounces, or 1 1/8 gallons of blood per minute. That's about 65 gallons of blood
per hour. Imagine having to do this much work, around the clock, every day of your life!
Can you see why your heart needs to be very strong?

A person's normal heart rate decreases with age. A newborn's heart rate can be as
high as 110 to 160 beats per minute. For 10-year-olds, it is around 90 beats per
minute; for adults, it is between 70 and 80 beats per minute. It is not unusual for older
people's hearts to beat as few as 50 to 65 times per minute.

Because cardiac output depends on a person's heart rate, it is not the same at all
times. The more often the heart beats in 1 minute, the more blood is pumped
throughout the body.

Exercise helps your heart grow larger and stronger. The larger and stronger your heart
is, the more blood it can pump with each heartbeat. A stronger heart needs fewer
heartbeats to pump the same amount of blood. This puts less of a strain on
the heart.

Math Journal 2, **p. 424**

Student Page

Date _____ Time _____

**LESSON
12·8**   **The Heart Pump** *continued*

Pretend that your heart has been pumping the same amount of blood all of your life—
so far, about 65 gallons of blood per hour.

1. a. At that rate, about how many gallons of blood would your heart pump per day?
   About ____1,560____ gallons

   b. About how many gallons per year? About ___569,400___ gallons

2. At that rate, about how many gallons would it have pumped from the time you
   were born to your last birthday?
   About __6,000,000__ gallons

3. Heart rate and cardiac output increase with exercise. Look at the table on journal
   page 418. Find the number of heartbeats in 15 seconds when you are at rest and
   the number of heartbeats after 25 step-ups. Record them below.   Answers vary.

   a. Heartbeats in 15 seconds at rest: _____

   b. Heartbeats in 15 seconds after 25 step-ups: _____

   Now figure out the number of heartbeats in 1 minute.

   c. Heartbeats in 1 minute at rest: _____

   d. Heartbeats in 1 minute after 25 step-ups: _____

4. If your heart pumps about 1.6 fluid ounces of blood per heartbeat, about how
   much blood does it pump in 1 minute when you are at rest?
   About _____ fl oz

5. A gallon is equal to 128 fluid ounces. About how many gallons of blood does
   your heart pump in 1 minute when you are at rest?
   About _____ gallon(s)

6. a. Use your answer to Problem 5 above to find about how many fluid ounces
      of blood your heart would pump in 1 minute after 25 step-ups.
      About _____ fl oz

   b. About how many gallons? About _____ gallon(s)

Math Journal 2, **p. 425**

Have students solve Problems 1 and 2 on journal page 425. Ask
whether they would have predicted the calculated magnitude of
the gallons of blood their hearts have pumped since birth. An
average 10-year-old has pumped about 6 million gallons of blood
since birth.

Adjusting the Activity

Have students solve the following problem:

• A gasoline tanker truck has a capacity of about 10,000 gallons. About how
many tanker trucks would be needed to carry the amount of blood pumped by
the heart in an average 10-year-old's life so far? About 600 tanker trucks

AUDITORY   ◆   KINESTHETIC   ◆   TACTILE   ◆   VISUAL

▶ ## Comparing Cardiac Output at
Rest and After Exercising

**PARTNER
ACTIVITY**

(*Math Journal 2,* pp. 418, 419, and 425)

Have partners complete the rest of journal page 425. The data
collected in Lesson 12-7 about their own heart rates is used to
find their cardiac outputs at rest and after 25 step-ups. Circulate
and assist.

When most students have finished, bring the class together to
share results. Ask students to look up their target heart rates
during exercise in Problem 3 on journal page 419 and answer the
following questions:

● If your heart beats at your target heart rate, about how many
gallons of blood will your heart pump in 1 minute?

● How does this compare to the amount of blood your heart
pumps in 1 minute when you are at rest?

2 Ongoing Learning & Practice

▶ ## Playing *Coordinate Search*

**INDEPENDENT
ACTIVITY**

(*Math Masters,* pp. 448 and 449)

Students practice plotting positions on a grid by playing
Coordinate Search. Read and discuss the directions on *Math
Masters,* page 449 as a class. When students understand the rules,
have them complete the grid independently or in partnerships.
Suggest that students use pencils, circle points that they think are
possible, but are not certain about, and check off the rows in the
tables as all points are found for that coordinate.

Math Boxes 12·8

(*Math Journal 2*, p. 426)

INDEPENDENT ACTIVITY

Mixed Practice Math Boxes in this lesson are paired with Math Boxes in Lesson 12-6.

Ongoing Assessment: Recognizing Student Achievement

Math Boxes Problem 1 ★

Use **Math Boxes, Problem 1** to assess students' ability to plot points in all four quadrants of a coordinate grid. Students are making adequate progress if they correctly plot and label the ordered number pairs.

[Measurement and Reference Frames Goal 4]

Study Link 12·8

(*Math Masters*, p. 366)

INDEPENDENT ACTIVITY

Home Connection Students solve rate and ratio problems.

---

3 Differentiation Options

ENRICHMENT

Reading about Ratios

SMALL-GROUP ACTIVITY

🕐 15–30 Min

Literature Link To explore ratios, have students discuss comparisons between human abilities and animal abilities. Read *If You Hopped Like a Frog* to the group. Then discuss the explanations and questions found at the end of the story. Consider having students make and illustrate posters of ratios, comparing themselves with specific animals, for display in the Rates and Ratio Museum.

If You Hopped Like a Frog

Summary: The abilities of a variety of animals are described in vignettes that compare them to what humans would be able to do given the same ratios of abilities. The book concludes with both mathematical and zoological explanations for the vignettes.

Game Master

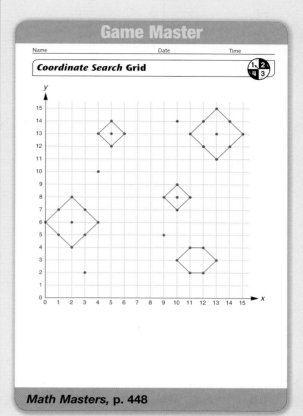

Coordinate Search Grid

Math Masters, p. 448

Student Page

LESSON 12·8 Math Boxes

1. Plot and label the ordered number pairs on the grid. ★

   E: (−2,5)
   F: (3,4)
   G: (−2,−4)
   H: (−1,0)
   I: (5,−1)
   J: (4,4)

2. ☐ = $\frac{45}{54}$

   Circle the best answer.

   A. $\frac{5}{8}$
   B. $\frac{4}{5}$
   C. $\frac{5}{6}$
   D. $\frac{3}{5}$

3. What is the measure of angle S? Do *not* use a protractor.

   A 26° 22° K

   ∠S = 132°

4. Name two equivalent fractions for each fraction below.

   a. $\frac{1}{3} = \frac{2}{6}, \frac{3}{9}$
   b. $\frac{3}{8} = \frac{6}{16}, \frac{9}{24}$
   c. $\frac{2}{7} = \frac{4}{14}, \frac{6}{21}$
   d. $\frac{9}{4} = \frac{18}{8}, \frac{27}{12}$
   e. $\frac{5}{3} = \frac{10}{6}, \frac{15}{9}$

5. Write > or <.

   a. 15 + 28 $<$ 10²
   b. 40 + 40 $<$ 3 * 30
   c. $\frac{1}{2} + \frac{1}{2}$ $>$ $\frac{3}{4}$
   d. $\frac{19}{20}$ $>$ 0.6 + 0.3
   e. 55 ÷ 5 $>$ 120 ÷ 12

Math Journal 2, p. 426

EXTRA PRACTICE

PARTNER ACTIVITY

5–15 Min

▶ **Solving Ratio Problems**

(*Math Masters*, p. 367)

Students use data about musical instruments to solve ratio problems.

ELL SUPPORT

SMALL-GROUP ACTIVITY

5–15 Min

▶ **Comparing Ratios and Rates**

To provide language support for ratios, have students draw a Venn diagram listing similarities and differences between ratios and rates. *For example:*

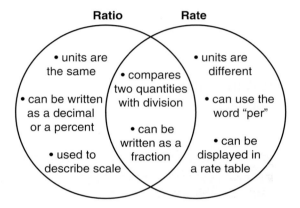

Objective To assess students' progress on mathematical content through the end of Unit 12.

1 Looking Back: Cumulative Assessment

The **End-of-Year Assessment** in the *Assessment Handbook* is a written assessment that you may use to assess students' proficiency with Grade-Level Goals.

 Input student data from Progress Check 12 and the End-of-Year Assessment into the **Assessment Management Spreadsheets**.

Materials
- ◆ Study Link 12◆8
- ◆ *Assessment Handbook,* pp. 142–149, 210–215, 227, and 280–283
- ◆ End-of-Year Assessment (*Assessment Handbook,* pp. 150, 151, 234–241, 245, and 245A)
- ◆ slate

CONTENT ASSESSED	LESSON(S)	SELF	ORAL/SLATE	WRITTEN PART A	WRITTEN PART B	OPEN RESPONSE
Find the greatest common factor of two numbers. [Number and Numeration Goal 3]	12·1	3		4		
Find least common multiple of two numbers. [Number and Numeration Goal 3]	12·1	4		5–9		
Find the prime factorization of numbers. [Number and Numeration Goal 3]	12·1	2		1–3		
Find the factors of numbers. [Number and Numeration Goal 3]	12·1	1	1, 3	1, 2		
Use least common multiples to find common denominators. [Number and Numeration Goal 5]				6–8		
Multiply and divide fractions. [Operations and Computation Goal 5]				14, 15		
Understand and use tree diagrams to solve problems. [Data and Chance Goal 4]	12·2	7	4		16	
Use the Multiplication Counting Principle to find the total number of possible outcomes of a sequence of choices. [Data and Chance Goal 4]	12·2	6	2		16	
Compute the probability of outcomes when choices are equally likely. [Data and Chance Goal 4]	12·2				17	
Solve ratio and rate problems. [Operations and Computation Goal 7]	12·3, 12·6, 12·8	5		10–13	18–22	✔

2 Looking Ahead: Preparing for Grade 6

 Math Boxes 12◆9

 Study Link 12◆9: End-of-Year Family Letter

Materials
- ◆ *Math Journal 2,* p. 427
- ◆ *Math Masters,* pp. 368–371

Getting Started

Math Message • Self Assessment

Complete the Self Assessment (Assessment Handbook, *page 210*).

Study Link 12·8 Follow-Up

Briefly review students' answers.

---

1 **Looking Back: Cumulative Assessment**

▶ ## Math Message Follow-Up

INDEPENDENT ACTIVITY

(Self Assessment, *Assessment Handbook*, p. 210)

The Self Assessment offers students the opportunity to reflect upon their progress.

▶ ## Oral and Slate Assessments

WHOLE-CLASS ACTIVITY

Problems 1 and 3 provide summative information that can be used for grading purposes. Problems 2 and 4 provide formative information that can be useful in planning future instruction.

Oral Assessment

1. Show thumbs up if the first number is a factor of the second and thumbs down if it is not.

   - 8; 64 up
   - 6; 303 down
   - 4; 256 up
   - 5; 8,045 up

2. Show thumbs up if the statement is true and thumbs down if it is false.

   - If there are 4 flavors of ice cream and 2 types of cones, there are 6 possible ice cream cone choices. down

   - If there are 8 notebook covers and 3 different colored pencils, there are 12 possible combinations of notebooks and pencils. down

   - If there are 2 styles of team uniforms and 4 colors of athletic shoes, there are 8 possible combinations of uniforms and shoes. up

   - If there are 6 pasta choices and 5 sauce choices, there are 30 possible combinations of sauce and pasta. up

Slate Assessment

3. Name all the factors of each number.

   - 12 1, 2, 3, 4, 6, 12
   - 16 1, 2, 4, 8, 16
   - 36 1, 2, 3, 4, 6, 9, 12, 18, 36
   - 47 1, 47

Assessment Master

Name _____ Date _____ Time _____

LESSON 12·9 **Self Assessment**

Progress Check 12

Think about each skill listed below. Assess your own progress by checking the most appropriate box.

Skills	I can do this on my own and explain how to do it.	I can do this on my own.	I can do this if I get help or look at an example.
1. Find all the factors of a number.			
2. Find the prime factorization of a number.			
3. Find the greatest common factor of two numbers.			
4. Find the least common multiple of two numbers.			
5. Solve rate and ratio number stories.			
6. Use the Multiplication Counting Principle to solve problems.			
7. Use tree diagrams to solve problems.			

Assessment Handbook, p. 210

4. Make a tree diagram to show the possible choices.

- There are 4 flavors of ice cream and 2 types of cones.

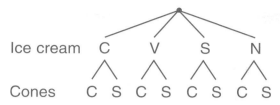

- There are 8 notebook covers and 3 different colored pencils.

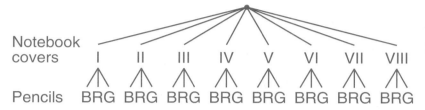

Written Assessment

 INDEPENDENT ACTIVITY

(*Assessment Handbook*, pp. 211–214)

Part A   Recognizing Student Achievement

Problems 1–13 provide summative information and may be used for grading purposes.

Problem(s)	Description
1, 2	Find the factors of numbers.
1–3	Find the prime factorizations of numbers.
4	Find the greatest common factor of two numbers.
5–9	Find the least common multiple of two numbers.
10–13	Solve ratio and rate number stories.
14	Solve a fraction multiplication number story.
15	Solve a fraction division number story.

Part B   Informing Instruction

Problems 14–20 provide formative information that can be useful in planning future instruction.

Problem(s)	Description
16	Understand and use tree diagrams.
17	Compute the probability of outcomes.
18–22	Solve ratio and rate number stories.

Use the checklists on pages 281 and 283 of the *Assessment Handbook* to record results. Then input the data into the **Assessment Management Spreadsheets** to keep an ongoing record of students' progress toward Grade-Level Goals.

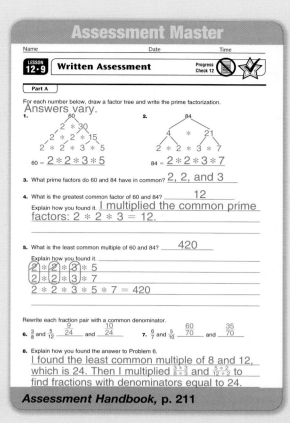

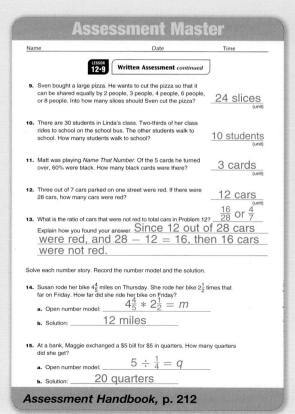

▶ Open Response

(*Assessment Handbook,* p. 215)

INDEPENDENT ACTIVITY

Counting Cars

 The open-response item requires students to apply skills and concepts from Unit 12 to solve a multistep problem. See *Assessment Handbook,* pages 145–149 for rubrics and students' work samples for this problem.

▶ End-of-Year Assessment

(*Assessment Handbook,* pp. 234–241)

INDEPENDENT ACTIVITY

The End-of-Year Assessment (*Assessment Handbook,* pages 234–241) provides an additional assessment opportunity that you may use as part of your balanced assessment plan. This assessment covers many of the important concepts and skills presented in *Fifth Grade Everyday Mathematics.* It should be used along with ongoing and periodic assessments. Please see the *Assessment Handbook* for further information.

▶ ## Math Boxes 12·9

(*Math Journal 2*, p. 427)

INDEPENDENT ACTIVITY

 Mixed Practice This Math Boxes page previews Grade 6 content.

▶ ## Study Link 12·9:
End-of-Year Family Letter

(*Math Masters*, pp. 368–371)

INDEPENDENT ACTIVITY

Home Connection The End-of-Year Family Letter thanks family members for their participation in *Fifth Grade Everyday Mathematics*, suggests activities that can be done at home during vacation, and provides a preview of *Sixth Grade Everyday Mathematics*.

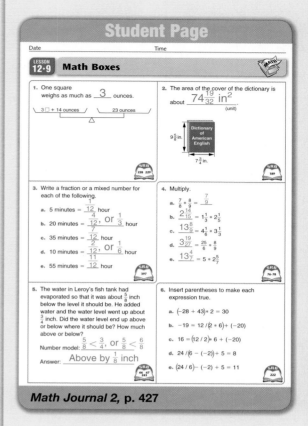

Math Journal 2, p. 427

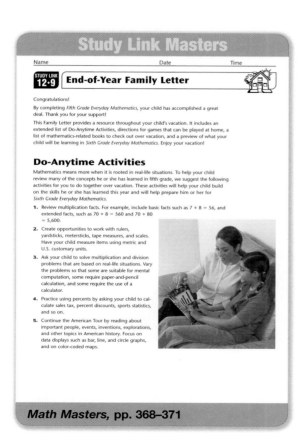

Math Masters, pp. 368–371

Appendices

Contents

The Sieve of Eratosthenes

 Objective To provide experiences with identifying prime numbers and patterns in prime numbers.

Technology Resources www.everydaymathonline.com

eToolkit

Algorithms
Practice

EM Facts
Workshop
Game™

Family
Letters

Assessment
Management

Common
Core State
Standards

Curriculum
Focal Points

Interactive
Teacher's
Lesson Guide

1 Doing the Project

Recommended Use During or after Unit 1

Key Concepts and Skills

• Use the Sieve of Eratosthenes to identify prime numbers.
[Number and Numeration Goal 3]

• Describe prime number patterns.
[Patterns, Functions, and Algebra Goal 1]

Key Activities

Students use the Sieve of Eratosthenes, an ancient graphic device, to identify prime numbers and explore prime number patterns.

Key Vocabulary

prime number ◆ composite number ◆ multiples ◆ factors ◆ Sieve of Eratosthenes ◆ twin primes

Materials

◆ *Math Masters,* pp. 374–378
◆ transparency of *Math Masters*, p. 376
◆ Class Data Pad
◆ different-colored crayons, markers, or pencils

2 Extending the Project

Students find more information on prime numbers.

Materials

◆ encyclopedia
◆ computer with Internet access

Advance Preparation

Make a transparency of *Math Masters,* page 376 to demonstrate how to use the Sieve of Eratosthenes.

① Doing the Project

▶ Introducing the Sieve of Eratosthenes

 **WHOLE-CLASS DISCUSSION**

(*Math Masters*, pp. 374–376)

Have students read and discuss the essay on *Math Masters*, page 374. Be sure to review the definitions of **prime number** and **composite number.** Have the class practice finding **multiples** of numbers. It is important for students to understand that every multiple of a number *n* has *n* as one of its **factors.** For example, 8 is a multiple of 2; therefore, 2 is a factor of 8.

Use a transparency of *Math Masters*, page 376 to demonstrate how to use the **Sieve of Eratosthenes** (ĕr´ə-tŏs´thə-nēz´). Do the first three steps on *Math Masters*, page 375 with the class.

▶ Using the Sieve of Eratosthenes to Identify the Prime Numbers from 1 to 100

 PARTNER ACTIVITY

(*Math Masters*, pp. 375–377)

Have students continue to circle numbers that have not already been crossed out and then cross out their multiples until all the numbers from 1 to 100 have either been circled or crossed out. Then have students list all prime numbers from 1 to 100 on *Math Masters*, page 375 and answer the questions on *Math Masters*, page 377.

Discuss students' answers. Have volunteers list the pairs of **twin primes** from 1 to 100 on the Class Data Pad. Encourage students to search for patterns, even if these are not obvious at first.

▶ Using the Sieve of Eratosthenes to Identify the Prime Numbers from 101 to 200

 **INDEPENDENT ACTIVITY**

(*Math Masters*, p. 378)

Encourage students to identify prime numbers greater than 100 by crossing out multiples of the prime numbers from 1 to 200. Students use the extended grid on *Math Masters*, page 378.

Project Master

Name _____ Date _____ Time _____

PROJECT 1 The Search for Prime Numbers

You probably know the following definitions of prime and composite numbers:

A **prime number** is a whole number that has exactly two **factors**. The factors are 1 and the number itself. For example, 7 is a prime number because its only factors are 1 and 7. A prime number is divisible by only 1 and itself.

A **composite number** is a whole number that has more than two factors. For example, 10 is a composite number because it has four factors: 1, 2, 5, and 10. A composite number is divisible by at least three whole numbers.

The number 1 is neither prime nor composite.

For centuries, mathematicians have been interested in prime and composite numbers because they are the building blocks of whole numbers. They have found that every composite number can be written as the product of prime numbers. For example, 18 can be written as 2 ∗ 3 ∗ 3.

Around 300 B.C., the Greek mathematician Euclid (yOO´klid) proved that there is no largest prime number. No matter how large a prime number you find, there will always be larger prime numbers. Since then, people have been searching for more prime numbers. In 1893, a mathematician was able to show that there are more than 50 million prime numbers between the numbers 1 and 1 billion.

The Greek mathematician Eratosthenes (ĕr´ə-tŏs´ thə-nēz´), who lived around 200 B.C., devised a simple method for finding prime numbers. His strategy was based on the fact that every **multiple of a number** is divisible by that number. For example, the numbers 2, 4, 6, 8, and 10 are multiples of 2, and each of these numbers is divisible by 2. Here is another way to say it: A whole number is a factor of every one of its multiples. For example, 2 is a factor of 4, 6, 8, and 10. The number 2 has only one other factor, the number 1, so 2 is a prime number. All other multiples of 2 are composite numbers.

Eratosthenes' method is called the **Sieve of Eratosthenes.** The directions for using the sieve to find prime numbers are given on *Math Masters*, page 375.

Since the time of Eratosthenes, mathematicians have invented more powerful methods for finding prime numbers. Some methods use formulas. Today, people use computers. The largest prime number known when this book went to press had 9,152,052 digits. If that number were printed in a book with pages the same size as this page, in the same size type, the book would be about 1,400 pages long.

Math Masters, p. 374

Project Master

Name _____ Date _____ Time _____

PROJECT 1 The Sieve of Eratosthenes

Follow the directions below for *Math Masters*, page 376. When you have finished, you will have crossed out every number from 1 to 100 that is not a prime number.

1. Because 1 is not a prime number, cross it out.

2. Circle 2 with a colored marker or crayon. Then count by 2, crossing out all multiples of 2; that is, 4, 6, 8, 10, and so on.

3. Circle 3 with a different colored marker or crayon. Cross out every third number after 3—6, 9, 12, and so on. If a number is already crossed out, make a mark in a corner of the box. The numbers you have crossed out or marked are multiples of 3.

4. Skip 4, because it is already crossed out, and go on to 5. Use a new color to circle 5, and cross out multiples of 5.

5. Continue in the same pattern. Start each time by circling the next number that is not crossed out. Cross out all multiples of that number. If a number is already crossed out, make a mark in a corner of the box. Use a different color for each new set of multiples.

6. Stop when there are no more numbers to be circled or crossed out. The circled numbers are the prime numbers from 1 to 100.

7. List all the prime numbers from 1 to 100.
   2, 3, 5, 7, 11, 13, 17, 19, 23, 29, 31, 37, 41,
   43, 47, 53, 59, 61, 67, 71, 73, 79, 83, 89, 97

Math Masters, p. 375

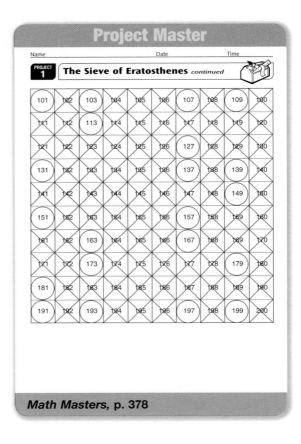
2 Extending the Project

▶ Learning about Prime Numbers

Invite students to find out more about prime numbers in encyclopedias and math books and to visit Internet sites regarding prime numbers. For example, the sites listed below have information on the search for larger prime numbers and links to other prime-number sites. The largest known prime number, as of this printing, was found in 2008. It contains 12,978,189 digits.

http://primes.utm.edu/
http://www.mersenne.org/prime.htm

Deficient, Abundant, and Perfect Numbers

 Objective To explore number properties.

Technology Resources www.everydaymathonline.com

| eToolkit | Algorithms Practice | EM Facts Workshop Game™ | Family Letters | Assessment Management | Common Core State Standards | Curriculum Focal Points | Interactive Teacher's Lesson Guide |

1 Doing the Project

Recommended Use After Unit 1

Key Concepts and Skills

• Factor numbers.
  [Number and Numeration Goal 3]

• Use parentheses to evaluate expressions.
  [Patterns, Functions, and Algebra Goal 3]

Key Activities

Students classify the whole numbers through 50 according to the sums of their proper factors.

Key Vocabulary

factor ◆ proper factor ◆ deficient number ◆ abundant number ◆ perfect number

Materials

◆ *Student Reference Book,* p. 306 (optional)
◆ *Math Masters,* pp. 379–382
◆ calculator

2 Extending the Project

Students find more information on perfect numbers and Mersenne numbers.

Materials

◆ encyclopedia
◆ computer with Internet access

Project Master

Name _____ Date _____ Time _____

PROJECT 2 · Deficient, Abundant, and Perfect Numbers

A **factor** of a whole number N is any whole number that can be multiplied by a whole number to give N as the product. For example, 5 is a factor of 30 because 6 * 5 = 30. Also, 6 is a factor of 30. Every whole number has itself and 1 as factors.

A **proper factor** of a whole number is any factor of that number except the number itself. For example, the factors of 10 are 1, 2, 5, and 10. The proper factors of 10 are 1, 2, and 5.

A whole number is a **deficient number** if the sum of its proper factors is less than the number. For example, 10 is a deficient number because the sum of its proper factors is 1 + 2 + 5 = 8, and 8 is less than 10.

A whole number is an **abundant number** if the sum of its proper factors is greater than the number. For example, 12 is an abundant number because the sum of its proper factors is 1 + 2 + 3 + 4 + 6 = 16, and 16 is greater than 12.

A whole number is a **perfect number** if the sum of its proper factors is equal to the number. For example, 6 is a perfect number because the sum of its proper factors is 1 + 2 + 3 = 6.

Exploration

List the proper factors of each number from 1 to 50 in the table on Math Masters, pages 380 and 381. Then find the sum of the proper factors of each number, and record it in the third column of the table. Finally, make a check mark in the appropriate column to show whether the number is deficient, abundant, or perfect.

Divide the work with the other members of your group. Have partners use factor rainbows to check each other's work. When you are satisfied that all the results are correct, answer the questions on page 381.

Project Master

Name _____ Date _____ Time _____

PROJECT 2 · Deficient, Abundant, and Perfect Numbers cont.

Number	Proper Factors	Sum of Proper Factors	Deficient	Abundant	Perfect
1		0	✓		
2	1	1	✓		
3	1	1	✓		
4	1, 2	3	✓		
5	1	1	✓		
6	1, 2, 3	6			✓
7	1	1	✓		
8	1, 2, 4	7	✓		
9	1, 3	4	✓		
10	1, 2, 5	8	✓		
11	1	1	✓		
12	1, 2, 3, 4, 6	16		✓	
13	1	1	✓		
14	1, 2, 7	10	✓		
15	1, 3, 5	9	✓		
16	1, 2, 4, 8	15	✓		
17	1	1	✓		
18	1, 2, 3, 6, 9	21		✓	
19	1	1	✓		
20	1, 2, 4, 5, 10	22		✓	
21	1, 3, 7	11	✓		
22	1, 2, 11	14	✓		
23	1	1	✓		
24	1, 2, 3, 4, 6, 8, 12	36		✓	
25	1, 5	6	✓		
26	1, 2, 13	16	✓		
27	1, 3, 9	13	✓		
28	1, 2, 4, 7, 14	28			✓
29	1	1	✓		
30	1, 2, 3, 5, 6, 10, 15	42		✓	
31	1	1	✓		
32	1, 2, 4, 8, 16	31	✓		
33	1, 3, 11	15	✓		
34	1, 2, 17	20	✓		

1 · Doing the Project

▶ Introducing Deficient, Abundant, and Perfect Numbers

WHOLE-CLASS DISCUSSION

(*Math Masters*, p. 379)

Ask students to read the definitions on *Math Masters*, page 379. Then go over the definitions of **factor**, **proper factor**, **deficient number**, **abundant number**, and **perfect number**.

Ask questions such as the following:

- What are the factors of 15? 1, 3, 5, 15
- What are the proper factors of 15? 1, 3, 5
- What is the sum of the proper factors of 15? 1 + 3 + 5 = 9
- Is 15 a deficient, abundant, or perfect number? deficient

If students have no trouble answering these questions, repeat the sequence with a more challenging number, such as 60. Point out that the terms *deficient, abundant,* and *perfect* have historical origins but do not define a number's importance. They are merely labels.

▶ Classifying Whole Numbers by the Sums of Their Proper Factors

SMALL-GROUP ACTIVITY

(*Math Masters*, pp. 379–381)

Have students read the instructions at the bottom of *Math Masters*, page 379. Suggest that each group divide the work among partnerships. Partners should check each other's work. When members of each group have reached agreement on the answers for each number, they record the results in the tables on *Math Masters*, pages 380 and 381. Then they answer the questions at the bottom of *Math Masters*, page 381.

Bring the groups together to report their findings. Problems 5 and 6 reveal an interesting pattern:

- The sum of the proper factors of a power of 2 (2^1, 2^2, 2^3, and so on) is 1 less than the power of 2. For example, $2^4 = 16$, and the sum of the proper factors of 2^4 (16), is $16 - 1 = 15$.

- The sum of all the factors of a power of 2 is equal to the sum of the proper factors plus the power itself. This can be found by doubling the number and subtracting 1. For example, the sum of all the factors of 2^4 (16), is $(2 * 16) - 1 = 31$.

The classification of whole numbers according to the sums of their proper factors can help students choose the best possible numbers when playing *Factor Captor*. Encourage students to refer to the tables on *Math Masters,* pages 380 and 381 when they play the game (*Student Reference Book,* page 306).

Looking for Additional Perfect Numbers

INDEPENDENT ACTIVITY

(*Math Masters,* p. 382)

Students work independently or in small groups to find the third and fourth perfect numbers. They use the method described on *Math Masters,* page 382.

Adjusting the Activity

Have students try to find the fifth perfect number. The next starting number whose factors add up to a prime number is 4,096. The sum of its factors is (2 ∗ 4,096) − 1 = 8,191. The product of 4,096 and 8,191 is 33,550,336, which is the fifth perfect number.

AUDITORY ◆ KINESTHETIC ◆ TACTILE ◆ VISUAL

2 Extending the Project

Learning More about Perfect Numbers

INDEPENDENT ACTIVITY

The search for perfect numbers is based on the ideas presented on *Math Masters,* page 382. As noted earlier, the sum of the proper factors of a power of 2 is equal to 1 less than the power of 2, or $2^n - 1$. Numbers of this form are called *Mersenne numbers*. If a Mersenne number is a prime number, it is called a *Mersenne prime*. Mersenne primes are used to generate perfect numbers.

Have students use encyclopedias or other reference books to find more information on perfect numbers and Mersenne numbers. Many Internet sites are devoted to prime numbers, perfect numbers, and Mersenne primes. For example, see http://www.mersenne.org/prime.htm.

Project Master

Name Date Time

PROJECT 2 **Deficient, Abundant, and Perfect Numbers** *cont.*

Number	Proper Factors	Sum of Proper Factors	Deficient	Abundant	Perfect
35	1, 5, 7	13	✓		
36	1, 2, 3, 4, 6, 9, 12, 18	55		✓	
37	1	1	✓		
38	1, 2, 19	22	✓		
39	1, 3, 13	17	✓		
40	1, 2, 4, 5, 8, 10, 20	50		✓	
41	1	1	✓		
42	1, 2, 3, 6, 7, 14, 21	54		✓	
43	1	1	✓		
44	1, 2, 4, 11, 22	40	✓		
45	1, 3, 5, 9, 15	33	✓		
46	1, 2, 23	26	✓		
47	1	1	✓		
48	1, 2, 3, 4, 6, 8, 12, 16, 24	76		✓	
49	1, 7	8	✓		
50	1, 2, 5, 10, 25	43	✓		

Source: *The Math Teacher's Book of Lists.* San Francisco: Jossey-Bass, 2005.

Refer to the results in your table.

1. What are the perfect numbers up to 50? 6 and 28
2. Is there an abundant number that is not an even number? No
3. Are all deficient numbers odd numbers? No
4. What is the next number greater than 50 for which the sum of its proper factors is 1? 53
5. The sum of the proper factors of 4 is 1 less than 4. List all the numbers through 50 for which the sum of the proper factors is 1 less than the number itself. 2, 4, 8, 16, 32
6. What do you think is the next number greater than 50 for which the sum of its proper factors is 1 less than the number itself? 64

Math Masters, p. 381

Project Master

Name Date Time

PROJECT 2 **A Perfect-Number Challenge**

Perfect numbers become big very quickly. The third perfect number has 3 digits, the fourth has 4 digits, the fifth has 8 digits, the sixth has 10 digits, and the thirty-second has 455,663 digits! In other words, perfect numbers are hard to find.

You can find perfect numbers without having to find the sum of the proper factors of every number. Here is what you do:

1. Complete the pattern of starting numbers in the first column of the table.
2. List the factors of each starting number in the second column.
3. Write the sum of the factors of each starting number in the third column.
4. If the sum of the factors of the starting number is prime, multiply this sum by the starting number itself. The product is a perfect number. Record it in the last column.

The first perfect number is 6. Try to find the next three perfect numbers.

Starting Number	Factors	Sum of Factors	Perfect Number
2	1, 2	3	6
4	1, 2, 4	7	28
8	1, 2, 4, 8	15	
16	1, 2, 4, 8, 16	31	496
32	1, 2, 4, 8, 16, 32	63	
64	1, 2, 4, 8, 16, 32, 64	127	8,128
128	1, 2, 4, 8, 16, 32, 64, 128	255	

People have been fascinated by perfect numbers for centuries. The ancient Greeks knew the first four. No one found the fifth perfect number until the year 1456. Computers now carry on the search for perfect numbers. When this book went to press, 42 perfect numbers had been identified. All the perfect numbers found so far are even numbers.

Math Masters, p. 382

An Ancient Multiplication Algorithm

◎ **Objective** To explore number theory concepts and multiplication algorithms.

Technology Resources www.everydaymathonline.com

eToolkit

Algorithms Practice

EM Facts Workshop Game™

Family Letters

Assessment Management

Common Core State Standards

NCTM Curriculum Focal Points

Interactive Teacher's Lesson Guide

1 Doing the Project

Recommended Use During or after Unit 2

Key Concepts and Skills

- Use exponential notation to represent whole numbers.
  [Number and Numeration Goal 4]

- Use paper-and-pencil algorithms to multiply whole numbers.
  [Operations and Computation Goal 3]

- Explain how multiplication strategies work.
  [Operations and Computation Goal 3]

Key Activities

Students examine a multiplication algorithm that was invented in Egypt more than 4,000 years ago. They compare multiplication algorithms and list their advantages and their disadvantages.

Key Vocabulary

powers of 2 ◆ partial products

Materials

- *Math Masters*, pp. 383–385
- Class Data Pad
- transparency (optional)

2 Extending the Project

Students use the Egyptian algorithm with hieroglyphs and Roman numerals.

Students use the Internet to learn more about different numeral systems.

Materials

- *Math Masters*, p. 386
- computer with Internet access

Exploring an Ancient Method of Multiplication

SMALL-GROUP ACTIVITY

(*Math Masters*, pp. 383 and 384)

Read and discuss the introduction and Problems 1 and 2 on *Math Masters*, page 383 as a class. On the Class Data Pad, list the **powers of 2** from the table on the *Math Masters* page. Model the steps for the Egyptian method of multiplication on the board or a transparency. Allow partners time to discuss Problem 3. Then ask volunteers to share their responses. Some students may have analyzed the Egyptian algorithm in Part 3 of Lesson 2-9; consider having these students lead the discussion.

Have students solve the three multiplication problems at the top of *Math Masters*, page 384 using the Egyptian algorithm.

Finally, have students look at the first two problems at the bottom of *Math Masters*, page 384, which have been solved using a variation of the Egyptian algorithm. Ask students to solve the third problem by the same method. Recreational mathematics books call this method the Russian Peasant Algorithm. It is performed by repeatedly halving the number in the left column, ignoring any nonzero remainders, and doubling the number in the right column. All rows that have an even number in the left column are crossed out, and the remaining numbers in the right column are added. The sum of these **partial products** is the answer to the multiplication problem.

Comparing Multiplication Algorithms

INDEPENDENT ACTIVITY

(*Math Masters*, p. 385)

Have students consider the multiplication algorithms they know and record the advantages and the disadvantages of each on *Math Masters*, page 385. This should help students decide which algorithm works best for them. However, this need not be the only algorithm they use. It is also important to emphasize that a paper-and-pencil algorithm might not be the most efficient way to solve a problem. Mental computation, a calculator, or an estimate might be a better choice.

When students have completed their comparison charts, bring them together to share preferences. Have students support their choices with examples.

Math Masters, p. 383

Math Masters, p. 384

② Extending the Project

▶ Using Ancient Numerals in Multiplication Algorithms

 PARTNER ACTIVITY

(*Math Masters*, p. 386)

Problem 1 on *Math Masters*, page 386 shows how the ancient
Egyptians might have used their hieroglyph numerals and
algorithm to multiply two numbers. Ask students to solve Problem
1 using hieroglyph numerals. When most students have finished,
have volunteers share their solutions on the board.

Problem 2 asks students to use the Egyptian algorithm to multiply
with Roman numerals. Ask students to solve Problem 2 using
Roman numerals. It is sometimes said that "multiplication with
Roman numerals was impossible," but, at least for smaller
numbers, it seems possible with this algorithm. Have volunteers
share their solutions on the board.

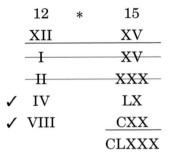

$$
\begin{array}{ccc}
12 & * & 15 \\
\hline
\text{XII} & & \text{XV} \\
\hline
\text{I} & & \text{XV} \\
\hline
\text{II} & & \text{XXX} \\
\checkmark \quad \text{IV} & & \text{LX} \\
\checkmark \quad \text{VIII} & & \text{CXX} \\
\hline
& & \text{CLXXX}
\end{array}
$$

Ask the class if they feel it would be possible to multiply Roman
numerals for larger numbers using the Egyptian algorithm. Allow
partners time to explore multiplying Roman numerals for larger
numbers.

▶ Learning More about Number Systems

 **INDEPENDENT ACTIVITY**

Much information about Egyptian mathematics is found on a scroll
called the Rhind papyrus. This scroll, copied about 1650 B.C., is
named after the man who purchased it in Egypt in A.D. 1858. It is
now in the British Museum in London.

Invite students to use the Internet to learn more about different
numeral systems, such as the Egyptian, Roman, and Babylonian
numeral systems. (The Babylonian numeral system uses a base
of 60.) Consider having students make Venn diagrams to compare
the similarities and differences between the base-10 number
system and a different numeral system of their choice.

The Web site below offers links to a variety of Internet sites on
number systems: http://mathforum.org/alejandre/numerals.html

"Magic" Computation Tricks

Objective To explore properties of arithmetic.

Technology Resources www.everydaymathonline.com

| eToolkit | Algorithms Practice | EM Facts Workshop Game™ | Family Letters | Assessment Management | Common Core State Standards | Curriculum Focal Points | Interactive Teacher's Lesson Guide |

1 Doing the Project

Recommended Use During or after Unit 2

Key Concepts and Skills

• Identify places in whole numbers and the values of the digits in those places.
[Number and Numeration Goal 1]

• Use algorithms to add and subtract whole numbers.
[Operations and Computation Goal 1]

• Apply properties of arithmetic.
[Patterns, Functions, and Algebra Goal 4]

Key Activities

Students read a description of a "magic" computation trick and try to figure out how it is done. They learn how to perform the trick and then teach it to other students. After completing this project, students should be able to perform and explain three computation tricks.

Materials

◆ *Math Masters,* pp. 387–393
◆ calculator
◆ 6 six-sided dice

2 Extending the Project

Students explore variations of their computation tricks.

Materials

◆ *Math Masters,* pp. 391–393
◆ computer with Internet access (optional)

Project Master

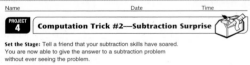

Name _____ Date _____ Time _____

PROJECT 4 | **Computation Trick #1—Super Speedy Addition**

Set the Stage: Tell a friend that you have become a whiz at addition. To prove it, you are going to add five 3-digit numbers in your head within seconds.

Props Needed: calculator

Performing the Trick:

	Examples:		
	Trial 1	**Trial 2**	**Trial 3**
1. Ask your friend to jot down a 3-digit number on a piece of paper. Each digit must be different.	493	261	682
2. Ask your friend to write another 3-digit number below the first number. Each digit must be different.	764	503	149
3. One more time. (This is the "notice-me number.")	175	935	306
4. Now it is your turn. Write a number so that the sum of your number and the first number is 999. (For example, in Trial 1, 493 + 506 = 999.)	506	738	317
5. Write another number so that the sum of this number and the second number is 999. (For example, in Trial 1, 764 + 235 = 999.)	+ 235	+ 496	+ 850
6. Pause a few seconds, and then give the sum of the five numbers. Have your friend check your super speedy addition on a calculator.	2,173	2,933	2,304

Figure out how to do this trick. How does it work?
You know that your partner's first 2 numbers and your last 2 numbers total 2 less than 2,000. Subtract 2 from the third number. Add the result to 2,000.

Math Masters, p. 387

Project Master

Name _____ Date _____ Time _____

PROJECT 4 | **Computation Trick #2—Subtraction Surprise**

Set the Stage: Tell a friend that your subtraction skills have soared. You are now able to give the answer to a subtraction problem without ever seeing the problem.

Props Needed: calculator

Performing the Trick:

	Examples:	
	Trial 1	**Trial 2**
1. Ask your friend to secretly write a 3-digit number on a piece of paper. Each digit must be different.	135	562
2. Tell your friend to reverse the digits and write the new number below the first number.	531	265
3. Now have your friend use a calculator to subtract the smaller number from the larger number.	531 − 135 = 396	562 − 265 = 297
4. Say: *Tell me either the digit in the hundreds place or the digit in the ones place.*	3 in the hundreds place	7 in the ones place
5. Pause a few seconds, and then give the answer.	396	297

Figure out how to do this trick. How does it work?
The sum of the digits in the ones place and the hundreds place is always 9. The tens place is always 9.

Math Masters, p. 388

1 Doing the Project

▶ Demonstrating a Magic Number Trick with Dice

WHOLE-CLASS DISCUSSION

Play "magician" and announce that you are going to perform a magic number trick. Tell students to watch you carefully and to try to figure out how you did it.

Ask a student to roll 5 dice and find the sum of all the numbers on the top and bottom of the dice. Before the student has had much time to think, announce that the sum of all the numbers on the top and bottom of the dice is 35.

Perform the trick again, this time with 6 dice. Again, give the answer quickly, 42. Repeat with other numbers of dice. Ask each time whether anyone has figured out how to do the trick. The sum is equal to 7 times the number of dice rolled. For example, the sum is 28 with 4 dice; the sum is 56 with 8 dice; and so on.

At some point, someone is likely to notice the pattern. If no one figures it out, share it with the class:

▷ On a six-sided die, the sum of the numbers on each pair of opposite faces is 7. Therefore, with 5 dice, the sum of the numbers on the top and bottom is $7 * 5 = 35$, no matter which numbers come up on top when the dice are rolled. With 6 dice, the sum is $7 * 6 = 42$, and so on.

▶ Learning a Magic Computation Trick

SMALL-GROUP ACTIVITY

(*Math Masters,* pp. 387–393)

Divide the class into three equal groups. Tell students that each group will figure out how to do a magic computation trick. When they have figured it out, each student in the group will teach it to one member in each of the other two groups.

Give each student in one group a copy of *Math Masters,* page 387. Give each student in a second group one copy of *Math Masters,* page 388 and each student in the third group a copy of *Math Masters,* pages 389 and 390. Give the groups 10–15 minutes to figure out how the tricks work and to write a brief explanation.

Then give one or more copies of *Math Masters,* page 391 to the first group; *Math Masters,* page 392 to the second group; and *Math Masters,* page 393 to the third group. The top section of each page explains the group's original trick. Ask students to compare their explanations with the *Math Masters* page. Then have each group work together until all members are certain they can perform and explain the trick.

Teaching Computation Tricks to Other Students

SMALL-GROUP ACTIVITY

Mix up the groups and form groups of three students, consisting of one student from each of the original three groups. Each student in a group performs a trick and teaches it to the other two students in the group.

You can form groups of three by having students in each of the original groups count off "1, 2, 3, ..." Then all the 1s form a group, all the 2s form another group, and so on. If the original groups do not have the same number of members, you can team up a pair of students to present the same trick in one of the other groups.

Discussing the Computation Tricks

WHOLE-CLASS DISCUSSION

Bring students together to discuss the computation tricks. Possible questions:

- Which trick did you find easiest to learn? The hardest to learn?
- Was it easy or hard to teach your trick to others? Why?
- Which trick would you most like to share with someone at home? Why?

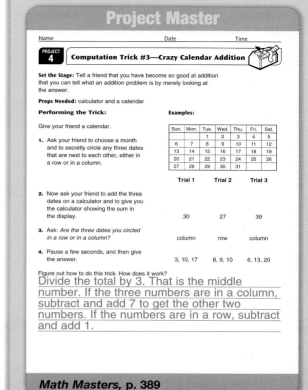

Math Masters, p. 389

Math Masters, p. 390

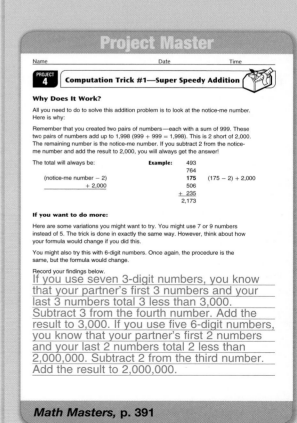

Math Masters, p. 391

② Extending the Project

▶ Exploring More Tricks

(*Math Masters*, pp. 391–393)

INDEPENDENT ACTIVITY

Math Masters, pages 391–393 contain variations of the computation tricks at the bottom of each page under the heading If You Want to Do More. Invite students to try these.

There are many books and Internet sites on recreational mathematics. The sites listed below provide a variety of links and approaches:

http://archives.math.utk.edu/popmath.html

www-history.mcs.st-andrews.ac.uk/HistTopics/Mathematical_games.html

Encourage students to find more computation tricks to share with the class.

How Would You Spend $1,000,000?

Objectives To provide experiences with large number computation; fraction, decimal, and percent conversions; and data display.

1 Doing the Project

Recommended Use During or after Unit 5

Key Concepts and Skills

- Solve problems involving percents.
  [Number and Numeration Goal 2]

- Convert between fractions, decimals, and percents.
  [Number and Numeration Goal 5]

- Collect and organize data to create a circle graph.
  [Data and Chance Goal 1]

Key Activities

In this long-term project, students work independently to research and plan how they would spend $1,000,000 while guided by a consistent, original theme. Students group their purchases into categories and record the items purchased in each category. They present their results to the class, using any appropriate format, such as a written report or a display board.

Key Vocabulary

major category ◆ unit price

Materials
- ◆ *Math Masters,* pp. 394–398
- ◆ calculator

2 Extending the Project

Students apply percent skills to analyze their project data and make circle graphs.

Materials
- ◆ *Math Masters,* pp. 399 and 400
- ◆ Geometry Template
- ◆ calculator

Additional Information

Allow about two weeks, outside of class time, for the project.

The project used as a model was done by Emily Maneck, a student in Glenview, Illinois. The project design was created by Catherine Tucci and Gayle Zis, teachers in Glenview, Illinois.

Advance Preparation

Each student will need several copies of *Math Masters,* page 398, one for each of their determined major categories.

Name _____ Date _____ Time _____

PROJECT 5 **How Would You Spend $1,000,000?—Emily's Idea**

Emily decided that if she had $1,000,000 she would spend it on a fabulous 10-day trip to Florida for her, 19 of her friends, and 4 chaperones—24 people altogether. With $1,000,000, she knew that she could make this a trip no one would ever forget.

Emily began by thinking about everything she and her friends might need for their trip. She visited a local department store to find out how much different items cost. She decided to purchase a **vacation wardrobe** for everyone, including the chaperones, at a cost of $50,750. Her next stop was a **sporting goods** store for items such as snorkel gear, swimsuits, and sunglasses. The store clerk calculated that all of her purchases there would cost $24,100.

Emily knew that she would need **transportation** to Florida and for traveling around while there. She made a few telephone calls to find out the prices for transportation. Emily found that when she politely explained her project to people, most of them were willing to help her. After doing some research, she chartered an airplane for a flight from Chicago to Orlando and back ($54,780). She purchased two stretch limos to use in Florida ($165,160 + $10,000 for gas and two around-the-clock chauffeurs). She also purchased a minivan to carry the chaperones and the luggage ($20,700) while in Florida.

Lodging was another consideration. Emily decided that her group would stay at one of the resorts inside a theme park ($33,550). She went to a travel agency to get some information about the **activities** that she and her friends might try while they were there. For $177,200, Emily made reservations for several special breakfasts as well as dinner shows, rented a water park for 12 hours, and purchased 10-day passes to the theme park where she and her group were staying.

Math Masters, p. 394

Name _____ Date _____ Time _____

PROJECT 5 **How Would You Spend $1,000,000?** *cont.*

Emily decided to keep a record of the money she was spending by listing her purchases in major categories. At the right is part of the chart that she made.

Major Category	Cost
Vacation Wardrobe	$ 50,750
Sports Equipment	$ 24,100
Transportation	$ 250,640
Lodging	$ 33,550
Activities	$ 177,200

Emily also decided that for each category she would keep a detailed record so that she would know exactly how she was spending the $1,000,000.

Below is an example of her record for one category.

Item	Quantity	Unit Price	Total Price
	Major Category—Vacation Wardrobe		
Boxer shorts	100	$ 12.50	$ 1,250.00
Socks	200	$ 5.50	$ 1,100.00
Shorts	240	$ 38.00	$ 9,120.00
T-shirts	200	$ 32.00	$ 6,400.00
Swimsuits	100	$ 36.00	$ 3,600.00
Jeans	100	$ 34.00	$ 3,400.00
Shoes	60	$ 50.00	$ 3,000.00
Flip-flops	60	$ 24.00	$ 1,440.00
Sunglasses	20	$ 29.50	$ 590.00
Long-sleeve shirts	40	$ 57.00	$ 2,280.00
Tax			$ 2,570.00
Chaperones' Wardrobe Allotment		$4,000.00 per person	$ 16,000.00
		Total	$50,750.00

These are examples of just a few of the expenses for Emily's amazing trip.

About how much money has Emily spent so far? $536,240

About how much money does Emily have left to spend? $463,760

Math Masters, p. 395

---

① Doing the Project

▶ **Introducing the Project**

WHOLE-CLASS DISCUSSION

(*Math Masters*, pp. 394 and 395)

Ask students to imagine that they have $1,000,000 and to think about ways they would spend it. Then have them share a few of their ideas.

Ask students to read *Math Masters*, pages 394 and 395. The essay describes how Emily decided on a theme and began her investigation of how she would spend $1,000,000. Discuss the essay to model an approach to the project. Include the following points:

▷ Emily's theme for spending her $1,000,000 was a Florida vacation.

Emily researched her project by going to stores and making phone calls. She found that when she politely explained her project to people, they were happy to help her. (Explain that not everyone students speak to will be enthusiastic about answering hypothetical purchasing questions. Realistically, many people do not have the time. Encourage students to politely thank those who are too busy to help and to try again somewhere else.)

▷ Emily organized her purchases into **major categories** and listed the items that made up each category.

Point out that the term ***unit price*** refers to the cost for one item. Unit costs should be rounded to the nearest dollar or half-dollar. Encourage students to round larger prices to larger values, for example, to the nearest $10 or nearest $100 for major category costs.

▷ Emily has spent about $536,240 for the items listed. She has about $463,760 left over for more purchases.

▶ **Assigning the Project**

WHOLE-CLASS DISCUSSION

(*Math Masters*, pp. 396–398)

The guidelines for completing the project are given on *Math Masters*, page 396. Review them with the class. The guidelines provide students with a common framework to begin. However, try to keep the spirit of the project as open-ended as possible.

Encourage students to pursue their own creative ideas, to imagine projects that entertain or make a profit, and to explore projects that benefit society. Projects have included starting a sports grill and ice-cream shop, modernizing a food depository, opening an animal shelter, investing in the stock market, and renovating the children's wing of a hospital.

One benefit of this project is that it provides students with the opportunity to investigate subjects of their own choosing. In gathering information, students will need to use a variety of resources and possibly speak with many different people. Because some students will have greater access to resources than others will, expect some projects to be more detailed than others.

Have students use *Math Masters,* pages 397 and 398 to organize and to record their purchases.

The goal of the project is to spend as close to $1,000,000 as possible, without going over. As this might be difficult to do, allow students to contribute a specified amount (for example, not less than $10,000 and not more than $50,000) to a charity to bring the total to $1,000,000. This contribution could be used to account for small, unspent amounts of money.

Presenting the Project

 **WHOLE-CLASS DISCUSSION**

Schedule time for students to present their completed projects to the class. Students will enjoy sharing their plans for spending $1,000,000, as well as hearing how other students choose to spend it. The presentations can be brief—students can give quick summaries of their themes and highlight any special parts of their projects.

Collect the accounting sheets (*Math Masters,* pages 397 and 398) from students after their presentations. Verify that the totals in all the categories do indeed total $1,000,000. If not, return the sheets to the students for correction before proceeding to the next activity.

2 Extending the Project

Displaying Project Data

 **INDEPENDENT ACTIVITY**

(*Math Masters,* pp. 399 and 400)

Distribute the accounting sheets that you collected after the students' presentations. Students use their data to complete *Math Masters,* pages 399 and 400.

You might need to clarify the directions on *Math Masters,* page 400. Because each percent has been rounded to the nearest whole percent, the percents might not total 100%. To compensate for this, the smaller categories should be graphed first and the largest one graphed last. If a category is only 2% of the total, and it is off by 1%, that is a relatively large error. However, if a category is 34% of the total, and it is off by 1%, the error is much less significant. By starting with the smallest category, the relative errors can be minimized.

Consider making a display of students' graphs.

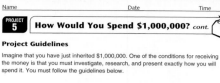

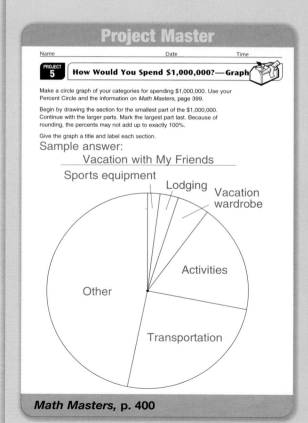

Math Masters, p. 396

Math Masters, p. 400

Project

6 Sports Areas

Objectives To provide experiences with calculating the areas of rectangles, converting between units, and converting mixed units to decimals.

1 Doing the Project

Recommended Use During or after Unit 9

Key Concepts and Skills

• Use appropriate formulas to calculate the areas of rectangles.
  [Measurement and Reference Frames Goal 2]

• Describe relationships among U.S. customary units for area, and convert units.
  [Measurement and Reference Frames Goal 3]

Key Activities

Students are given the dimensions of the playing field or surface for a variety of sports. They calculate the area of each and identify areas greater than 1 acre.

Key Vocabulary

scale drawing ◆ perspective drawing

Materials
◆ *Math Masters,* pp. 401 and 402
◆ calculator
◆ ruler

2 Extending the Project

Students convert the ground area of several large buildings to estimated area in acres.

Materials
◆ *Math Masters,* p. 403
◆ calculator

1 ⃝ Doing the Project

Discussing Scale Drawings and Dimensions of Sports Surfaces

👥👥 **WHOLE-CLASS DISCUSSION**

(*Math Masters*, pp. 401 and 402)

The dimensions of the playing surface for each sport are given in the rules for that sport. Playing areas vary greatly from sport to sport.

Discuss the two scale drawings on *Math Masters*, pages 401 and 402. Include the following points:

▷ The drawings are **scale drawings**. The relationships between lengths in a scale drawing are the same as the relationships between lengths in the actual object. For example, the playing surface for field hockey is 300 feet by 180 feet, or 100 yards by 60 yards. Its scale drawing on *Math Masters*, page 402 is 100 millimeters by 60 millimeters.

▷ The drawings are not **perspective drawings**. In perspective drawings, parallel lines that move away from the viewer are drawn so they come together at a vanishing point. The proportions in a perspective drawing are not the same as the proportions of the actual object.

The surfaces for contact sports shown on *Math Masters*, page 401 are drawn to a scale of 1 millimeter to 1 foot. Have students measure the boxing ring or one of the other surfaces with a ruler and use the scale to convert their measurements to feet. They can check their measurements against the dimensions listed below the drawing.

The surfaces for other popular sports shown on *Math Masters*, page 402 were too large to draw with the same scale used on *Math Masters*, page 401. The scale is 1 millimeter to 1 yard (3 feet). If each length and width of the scale drawing on page 402 were enlarged to three times the current size, then the playing surfaces shown on both pages would be drawn to the same scale.

Remind students of the work they did in Lesson 4-3, when they learned how to use a map scale to measure distances on a map. For example, 1 inch on a map might represent 10 miles. On another map, 1 inch might represent 100 miles.

Work through at least one problem from each page with the class. Have students write the formula for area at the bottom of page 401. $A = b * h$, or $A = l * w$ Point out that some dimensions are given in feet and inches. Such measures must be converted to decimals to enter them into a calculator.

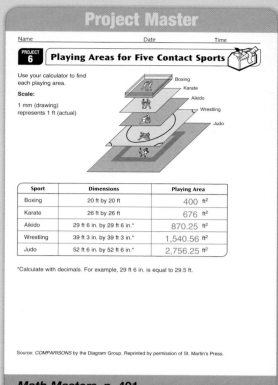

Project Master

Name _____ Date _____ Time _____

PROJECT 6 — Playing Areas for Five Contact Sports

Use your calculator to find each playing area.

Scale:
1 mm (drawing) represents 1 ft (actual)

Sport	Dimensions	Playing Area
Boxing	20 ft by 20 ft	400 ft²
Karate	26 ft by 26 ft	676 ft²
Aikido	29 ft 6 in. by 29 ft 6 in.*	870.25 ft²
Wrestling	39 ft 3 in. by 39 ft 3 in.*	1,540.56 ft²
Judo	52 ft 6 in. by 52 ft 6 in.*	2,756.25 ft²

*Calculate with decimals. For example, 29 ft 6 in. is equal to 29.5 ft.

Source: *COMPARISONS* by the Diagram Group. Reprinted by permission of St. Martin's Press.

***Math Masters*, p. 401**

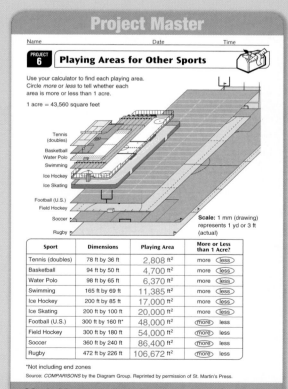

Project Master

Name _____ Date _____ Time _____

PROJECT 6 — Playing Areas for Other Sports

Use your calculator to find each playing area. Circle *more* or *less* to tell whether each area is more or less than 1 acre.

1 acre = 43,560 square feet

Scale: 1 mm (drawing) represents 1 yd or 3 ft (actual)

Sport	Dimensions	Playing Area	More or Less than 1 Acre?
Tennis (doubles)	78 ft by 36 ft	2,808 ft²	more (less)
Basketball	94 ft by 50 ft	4,700 ft²	more (less)
Water Polo	98 ft by 65 ft	6,370 ft²	more (less)
Swimming	165 ft by 69 ft	11,385 ft²	more (less)
Ice Hockey	200 ft by 85 ft	17,000 ft²	more (less)
Ice Skating	200 ft by 100 ft	20,000 ft²	more (less)
Football (U.S.)	300 ft by 160 ft*	48,000 ft²	(more) less
Field Hockey	300 ft by 180 ft	54,000 ft²	(more) less
Soccer	360 ft by 240 ft	86,400 ft²	(more) less
Rugby	472 ft by 226 ft	106,672 ft²	(more) less

*Not including end zones

Source: *COMPARISONS* by the Diagram Group. Reprinted by permission of St. Martin's Press.

***Math Masters*, p. 402**

► Calculating Sports Areas

(*Math Masters,* pp. 401 and 402)

PARTNER ACTIVITY

Have students complete *Math Masters,* pages 401 and 402. Remind them that they can compare an area to an acre if they know the area in square feet. A sports area of more than 43,560 square feet will be more than 1 acre.

Students might note that a football field (minus the end zones) is about 1 acre. They will have little difficulty identifying football, field hockey, soccer, and rugby as sports whose playing areas exceed 1 acre.

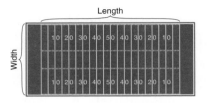

The area of a football field without the end zones is approximately 1 acre.

2 Extending the Project

► Finding the Footprints of Famous Buildings

(*Math Masters,* p. 403)

PARTNER ACTIVITY

Students are given the ground areas in square feet, or footprints, of seven famous, large buildings. Using an equivalence of 1 acre to about 50,000 ft², they convert these areas to acres.

Name _____ Date _____ Time _____

PROJECT 6 — Ground Areas of Famous Large Buildings

The ground areas of buildings, their footprints, are almost always given in square feet or square meters. Some buildings have very large ground areas. When their areas are given in square feet, the numbers are so large that it is hard to imagine how big the buildings really are.

For large buildings, if you convert the area in square feet to an estimate in acres, you can get a better idea of the size of the building.

Estimate the ground area, in acres, of each building in the table below:

Example: The Colosseum, in Italy, covers an area of about 250,000 ft².

One acre is about 50,000 ft².

So 5 acres is about 250,000 ft².

The Colosseum covers an area of about 5 acres (5 football fields).

Reference

1 acre = 43,560 square feet

For estimating, think of 1 acre as about 50,000 square feet.

A football field (excluding the end zones) is approximately 1 acre.

Building	Country	Date Built	Ground Area (ft²)	Estimated Area (in acres)	
Colosseum	Italy	70–224	250,000 ft²	5	acres
Pyramid of Cheops	Egypt	c. 2600 B.C.	571,500 ft²	11	acres
Chartres Cathedral	France	1194–1514	60,000 ft²	1	acres
St. Peter's Basilica	Vatican City	1506–1626	392,300 ft²	8	acres
Taj Mahal	India	1636–1653	78,000 ft²	1.5	acres
Pentagon	U.S. (Virginia)	1941–1943	1,263,000 ft²	25	acres
Ford Parts Center	U.S. (Michigan)	1936	2,800,000 ft²	56	acres

Math Masters, p. 403

Polygon Areas and Pick's Formula

 Objective To explore Pick's Formula for finding the area of a polygon.

Technology Resources www.everydaymathonline.com

| eToolkit | Algorithms Practice | EM Facts Workshop Game™ | Family Letters | Assessment Management | Common Core State Standards | Curriculum Focal Points | Interactive Teacher's Lesson Guide |

1 Doing the Project

Recommended Use During or after Unit 9

Key Concepts and Skills

• Measure length with tools to the nearest millimeter.
[Measurement and Reference Frames Goal 1]

• Use appropriate formulas to calculate the areas of polygons.
[Measurement and Reference Frames Goal 2]

Key Activities

Students extend the rectangle method or choose other methods to find areas of polygons. They are introduced to Pick's Formula as an alternative way to find the area of a figure drawn on a square grid or formed on a geoboard.

Key Vocabulary

grid points ◆ vertices ◆ interior

Materials

◆ *Math Masters,* pp. 404 and 405
◆ Geometry Template or ruler
◆ Class Data Pad
◆ calculator
◆ for demonstration: overhead geoboard and elastic bands or transparency of geoboard dot paper
◆ per partnership: geoboard and rubber bands or geoboard dot paper

2 Extending the Project

Students use Pick's Formula to find the area of an irregular path.

Materials

◆ *Math Masters,* p. 406

Advance Preparation

As an alternative to an overhead geoboard and elastic bands, make a transparency of geoboard dot paper.

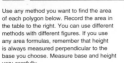

Name _____ Date _____ Time _____

PROJECT 7 | **Finding Areas with Standard Methods**

Use any method you want to find the area of each polygon below. Record the area in the table to the right. You can use different methods with different figures. If you use any area formulas, remember that height is always measured perpendicular to the base you choose. Measure base and height very carefully.

Figure	Area
A	about __4.5__ cm²
B	about __13__ cm²
C	about __7__ cm²
D	about __12__ cm²
E	about __7.5__ cm²
F	about __7.5__ cm²

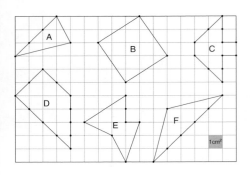

Math Masters, p. 404

Name _____ Date _____ Time _____

PROJECT 7 | **Finding Areas with Pick's Formula**

Read the paragraphs below, and then use Pick's Formula to find the areas of the polygons on the previous page. Record your results in the table below. Compare them to the results you recorded in the table on the previous page. You should expect some differences—measures are always estimates.

Pick's Formula for Finding Polygon Areas by Counting
In 1899, Georg Pick, an Austrian mathematician, discovered a formula for finding the area of a polygon on a square grid (such as graph paper). If a polygon has its vertices at grid points, its area can be found by counting the number of grid points on the polygon (P) and the number of grid points in the interior of the polygon (I) and then by using the formula $A = (\frac{1}{2} * P) + I - 1$. The unit of area is one square on the grid.

For figure B on the previous page, the unit of area is cm².

P = 4 (grid points on polygon)

I = 12 (grid points in interior)

$A = (\frac{1}{2} * P) + I - 1$
  $= (\frac{1}{2} * 4) + 12 - 1$
  $= 13$ cm²

Figure	P	I	Area $= (\frac{1}{2} * P) + I +- 1$
A	5	3	4.5 cm²
B	4	12	13 cm²
C	12	2	7 cm²
D	12	7	12 cm²
E	7	5	7.5 cm²
F	7	5	7.5 cm²

Draw two polygons. Be sure that the vertices are at grid points. Use Pick's Formula to find the areas of the polygons.

Sample answers: 1 cm²

Area: __6.5 cm²__   Area: _____

Math Masters, p. 405

---

① Doing the Project

▶ Finding Areas of Polygons

PARTNER ACTIVITY

(*Math Masters*, p. 404)

Students find the areas of the polygons on *Math Masters*, page 404 and record them in the table. Encourage students to use any of the strategies they know for finding areas.

NOTE For figures that are "tilted" on the grid, it might not be possible to read lengths of bases or heights directly from the grid. Advise students using area formulas to measure slant lengths very carefully (in millimeters) and to use their calculators to multiply the resulting decimals to get close approximations of the areas.

When most students have completed the page, discuss the methods they used to find the areas, and list the strategies on the Class Data Pad. The rectangle method can be used with all the figures. Examples of other strategies:

▷ **Figure A**
Measure a base and height, and use the formula for the area of a triangle. Remind students that the height of the triangle must be measured perpendicular to the base of the triangle.

▷ **Figure B**
Carefully measure the sides (about 3.6 cm each), and use the formula for the area of a rectangle.

▷ **Figure C**
Count squares and half-squares to find the area of the figure.

▷ **Figure D**
Partition the trapezoid into a square and a triangle. Measure bases and heights carefully. Then calculate the areas, and add them together

▷ **Figure E**
This figure is challenging to most students. The rectangle method works very nicely here. Partitioning the polygon into many triangles is possible but tedious.

▷ **Figure F**
Measure carefully, and use the formula for the area of a triangle. Once again, remind students that the height of the triangle is measured perpendicular to the base of the triangle.

▶ Introducing Pick's Formula

WHOLE-CLASS DISCUSSION

(*Math Masters*, p. 405)

Pick's Formula can be used to find the area of any polygon that has its vertices at grid points on a square grid or geoboard.

Have students read the description of Pick's Formula and the example on *Math Masters*, page 405. Discuss the formula. Be sure students understand how P (the number of **grid points** on the polygon, including **vertices**) and *I* (the number of grid points in the **interior** of the polygon) are counted and how they are used in the calculation of area.

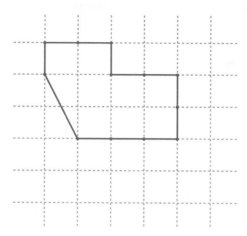

Use an overhead geoboard, or draw several figures on a transparency of geoboard dot paper. Work through Pick's Formula with the class to find the areas of the figures.

NOTE Pick's Formula, also called *Pick's Theorem,* was first published in 1899 by Austrian mathematician Georg Alexander Pick (1859–1942). The proof of this odd, but elegant formula is beyond the scope of this book, as is the proof that it is equivalent to the formula linking the number of edges (*e*), faces (*f*), and vertices (*v*) of any polyhedron: $e = f + v - 2$.

▶ Using Pick's Formula

PARTNER ACTIVITY

(*Math Masters,* pp. 404 and 405)

Have students use Pick's Formula to find the areas of the polygons on *Math Masters,* page 404. They record the areas on *Math Masters,* page 405.

If students have geoboards, have them form the figures before using Pick's Formula. Encourage partners who finish early to create new problems for each other on a geoboard or geoboard dot paper.

2 Extending the Project

▶ Using Pick's Formula to Find the Area of an Irregular Path

INDEPENDENT ACTIVITY

(*Math Masters,* p. 406)

Have students use Pick's Formula to find the area of the path on *Math Masters,* page 406. This path appeared in Lesson 9-6 (*Math Masters,* page 273). When students have completed the page, discuss whether they think Pick's Formula is an efficient method for calculating this area.

Project
8
Pendulums

Objectives To provide experiences with collecting, displaying, and analyzing data.

Technology Resources www.everydaymathonline.com

eToolkit

Algorithms Practice

EM Facts Workshop Game™

Family Letters

Assessment Management

CCSS

Common Core State Standards

NCTM

Curriculum Focal Points

*i*TLG

Interactive Teacher's Lesson Guide

1 Doing the Project

Recommended Use During or after Unit 10

Key Concepts and Skills

• Collect and organize data to create a line graph.
  [Data and Chance Goal 1]

• Predict the outcomes of experiments, test the predictions using manipulatives, and summarize the results.
  [Data and Chance Goal 4]

Key Activities

Students record and graph the time and length of pendulum swings. They investigate whether the length of a pendulum affects the duration of one complete swing of the pendulum; whether the length of the arc of a pendulum affects the duration of the swing; and whether the amount of weight at the end of a pendulum affects the duration of the swing.

Key Vocabulary

pendulum ◆ complete swing

Materials

◆ *Math Masters,* pp. 407–409

Per small group:

◆ string pendulum

◆ ruler or meterstick

◆ watch or clock to time seconds (preferable to tenths of a second)

◆ 10 metal washers or similar weights

2 Extending the Project

Students research pendulums.

Materials

◆ encyclopedia

◆ *Longitude*

◆ *Sea Clocks: The Story of Longitude*

◆ computer with Internet access (optional)

Advance Preparation

Prepare one string pendulum for each small group. Cut as many $1\frac{1}{2}$ m strings as there are groups. Tie a paper clip to one end of each string. Use a marker to mark each string 5 cm, 10 cm, 20 cm, 30 cm, 50 cm, 75 cm, and 1 m from the end of the paper clip. Open up the clip so large metal washers or similar weights can be hung on it.

Prepare one additional pendulum with a string at least 2 m long and a paper clip at one end for demonstration purposes. Mark the string 50 cm, 75 cm, and 2 m from the paper clip.

For Part 2, obtain a copy of *Longitude* by Dava Sobel (Walker, 2005) and/or *Sea Clocks: The Story of Longitude* by Louise Bordon (Margaret K. McElderry, 2004).

1 Doing the Project

Discussing Pendulums

Explain that according to legend, Galileo discovered the principle of the pendulum in 1583 while watching a hanging lamp swing back and forth in a cathedral in Pisa. Galileo and Christiaan Huygens (1656) are each credited with designing a clock controlled by the motion of a pendulum.

A **pendulum** consists of an object, called the bob, suspended from a fixed support in such a way that the object can swing freely back and forth under the influence of gravity.

Ask students to describe the instances of pendulums they have seen. One example would be the pendulum in a clock. Some students might have been to a science museum and seen a very long pendulum (a Foucault pendulum) that demonstrates the rotation of the Earth.

Demonstrating and Timing a Pendulum

WHOLE-CLASS ACTIVITY

(*Math Masters,* p. 407)

Demonstrate how to set up a string pendulum on a desk or table (*see margin*):

▷ Form a pendulum that is 50 cm long.

▷ Hold the pendulum fairly high (approximately parallel to the floor) and release the bob. In a **complete swing,** the pendulum swings forward, stops for an instant, swings back (almost) to its starting position, and stops for an instant. Swinging in just one direction is a half-swing.

Tell students that they will perform experiments to try to answer the question, *Does the time it takes a pendulum to make a complete swing depend on the length of the string?* Ask students to predict what the answer will be.

Now use the pendulum to demonstrate how to time 10 complete swings of the pendulum:

1. Ask a student to keep time with a seconds timer.

2. Pull the pendulum to one side. As you release it, say, *Go.* The student starts timing.

3. With the class, count out 10 complete swings (not half-swings).

4. When the pendulum finishes its tenth complete swing, say, *Stop.* The student stops timing.

5. The student gives the elapsed time (to the nearest tenth of a second, if possible).

Name   Date   Time

PROJECT 8 The Swing Time of Pendulums

1. Your teacher will demonstrate an experiment with a pendulum that is 50 cm long. Record the results below. Sample answers:

   a. It took about ___14___ seconds for 10 complete swings of the pendulum.

   b. About how much time did it take for one swing? Round your answer to the nearest 0.1 second.
   ___1.4___ second(s)

2. Form a pendulum that is 75 cm long. Time 10 complete swings of the pendulum. Time the swings to the nearest second.

   Practice timing 10 complete swings several times. Then time 10 swings and record the results below. Sample answers:

   a. It took about ___17___ seconds for 10 complete swings of the pendulum.

   b. About how much time did it take for one swing? Round your answer to the nearest 0.1 second. ___1.7___ second(s)

3. Record the results for a 50-cm and a 75-cm pendulum in the table at the right. Sample answers:

4. Experiment with different lengths of pendulum string.

   Find the time for 10 complete swings for each of the other pendulum lengths. Time the 10 swings to the nearest 0.1 second. Record your results in the table.

   After collecting your data, divide each of the times by 10 to estimate the time for one complete swing. Record your answers in the table, rounded to the nearest 0.1 second.

Length of Pendulum	Time for: Ten Complete Swings (to nearest 0.1 sec)	Time for: One Complete Swing (to nearest 0.1 sec)
5 cm	4.5 sec	0.5 sec
10 cm	6.3 sec	0.6 sec
20 cm	9.0 sec	0.9 sec
30 cm	11.0 sec	1.1 sec
50 cm	14.0 sec	1.4 sec
75 cm	17.4 sec	1.7 sec
100 cm	20.0 sec	2.0 sec
200 cm	28.4 sec	2.8 sec

Math Masters, p. 407

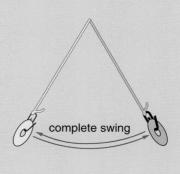

heavy object

pendulum

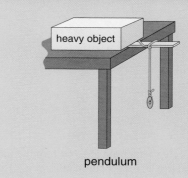

floor

Hold pendulum parallel to floor.

complete swing

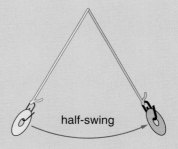

half-swing

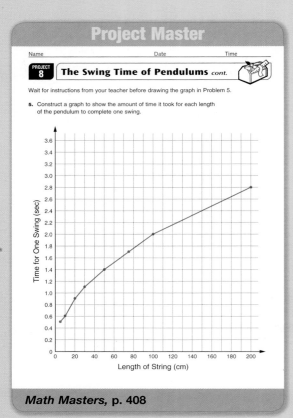
NOTE For your information, the formula for calculating the time of a complete swing of a pendulum is based on its length.

Time in seconds $= 2 * \pi * \sqrt{\dfrac{\text{length in meters}}{9.8}}$

Ask students to use the time for 10 swings to calculate the approximate time for one complete swing, to the nearest tenth or hundredth of a second. Divide by 10. Have students record the times for 10 swings and for 1 swing in Problem 1 on *Math Masters,* page 407, and in the table at the bottom of the page.

Some students might wonder why it is necessary to time 10 complete swings to obtain an accurate time measurement for a single swing. Why not simply time a single swing? Point out that timing a single, complete swing can be tricky, and the chance of error is great. But timing 10 swings is easy—even the shortest pendulum will take about 5 seconds for 10 swings.

▶ **Investigating the Swing Times for Pendulums of Various Lengths**

SMALL-GROUP ACTIVITY

(*Math Masters,* pp. 407 and 408)

1. **Practicing Timing Swings of a 75-centimeter Pendulum**
   Have each group form a 75-centimeter pendulum and time 10 swings. Ask groups to do several additional practice trials. Circulate and assist.

   When students have demonstrated that they have acquired the knack for timing the pendulum, have them do a final trial that they will record. They should then record the time for 10 complete swings and 1 complete swing in Problem 2 and in the table at the bottom of *Math Masters,* page 407.

2. **Collecting Data for Pendulums of Various Lengths**
   Ask for three volunteers. Two students stand on chairs about 2 meters apart. One of them holds the demonstration pendulum by the weighted end. The other holds the string at the 2-meter mark. The third student prepares to keep time. The volunteers then time 10 complete swings of this pendulum. Students calculate the duration of one swing and record the results in the table.

NOTE If a group's results are markedly different from the others, discuss how this might have happened (for example, counting half-swings instead of complete swings; timing is started or stopped too early or too late; making the pendulum the wrong length). In such cases, suggest that the group use data from another group for the graphing exercise.

⬆ Adjusting the Activity

Suggest students make long pendulums that they can safely swing from high places, time the swings, and report the results to the class. Have students prepare a larger graph incorporating the results.

AUDITORY ◆ KINESTHETIC ◆ TACTILE ◆ VISUAL

Have students work in groups to continue the investigation by timing 10 swings for pendulums with 5 cm, 10 cm, 20 cm, 30 cm, and 1 m string lengths. Circulate and assist. Each student records the time for 10 swings and then divides by 10 to find the average time for a single swing, to the nearest tenth of a second.

Check the reasonableness of data entries of groups that finish early. They may go on to Problem 6 on *Math Masters,* page 409 while waiting for the others to catch up. They should not begin the graphing exercise in Problem 5 on *Math Masters,* page 408 until their data entries have been checked.

3. Graphing the Results

After all groups have completed their trials and found the average time for 10 swings to the nearest tenth of a second, help students plot one or two data points on the grid in Problem 5 on *Math Masters,* page 408. Students then plot the rest of the results recorded in the table on *Math Masters,* page 407.

Ask students to connect the dots to form a broken-line graph. In discussing the graph, ask questions such as the following:

- Does the length of the string affect the duration of the swing? The time for one complete swing increases as the length of the pendulum string increases. Some students might notice that quadrupling the length of the pendulum string doubles the swing time.

- About how many seconds, to the nearest tenth of a second, would it take for a complete swing of a 150-centimeter pendulum? About 2.4 sec

- About how long is a pendulum that takes 2 seconds to complete a swing? 100 cm

- Based on the results, what might be the swing time for a much longer pendulum—say 10 m, 20 m, or even 30 m long? Possible responses: 10 m: about 6 sec; 20 m: about 9 sec; 30 m: about 11 sec

▶ Investigating the Effect of the Arc on Swing Time

SMALL-GROUP ACTIVITY

(*Math Masters,* p. 409)

Have students start the swing of a pendulum at various positions. They try to answer the question, *Does the size of the arc make much difference in the amount of time it takes for 10 complete swings?* They record their answer in Problem 6 on *Math Masters,* page 409. For a given pendulum length, the position of the starting point should not significantly affect the time for a complete swing.

▶ Investigating the Effect of Weight on Swing Time

(*Math Masters*, p. 409)

Have students explore whether the amount of weight at the end of a pendulum affects the time for 10 complete swings. Using the 50-centimeter pendulum, students vary the weight by adding or removing washers. For a given pendulum length, different weights should make little difference in the time for a complete swing. However, the heavier the weight is, the longer the pendulum is likely to keep swinging. They record their conclusions in Problem 7 on *Math Masters,* page 409.

2 Extending the Project

▶ Learning More about Pendulums

 INDEPENDENT ACTIVITY

Invite students to find out more about the history, types, and uses of pendulums by looking in encyclopedias or searching the Internet.

Pendulums were integral to the development of clocks. Clocks, in turn, made possible the long-sought solution to measuring longitude. Two books that discuss this solution are *Longitude* and *Sea Clocks: The Story of Longitude.*

Longitude
Summary: This is the story of the search for a way to determine longitude aboard ships at sea. The solution came in the 18th century in the form of precise clocks designed so a ship's motion and variations in temperature and humidity did not affect the clocks' pendulums.

Sea Clocks: The Story of Longitude
Summary: This juvenile literature biography is the dramatic story of John Harrison. Harrison dedicated more than 40 years of his life to the design of the perfect sea clock.

Project

9

Adding Volumes of Solid Figures

Objectives To find the volumes of solid figures composed of two non-overlapping rectangular prisms.

Technology Resources www.everydaymathonline.com

eToolkit

Algorithms
Practice

EM Facts
Workshop
Game™

Family
Letters

Assessment
Management

CCSS
Common
Core State
Standards

NCTM
Curriculum
Focal Points

iTLG
Interactive
Teacher's
Lesson Guide

1 Doing the Project

Recommended Use During or after Unit 9

Key Concepts and Skills

- Use unit cubes to calculate volume.
  [Measurement and Reference Frames Goal 2]

- Use a formula to calculate the volumes of rectangular prisms.
  [Measurement and Reference Frames Goal 2]

- Explore properties of solid figures.
  [Geometry Goal 2]

- Write number sentences with variables to model volume problems.
  [Patterns, Functions, and Algebra Goal 2]

Key Activities

Students use centimeter cubes and formulas to explore the volumes of solid figures composed of two rectangular prisms.

Key Vocabulary

unit cube

Materials

- *Math Journal 2,* Activity Sheet 8
- *Math Masters,* p. 410
- transparent tape
- per group of students: about 100 centimeter cubes

2 Extending the Project

Students find the volumes of rectangular prisms to find the total approximate volume of Willis Tower.

Materials

- *Math Masters,* p. 410A

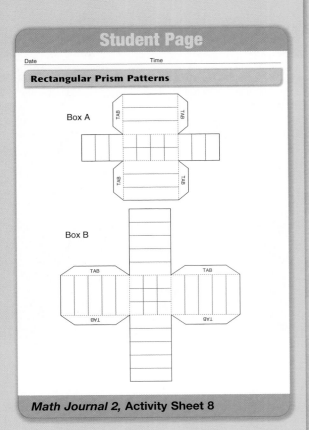

1 Doing the Projects

▶ Exploring the Volume of Solid Figures

SMALL-GROUP ACTIVITY

(*Math Journal 2,* Activity Sheet 8)

Provide each group of students with about 100 centimeter cubes. In each group, students should display the two open boxes that they constructed in Lesson 9-8 from Activity Sheet 8. If the constructed boxes are no longer available, distribute copies of Activity Sheet 8 as needed.

Have students tape together Boxes A and B to form one solid figure. Specify that they should put the prisms together so that two faces are together and edges line up where possible. Note that students may tape the prisms together in different ways. The figure below is one example.

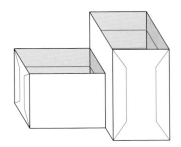

Ask: *Suppose each box has a lid so that each is a rectangular prism. Is the figure formed by the two rectangular prisms also a rectangular prism? Explain.* Sample answer: No. A rectangular prism is formed by six faces that are rectangles. The new figure that is formed has more than six rectangular faces. Mention that a three-dimensional shape that is not of a specific type is simply called a *solid figure.*

Ask: *How could you use the centimeter cubes to find the volume of the solid figure you formed?* Sample answer: Fill each box with centimeter cubes. Add or count the cubes used in all. *What is the volume of the solid figure?* 69 cubic centimeters

Ask students to attach the two prisms in different ways (such as one above the other or one next to the other) and compare the volume of each new solid that has been formed. Students should recognize that the volume is the same no matter how the prisms are attached. Ask a volunteer to explain why this is so. Sample answer: The two prisms have the same volumes no matter how they are put together, so the sum of the two volumes is the same.

Explain that in this case we can consider each dimension of a centimeter cube as being 1 unit long. Mention that a cube with side lengths of 1 unit is called a **unit cube.** Explain that in general, when a solid figure can be packed without gaps and overlaps using n unit cubes, the volume of the solid figure is n cubic units.

Building a Solid Figure to Find Volume

👥 **SMALL-GROUP ACTIVITY**

(*Math Masters,* p. 410)

Have students use the centimeter cubes to build the two rectangular prisms in each of Problems 1–3 on *Math Masters,* page 410. Students find the volume of each prism and then find the volume of the solid figure formed by the two prisms. Encourage students to use a formula (either $V = B * h$ or $V = l * w * h$) to find the volumes of the rectangular prisms. Students should use the cubes to check their results.

When students complete Problem 4, they should conclude that you can find the volume of a solid figure formed by two rectangular prisms by adding the two volumes. So, finding the volume of a solid figure that includes more than one rectangular prism is an additive process. You may want to explain that if a solid figure has overlapping parts, as in the solid figure below, you add the volumes of the *non-overlapping* parts to the volumes of the parts that overlap.

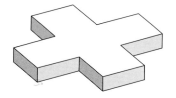

2 Extending the Project

Finding the Volume of Willis Tower in Chicago

🧍 **INDEPENDENT ACTIVITY**

(*Math Masters,* p. 410A)

Mention that at 1,450 feet tall (excluding antennas), Willis Tower in Chicago (formerly named Sears Tower) is the tallest building in the United States. When it was built in 1974, it was the tallest building in the world.

Project Master

Name _____ Date _____ Time _____

PROJECT 9 | **Building a Solid Figure to Find Volume**

For Problems 1–3, do the following:
  a. Use centimeter cubes to build each rectangular prism.
  b. Find the volume of each rectangular prism.
  c. Find the volume of the solid figure formed by the two rectangular prisms.

1.

	Length l	Width w	Height h	Volume V (cubic units)
Rectangular Prism A	1	2	3	6
Rectangular Prism B	2	3	4	24
Solid Figure Formed by Prisms A and B				30

2.

	Length l	Width w	Height h	Volume V (cubic units)
Rectangular Prism C	5	3	2	30
Rectangular Prism D	2	3	5	30
Solid Figure Formed by Prisms C and D				60

3.

	Length l	Width w	Height h	Volume V (cubic units)
Rectangular Prism E	12	3	1	36
Rectangular Prism F	3	3	3	27
Solid Figure Formed by Prisms E and F				63

4. Explain how to find the volume of a solid figure made from two rectangular prisms, one with dimensions 3 cm by 4 cm by 5 cm and one with dimensions 2 cm by 5 cm by 4 cm.
   Sample answer: I would use the formula $V = l * w * h$ to find the volume of each rectangular prism and then add the volumes. So, the total volume is $3 * 4 * 5 + 2 * 5 * 4 = 60 + 40$, or 100 cm³.

Math Masters, p. 410

Project Master

Name   Date   Time

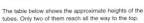

PROJECT 9 **Finding the Volume of Willis Tower**

At 1,450 feet tall, Willis Tower in Chicago is the tallest
building in the United States. It is composed of nine
rectangular prisms known as "tubes." The tubes are built
in a 3-by-3 arrangement. Although the tubes are of various
heights, each one has a square base that measures
75 feet on a side.

Willis Tower

1. What is the area of the base of each tube?

    5,625 ft²

The table below shows the approximate heights of the
tubes. Only two of them reach all the way to the top.

2. What formula could you use to find the volume
of one tube?   Sample answer:
$V = B * h$

3. Complete the table to find the volume of one tube at each given height. Then
find the total volume of the tubes for each height.

Approximate Height of Tube	Number of Tubes at this Height	Volume of One Tube at this Height (ft³)	Total Volume of Tubes at this Height (ft³)
646 ft	3	3,633,750	10,901,250
672 ft	2	3,780,000	7,560,000
1,200 ft	2	6,750,000	13,500,000
1,450 ft	2	8,156,250	16,312,500

4. Describe what you will do to find the total approximate volume of Willis Tower.

Sample answer: I will find the sum of the total volumes of
the tubes for each height.

5. The total volume of Willis Tower is about ___48,273,750___ ft³.

Math Masters, p. 410A

The building consists of nine square "tubes" constructed in a 3-by-3
arrangement. Each tube measures 75 feet on a side. Ask students to
explain how to find the dimensions of the entire base of Willis Tower.
Sample answer: There are three tubes on a side, and each is 75 feet
long. So each side is 225 feet long, making the dimensions of the
base 225 ft by 225 ft. Ask: *What is the area of the base?* 225 * 225,
or 50,625 ft²

Explain that the nine tubes are of various heights, with some being
the same height. For example, although all nine tubes extend up
through the 49th story, only two tubes extend to the full height
of 110 stories. So to find the volume of Willis Tower, you need to
find the volumes of the different tubes and then add. Of course,
multiplication could be used to find the total volume of tubes with
the same dimensions.

Math Masters, page 410A guides students in finding the
approximate volume of Willis Tower.

Algorithm
1
Project

U.S. Traditional Addition

Objective To introduce U.S. traditional addition.

Technology Resources www.everydaymathonline.com

eToolkit

Algorithms
Practice

EM Facts
Workshop
Game™

Family
Letters

Assessment
Management

Common
Core State
Standards

Curriculum
Focal Points

Interactive
Teacher's
Lesson Guide

1 Doing the Project

Recommended Use After Lesson 2◆2

Key Concepts and Skills

• Identify places in whole numbers and the values of the digits in those places.
[Number and Numeration Goal 1]

• Add multidigit whole numbers.
[Operations and Computation Goal 1]

• Solve addition number stories.
[Operations and Computation Goal 1]

• Make reasonable estimates for addition problems.
[Operations and Computation Goal 6]

Key Activities

Students explore and practice U.S. traditional addition with multidigit whole numbers.

Key Vocabulary

U.S. traditional addition

Materials

◆ *Math Journal 1* or *2,* pp. 1P and 2P
◆ *Student Reference Book,* p. 24A

2 Extending the Project

Students solve multidigit addition problems, first using the focus algorithm (partial-sums addition) and then using any algorithm they choose.

Materials

◆ *Math Journal 1* or *2,* pp. 3P and 4P
◆ Online Additional Practice, pp. 4A–4D
◆ *Student Reference Book,* pp. 13, 14, and 24A

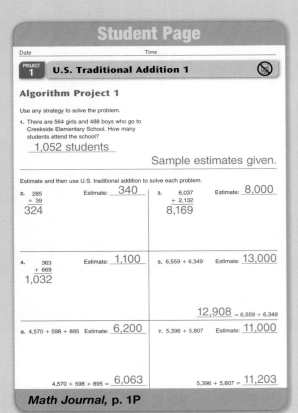

Student Page

Date _____ Time _____

PROJECT 1 **U.S. Traditional Addition 1**

Algorithm Project 1

Use any strategy to solve the problem.

1. There are 564 girls and 488 boys who go to Creekside Elementary School. How many students attend the school?

   1,052 students

   Sample estimates given.

Estimate and then use U.S. traditional addition to solve each problem.

2. 285
    + 39   Estimate: __340__
    324

3. 6,037
    + 2,132   Estimate: __8,000__
    8,169

4. 363
    + 669   Estimate: __1,100__
    1,032

5. 6,559 + 6,349   Estimate: __13,000__

    12,908 = 6,559 + 6,349

6. 4,570 + 598 + 895   Estimate: __6,200__

7. 5,396 + 5,807   Estimate: __11,000__

    4,570 + 598 + 895 = __6,063__

    5,396 + 5,807 = __11,203__

Math Journal, p. 1P

NOTE Reinforce the use of estimation by asking students to make an estimate prior to solving each problem. The estimate is then used to check the reasonableness of the solution to the problem.

1 Doing the Project

▶Solving an Addition Problem

INDEPENDENT ACTIVITY

(*Math Journal 1 or 2*, p. 1P)

Ask students to solve Problem 1 on journal page 1P. Tell them they may use any methods they wish, but they may not use calculators.

▶Discussing Solutions

WHOLE-CLASS ACTIVITY

(*Math Journal 1 or 2*, p. 1P)

Discuss students' solutions to Problem 1 on journal page 1P. $564 + 488 = 1,052$ students Expect that students will use several different methods, including partial-sums addition, column addition, and the opposite-change rule for addition. Some students may also use U.S. traditional addition. *Possible strategies:*

▷ Using partial-sums addition

$$\begin{array}{r} 5\,6\,4 \\ +\ 4\,8\,8 \\ \hline \end{array}$$

Add the 100s.	$500 + 400 \rightarrow$	9 0 0
Add the 10s.	$60 + 80 \rightarrow$	1 4 0
Add the 1s.	$4 + 8 \rightarrow$	1 2
Add the partial sums.	$900 + 140 + 12 \rightarrow$	**1 0 5 2**

▷ Using column addition

	100s	10s	1s
	5	6	4
+	4	8	8
Add the numbers in each column.	9	14	12
Trade 10 ones for 1 ten.	9	15	2
Trade 10 tens for 1 hundred.	**10**	**5**	**2**

▷ Using the opposite-change rule for addition

Adjust 564 down (by 2) to 562 and adjust 488 up (by 2) to 490.
Adjust 562 down (by 10) to 552 and adjust 490 up (by 10) to 500.

$$\begin{array}{r} 5\,6\,4 \\ +\ 4\,8\,8 \\ \hline 5\,6\,2 \\ +\ 4\,9\,0 \\ \hline 5\,5\,2 \\ +\ 5\,0\,0 \\ \hline 1\,0\,5\,2 \end{array}$$

▷ Using U.S. traditional addition

$$\begin{array}{r} 1\,1 \\ 5\,6\,4 \\ +\ 4\,8\,8 \\ \hline 1\,0\,5\,2 \end{array}$$

▶ Introducing U.S. Traditional Addition

 **WHOLE-CLASS ACTIVITY**

After you have discussed students' solutions, and even if one or more students used **U.S. traditional addition,** demonstrate it as described below.

Example 1: 564 + 488

Step 1:

Add the 1s: 4 + 8 = 12.

12 = 1 ten + 2 ones

Write 2 in the 1s place below the line.

Write 1 above the numbers in the 10s place.

```
    1
  5 6 4
+ 4 8 8
      2
```

Step 2:

Add the 10s: 1 + 6 + 8 = 15.

15 tens = 1 hundred + 5 tens

Write 5 in the 10s place below the line.

Write 1 above the numbers in the 100s place.

```
  1 1
  5 6 4
+ 4 8 8
    5 2
```

Step 3:

Add the 100s: 1 + 5 + 4 = 10.

10 hundreds = 1 one thousand + 0 hundreds

Write 0 in the 100s place below the line.

Write 1 in the 1,000s place below the line.

```
  1 1
  5 6 4
+ 4 8 8
1 0 5 2
```

564 + 488 = 1,052

There are 1,052 students at Creekside Elementary School.

NOTE Throughout the discussion of U.S. traditional addition, be sure that students understand the values of the digits. For instance, in Step 2 of Example 1, 1 + 6 + 8 = 15 means 1 ten + 6 tens + 8 tens = 15 tens (1 hundred + 5 tens) or 10 + 60 + 80 = 150.

Example 2: 7,446 + 3,579

Step 1:

Add the 1s: 6 + 9 = 15.

15 = 1 ten + 5 ones

Write 5 in the 1s place below the line.

Write 1 above the numbers in the 10s place.

```
      1
  7 4 4 6
+ 3 5 7 9
        5
```

Student Page

Date _____ Time _____

PROJECT 1 | **U.S. Traditional Addition 2** 🚫

Algorithm Project 1

Use U.S. traditional addition to solve each problem.

1. A librarian reshelved 319 books before her lunch hour on Monday. After lunch, she reshelved 295 more books. How many books did the librarian reshelve on Monday?

__614 books__

2. Write a number story for 259 + 86. Solve your number story.

__345; Number stories vary.__

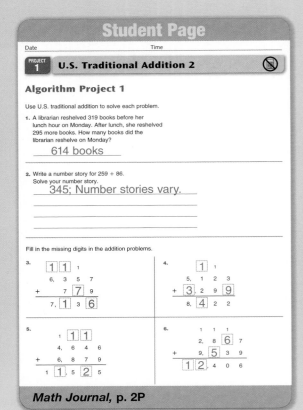

Fill in the missing digits in the addition problems.

Math Journal, p. 2P

Step 2:

Add the 10s: $1 + 4 + 7 = 12$.

12 tens = 1 hundred + 2 tens

Write 2 in the 10s place below the line.

Write 1 above the numbers in the 100s place.

$$\begin{array}{r} 1\ 1 \\ 7\ 4\ 4\ 6 \\ +\ 3\ 5\ 7\ 9 \\ \hline 2\ 5 \end{array}$$

Step 3:

Add the 100s: $1 + 4 + 5 = 10$.

10 hundreds = 1 thousand + 0 hundreds

Write 0 in the 100s place below the line.

Write 1 above the numbers in the 1,000s place.

$$\begin{array}{r} 1\ 1\ 1 \\ 7\ 4\ 4\ 6 \\ +\ 3\ 5\ 7\ 9 \\ \hline 0\ 2\ 5 \end{array}$$

Step 4:

Add the 1,000s: $1 + 7 + 3 = 11$.

11 thousands = 1 ten thousand + 1 thousand

Write 1 in the 1,000s place below the line.

Write 1 in the 10,000s place below the line.

$$\begin{array}{r} 1\ 1\ 1 \\ 7\ 4\ 4\ 6 \\ +\ 3\ 5\ 7\ 9 \\ \hline 1\ 1\ 0\ 2\ 5 \end{array}$$

$7,446 + 3,579 = 11,052$

You may want to work several more examples with the whole class.

Suggestions:

▷ $77 + 58 = ?$ 135

▷ $581 + 69 = ?$ 650

▷ $517 + 362 = ?$ 879

▷ $763 + 245 + 528 = ?$ 1,536

▷ $8,075 + 6,997 = ?$ 15,072

▷ $6,488 + 7,556 = ?$ 14,044

▶ Practicing U.S. Traditional Addition

 PARTNER ACTIVITY

(*Math Journal 1* or *2*, pp. 1P and 2P; *Student Reference Book*, p. 24A)

When students are ready, have them estimate and then solve Problems 2–7 on journal page 1P. They may find the example on *Student Reference Book*, page 24A helpful.

Journal page 2P provides students with additional practice using U.S. traditional addition. Use this journal page as necessary.

Student Page

Date _____ Time _____

PROJECT 1 | **Partial-Sums Addition** 🚫

Algorithm Project 1

Use partial-sums addition to solve each problem.

1. The camp cook made breakfast for 286 campers and 44 counselors. For how many people did the cook make breakfast?

__330 people__

Sample estimates given.

2. $\begin{array}{r} 555 \\ +\ 789 \\ \hline 1,344 \end{array}$ Estimate: __1,400__

3. $\begin{array}{r} 7,644 \\ +\ 3,648 \\ \hline 11,292 \end{array}$ Estimate: __12,000__

4. $\begin{array}{r} 388 \\ 414 \\ +\ 779 \\ \hline 1,581 \end{array}$ Estimate: __1,600__

5. $8,668 + 8,759$ Estimate: __18,000__

__17,427__ = 8,668 + 8,759

6. $396 + 2,502$ Estimate: __2,900__

$396 + 2,502 =$ __2,898__

7. $9,982 + 6,439$ Estimate: __16,000__

$9,982 + 6,439 =$ __16,421__

Math Journal, p. 3P

② Extending the Project

▶ Solving Multidigit Addition Problems

 **INDEPENDENT ACTIVITY**

(*Math Journal 1* or *2,* pp. 3P and 4P; Online Additional Practice, pp. 4A–4D; *Student Reference Book,* pp. 13, 14, and 24A)

Journal pages 3P and 4P provide students with additional practice solving multidigit addition problems. Use these journal pages as necessary.

Encourage students to estimate and then use the focus algorithm (partial-sums addition) to solve the problems on journal page 3P. Invite them to use any algorithm they wish to solve the problems on journal page 4P. Online practice pages 4A–4D provide students with additional practice with multidigit addition problems.

Students may find the examples on *Student Reference Book,* pages 13, 14, and 24A helpful.

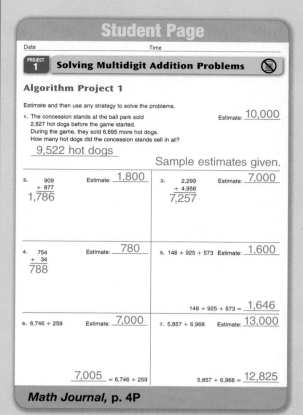

Student Page

Date _____ Time _____

PROJECT 1 | **Solving Multidigit Addition Problems** 🚫

Algorithm Project 1

Estimate and then use any strategy to solve the problems.

1. The concession stands at the ball park sold 2,827 hot dogs before the game started. During the game, they sold 6,695 more hot dogs. How many hot dogs did the concession stands sell in all?   Estimate: 10,000
   9,522 hot dogs

Sample estimates given.

2. 909 + 877   Estimate: 1,800
   1,786

3. 2,299 + 4,958   Estimate: 7,000
   7,257

4. 754 + 34   Estimate: 780
   788

5. 148 + 925 + 573   Estimate: 1,600
   148 + 925 + 573 = **1,646**

6. 6,746 + 259   Estimate: 7,000
   7,005 = 6,746 + 259

7. 5,857 + 6,968   Estimate: 13,000
   5,857 + 6,968 = **12,825**

Math Journal, p. 4P

 Go to www.everydaymathonline.com to access the additional practice pages.

Online Master

Name _____ Date _____ Time _____

PROJECT 1 | **Solving Multidigit Addition Problems 1** 🚫 Online Additional Practice 💻

Algorithm Project 1

Estimate and then use any strategy to solve the problems.

1. Lamar and his classmates held a food drive. They collected 1,973 cans of food and 2,634 boxes of food. How many food items did they collect in all?   Estimate: 5,000
   4,607 food items

Sample estimates given.

2. 492 + 627   Estimate: 1,100
   1,119

3. 8,230 + 3,576   Estimate: 12,000
   11,806

4. 133 209 + 75   Estimate: 400
   417

5. 7,138 + 4,593   Estimate: 12,000
   11,731 = 7,138 + 4,593

6. 2,945 382 + 68   Estimate: 3,400
   3,395

7. 5,792 + 8,821   Estimate: 15,000
   5,792 + 8,821 = **14,613**

Online Additional Practice, p. 4A

Algorithm
2
Project

U.S. Traditional Addition: Decimals

◎ **Objective** To introduce U.S. traditional addition for decimals.

Technology Resources www.everydaymathonline.com

eToolkit

Algorithms Practice

EM Facts Workshop Game™

Family Letters

Assessment Management

Common Core State Standards

NCTM Curriculum Focal Points

iTLG
Interactive Teacher's Lesson Guide

1 Doing the Project

Recommended Use After Lesson 2♦2

Key Concepts and Skills

• Identify places in whole numbers and decimals and the values of the digits in those places.
[Number and Numeration Goal 1]

• Add decimals.
[Operations and Computation Goal 1]

• Solve addition number stories with decimals.
[Operations and Computation Goal 1]

• Make reasonable estimates for addition with decimals.
[Operations and Computation Goal 6]

Key Activities

Students explore and practice U.S. traditional addition with decimals.

Materials

◆ *Math Journal 1* or *2*, pp. 5P–8P
◆ *Student Reference Book,* p. 54A
◆ base-10 blocks (optional)

2 Extending the Project

Students solve decimal addition problems, first using the focus algorithm (partial-sums addition) and then using any algorithm they choose.

Materials

◆ Online Additional Practice, pp. 8A–8D
◆ *Student Reference Book,* pp. 34, 35, and 54A

① Doing the Project

▶ Solving a Decimal Addition Problem

INDEPENDENT ACTIVITY

(*Math Journal 1* or *2*, p. 5P)

Ask students to solve Problem 1 on journal page 5P. Tell them they may use base-10 blocks, paper and pencil, or any other tools they wish, except calculators.

▶ Discussing Solutions

WHOLE-CLASS ACTIVITY

(*Math Journal 1* or *2*, p. 5P)

Discuss students' solutions to Problem 1 on journal page 5P. $4.85 + $2.69 = $7.54 Expect that students will use several different methods, including base-10 blocks, partial-sums addition, and column addition. Some students may also use U.S. traditional addition. *Possible strategies:*

▷ Modeling with base-10 blocks

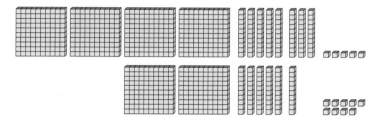

Show 4.85 and 2.69 with blocks.

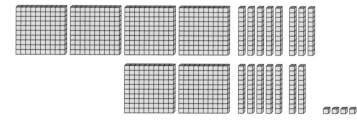

Trade 10 cubes for 1 long.

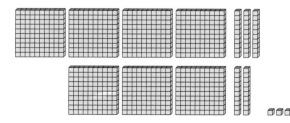

Trade 10 longs for 1 flat.

$4.85 + $2.69 = $7.54

Student Page

Date _____ Time _____

PROJECT 2 U.S. Traditional Addition: Decimals 1 🚫

Algorithm Project 2

Estimate and then use any strategy to solve the problem.

1. Karim spent $4.85 on a drawing pad. He spent $2.69 on a drawing pencil. How much money did Karim spend in all?   Estimate: $8.00

   $7.54

Sample estimates given.

Estimate and then use U.S. traditional addition to solve each problem.

2. 5.215 + 3.362   Estimate: 8   3. 34.89 + 7.7   Estimate: 40

   5.215 + 3.362 = 8.577   42.59 = 34.89 + 7.7

4. 88.8 + 6.45   Estimate: 96   5. $19.98 + $4.26   Estimate: $24.00

   88.8 + 6.45 = 95.25 $19.98 + $4.26 = $24.24

6. 34.56 + 65.787   Estimate: 100   7. 5.699 + 8.55   Estimate: 15

   34.56 + 65.787 = 100.347   14.249 = 5.699 + 8.55

Math Journal, p. 5P

NOTE Reinforce the use of estimation by asking students to make an estimate prior to solving each problem. The estimate is then used to check the reasonableness of the solution to the problem.

▷ Using shorthand pictures of base-10 blocks

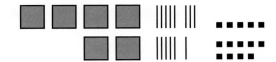

Draw a picture for each number.

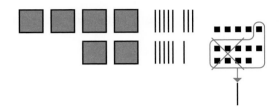

Draw a ring around 10 cubes and trade them for 1 long.

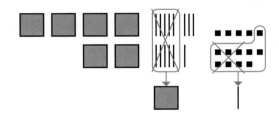

Draw a ring around 10 longs and trade them for 1 flat.

This drawing shows 7.54.

$4.85 + $2.69 = $7.54

▷ Using partial-sums addition

$$\begin{array}{r} 4.85 \\ +2.69 \end{array}$$

Add the 1s.	$4 + 2 \rightarrow$	6.00
Add the 0.1s.	$0.8 + 0.6 \rightarrow$	1.40
Add the 0.01s.	$0.05 + 0.09 \rightarrow$	0.14
Add the partial sums.	$6.00 + 1.40 + 0.14 \rightarrow$	**7.54**

$6.00 + $1.40 + $0.14 = $7.54

▷ Using column addition

	1s	0.1s	0.01s
	4 .	**8**	**5**
	+ 2 .	**6**	**9**
Add the numbers in each column.	6 .	14	14
Trade 14 hundredths for 1 tenth and 4 hundredths.	6 .	15	4
	7 .	**5**	**4**

Trade 15 tenths for one and 5 tenths.

$4.85 + $2.69 = $7.54

▷ Using U.S. traditional addition

$$\begin{array}{r} \overset{1}{} \ \overset{1}{} \\ 4.85 \\ +2.69 \\ \hline 7.54 \end{array}$$

$4.85 + $2.69 = $7.54

► Introducing U.S. Traditional Addition for Decimals

After you have discussed students' solutions, and even if one or more students used U.S. traditional addition, demonstrate it again as described below.

Example 1: $4.85 + $2.69

Step 1:

Start with the 0.01s: 5 + 9 = 14.
14 hundredths = 1 tenth + 4 hundredths

```
    1
  4.85
+ 2.69
     4
```

Step 2:

Add the 0.1s: 1 + 8 + 6 = 15.
15 tenths = 1 whole + 5 tenths

```
 1  1
  4.85
+ 2.69
    54
```

Step 3:

Add the 1s: 1 + 4 + 2 = 7.
Remember to include the decimal point in the answer.

```
 1  1
  4.85
+ 2.69
  7.54
```

$4.85 + $2.69 = $7.54

Karim spent $7.54.

Be sure that students understand how to properly line up the places when adding decimals so that hundredths are added to hundredths, tenths to tenths, and so on. In the example below, write 28.38 as 28.380 so that both numbers have the same number of digits after the decimal point.

Example 2: 37.966 + 28.38

Step 1:

Start with the 0.001s: 6 + 0 = 6.

```
  37.966
+ 28.380
       6
```

Step 2:

Add the 0.01s: 6 + 8 = 14.
14 hundredths = 1 tenth + 4 hundredths

```
      1
  37.966
+ 28.380
      46
```

Step 3:

Add the 0.1s: 1 + 9 + 3 = 13.
13 tenths = 1 whole + 3 tenths

```
   1  1
  37.966
+ 28.380
     346
```

Step 4:

Add the 1s: 1 + 7 + 8 = 16.
16 = 1 ten + 6 ones

```
  11  1
  37.966
+ 28.380
  6 346
```

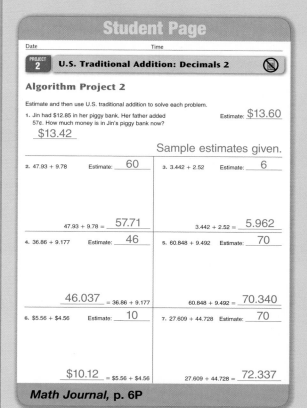

Math Journal, p. 6P

NOTE Throughout the discussion of U.S. traditional addition, be sure that students understand the values of the digits. For example, in Step 1 of Example 1, 5 + 9 = 14 means 5 hundredths + 9 hundredths = 14 hundredths (1 tenth + 4 hundredths), or 0.05 + 0.09 = 0.14. The same structure applies to the carry digits.

Student Page

Date   Time

PROJECT 2 **U.S. Traditional Addition: Decimals 3**

Algorithm Project 2

Use U.S. traditional addition to solve each problem.

1. Abby and Ben bought their mother a present. Abby paid $7.85, and Ben paid $6.68. How much did they pay together?

   $14.53

2. Write a number story for $23.55 + $8.96. Solve your number story.
   $32.51; Number stories vary.

Fill in the missing digits in the addition problems.

3.
```
    1    1
      7 . 7 6
 +  5 4 . 0 6
   6 1 . 8 2
```

4.
```
   1  1 1  1
    3 8 . 4 6 7
 +    8 . 6 7 4
    4 7 . 1 4 1
```

5.
```
    1  1  1  1
    2 5 . 4 5 9
 +  1 4 . 6 8 8
    4 0 . 1 4 7
```

6.
```
      1  1
    6 3 . 3 9
 +  3 5 . 9 8
    9 9 . 3 7
```

Math Journal, p. 7P

Student Page

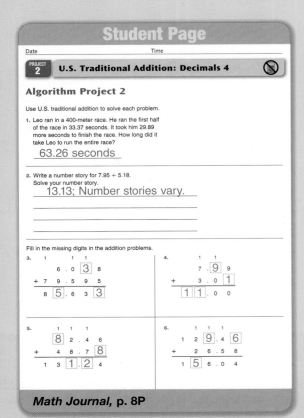

Math Journal, p. 8P

Go to www.everydaymathonline.com to access the additional practice pages.

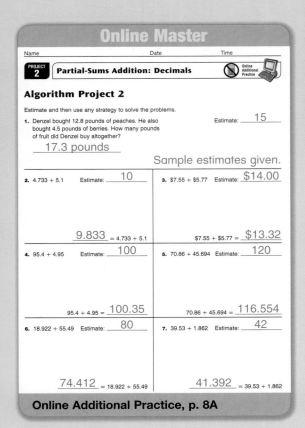

Online Additional Practice, p. 8A

Step 5:

Add the 10s: $1 + 3 + 2 = 6$.
Remember to include the decimal point in the answer.

$$\begin{array}{r} \overset{1\;1\;\;\;1}{3\,7.9\,6\,6} \\ +\,2\,8.3\,8\,0 \\ \hline 6\,6.3\,4\,6 \end{array}$$

$37.966 + 28.38 = 66.346$

You may want to work several more examples with the whole class.

Suggestions:

▷ $\$2.32 + \$6.55 = ?$ $\$8.87$

▷ $7.809 + 1.395 = ?$ 9.204

▷ $4.77 + 8.259 = ?$ 13.029

▷ $63.9 + 8.72 = ?$ 72.62

▷ $\$38.83 + \$94.07 = ?$ $\$132.90$

▷ $60.498 + 45.664 = ?$ 106.162

▶ Practicing U.S. Traditional Addition for Decimals

PARTNER ACTIVITY

(*Math Journal 1 or 2*, pp. 5P–8P; *Student Reference Book*, p. 54A)

When students are ready, have them estimate and then solve Problems 2–7 on journal page 5P. They may find the example on *Student Reference Book*, page 54A helpful.

Journal pages 6P–8P provide students with additional practice using U.S. traditional addition. Use these journal pages as necessary.

② Extending the Project

▶ Solving Decimal Addition Problems

INDEPENDENT ACTIVITY

(Online Additional Practice, pp. 8A–8D; *Student Reference Book*, pp. 34, 35, and 54A)

Online practice pages 8A–8D provide students with additional practice solving decimal addition problems. Use these pages as necessary.

Encourage students to use the focus algorithm (partial-sums addition) to solve the problems on practice page 8A. Invite them to use any algorithm they wish to solve the problems on the remaining pages.

Students may find the examples on *Student Reference Book*, pages 34, 35, and 54A helpful.

Algorithm

3

Project

U.S. Traditional Subtraction

 Objective To introduce U.S. traditional subtraction.

Technology Resources www.everydaymathonline.com

| eToolkit | Algorithms Practice | EM Facts Workshop Game™ | Family Letters | Assessment Management | Common Core State Standards | Curriculum Focal Points | Interactive Teacher's Lesson Guide |

1 Doing the Project

Recommended Use After Lesson 2•3

Key Concepts and Skills

• Identify places in whole numbers and the values of the digits in those places.
[Number and Numeration Goal 1]

• Subtract multidigit numbers.
[Operations and Computation Goal 1]

• Solve subtraction number stories.
[Operations and Computation Goal 1]

• Make reasonable estimates for subtraction problems.
[Operations and Computation Goal 6]

Key Activities

Students explore and practice U.S. traditional subtraction with multidigit whole numbers.

Key Vocabulary

U.S. traditional subtraction

Materials

◆ *Math Journal 1 or 2,* pp. 9P and 10P
◆ *Student Reference Book,* p. 24B
◆ play money (optional)
◆ base-10 blocks (optional)

2 Extending the Project

Students solve multidigit subtraction problems, first using the focus algorithm (trade-first subtraction) and then using any algorithm they choose.

Materials

◆ *Math Journal 1 or 2,* pp. 11P and 12P
◆ Online Additional Practice, pp. 12A–12D
◆ *Student Reference Book,* pp. 15–17 and 24B

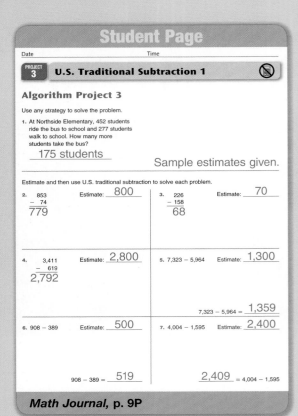

Math Journal, p. 9P

NOTE Reinforce the use of estimation by asking students to make an estimate prior to solving each problem. The estimate is then used to check the reasonableness of the solution to the problem.

▶ **Solving a Subtraction Problem**

   INDEPENDENT ACTIVITY

(*Math Journal 1* or *2*, 9P)

Ask students to solve Problem 1 on journal page 9P. Tell them they may use base-10 blocks, play money, paper and pencil, or any other tools they wish, except calculators.

▶ **Discussing Solutions**

   WHOLE-CLASS ACTIVITY

(*Math Journal 1* or *2*, p. 9P)

Discuss students' solutions to Problem 1 on journal page 9P. $452 - 277 = 175$ students Expect that students will use several different methods. Some may use base-10 blocks, play money, or other manipulatives. Others may use paper-and-pencil methods, including the same-change rule, counting up, partial-differences subtraction, and trade-first subtraction. Some students may also use U.S. traditional subtraction. *Possible strategies:*

▷ Using the same-change rule

$$
\begin{array}{rl}
\mathbf{452} & \text{(add 23)} \\
\mathbf{-\ 277} & \text{(add 23)}
\end{array}
\qquad
\begin{array}{r}
475 \\
-\ 300 \\
\hline
175
\end{array}
$$

▷ Counting up

$$277 \xrightarrow{+3} 280 \xrightarrow{+20} 300 \xrightarrow{+100} 400 \xrightarrow{+52} 452$$

$$
\begin{array}{rcl}
277 + 3 &=& 280 \\
280 + 20 &=& 300 \\
300 + 100 &=& 400 \\
400 + 52 &=& 452
\end{array}
$$

$$3 + 20 + 100 + 52 = 175$$
$$452 - 277 = 175$$

▷ Using partial-differences subtraction

$$
\begin{array}{r}
4\ 5\ 2 \\
-\ 2\ 7\ 7 \\
\end{array}
$$

Subtract the 100s.	$400 - 200 \rightarrow$	$+\,2\,0\,0$
Subtract the 10s.	$50 - 70 \rightarrow$	$-\quad 2\,0$
Subract the 1s.	$2 - 7 \rightarrow$	$-\qquad 5$
Find the total.	$200 - 20 - 5 \rightarrow$	$\mathbf{1\,7\,5}$

▷ Using trade-first subtraction

$$
\begin{array}{r}
\,\overset{\displaystyle 14}{} \\
3 \;\; \not\!4 \;\; 12 \\
\not\!4 \;\; \not\!5 \;\; \not\!2 \\
-\; 2 \;\; 7 \;\; 7 \\
\hline
1 \;\; 7 \;\; 5
\end{array}
$$

▷ Using U.S. traditional subtraction

$$
\begin{array}{r}
\,\overset{\displaystyle 14}{} \\
3 \;\; \not\!4 \;\; 12 \\
\not\!4 \;\; \not\!5 \;\; \not\!2 \\
-\; 2 \;\; 7 \;\; 7 \\
\hline
1 \;\; 7 \;\; 5
\end{array}
$$

NOTE Trade-first subtraction resembles U.S. traditional subtraction, except that in trade-first subtraction, as the name implies, all the trading is done before any subtractions are carried out, allowing the person to concentrate on one task at a time.

▶ Introducing U.S. Traditional Subtraction

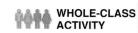 **WHOLE-CLASS ACTIVITY**

After you have discussed students' solutions, and even if one or more students used **U.S. traditional subtraction,** demonstrate it again as described below.

Example 1: 452 − 277

Step 1:

Start with the 1s.

Since 7 > 2, you need to regroup.

Trade 1 ten for 10 ones:
452 = 4 hundreds + 4 tens + 12 ones.

Subtract the 1s: 12 − 7 = 5.

$$
\begin{array}{r}
\; 4 \;\; 12 \\
4 \;\; \not\!5 \;\; \not\!2 \\
-\; 2 \;\; 7 \;\; 7 \\
\hline
5
\end{array}
$$

Step 2:

Go to the 10s.

Since 7 > 4, you need to regroup.

Trade 1 hundred for 10 tens:
452 = 3 hundreds + 14 tens + 12 ones.

Subtract the 10s: 14 − 7 = 7.

$$
\begin{array}{r}
\,\overset{\displaystyle 14}{} \\
3 \;\; \not\!4 \;\; 12 \\
\not\!4 \;\; \not\!5 \;\; \not\!2 \\
-\; 2 \;\; 7 \;\; 7 \\
\hline
7 \;\; 5
\end{array}
$$

Step 3:

Go to the 100s. You don't need to regroup.

Subtract the 100s: 3 − 2 = 1.

452 − 277 = 175

There are 175 more students who take the bus.

$$
\begin{array}{r}
\,\overset{\displaystyle 14}{} \\
3 \;\; \not\!4 \;\; 12 \\
\not\!4 \;\; \not\!5 \;\; \not\!2 \\
-\; 2 \;\; 7 \;\; 7 \\
\hline
1 \;\; 7 \;\; 5
\end{array}
$$

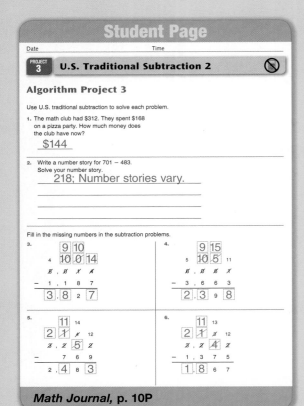

Math Journal, p. 10P

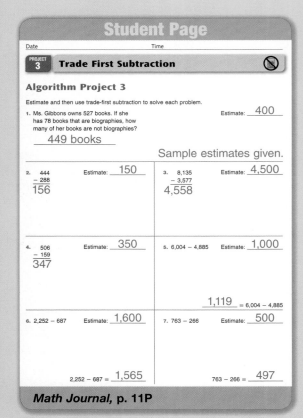

Math Journal, p. 11P

Example 2: 503 − 386

Step 1:

Start with the 1s.

Since 6 > 3, you need to regroup.

There are no tens in 503, so trade 1 hundred for 10 tens and then trade 1 ten for 10 ones: 503 = 4 hundreds + 9 tens + 13 ones.

Subtract the 1s: 13 − 6 = 7.

$$\begin{array}{r} 9 \\ 4 \quad \cancel{10} \quad 13 \\ \cancel{5} \quad \cancel{0} \quad \cancel{3} \\ - \; 3 \quad 8 \quad 6 \\ \hline 7 \end{array}$$

Step 2:

Go to the 10s. You don't need to regroup.

Subtract the 10s: 9 − 8 = 1.

$$\begin{array}{r} 9 \\ 4 \quad \cancel{10} \quad 13 \\ \cancel{5} \quad \cancel{0} \quad \cancel{3} \\ - \; 3 \quad 8 \quad 6 \\ \hline 1 \quad 7 \end{array}$$

Step 3:

Go to the 100s. You don't need to regroup.

Subtract the 100s: 4 − 3 = 1.

503 − 386 = 117

$$\begin{array}{r} 9 \\ 4 \quad \cancel{10} \quad 13 \\ \cancel{5} \quad \cancel{0} \quad \cancel{3} \\ - \; 3 \quad 8 \quad 6 \\ \hline 1 \quad 1 \quad 7 \end{array}$$

You may want to work several more examples with the whole class.

Suggestions:

▷ 231 − 69 = ? 162

▷ 643 − 447 = ? 196

▷ 5,318 − 349 = ? 4,969

▷ 707 − 488 = ? 219

▷ 4,610 − 1,773 = ? 2,837

▷ 8,002 − 3,626 = ? 4,376

▶ Practicing U.S. Traditional Subtraction

 PARTNER ACTIVITY

(*Math Journal 1 or 2,* pp. 9P and 10P; *Student Reference Book,* p. 24B)

When students are ready, have them estimate and then solve Problems 2–7 on journal page 9P. They may find the example on *Student Reference Book,* page 24B helpful.

Journal page 10P provides students with additional practice using U.S. traditional subtraction. Use this journal page as necessary.

② Extending the Project

▶ Solving Multidigit Subtraction Problems

INDEPENDENT ACTIVITY

(*Math Journal 1* or *2*, pp. 11P and 12P; Online Additional Practice, pp. 12A–12D; *Student Reference Book*, pp. 15–17 and 24B)

Journal pages 11P and 12P provide students with additional practice solving multidigit subtraction problems. Use these journal pages as necessary. Encourage students to use the focus algorithm (trade-first subtraction) to solve the problems on journal page 11P. Invite them to use any algorithm they wish to solve the problems on journal page 12P.

Online practice pages 12A–12D provide students with additional practice with multidigit subtraction problems.

Students may find the examples on *Student Reference Book,* pages 15–17 and 24B helpful.

Date _____ Time _____

PROJECT 3 Solving Multidigit Subtraction Problems

Algorithm Project 3

Estimate and then use any strategy to solve the problems.

1. On Saturday, 5,007 people went to the county fair. On Sunday, 3,889 people went to the county fair. How many more people went to the fair on Saturday?
   Estimate: __1,000__

   __1,118 people__

   Sample estimates given.

2. 402
   − 234   Estimate: __200__
   __168__

3. 7,430
   − 3,583   Estimate: __4,000__
   __3,847__

4. 624
   − 86   Estimate: __500__
   __538__

5. 945 − 277   Estimate: __700__

   945 − 277 = __668__

6. 3,613 − 859   Estimate: __2,600__

   __2,754__ = 3,613 − 859

7. 521 − 333   Estimate: __200__

   521 − 333 = __188__

Math Journal, p. 12P

Go to www.everydaymathonline.com to access the additional practice pages.

Name _____ Date _____ Time _____

PROJECT 3 Solving Multidigit Subtraction Problems 1  Online Additional Practice

Algorithm Project 3

Estimate and then use any strategy to solve the problems.

1. The winner of the student-council election received 368 votes. The runner-up received 179 votes. How many more votes did the winner receive?
   Estimate: __200__

   __189 votes__

   Sample estimates given.

2. 761
   − 83   Estimate: __700__
   __678__

3. 314
   − 235   Estimate: __100__
   __79__

4. 7,020
   − 514   Estimate: __6,500__
   __6,506__

5. 4,189 − 2,999   Estimate: __1,000__

   4,189 − 2,999 = __1,190__

6. 756 − 177   Estimate: __600__

   __579__ = 756 − 177

7. 6,150 − 2,459   Estimate: __4,000__

   __3,691__ = 6,150 − 2,459

Online Additional Practice, p. 12A

Algorithm Project 3   **A15**

Algorithm 4 Project

U.S. Traditional Subtraction: Decimals

 Objective To introduce U.S. traditional subtraction with decimals.

Technology Resources www.everydaymathonline.com

| eToolkit | Algorithms Practice | EM Facts Workshop Game™ | Family Letters | Assessment Management | Common Core State Standards | Curriculum Focal Points | Interactive Teacher's Lesson Guide |

---

1 Doing the Project

Recommended Use After Lesson 2◆3

Key Concepts and Skills

- Identify places in whole numbers and decimals and the values of the digits in those places.
  [Number and Numeration Goal 1]

- Subtract decimals.
  [Operations and Computation Goal 1]

- Solve subtraction number stories with decimals.
  [Operations and Computation Goal 1]

- Make reasonable estimates for subtraction with decimals.
  [Operations and Computation Goal 6]

Key Activities

Students explore and practice U.S. traditional subtraction for decimals.

Materials
- *Math Journal 1* or *2*, pp. 13P–16P
- *Student Reference Book,* p. 54B
- play $10 and $1 bills (optional)
- dimes, pennies (optional)
- base-10 blocks (optional)

2 Extending the Project

Students solve decimal subtraction problems, first using the focus algorithm (trade-first subtraction) and then using any algorithm they choose.

Materials
- Online Additional Practice, pp. 16A–16D
- *Student Reference Book,* pp. 34–37 and 54B

① Doing the Project

Solving a Decimal Subtraction Problem

INDEPENDENT ACTIVITY

(*Math Journal 1* or *2*, p. 13P)

Ask students to solve Problem 1 on journal page 13P. Tell them they may use base-10 blocks, play money, paper and pencil, or any other tools they wish, except calculators.

Discussing Solutions

WHOLE-CLASS ACTIVITY

(*Math Journal 1* or *2*, p. 13P)

Discuss students' solutions to Problem 1 on journal page 13P. $7.24 − $5.86 = $1.38 Expect that students will use several different methods, including modeling with base-10 blocks, counting up, using partial-differences subtraction, and using trade-first subtraction. Some students may also use U.S. traditional subtraction. *Possible strategies:*

▷ Modeling with base-10 blocks

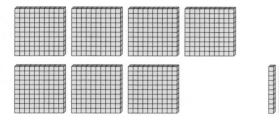

Show 7.24 with blocks.

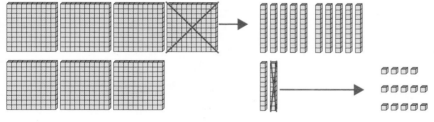

You want to take away 5.86. To do this, you need to first trade 1 flat for 10 longs and 1 long for 10 cubes.

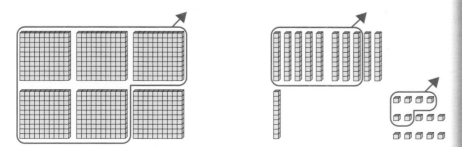

Now remove 5 flats, 8 longs, and 6 cubes (5.86). One flat, 3 longs, and 8 cubes are left. These blocks show 1.38.

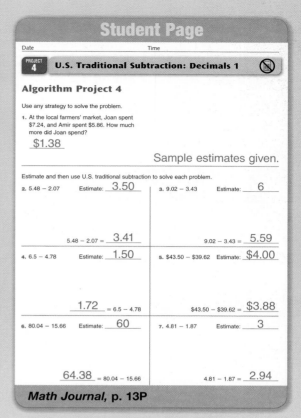

Date _____ Time _____

PROJECT 4 **U.S. Traditional Subtraction: Decimals 1**

Algorithm Project 4

Use any strategy to solve the problem.

1. At the local farmers' market, Joan spent $7.24, and Amir spent $5.86. How much more did Joan spend?

   $1.38

   Sample estimates given.

Estimate and then use U.S. traditional subtraction to solve each problem.

2. 5.48 − 2.07   Estimate: 3.50
   5.48 − 2.07 = 3.41

3. 9.02 − 3.43   Estimate: 6
   9.02 − 3.43 = 5.59

4. 6.5 − 4.78   Estimate: 1.50
   1.72 = 6.5 − 4.78

5. $43.50 − $39.62   Estimate: $4.00
   $43.50 − $39.62 = $3.88

6. 80.04 − 15.66   Estimate: 60
   64.38 = 80.04 − 15.66

7. 4.81 − 1.87   Estimate: 3
   4.81 − 1.87 = 2.94

Math Journal, p. 13P

NOTE Reinforce the use of estimation by asking students to make an estimate prior to solving each problem. The estimate is then used to check the reasonableness of the solution to the problem.

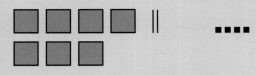

Draw a picture for 7.24.

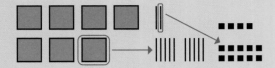

Trade 1 flat for 10 longs and
1 long for 10 cubes.

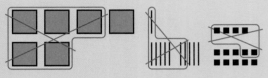

Remove 5 flats, 8 longs, and 6 cubes.
The drawing shows 1.38.

$7.24 - $5.86 = $1.38

▷ Using shorthand pictures of base-10 blocks (*See margin.*)

▷ Counting up

$$
\begin{array}{r}
5.86 \\
+\,\boxed{0.04} \\
\hline
5.90 \\
+\,\boxed{0.10} \\
\hline
6.00 \\
+\,\boxed{1.24} \\
\hline
7.24
\end{array}
\qquad
\begin{array}{r}
0.04 \\
0.10 \\
+\,1.24 \\
\hline
1.38
\end{array}
$$

$7.24 - $5.86 = $1.38

▷ Using partial-differences subtraction

$$
\begin{array}{r}
\mathbf{7.2\,4} \\
-\,\mathbf{5.8\,6}
\end{array}
$$

Subtract the 1s.	$7 - 5 \rightarrow$	$2.0\,0$
Subtract the 0.1s.	$0.2 - 0.8 \rightarrow$	$-\,0.6\,0$
Subtract the 0.01s.	$0.04 - 0.06 \rightarrow$	$-\,0.0\,2$
Find the total.	$2 - 0.60 - 0.02 \rightarrow$	$\mathbf{1.3\,8}$

$7.24 - $5.86 = $1.38

▷ Using trade-first subtraction

1s	0.1s	0.01s
	11	
6	$\not{X}$	14
$\not{7}.$	$\not{2}$	$\not{4}$
$-\,5.$	8	6
1.	3	8

$7.24 - $5.86 = $1.38

▷ Using U.S. traditional subtraction

1s	0.1s	0.01s
	11	
6	$\not{X}$	14
$\not{7}.$	$\not{2}$	$\not{4}$
$-\,5.$	8	6
1.	3	8

$7.24 - $5.86 = $1.38

NOTE Trade-first subtraction resembles U.S. traditional subtraction, except that in trade-first subtraction, as the name implies, all the trading is done before any subtractions are carried out, allowing the person to concentrate on one task at a time.

▶ **Introducing U.S. Traditional Subtraction for Decimals**

 **WHOLE-CLASS ACTIVITY**

After you have discussed students' solutions, and even if one or more students used U.S. traditional subtraction, demonstrate it again as described on the next page.

Example 1: 7.24 − 5.86

Step 1:

Start with the 0.01s.

Since 6 > 4, you need to regroup.

Trade 1 tenth for 10 hundredths:

7.24 = 7 ones + 1 tenth + 14 hundredths.

Subtract the 0.01s: 14 − 6 = 8.

```
          1   14
     7 . 2   4
   − 5 . 8   6
   ─────────────
              8
```

Step 2:

Go to the 0.1s.

Since 8 > 1, you need to regroup.

Trade 1 one for 10 tenths:

7.24 = 6 ones + 11 tenths + 14 hundredths.

Subtract the 0.1s: 11 − 8 = 3.

```
         11
     6    1   14
     7 . 2   4
   − 5 . 8   6
   ─────────────
          3   8
```

Step 3:

Go to the 1s. You don't need to regroup.

Subtract the 1s: 6 − 5 = 1.

Remember to include the decimal point in the answer.

```
         11
     6    1   14
     7 . 2   4
   − 5 . 8   6
   ─────────────
     1 . 3   8
```

$7.24 − $5.86 = $1.38

Joan spent $1.38 more than Amir.

Example 2: 62.05 − 34.29

Step 1:

Start with the 0.01s.

Since 9 > 5, you need to regroup.

There are no tenths in 62.05, so trade 1 one for 10 tenths and then trade 1 tenth for 10 hundredths: 62.05 = 6 tens + 1 one + 9 tenths + 15 hundredths.

Subtract the 0.01s: 15 − 9 = 6.

```
              9
          1  10   15
     6    2 . 0   5
   − 3    4 . 2   9
   ─────────────────
                  6
```

Step 2:

Go to the 0.1s.

You don't need to regroup.

Subtract the 0.1s: 9 − 2 = 7.

```
              9
          1  10   15
     6    2 . 0   5
   − 3    4 . 2   9
   ─────────────────
              7   6
```

Step 3:

Go to the 1s.

Since 4 > 1, you need to regroup.

Trade 1 ten for 10 ones:

62.05 = 5 tens + 11 ones + 9 tenths + 15 hundredths.

Subtract the ones: 11 − 4 = 7.

```
         11   9
     5    1  10   15
     6    2 . 0   5
   − 3    4 . 2   9
   ─────────────────
     7    7 . 7   6
```

Math Journal, p. 14P

Student Page

Date   Time

PROJECT 4   **U.S. Traditional Subtraction: Decimals 3**

Algorithm Project 4

Use U.S. traditional subtraction to solve each problem.

1. Wenona bought a sandwich and a bowl of soup. The total cost (before tax) was $6.35. The sandwich cost $3.79. How much did the soup cost?

   $2.56

2. Write a number story for $47.25 − $25.89. Solve your number story.

   $21.36; Number stories vary.

Fill in the missing numbers in the subtraction problems.

Math Journal, p. 15P

Step 4:

Go to the 10s.
You don't need to regroup.
Subtract the 10s: 5 − 3 = 2.
Remember to include the decimal point in the answer.

$$62.05 − 34.29 = 27.76$$

Example 3: 8.3 − 2.74

Step 1:

Write the problem in columns.
Be sure to line up the places correctly.
Since 2.74 has two decimal places, write 8.3 as 8.30.

Step 2:

Start with the 0.01s.
Since 4 > 0, you need to regroup.
Trade 1 tenth for 10 hundredths:
8.30 = 8 ones + 2 tenths + 10 hundredths.
Subtract the 0.01s: 10 − 4 = 6.

Step 3:

Go to the 0.1s.
Since 7 > 2, you need to regroup.
Trade 1 one for 10 tenths:
8.30 = 7 ones + 12 tenths + 10 hundredths.
Subtract the 0.1s: 12 − 7 = 5.

Step 4:

Go to the 1s. You don't need to regroup.
Subtract the 1s: 7 − 2 = 5.
Remember to include the decimal point in the answer.

$$8.3 − 2.74 = 5.56$$

You may want to work several more examples with the whole class.

Suggestions:

▷ $5.65 − $3.22 = ? $2.43

▷ 7.32 − 1.47 = ? 5.85

▷ 3.03 − 2.36 = ? 0.67

▷ 8.4 − 5.69 = ? 2.71

▷ $62.25 − $49.89 = ? $12.36

▷ 70.06 − 38.88 = ? 31.18

Practicing U.S. Traditional Subtraction for Decimals

PARTNER ACTIVITY

(*Math Journal 1 or 2*, pp. 13P–16P; *Student Reference Book*, p. 54B)

When students are ready, have them estimate and then solve Problems 2–7 on journal page 13P. They may find the example on *Student Reference Book*, page 54B helpful.

Journal pages 14P–16P provide students with additional practice using U.S. traditional subtraction. Use these journal pages as necessary.

2 Extending the Project

Solving Decimal Subtraction Problems

INDEPENDENT ACTIVITY

(Online Additional Practice, pp. 16A–16D; *Student Reference Book*, pp. 34–37 and 54B)

Online practice pages 16A–16D provide students with additional practice solving decimal subtraction problems. Use these pages as necessary.

Encourage students to use the focus algorithm (trade-first subtraction) to solve the problems on practice page 16A. Invite them to use any algorithm they wish to solve the problems on the remaining pages.

Students may find the examples on *Student Reference Book*, pages 34–37 and 54B helpful.

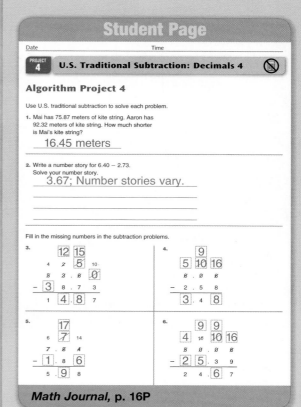

Math Journal, p. 16P

 Go to www.everydaymathonline.com to access the additional practice pages.

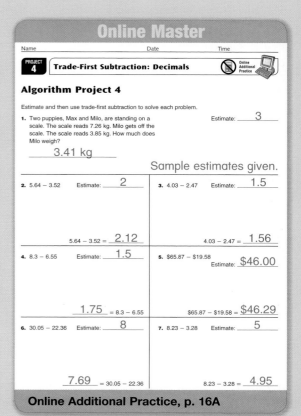

Online Additional Practice, p. 16A

Algorithm 5 Project

U.S. Traditional Multiplication

◎ **Objective** To introduce U.S. traditional multiplication.

Technology Resources www.everydaymathonline.com

eToolkit

Algorithms Practice

EM Facts Workshop Game™

Family Letters

Assessment Management

Common Core State Standards

Curriculum Focal Points

Interactive Teacher's Lesson Guide

1 Doing the Project

Recommended Use After Lesson 2◆9

Key Concepts and Skills

• Identify places in whole numbers and the values of the digits in those places.
[Number and Numeration Goal 1]

• Use multiplication facts to find products of multidigit whole numbers.
[Operations and Computation Goal 3]

• Multiply multidigit whole numbers.
[Operations and Computation Goal 4]

• Solve multiplication number stories.
[Operations and Computation Goal 4]

• Make reasonable estimates for multiplication problems.
[Operations and Computation Goal 6]

Key Activities

Students explore and practice U.S. traditional multiplication with multidigit whole numbers.

Key Vocabulary

U.S. traditional multiplication

Materials

◆ *Math Journal 1* or *2*, pp. 17P–20P
◆ *Student Reference Book,* pp. 24C and 24D

2 Extending the Project

Students solve multidigit multiplication problems, first using the focus algorithm (partial-products multiplication) and then using any algorithm they choose.

Materials

◆ Online Additional Practice, pp. 20A–20D
◆ *Student Reference Book,* pp. 19, 20, 24C, and 24D

▶ Solving a Multiplication Problem

INDEPENDENT ACTIVITY

(*Math Journal 1* or *2*, p. 17P)

Ask students to solve Problem 1 on journal page 17P. Tell them they may use any methods they wish, except calculators.

▶ Discussing Solutions

WHOLE-CLASS ACTIVITY

(*Math Journal 1* or *2*, p. 17P)

Discuss students' solutions to Problem 1 on journal page 17P.
86 * 24 = 2,064 bottles Expect that students will use several different methods, including partial-products multiplication and lattice multiplication. Some students may also use U.S. traditional multiplication. *Possible strategies:*

▷ Using partial-products multiplication

```
        8 6
    *   2 4
20 * 80 →  1 6 0 0
20 * 6 →    1 2 0
 4 * 80 →     3 2 0
  4 * 6 →        2 4
           2 0 6 4
```

▷ Using lattice multiplication

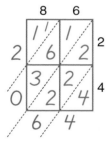

▷ Using U.S. traditional multiplication

```
        1
        2
        8 6
    *   2 4
        3 4 4
    + 1 7 2 0
      2 0 6 4
```

Date _____ Time _____

PROJECT 5 — **U.S. Traditional Multiplication 1**

Algorithm Project 5

Use any strategy to solve the problem.

1. A truck delivered 86 cases of juice to a grocery store. Each case contains 24 bottles of juice. How many bottles of juice did the store get?

   __2,064 bottles__   Sample estimates given.

Estimate and then use U.S. traditional multiplication to solve each problem.

2. 12 * 34   Estimate: __350__   3. 455 * 600   Estimate: __300,000__

   12 * 34 = __408__   455 * 600 = __273,000__

4. 73 * 288   Estimate: __21,000__   5. 49 * 60   Estimate: __3,000__

   __21,024__ = 73 * 288   49 * 60 = __2,940__

6. 92 * 46   Estimate: __4,500__   7. 305 * 592   Estimate: __180,000__

   92 * 46 = __4,232__   __180,560__ = 305 * 592

Math Journal, p. 17P

NOTE Reinforce the use of estimation by asking students to make an estimate prior to solving each problem. The estimate is then used to check the reasonableness of the solution to the problem.

▶ Introducing U.S. Traditional Multiplication

After you have discussed students' solutions, and even if one or more students used **U.S. traditional multiplication,** demonstrate it again as described below.

Example 1: 24 * 86

Step 1:

Multiply 86 by the 4 in 24, as if the problem were 4 * 86.

$$
\begin{array}{r}
2 \\
8\,6 \\
*\quad 2\,4 \\
\hline
3\,4\,4
\end{array}
$$
← The partial product 4 * 86 = 344

Step 2:

Multiply 86 by the 2 in 24, as if the problem were 2 * 86.

The 2 in 24 stands for 2 tens, so write the partial product one place to the left.

Write a 0 in the 1s place to show you are multiplying by tens.

Write the new carry above the old carry.

$$
\begin{array}{r}
1 \\
2 \\
8\,6 \\
*\quad 2\,4 \\
\hline
3\,4\,4 \\
1\,7\,2\,0
\end{array}
$$
← 20 * 86 = 1,720

Step 3:

Add the two partial products to get the final answer.

24 * 86 = 2,064

$$
\begin{array}{r}
1 \\
2 \\
8\,6 \\
*\quad 2\,4 \\
\hline
3\,4\,4 \\
+\,1\,7\,2\,0 \\
\hline
2\,0\,6\,4
\end{array}
$$
← 24 * 86 = 2,064

The store purchased 2,064 bottles of juice.

NOTE U.S. traditional multiplication is so familiar that the details of its working may appear more meaningful than they are. Consider the following example:

$$
\begin{array}{r}
1\ \ 2 \\
3\ \ 5 \\
1\,4\,7 \\
*\quad 3\,8 \\
\hline
1\,1\,7\,6 \\
+\,4\,4\,1\,0 \\
\hline
5\,5\,8\,6
\end{array}
$$

Many people, when asked why the "2" carried from "3 * 7" is written in the 10s place, will explain that it stands for "2 tens." But this "2" really means "2 hundreds" because the "3" is really "3 tens." U.S. traditional multiplication is efficient—though not as efficient as a calculator—but it is not, despite its familiarity, conceptually transparent.

Example 2: 237 * 456

Step 1:

Multiply 456 by the 7 in 237,
as if the problem were 7 * 456.

```
      3 4
    4 5 6
  *   2 3 7
    3 1 9 2   ← The partial product
               7 * 456 = 3,192
```

Step 2:

Multiply 456 by the 3 in 237,
as if the problem were 3 * 456.

The 3 in 237 stands for 3 tens,
so write the partial product one
place to the left.

Write a 0 in the 1s place to show
you are multiplying by tens.

Write the new carries above
the old carries.

```
      1 1
      3 4
    4 5 6
  *   2 3 7
    3 1 9 2
  1 3 6 8 0   ← 30 * 456 = 13,680
```

Step 3:

Multiply 456 by the 2 in 237,
as if the problem were 2 * 456.

The 2 in 237 stands for
2 hundreds, so write the partial
product two places to the left.

Write 0s in the 10s and 1s places
to show you are multiplying by
hundreds.

Write the new carries above
the old carries.

```
      1 1
      1 1
      3 4
    4 5 6
  *   2 3 7
    3 1 9 2
  1 3 6 8 0
  9 1 2 0 0   ← 200 * 456 = 91,200
```

Step 4:

Add the three partial products
to get the final answer.

237 * 456 = 108,072

```
      1 1
      1 1
      3 4
    4 5 6
  *   2 3 7
    3 1 9 2
  1 3 6 8 0
+ 9 1 2 0 0
1 0 8 0 7 2   ← 237 * 456 = 108,072
```

You may want to work several more examples with the whole class.

Suggestions:

▷ 320 * 21 = ? 6,720

▷ 48 * 73 = ? 3,504

▷ 675 * 50 = ? 33,750

▷ 59 * 302 = ? 17,818

▷ 700 * 36 = ? 25,200

▷ 284 * 77 = ? 21,868

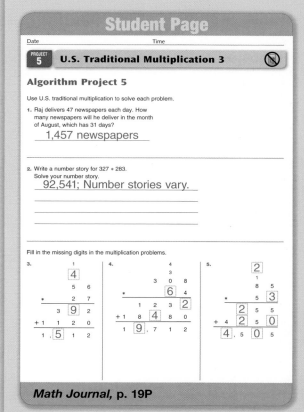

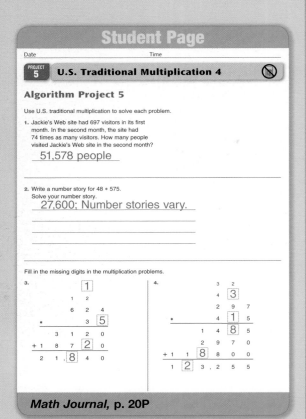

Student Page

Date _____ Time _____

PROJECT 5 U.S. Traditional Multiplication 4

Algorithm Project 5

Use U.S. traditional multiplication to solve each problem.

1. Jackie's Web site had 697 visitors in its first
month. In the second month, the site had
74 times as many visitors. How many people
visited Jackie's Web site in the second month?

    __51,578 people__

2. Write a number story for 48 ∗ 575.
Solve your number story.
    __27,600; Number stories vary.__

Fill in the missing digits in the multiplication problems.

3.

```
              1
        1   2
      6   2   4
    *     3 [5]
      3   1   2   0
  + 1   8   7 [2] 0
    2   1 , [8]  4   0
```

4.

```
              3   2
          4 [3]
          2   9   7
      *   4 [1]  5
        1   4 [8]  5
      2   9   7   0
  + 1   1 [8]  8   0   0
    1 [2]  3 ,  2   5   5
```

Math Journal, p. 20P

Go to www.everydaymathonline.com
to access the additional practice
pages.

Online Master

Name _____ Date _____ Time _____

PROJECT 5 Partial-Products Multiplication

Algorithm Project 5

Estimate and then use partial-products multiplication to solve each problem.

1. Last week, a theater showed a popular movie
35 times. Each time, all 218 seats in the theater
were full. How many people saw the movie at
that theater last week?

    Estimate: __8,000__

    __7,630 people__

Sample estimates given.

2. 300 ∗ 21   Estimate: __6,000__

3. 75 ∗ 363   Estimate: __28,000__

300 ∗ 21 = __6,300__

__27,225__ = 75 ∗ 363

4. 23 ∗ 84   Estimate: __1,600__

5. 38 ∗ 59   Estimate: __2,400__

23 ∗ 84 = __1,932__

38 ∗ 59 = __2,242__

6. 60 ∗ 504   Estimate: __30,000__

7. 182 ∗ 797   Estimate: __160,000__

60 ∗ 504 = __30,240__

__145,054__ = 182 ∗ 797

Online Additional Practice, p. 20A

▶ Practicing U.S. Traditional Multiplication

(*Math Journal 1* or *2,* pp. 17P–20P; *Student Reference Book,*
pp. 24C and 24D)

When students are ready, have them estimate and then solve
Problems 2–7 on journal page 17P. They may find the examples
on *Student Reference Book,* pages 24C and 24D helpful.

Journal pages 18P–20P provide students with additional practice
using U.S. traditional multiplication. Use these journal pages as
necessary.

(2) Extending the Project

▶ Solving Multidigit Multiplication Problems

INDEPENDENT ACTIVITY

(Online Additional Practice, pp. 20A–20D; *Student Reference Book,*
pp. 19, 20, 24C, and 24D)

Online practice pages 20A–20D provide students with additional
practice solving multidigit multiplication problems. Use these
pages as necessary.

Encourage students to use the focus algorithm (partial-products
multiplication) to solve the problems on practice page 20A. Invite
them to use any algorithm they wish to solve the problems on the
remaining pages.

Students may find the examples on *Student Reference Book,*
pages 19, 20, 24C, and 24D helpful.

Algorithm 6 Project

U.S. Traditional Multiplication: Decimals

Objective To introduce U.S. traditional multiplication for decimals.

Technology Resources www.everydaymathonline.com

eToolkit

Algorithms Practice

EM Facts Workshop Game™

Family Letters

Assessment Management

Common Core State Standards

NCTM Curriculum Focal Points

iTLG Interactive Teacher's Lesson Guide

1 Doing the Project

Recommended Use After Lesson 2•9

Key Concepts and Skills

• Identify places in whole numbers and decimals and the values of the digits in those places.
[Number and Numeration Goal 1]

• Calculate products of decimals and whole numbers and of decimals and decimals.
[Operations and Computation Goal 3]

• Solve multiplication number stories with decimals.
[Operations and Computation Goal 3]

• Make reasonable estimates for multiplication with decimals.
[Operations and Computation Goal 6]

Key Activities

Students explore and practice U.S. traditional multiplication with decimals.

Materials
◆ *Math Journal 1* or *2*, pp. 21P–24P
◆ *Student Reference Book,* pp. 54C and 54D
◆ play money (optional)

2 Extending the Project

Students solve decimal multiplication problems, first using the focus algorithm (partial-products multiplication) and then using any algorithm they choose.

Materials
◆ Online Additional Practice, pp. 24A–24D
◆ *Student Reference Book,* pp. 37–40, 54C, and 54D

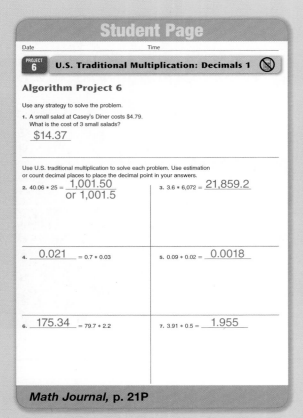

Math Journal, p. 21P

1 Doing the Project

▶ Solving a Decimal Multiplication Problem

(*Math Journal 1* or *2*, p. 21P)

Ask students to solve Problem 1 on journal page 21P. Tell them they may use play money, paper and pencil, or any other tools they wish, except calculators.

▶ Discussing Solutions

(*Math Journal 1* or *2*, p. 21P)

Discuss students' solutions to Problem 1 on journal page 21P. $4.79 * 3 = $14.37 Expect that students will use several different methods, which may include modeling with play money, using repeated addition, using lattice multiplication, and using partial-products multiplication. Some students may also use U.S. traditional multiplication. *Possible strategies:*

▷ Modeling with play money

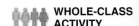

Use play money to show the cost of 3 salads.

$$4\boxed{\$1} + 4\boxed{\$1} + 4\boxed{\$1} = 12\boxed{\$1} \text{ or } 1\boxed{\$10} \text{ and } 2\boxed{\$1}$$

Combine the bills.

$$7\text{Ⓓ} + 7\text{Ⓓ} + 7\text{Ⓓ} = 21\text{Ⓓ} \text{ or } 2\boxed{\$1} \text{ and } 1\text{Ⓓ}$$

Combine the dimes.

$$9\text{Ⓟ} + 9\text{Ⓟ} + 9\text{Ⓟ} = 27\text{Ⓟ} \text{ or } 2\text{Ⓓ} \text{ and } 7\text{Ⓟ}$$

Combine the pennies.

$$1\boxed{\$10} + 2\boxed{\$1} + 2\boxed{\$1} + 1\text{Ⓓ} + 2\text{Ⓓ} + 7\text{Ⓟ} = \$14.37$$

Combine the bills and coins.

▷ Using repeated addition

$4.79	$9.58
+ $4.79	+ $4.79
$8.00	$13.00
$1.40	$1.20
+ $0.18	+ $0.17
$9.58	$14.37

$4.79 * 3 = $14.37

▷ Using lattice multiplication

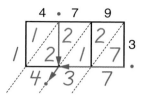

$4.79 * 3 = $14.37

▷ Using partial-products multiplication

$$\$4\,.\,7\,9$$
$$*\qquad 3$$

3 [$4.00s] →	1 2 . 0 0	
3 [$0.70s] →	2 . 1 0	
3 [$0.09s] →	+ 0 . 2 7	
	$1 4 . 3 7	

$4.79 * 3 = $14.37

▷ Using U.S. traditional multiplication

$$\overset{2\ \ 2}{\$4\,.\,7\,9}$$
$$*\qquad 3$$
$$\$1\,4\,.\,3\,7$$

$4.79 * 3 = $14.37

▶ Introducing U.S. Traditional Multiplication for Decimals

 **WHOLE-CLASS ACTIVITY**

After you have discussed students' solutions, and even if one or more students used U.S. traditional multiplication, demonstrate it again as described below.

Example 1: $4.79 * 3

Step 1:

Start with the pennies.

3 * 9 pennies = 27 pennies

27 pennies = 2 dimes + 7 pennies

$$\overset{\qquad 2}{4\,.\,7\,\mathbf{9}}$$
$$*\qquad \mathbf{3}$$
$$\mathbf{7}$$

Step 2:

Multiply the dimes.

3 * 7 dimes = 21 dimes

Remember the 2 dimes from Step 1.

21 dimes + 2 dimes = 23 dimes in all

23 dimes = $2 + 3 dimes

$$\overset{2\ \ 2}{4\,.\,\mathbf{7}\,9}$$
$$*\qquad \mathbf{3}$$
$$\mathbf{3}\,7$$

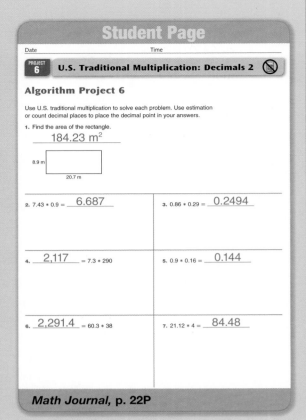

NOTE This second method for multiplying decimals (used in Example 3) is useful when there are many decimal places in the factors, making it difficult to estimate the answer. For example, 0.078 * 0.029 = 0.002262.

Student Page

Date _____ Time _____

PROJECT 6 **U.S. Traditional Multiplication: Decimals 3**

Algorithm Project 6

Use U.S. traditional multiplication to solve each problem. Use estimation or count decimal places to place the decimal point in your answers.

1. A model train caboose is 7.75 inches long. The actual caboose is 48 times as long as this. How long is the actual caboose?

   __372.00 or 372 in.__

2. Write a number story for 40.06 * 67. Solve your number story.

   __2,684.02; Number stories vary.__

Fill in the missing digits in the multiplication problems.

3.
```
      1  3
      1  4
     3  2 . 7
   *      5 . 6
     1  9  6  2
  + 1  6  3  5  0
   1  8  3 . 1  2
```

4.
```
       3
     8 . 0  5
   *     0 . 6
     4 . 8  3  0
```

5.
```
          4
        0 . 1  9
   *      0 . 5
     0 . 0  9  5
```

Step 3:

Multiply the dollars.

$3 * \$4 = \$12$

Remember the $2 from Step 2.

$\$12 + \$2 = \$14$ in all

$\$14 = 1 [\$10] + 4 [\$1]s$

Remember to include the decimal point.

$\$4.79 * 3 = \$14.37$

Three small salads cost $14.37.

```
      2  2
   4 . 7 9
 *       3
  1 4 . 3 7
```

One way to use U.S. traditional multiplication with decimals is to multiply the factors as though they were whole numbers and then use estimation to place the decimal point.

Example 2: $6.07 * 0.5$

Step 1:

Multiply as though both factors were whole numbers.

Step 2:

Estimate the product: $6.07 * 0.5 \approx 6 * 0.5 = 3$.

```
        3
     6 0 7
 *       5
   3 0 3 5
```

Step 3:

Use the estimate to place the decimal point in the answer. The estimate is 3, so place the decimal point to make the answer close to 3: 3.035 is close to 3.

$6.07 * 0.5 = 3.035$

Another way to use U.S. traditional multiplication with decimals is to multiply as though both factors were whole numbers and then find the total number of places to the right of the decimal points of both factors to decide where to place the decimal point.

Example 3: $0.47 * 0.82$

Step 1:

Multiply as though both factors were whole numbers.

Step 2:

Count the total number of places to the right of the decimal points of both factors. There are 2 places to the right of the decimal point in 0.47. There are 2 places to the right of the decimal point in 0.82. There are 4 decimal places in all.

```
       5
       1
       4 7
   *   8 2
       9 4
   + 3 7 6 0
     3 8 5 4
```

Step 3:

Place the decimal point 4 places from the right.

$0.47 * 0.82 = 0.3854$

You may want to work several more examples with the whole class.

Suggestions:

▷ 4.64 * 24 = ? 111.36

▷ 30.8 * 52 = ? 1,601.6

▷ 5.3 * 953 = ? 5,050.9

▷ 0.8 * 0.38 = ? 0.304

▷ 0.71 * 0.04 = ? 0.0284

▷ 82.9 * 8.1 = ? 671.49

▶ Practicing U.S. Traditional Multiplication for Decimals

PARTNER ACTIVITY

(*Math Journal 1* or *2*, pp. 21P–24P; *Student Reference Book*, pp. 54C and 54D)

When students are ready, have them solve Problems 2–7 on journal page 21P. They may find the examples on *Student Reference Book*, pages 54C and 54D helpful.

Journal pages 22P–24P provide students with additional practice using U.S. traditional multiplication. Use these journal pages as necessary.

2 Extending the Project

▶ Solving Decimal Multiplication Problems

INDEPENDENT ACTIVITY

(Online Additional Practice, pp. 24A–24D; *Student Reference Book*, pp. 37–40, 54C, and 54D)

Online practice pages 24A–24D provide students with additional practice solving decimal multiplication problems. Use these pages as necessary.

Encourage students to use the focus algorithm (partial-products multiplication) to solve the problems on practice page 24A. Invite them to use any algorithm they wish to solve the problems on the remaining pages.

Students may find the examples on *Student Reference Book*, pages 37–40, 54C, and 54D helpful.

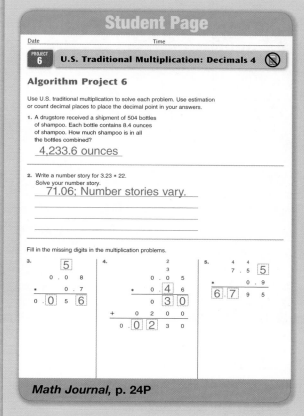

Math Journal, p. 24P

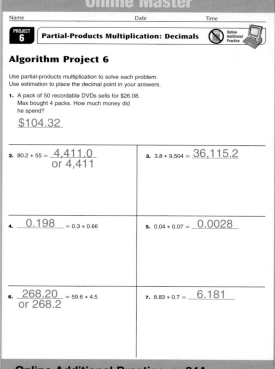

Online Additional Practice, p. 24A

Algorithm 7 Project

U.S. Traditional Long Division

 Objective To review and practice U.S. traditional long division with whole numbers.

Technology Resources www.everydaymathonline.com

eToolkit

Algorithms
Practice

EM Facts
Workshop
Game™

Family
Letters

Assessment
Management

Common
Core State
Standards

Curriculum
Focal Points

iTLG
Interactive
Teacher's
Lesson Guide

---

1 Doing the Project

Recommended Use After Lesson 4◆2

Key Concepts and Skills

• Apply multiplication and division facts with long division.
[Operations and Computation Goal 2]

• Use long division to divide whole numbers by single-digit and multidigit whole numbers.
[Operations and Computation Goal 3]

• Use estimation to carry out long division efficiently.
[Operations and Computation Goal 6]

Key Activities

Students review, practice, and extend U.S. traditional long division with whole numbers.

Key Vocabulary

U.S. traditional long division ◆ dividend ◆ divisor ◆ quotient ◆ remainder

Materials

◆ *Math Journal 1* or *2*, pp. 25P–28P
◆ *Student Reference Book,* pp. 24E–24H
◆ play money (optional)

---

2 Extending the Project

Students create and solve long division puzzles.

For additional practice, students solve division problems, first using the focus algorithm (partial-quotients division) and then using any algorithm they choose.

Materials

◆ *Math Journal 1* or *2*, p. 28P
◆ *Math Masters,* p. 415
◆ Online Additional Practice, pp. 28A–28D
◆ *Student Reference Book,* pp. 22, 23, and 24E–24H

1 Doing the Project

► Reviewing Long Division with Single-Digit Divisors

WHOLE-CLASS DISCUSSION

(*Math Journal 1 or 2*, p. 25P)

Have students solve Problem 1 on journal page 25P. Tell them they may use paper and pencil, or any manipulatives or tools that they wish, except calculators.

Have volunteers explain their solutions. $2,365 / 6 = $394 R$1 Expect that students will use several different methods, including partial-quotients division, various informal paper-and-pencil approaches, dealing with manipulatives, and drawing pictures. Some students may also use U.S. traditional long division, which was introduced and practiced in fourth-grade algorithm projects. *For example:*

▷ Using partial-quotients division

```
6 ) 2365
  - 1200 | 200
    1165
   - 600 | 100
     565
   - 300 |  50
     265
   - 240 |  40
      25
    - 24 |   4
       1 | 394
```

$$\$2365 \div 6 = \$394 \text{ R}\$1$$

▷ Using an informal paper-and-pencil method

```
  $2365
  - 600  ◄── $100 for each worker
   1765
  - 600  ◄── $100 for each worker
   1165
  - 600  ◄── $100 for each worker
    565
  - 300  ◄── $50 for each worker
    265
  - 240  ◄── $40 for each worker
     25
   - 24  ◄── $4 for each worker
```

▷ Using U.S. traditional long division (*See margin.*)

```
    394
6 2365
  - 18
    56
  - 54
    25
  - 24
     1
```

$$\$2365 \div 6 = \$394$$
$$\text{remainder} = \$1$$

Long division

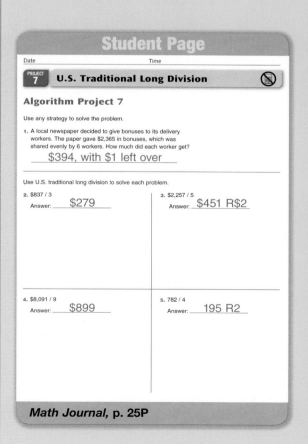

Date _____ Time _____

PROJECT 7 **U.S. Traditional Long Division**

Algorithm Project 7

Use any strategy to solve the problem.

1. A local newspaper decided to give bonuses to its delivery workers. The paper gave $2,365 in bonuses, which was shared evenly by 6 workers. How much did each worker get?
   $394, with $1 left over

Use U.S. traditional long division to solve each problem.

2. $837 / 3
   Answer: $279

3. $2,257 / 5
   Answer: $451 R$2

4. $8,091 / 9
   Answer: $899

5. 782 / 4
   Answer: 195 R2

Math Journal, p. 25P

Step 1

Bonus to be Shared

2	$1,000	s
3	$100	s
6	$10	s
5	$1	s

Step 2

Bonus to be Shared

23	$100	s
6	$10	s
5	$1	s

Step 3

Step 4

NOTE Sharing money is a useful context for teaching and learning long division. The process of sharing bills of various denominations ($100 bills, $10 bills, and $1 bills) and coins (dimes and pennies), starting with the largest denomination and trading for smaller denominations as necessary, is broadly parallel to the steps in long division.

Review how to solve the problem using **U.S. traditional long division.** Illustrate each step with pictures and, if possible, model the steps using play money. Emphasize the connections between the steps in long division and the process of sharing money.

Step 1:

Write the problem $2,365 / 6 in the long division format on the board or a transparency.

$6 \overline{)2\ 3\ 6\ 5}$ ← $2,365 is to be shared: $2,365 is the **dividend.**
↑
The money is to be
shared by 6 workers:
6 is the **divisor.**

Step 2:

Encourage students to think about sharing actual bills: 2 [$1,000]s, 3 [$100]s, 6 [$10]s, and 5 [$1]s. There are not enough [$1,000]s for 6 equal shares, so trade the 2 [$1,000]s for 20 [$100]s. There were 3 [$100]s already, so there are 20 + 3 = 23 [$100]s after the trade.

$6 \overline{)2\ 3\ 6\ 5}$ ← 20 [$100]s from the 2 [$1,000]s +
　　　　　　　3 [$100]s = 23 [$100]s

Step 3:

Share the 23 [$100]s. Each worker gets 3 [$100]s; 5 [$100]s are left over.

$\begin{array}{r} 3 \\ 6\overline{)2\ 3\ 6\ 5} \\ -1\ 8 \\ \hline 5 \end{array}$

← Each worker gets 3 [$100]s.

← 3 [$100]s each for 6 workers = 18 [$100]s

← 5 [$100]s are left.

Step 4:

Trade the 5 [$100]s for 50 [$10]s. There were 6 [$10]s already, so there are 50 + 6 = 56 [$10]s.

$\begin{array}{r} 3 \\ 6\overline{)2\ 3\ \mathbf{6}\ 5} \\ -1\ 8 \downarrow \\ \hline \mathbf{5\ 6} \end{array}$

← 50 [$10]s from the 5 [$100]s + 6 [$10]s = 56 [$10]s

Step 5:

Share the 56 [$10]s. Each worker gets 9 [$10]s; there are 2 [$10]s left over.

```
    3 9   ← Each worker gets 9 [$10]s.
6)2 3 6 5
 − 1 8
    5 6
  − 5 4   ← 9 [$10]s each for 6 workers = 54 [$10]s
      2   ← 2 [$10]s are left.
```

Step 6:

Trade the 2 [$10]s for 20 [$1]s. There were 5 [$1]s already, so there are 20 + 5 = 25 [$1]s.

```
    3 9
6)2 3 6 5
 − 1 8
    5 6
  − 5 4
      2 5   ← 20 [$1]s from the 2 [$10]s + 5 [$1]s = 25 [$1]s
```

Step 7:

Share the 25 [$1]s. Each worker gets 4 [$1]s; 1 [$1] is left over.

```
    3 9 4   ← Each worker gets 4 [$1]s.
6)2 3 6 5
 − 1 8
    5 6
  − 5 4
      2 5
    − 2 4   ← 4 [$1]s each for 6 workers = 24 [$1]s
        1   ← 1 [$1] is left.
```

Step 8:

Each worker gets $394: $394 is the **quotient.** The $1 that is left over is the **remainder.** A number model is a good way to show the answer:

$2,365 / 6 → $394 R$1

U.S. traditional long division is complicated, so consider working one or two more examples with the whole class. Continue to use sharing money as a context and drawing pictures to show actions with money, as needed.

Suggestions:

▷ $4,967 / 6 $827 R$5   ▷ $2,850 / 8 $356 R$2

▷ $705 / 5 $141   ▷ $1,008 / 9 $112

▷ $2,048 / 4 $512   ▷ $402 / 4 $100 R$2

▷ $4,290 / 7 $612 R$6   ▷ $2,040 / 8 $255

Step 5

Step 6

Step 7

$2,365 shared by 6 workers

NOTE Some students may benefit from seeing long division on a computation grid that shows place-value column names.

	Thousands	Hundreds	Tens	Ones
		3	9	4
6	2	3	6	5
−	1	8		
		5	6	
	−	5	4	
			2	5
		−	2	4
				1

Student Page

Date _____ Time _____

PROJECT **7** **U.S. Traditional Long Division** *cont.*

Algorithm Project 7

6. The fifth graders at Freemont School washed cars to raise money for instruments for their music classes. They worked for two Saturdays and raised $632. If they charged $8 for each car they washed, how many cars did they wash?

_____ **79 cars** _____

7. Write a number story that fits $750 / 8. Then solve your number story.

_____ **$93 R$6; Number stories vary.** _____

Fill in the missing digits in these long division problems.

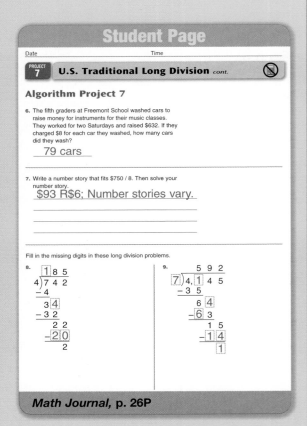

***Math Journal*, p. 26P**

Student Page

Date _____ Time _____

PROJECT **7** **Long Division with Multidigit Divisors**

Algorithm Project 7

Use any strategy to solve the problem.

1. Holmes School had a carnival to raise money for classroom supplies. The carnival raised $6,714, which was to be shared equally by all 27 teachers at Holmes. How much should each teacher have received?

_____ **$248, with $18 left over** _____

Use U.S. traditional long division to solve each problem.

2. $4,864 / 32
Answer: _____ **$152** _____

3. $17,187 / 43
Answer: **$399 R$30**

4. 5,238 / 27
Answer: _____ **194** _____

5. 4,785 / 87
Answer: _____ **55** _____

***Math Journal*, p. 27P**

▶ **Solving Long Division Problems with One-Digit Divisors**   **PARTNER ACTIVITY**

(*Math Journal 1* or *2*, pp. 25P and 26P; *Student Reference Book,* pp. 24E and 24F)

Have students use U.S. traditional long division to solve Problems 2–9 on journal pages 25P and 26P. They might find the examples on *Student Reference Book,* pages 24E and 24F helpful.

▶ **Introducing Long Division with Multidigit Divisors**  **WHOLE-CLASS DISCUSSION**

(*Math Journal 1* or *2*, p. 27P)

Have students solve Problem 1 on journal page 27P. Circulate and assist.

When most students have finished, discuss students' solutions. $6,714 / 27 → $248 R$18 Expect that students will use various methods.

```
27) 6714
  − 2700   | 100
  ─────
    4014
  − 2700   | 100
  ─────
    1314
  −  540   | 20
  ─────
     774
  −  540   | 20
  ─────
     234
  −  135   | 5
  ─────
      99
  −   54   | 2
  ─────
      45
  −   27   | 1
  ─────
      18   | 248
```

6714 ÷ 27 ──▶ 248 R18

Partial quotients

```
        248
27) 6714
  −  54
  ─────
     131
  −  108
  ─────
     234
  −  216
  ─────
      18
```

$27 * 1 = 27$
$27 * 2 = 54$
$27 * 3 = 81$
$27 * 4 = 108$
$27 * 5 = 135$
$27 * 6 = 162$
$27 * 8 = 216$
$27 * 10 = 270$

6714 ÷ 27 ──▶ 248 R18

Long division

Demonstrate how to solve the problem using long division. Illustrate each step on the board or a transparency.

Carrying out long division with multidigit divisors can be challenging, particularly for students whose estimation skills are not well developed. Have students make a table of simple multiples of the divisor to use in deciding how many to share at each step.

Example: Solve: $6,714 / 27

$6,714 has only 6 [$1,000]s, which are not enough to share among 27 teachers. Trade the 6 [$1,000]s for 60 [$100]s, which makes 67 [$100]s in all. Share the 67 [$100]s among the 27 teachers. Use the table of multiples to help decide how many each teacher should get.

```
        2     ← Each teacher gets 2 [$100]s.
  27)6 7 1 4  ← Trade 6 [$1,000]s for 60 [$100]s.
   − 5 4         There are 67 [$100]s to share
     1 3       ← 2 [$100]s * 27 teachers
               ← 13 [$100]s are left.
```

Trade the 13 [$100]s for 130 [$10]s. There was 1 [$10] already, so there are 131 [$10]s after the trade. Share the 131 [$10]s among the 27 teachers.

```
        2 4   ← Each teacher gets 4 [$10]s.
  27)6 7 1 4
   − 5 4
     1 3 1    ← 13 [$100]s + 1 [$10] = 131 [$10]s
   − 1 0 8    ← 4 [$10]s * 27 teachers
       2 3    ← 23 [$10]s are left.
```

Trade the 23 [$10]s for 230 [$1]s. There were 4 [$1]s already, so there are 234 [$1]s altogether. Share the 234 [$1]s among the 27 teachers.

```
        2 4 8  ← Each teacher gets 8 [$1]s.
  27)6 7 1 4
   − 5 4
     1 3 1
   − 1 0 8
       2 3 4   ← 23 [$10]s + 4 [$1] = 234 [$1]s
     − 2 1 6   ← 8 [$1] * 27 teachers
         1 8   ← 18 [$1]s are left.
```

$6,714 / 27 → $248 R$18

Each teacher gets $248. $18 are left over.

Discuss what the remainder means in this problem. It's the part of the original $6,714 raised by the carnival that is left over after each of the 27 teachers receives $248. Ask students what they think should be done with the leftover money. Some students may want to continue dividing. The $18 left over could be traded for 180 dimes, shared 27 ways, and so on. The quotient, even carried to pennies, won't come out evenly. There will be 18 pennies left over. However, by continuing the division, a bit more of the carnival proceeds could be distributed. Project 8 will extend long division to decimal dividends. Some students might want to attempt to extend the method on their own.

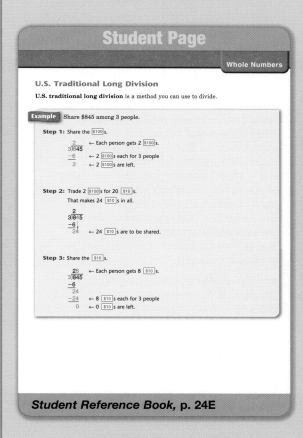

U.S. Traditional Long Division

U.S. traditional long division is a method you can use to divide.

Example Share $845 among 3 people.

Step 1: Share the [$100]s.

```
       2     ← Each person gets 2 [$100]s.
  3)845
   −6        ← 2 [$100]s each for 3 people
    2        ← 2 [$100]s are left.
```

Step 2: Trade 2 [$100]s for 20 [$10]s. That makes 24 [$10]s in all.

```
       2
  3)845
   −6
    24       ← 24 [$10]s are to be shared.
```

Step 3: Share the [$10]s.

```
      28     ← Each person gets 8 [$10]s.
  3)845
   −6
    24
   −24       ← 8 [$10]s each for 3 people
     0       ← 0 [$10]s are left.
```

Student Reference Book, p. 24E

Example

Step 4: Share the [$1]s.

```
      281    ← Each person gets 1 [$1].
  3)845
   −6
    24
   −24
     05      ← 5 [$1]s are to be shared.
     −3      ← 1 [$1] each for 3 people
      2      ← 2 [$1]s are left.
```

Each person gets $281; $2 is left over.
$845 / 3 → $281 R$2

Check Your Understanding

Divide.
1. $780 / 6   2. $973 / 4   3. $729 / 6   4. $828 / 8
Check your answers on page 442.

Student Reference Book, p. 24F

Work more examples as necessary until students understand the procedure.

Suggestions:

▷ $9,475 / 26 $364 R$11   ▷ $19,240 / 33 $583 R$1

▷ $16,248 / 13 $1,249 R$11   ▷ $5,535 / 12 $461 R$3

▷ $7,089 / 47 $150 R$39   ▷ $3,749 / 25 $149 R$24

▶ Solving Long Division Problems with Multidigit Divisors PARTNER ACTIVITY

(*Math Journal 1* or *2*, pp. 27P and 28P; *Student Reference Book,*
pp. 24G and 24H)

Have students use U.S. traditional long division to solve
Problems 2–9 on journal pages 27P and 28P. They may find the
examples on *Student Reference Book*, pages 24G and 24H helpful.

One of the hardest steps in carrying out U.S. traditional long
division is accurately estimating the quotient at each step. As
traditionally performed, any wrong estimate, either too high or
too low, will cause the algorithm to fail—the incorrect estimate
must be erased and replaced. Using a table of easy multiples is
one way to address this problem.

Another approach, which combines features of Partial Quotients
Division with U.S. Traditional Long Division, is illustrated below.
The stacked digits in the place-value positions of the quotient
represent partial quotients that must be added to yield the final
quotient. For example, the 6 in the hundreds place is from
6 * 7 = 42 (actually 600 * 7 = 4,200). The 2 above the 6 is from
2 * 7 = 14 (actually 200 * 7 = 1,400). The 6 and 2 must be added
to determine the hundreds digit in the final quotient. Similarly,
the 8 and the 1 must be added to determine the ones digit in the
final quotient. So, the final quotient for 6,225 / 7 is 889 R2.

```
      2   1
      6 8 8   → 889 R2
    7)6 2 2 5
    − 4 2
      2 0
    − 1 4
        6 2
      − 5 6
        6 5
      − 5 6
          9
        − 7
          2
```

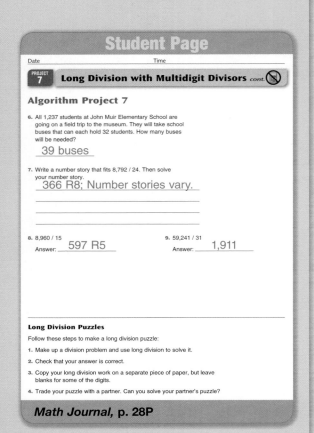

② Extending the Project

▶ Long Division Puzzles

PARTNER ACTIVITY

(*Math Journal 1* or *2*, p. 28P; *Math Masters*, p. 415)

Have partners follow the directions at the bottom of journal page 28P. Provide copies of the computation grid (*Math Masters*, page 415). Ask volunteers to explain how they checked their answers in Step 2. Consider having students make long division puzzles for classroom display.

▶ Solving Division Problems

INDEPENDENT ACTIVITY

(Online Additional Practice, pp. 28A–28D; *Student Reference Book*, pp. 22, 23, and 24E–24H)

Online practice pages 28A–28D provide students with additional practice solving division problems. Use these pages as necessary.

Encourage students to use the focus algorithm (partial-quotients division) to solve the problems on practice page 28A. Invite them to use any algorithm they wish to solve the problems on the remaining pages. Students may find the examples on *Student Reference Book*, pages 22, 23, and 24E–24H helpful.

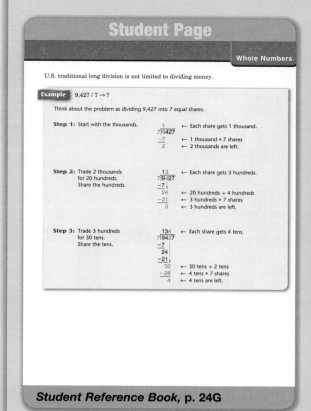

Student Reference Book, p. 24G

Go to www.everydaymathonline.com to access the additional practice pages.

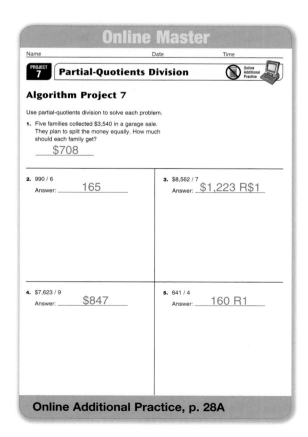

Online Additional Practice, p. 28A

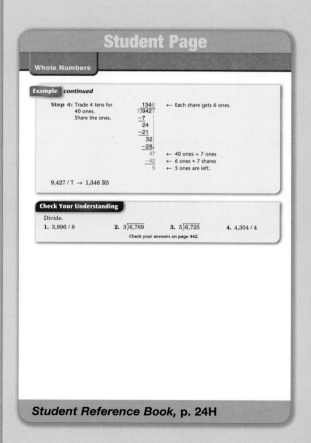

Student Reference Book, p. 24H

Algorithm 8 Project

U.S. Traditional Long Division with Decimal Dividends

Objective To extend long division to problems in which a decimal is divided by a whole number.

Technology Resources www.everydaymathonline.com

| eToolkit | Algorithms Practice | EM Facts Workshop Game™ | Family Letters | Assessment Management | Common Core State Standards | Curriculum Focal Points | Interactive Teacher's Lesson Guide |

① Doing the Project

Recommended Use After Lesson 4•5 and Algorithm Project 7

Key Concepts and Skills

• Apply multiplication facts in carrying out long division.
[Operations and Computation Goal 2]

• Use long division to solve division problems with decimal dividends.
[Operations and Computation Goal 3]

• Estimate products and quotients.
[Operations and Computation Goal 6]

• Find average speeds, given times and distances.
[Operations and Computation Goal 7]

Key Activities

Students extend the whole-number long division algorithm to decimal dividends.

Materials

◆ *Math Journal 1* or *2,* pp. 29P and 30P

◆ *Student Reference Book,* pp. 54E and 54F

② Extending the Project

Students use long division to rename fractions as decimals.

For additional practice, students solve division problems, first using the focus algorithm (partial-quotients division) and then using any algorithm they choose.

Materials

◆ *Math Journal 1* or *2,* p. 31P

◆ *Student Reference Book,* pp. 42, 43, 54E, 54F, 54I, and 54J

◆ Online Additional Practice, pp. 31A–31C

① Doing the Project

▶ Long Division with Dollars and Cents

(*Math Journal 1 or 2, p. 29P; Student Reference Book,* pp 54E and 54F)

WHOLE-CLASS DISCUSSION

Have students solve Problems 1–3 on journal page 29P. When most students have finished, write Emma's long division work from the journal page introduction on the board or a transparency. Ask questions such as the following:

- Where does the 53 in the fourth line of Emma's method come from? The 53 refers to 53 dimes, 50 dimes from the $5 left over after the whole dollars were shared and 3 dimes in the original dividend: 50 dimes + 3 dimes = 53 dimes.

- Where does the 48 in the fifth line of Emma's method come from? The 48 is the number of dimes shared when each of 6 shares gets 8 dimes: 6 * 8 dimes = 48 dimes.

- What is the 1 at the very bottom? It is the remainder; it represents $0.01 that is left over after $17.35 is divided by 6.

Have students make up a number story that fits 17.35 / 6. Ask volunteers to share their number stories and explain what should be done with the remainder in each case. Emphasize that what to do with the remainder depends on the problem situation.

Have partners complete journal page 29P. Students may find the examples on *Student Reference Book,* pages 54E and 54F helpful.

▶ Long Division with Decimal Dividends

WHOLE-CLASS DISCUSSION

(*Math Journal 1 or 2, p. 30P*)

Have students solve Problems 1 and 2 on journal page 30P. For Problem 2, remind students that a decimal point and trailing 0s can be attached to the dividend: 224 = 224.000 . . . and that a table of easy multiples of 12 might be helpful. Problem 2 involves a division that will never come out evenly and introduces students to a process that repeats forever. This idea is explored further in Part 2 of this project.

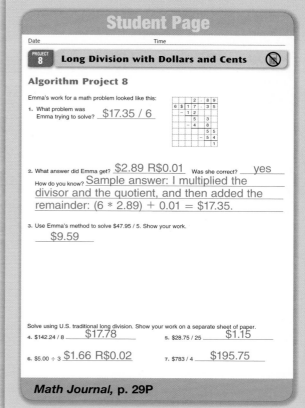

Math Journal, p. 29P

NOTE Extending whole-number long division to money in dollars-and-cents notation is relatively straightforward. One of the most useful characteristics of our base-10 place-value number system is that many whole-number algorithms can be easily adapted to work with decimals.

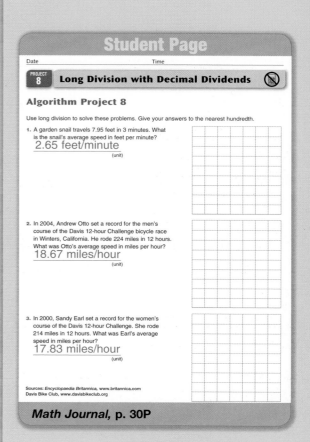

Math Journal, p. 30P

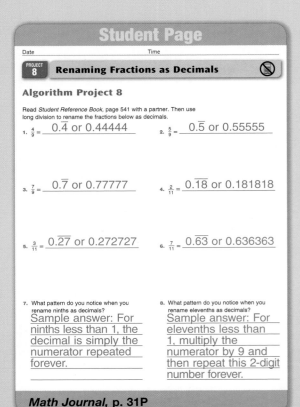

Date _____ Time _____

PROJECT 8 **Renaming Fractions as Decimals**

Algorithm Project 8

Read *Student Reference Book*, page 541 with a partner. Then use long division to rename the fractions below as decimals.

1. $\frac{4}{9}$ = _$0.\overline{4}$ or 0.44444_   2. $\frac{5}{9}$ = _$0.\overline{5}$ or 0.55555_

3. $\frac{7}{9}$ = _$0.\overline{7}$ or 0.77777_   4. $\frac{2}{11}$ = _$0.\overline{18}$ or 0.181818_

5. $\frac{3}{11}$ = _$0.\overline{27}$ or 0.272727_   6. $\frac{7}{11}$ = _$0.\overline{63}$ or 0.636363_

7. What pattern do you notice when you rename ninths as decimals?
Sample answer: For ninths less than 1, the decimal is simply the numerator repeated forever.

8. What pattern do you notice when you rename elevenths as decimals?
Sample answer: For elevenths less than 1, multiply the numerator by 9 and then repeat this 2-digit number forever.

Math Journal, p. 31P

Go to www.everydaymathonline.com to access the additional practice pages.

Name _____ Date _____ Time _____

PROJECT 8 **Partial-Quotients Division**

Algorithm Project 8

Use partial-quotients division to solve each problem.

1. Leah spent $28.25 on lunch for five days. If she spent the same amount each day, how much did each lunch cost?
$ _5.65_

2. Jackson spent $32.46 on gifts for three of his friends. How much did he spend on each friend?
$10.82

3. $28.42 / 7   Answer: _$4.06_   4. $229.50 / 9   Answer: _$25.50_

5. $5.92 / 4   Answer: _$1.48_   6. $157.26 / 6   Answer: _$26.21_

Online Additional Practice, p. 31A

When most students have finished, have volunteers copy their work on the board or a transparency and explain their solutions. Ask questions such as the following:

Problem 1

● Why does dividing 7.95 by 3 give the average speed in feet per minute? Feet per minute means feet in 1 minute. At the average speed, the snail would go 7.95 feet in 3 minutes; 7.95 / 3 gives the distance traveled in 1 minute.

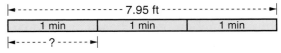

7.95 feet / 3 minutes = ? feet / 1 minute

● What does the digit 2 in the quotient mean? If 7 feet are shared into 3 equal parts, then each part would get 2 feet with 1 foot left over.

Problem 2

● Why does dividing 224 by 12 give the average speed in miles per hour? Miles per hour means miles in 1 hour. At the average speed, Otto would go 224 miles in 12 hours. 224 / 12 gives the distance traveled in 1 hour.

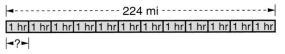

224 miles / 12 hours = ? miles / 1 hour

Have partners complete journal page 30P.

2 Extending the Project

▶ Using Long Division to Rename Fractions as Decimals
PARTNER ACTIVITY

(*Student Reference Book*, pp. 54I and 54J; *Math Journal 1 or 2*, p. 31P)

Have students solve Problems 1–8 on journal page 31P.

▶ Solving Division Problems
INDEPENDENT ACTIVITY

(Online Additional Practice, pp. 31A–31C; *Student Reference Book*, pp. 42, 43, 54E, 54F, 54I, and 54J)

Online practice pages 31A–31C provide students with additional practice solving division problems. Use these pages as necessary.

Encourage students to use the focus algorithm (partial-quotients division) to solve the problems on practice page 31A. Invite them to use any algorithm they wish to solve the problems on the remaining pages. Students may find the examples on *Student Reference Book*, pages 42, 43, 54E, 54F, 54I, and 54J helpful.

Algorithm 9 Project

U.S. Traditional Long Division: Decimals

 Objective To extend long division to problems in which both the divisor and the dividend are decimals.

Technology Resources www.everydaymathonline.com

 eToolkit

 Algorithms Practice

 EM Facts Workshop Game™

 Family Letters

 Assessment Management

 Common Core State Standards

 Curriculum Focal Points

 Interactive Teacher's Lesson Guide

---

1 Doing the Project

Recommended Use After Lesson 4◆5 and Algorithm Project 8

Key Concepts and Skills

• Use the Multiplication Rule to find equivalent fractions.
  [Number and Numeration Goal 5]

• Use long division to solve division problems with decimal divisors.
  [Operations and Computation Goal 3]

• Multiply numbers by powers of 10.
  [Operations and Computation Goal 3]

• Explore the meaning of division by a decimal.
  [Operations and Computation Goal 7]

Key Activities

Students explore the meaning of division by a decimal and extend long division to decimal divisors.

Key Vocabulary

decimal divisors

Materials

◆ *Math Journal 1* or *2*, p. 32P

◆ *Student Reference Book,* pp. 37, 54G, 54H, and 60

2 Extending the Project

Students express the remainder in a division problem as a whole number, a fraction, an exact decimal, and a decimal rounded to the nearest hundredth.

For additional practice, students solve division problems, first using the focus algorithm (partial-quotients division) and then using any algorithm they choose.

Materials

◆ *Math Journal 1* or *2*, p. 33P

◆ *Student Reference Book,* pp. 54E–54J

◆ Online Additional Practice, pp. 33A–33B

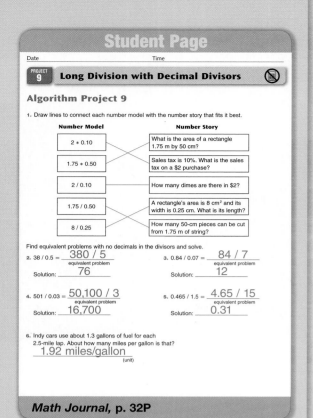

Student Page

Date _____ Time _____

PROJECT 9 Long Division with Decimal Divisors

Algorithm Project 9

1. Draw lines to connect each number model with the number story that fits it best.

Number Model	Number Story
2 * 0.10	What is the area of a rectangle 1.75 m by 50 cm?
1.75 * 0.50	Sales tax is 10%. What is the sales tax on a $2 purchase?
2 / 0.10	How many dimes are there in $2?
1.75 / 0.50	A rectangle's area is 8 cm² and its width is 0.25 cm. What is its length?
8 / 0.25	How many 50-cm pieces can be cut from 1.75 m of string?

Find equivalent problems with no decimals in the divisors and solve.

2. 38 / 0.5 = **380 / 5**
equivalent problem
Solution: **76**

3. 0.84 / 0.07 = **84 / 7**
equivalent problem
Solution: **12**

4. 501 / 0.03 = **50,100 / 3**
equivalent problem
Solution: **16,700**

5. 0.465 / 1.5 = **4.65 / 15**
equivalent problem
Solution: **0.31**

6. Indy cars use about 1.3 gallons of fuel for each 2.5-mile lap. About how many miles per gallon is that?
1.92 miles/gallon
(unit)

Math Journal, p. 32P

Student Page

Date _____ Time _____

PROJECT 9 Representing Remainders as Decimals

Algorithm Project 9

You might write the answer to a problem such as 17 / 6 in two ways: 17 / 6 → 2 R5, or by rewriting the remainder as a fraction: 17 / 6 = 2⅚.

With decimal long division, you can show the quotient as a decimal: 17 / 6 = 2.8$\overline{3}$. The repeat bar means that the 3s repeat forever. But, in most situations, having infinitely many 3s is not practical, so answers are often rounded to some reasonable number of decimal places, usually two or three: 17 / 6 = 2.83, or 17 / 6 = 2.833.

Notice that 17 / 6 = 2.83 is not actually true. You can check this by multiplying 2.83 by 6. You won't get 17. But, for most practical purposes, 2.83 or 2.833 is close enough to 17 / 6 that most people aren't bothered by a rounded number model.

Complete the table.

Problem	Answer as			
	Quotient and Remainder	Mixed Number	Exact Decimal	Decimal Rounded to Hundredths
1. 17 / 6	2 R5	2⅚	2.8$\overline{3}$	2.83
2. 15 / 4	3 R3	3¾	3.75	3.75
3. 5 / 8	0 R5	⅝	0.625	0.63
4. 17 / 3	5 R2	5⅔	5.6$\overline{6}$	5.67
5. 56 / 9	6 R2	6 2/9	6.2$\overline{2}$	6.22

Math Journal, p. 33P

① Doing the Project

▶ Exploring Meanings for Decimal Division

 **WHOLE-CLASS DISCUSSION**

(*Math Journal 1* or *2*, p. 32P)

Have partners solve Problem 1 on journal page 32P. When most students have finished, have volunteers explain their solutions. Use student responses to emphasize the following ideas:

▷ One way to think about division is as "How many ___ are in ___?"

▷ Think of missing factors. Given the area and one dimension of a rectangle, for example, we can use division to find the other dimension.

▷ Numbers in problems can be represented one way in the problem's number story and another way in the matching number model. For example, 10% in one of the number stories corresponds to 0.10 in the matching number model.

▷ The idea that multiplication makes bigger and division makes smaller, which many students have formed from their work with whole numbers, does not apply to multiplication and division by numbers less than 1.

▶ Dividing with Decimal Divisors

WHOLE-CLASS DISCUSSION

(*Math Journal 1* or *2*, p. 32P)

Remind students of two key facts that may be used to solve division problems with **decimal divisors:**

● A fraction can be interpreted as a division problem, and vice versa.

● Multiplying the numerator and denominator of a fraction by the same nonzero number results in an equivalent fraction.

Write 27 / 0.3 = ? on the board or a transparency. Using division methods such as partial quotients and long division is cumbersome with decimal divisors. Ask students how they might use multiplication to rename the problem to an equivalent problem that is easier to solve.

27 / 0.3 can be thought of as $\frac{27}{0.3}$.

$$\frac{27}{0.3} = \frac{27}{0.3} * \frac{10}{10} = \frac{270}{3}$$

But $\frac{270}{3}$ can be thought of as 270 / 3.

So, 27 / 0.3 = 270 / 3.

The resulting problem, 270 / 3, is easier to solve than the original problem, 27 / 0.3, but has the same answer.

Work through similar problems until students understand the principle:

> Multiplying the dividend and the divisor in a division problem by the same nonzero number does not change the quotient.

Suggestions:

▷ **45 / 0.9** $45 / 0.9 = \frac{45}{0.9} * \frac{10}{10} = \frac{450}{9} = 450 / 9 = 50$

▷ **12 / 0.03** $12 / 0.03 = \frac{12}{0.03} * \frac{100}{100} = \frac{1,200}{3} = 1,200 / 3 = 400$

▷ **105 / 0.015** $105 / 0.015 = \frac{105}{0.015} * \frac{1,000}{1,000} = \frac{105,000}{15} =$ $105,000 / 15 = 7,000$

Have students complete journal page 32P. Circulate and assist.

2 Extending the Project

▶ Using Long Division to Rename Fractions as Decimals

PARTNER ACTIVITY

(*Student Reference Book,* pp. 54I and 54J; *Math Journal,* p. 33P)

Have partners read *Student Reference Book,* pages 54I and 54J and then complete journal page 33P. When students have finished, discuss any difficulties or curiosities they encountered.

NOTE *Student Reference Book,* pages 54G and 54H provide a detailed step-by-step explanation of how to "clear decimals" in the divisor so that the long division algorithm can be applied. Other relevant *Student Reference Book* pages include page 37 (multiplication by powers of 10) and 60 (using multiplication to find equivalent fractions).

▶ Solving Division Problems

INDEPENDENT ACTIVITY

(*Online Additional Practice,* pp. 33A and 33B; *Student Reference Book,* pp. 42, 43, and 54E–54J)

Online practice pages 33A and 33B provide students with additional practice solving division problems. Use these pages as necessary.

Encourage students to use the focus algorithm (partial-quotients division) to solve the problems on practice page 33A. Invite them to use any algorithm they wish to solve the problems on the remaining page. Students may find the examples on *Student Reference Book,* pages 42, 43, and 54E–54J helpful.

Go to www.everydaymathonline.com to access the additional practice pages.

Fifth Grade Key Vocabulary

For a more comprehensive glossary that includes additional entries and illustrations, please refer to the *Teacher's Reference Manual.*

NOTE: Within a definition, terms in italics are defined elsewhere in the glossary.

account balance An amount of money that you have or that you owe. See *"in the black"* and *"in the red."*

acute angle An angle with a measure less than 90°.

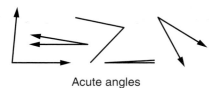

Acute angles

adjacent angles Two angles with a common side and *vertex* that do not otherwise overlap.

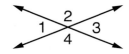

Angles 1 and 2, 2 and 3, 3 and 4, and 4 and 1 are pairs of adjacent angles.

adjacent sides (1) Two sides in a *polygon* that share a common *vertex*. (2) Two sides of a *polyhedron* with a common *edge*.

algebraic expression An *expression* that contains a *variable*. For example, if Maria is 2 inches taller than Joe and if the variable M represents Maria's height, then the algebraic expression $M - 2$ represents Joe's height.

algorithm A set of step-by-step instructions for doing something, such as carrying out a computation or solving a problem. The most common algorithms are those for basic arithmetic computation, but there are many others. Some mathematicians and many computer scientists spend a great deal of time trying to find more efficient algorithms for solving problems.

apex In a *pyramid* or *cone*, the *vertex* opposite the *base*. In a pyramid, all the nonbase faces meet at the apex.

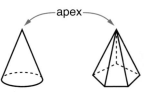

arc of a circle A part of a circle between and including two endpoints on the circle. For example, the endpoints of the *diameter* of a circle define an arc called a semicircle. An arc is named by its endpoints.

Arcs

area The amount of *surface* inside a 2-dimensional figure. The figure might be a triangle or rectangle in a plane, the curved surface of a *cylinder*, or a state or country on Earth's surface. Commonly, area is measured in *square units* such as square miles, square inches, or square centimeters.

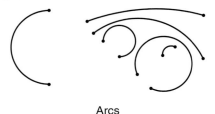

A triangle with area 21 square units

A rectangle with area 1.2 cm ∗ 2 cm = 2.4 square centimeters

The area of the United States is about 3,800,000 square miles.

area model (1) A model for multiplication in which the length and width of a rectangle represent the *factors,* and the *area* of the rectangle represents the *product.*

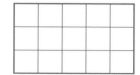

Area model for 3 ∗ 5 = 15

(2) A model showing fractions as parts of a whole. The *whole* is a region, such as a circle or a rectangle, representing the number *ONE*.

Area model for $\frac{2}{3}$

Associative Property A property of addition and multiplication (but not of subtraction or division) that says that when you add or multiply three numbers, it does not matter which two you add or multiply first. For example:

$$(4 + 3) + 7 = 4 + (3 + 7)$$
and
$$(5 * 8) * 9 = 5 * (8 * 9)$$

attribute blocks A set of blocks in which each block has one each of four attributes including color, size, thickness, and shape. The blocks are used for attribute identification and sorting activities. Compare to *pattern blocks.*

axis of a coordinate grid Either of the two number lines used to form a *coordinate grid.* Plural is axes.

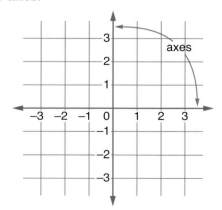

axis of rotation A line about which a solid figure rotates.

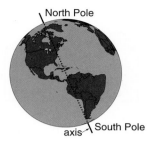

B

ballpark estimate A rough *estimate;* "in the ballpark." A ballpark estimate can serve as a check of the reasonableness of an answer obtained through some other procedure, or it can be made when an exact value is unnecessary or is impossible to obtain.

bar graph A graph with *horizontal* or *vertical* bars that represent data.

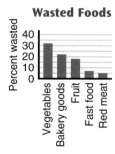

Wasted Foods

Source: *The Garbage Product*

Fat Content of Foods

Source: *The New York Public Library Desk Reference*

base (in exponential notation) A number that is raised to a *power.* For example, the base in 5^3 is 5.

base of a parallelogram (1) The side of a *parallelogram* to which an altitude is drawn. (2) The *length* of this side. The *area* of a parallelogram is the length of the base times the altitude or *height perpendicular* to it.

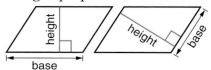

base of a prism or cylinder   Either of the two parallel and congruent *faces* that define the shape of a *prism* or *cylinder*. In a cylinder, the base is a circle.

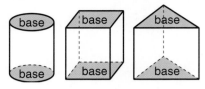

base of a pyramid or cone   The *face* of a *pyramid* or *cone* that is opposite its *apex*. The base of a cone is a circle.

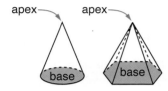

base of a rectangle   (1) One of the sides of a rectangle. (2) The *length* of this side. The *area* of a rectangle is the length of the base times the altitude, or *height*.

base of a triangle   (1) Any side of a triangle to which an *altitude* is drawn. (2) The *length* of this side. The *area* of a triangle is half the length of the base times the altitude, or *height*.

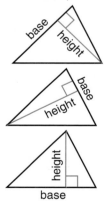

base-10 blocks   A set of blocks to represent ones, tens, hundreds, and thousands in the base-10 *place-value* system. In *Everyday Mathematics,* the unit block, or *cube,* has 1-cm edges; the ten block, or *long,* is 10 unit blocks in *length;* the hundred block, or *flat,* is 10 longs in width; and the thousand block, or big cube, is 10 flats high.

benchmark   A well-known count or measure that can be used to evaluate the reasonableness of other counts, measures, or estimates. The benchmarks often used when estimating with fractions are 0, $\frac{1}{2}$, and 1.

biased sample   A *sample* that does not fairly represent the total *population* from which it was selected. A sample is biased if every member of the population does not have the same chance of being selected for the sample.

C

calibrate   (1) To divide or mark a measuring tool with gradations, such as the degree marks on a *thermometer*. (2) To test and adjust the accuracy of a measuring tool.

capacity   (1) The amount of space occupied by a 3-dimensional figure. Same as *volume*. The amount a container can hold. Capacity is often measured in *units* such as *quarts,* gallons, *cups,* or *liters*. (2) The maximum weight a scale can measure.

census   An official count of population and the recording of other demographic data such as age, gender, income, and education.

center of a circle   The point in the plane of a circle equally distant from all points on the circle.

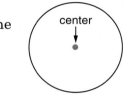

century   One hundred years.

change diagram   A diagram used in *Everyday Mathematics* to model situations in which quantities are either increased or decreased by addition or subtraction. The diagram includes a starting quantity, an ending quantity, and an amount of change.

A change diagram for 14 − 5 = 9

change-to-less story   A number story about a change situation in which the ending quantity is less than the starting quantity. For example, a story about spending money is a change-to-less story. Compare to *change-to-more story*.

change-to-more story   A number story about a change situation in which the ending quantity is more than the starting quantity. For example, a story about earning money is a change-to-more story. Compare to *change-to-less story*.

circle graph A graph in which a circle and its interior are divided into *sectors* corresponding to parts of a set of data. The whole circle represents the whole set of data. Same as *pie graph* and sometimes called a pie chart.

circumference The distance around a circle; its *perimeter*. The circumference of a *sphere* is the circumference of a circle on the sphere with the same center as the sphere.

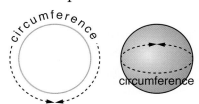

coefficient The number, or constant, *factor* in a *variable* term in an *expression*. For example, in $3c + 8d$, 3 and 8 are coefficients.

column addition An addition *algorithm* in which the addends' *digits* are first added in each *place-value* column separately, and then 10-for-1 trades are made until each column has only one digit. Lines may be drawn to separate the place-value columns.

combine like terms To rewrite the sum or difference of like terms as a single term. For example, $5a + 6a$ can be rewritten as $11a$, because $5a + 6a = (5 + 6)a = 11a$. Similarly, $16t - 3t = 13t$.

common denominator A nonzero number that is a multiple of the *denominators* of two or more fractions. For example, the fractions $\frac{1}{2}$ and $\frac{2}{3}$ have common denominators 6, 12, 18, and other multiples of 6. Fractions with the same denominator already have a common denominator.

common factor A *factor* of each of two or more counting numbers. For example, 4 is a common factor of 8 and 12.

Commutative Property of Multiplication A property of multiplication that two numbers can be multiplied in either order without changing the *product*. For example, $5 * 10 = 10 * 5$. In *Everyday Mathematics,* this is called a turn-around fact, and the two Commutative Properties are called *turn-around rules.* In symbols:

For any numbers a and b, $a * b = b * a$.

Division is not commutative. For example, $10 / 5 \neq 5 / 10$ because $2 \neq \frac{1}{2}$.

complement of a number n (1) In *Everyday Mathematics,* the *difference* between n and the next multiple of 10. For example, the complement of 4 is $10 - 4 = 6$ and the complement of 73 is $80 - 73 = 7$. (2) The difference between n and the next higher *power of 10*. In this definition, the complement of 73 is $100 - 73 = 27$.

composite number A counting number greater than 1 that has more than two *factors*. For example, 10 is a composite number because it has four factors: 1, 2, 5, and 10. A composite number is divisible by at least three whole numbers. Compare to *prime number.*

cone A *geometric solid* with a circular *base,* a *vertex* called an *apex* not in the plane of the base, and all of the line segments with one endpoint at the apex and the other endpoint on the *circumference* of the base.

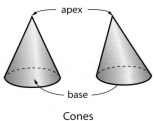

Cones

congruent figures ($\cong$) Figures having the same size and shape. Two figures are congruent if they match exactly when one is placed on top of the other after a combination of *slides,* flips, and/or turns. In diagrams of congruent figures, the corresponding congruent sides may be marked with the same number of hash marks. The symbol $\cong$ means "is congruent to."

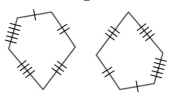

Congruent pentagons

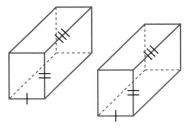

Congruent prisms

contour line A curve on a map through places where a measurement such as temperature, elevation, air pressure, or growing season is the same. Contour lines often separate regions that have been differently colored to show a range of conditions. See *contour map*.

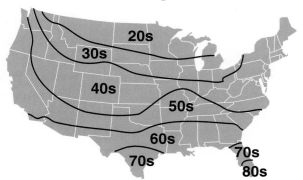

A contour map

contour map A map that uses *contour lines* to indicate areas having a particular feature, such as elevation or climate.

coordinate (1) A number used to locate a point on a number line; a point's distance from an *origin*. (2) One of the numbers in an *ordered pair* or triple that locates a point on a *coordinate grid* or in coordinate space, respectively.

coordinate grid (rectangular coordinate grid) A reference frame for locating points in a plane by means of *ordered pairs* of numbers. A rectangular coordinate grid is formed by two number lines that intersect at *right angles* at their zero points.

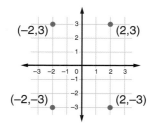

A coordinate grid

cube (1) A regular *polyhedron* with 6 square faces. A cube has 8 *vertices* and 12 *edges*.

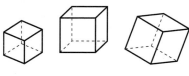

Cubes

(2) In *Everyday Mathematics,* the smaller cube of the *base-10 blocks,* measuring 1 cm on each edge.

cube of a number The *product* of a number used as a *factor* three times. For example, the cube of 5 is $5 * 5 * 5 = 5^3 = 125$.

cubic centimeter (cc or cm³) A metric *unit* of *volume* or *capacity* equal to the volume of a *cube* with 1-cm edges. 1 cm³ = 1 milliliter (mL).

cubic unit A *unit* such as *cubic centimeters,* cubic inches, cubic feet, and cubic meters used to measure *volume* or *capacity.*

cubit An ancient *unit* of *length,* measured from the point of the elbow to the end of the middle finger. The cubit has been standardized at various times between 18 and 22 inches. The Latin word "cubitum" means elbow.

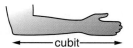

cubit

cup (c) A U.S. customary *unit* of *volume* or *capacity* equal to 8 fluid ounces or $\frac{1}{2}$ pint.

curved surface A 2-dimensional surface that does not lie in a plane. *Spheres, cylinders,* and *cones* each have one curved surface.

cylinder A *geometric solid* with two congruent, parallel circular regions for *bases* and a curved *face* formed by all the segments with an endpoint on each circle that are parallel to a segment with endpoints at the centers of the circles. Also called a circular cylinder.

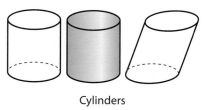

Cylinders

D

data bank (1) In *Third Grade Everyday Mathematics,* a collection of data sets presented in posters, tables, graphs, and maps. (2) In general, any established data set or database.

debit An amount subtracted from a bank balance; a withdrawal.

decade Ten years.

decimal point A mark used to separate the ones and tenths places in decimals. A decimal point separates dollars from cents in *dollars-and-cents notation*. The mark is a dot in the U.S. customary system and a comma in Europe and some other countries.

denominator The nonzero divisor b in a fraction $\frac{a}{b}$ and a/b. In a part-whole fraction, the denominator is the number of equal parts into which the *whole,* or ONE, has been divided. Compare to *numerator.*

diameter (1) A line segment that passes through the *center of a circle* or *sphere* and has endpoints on the circle or *sphere.* (2) The *length* of such a segment. The *diameter* of a circle or sphere is twice the length of the *radius.*

difference The result of subtracting one number from another. For example, the difference of 12 and 5 is $12 - 5 = 7$.

digit (1) Any one of the symbols 0, 1, 2, 3, 4, 5, 6, 7, 8, and 9 in the base-10 numeration system. For example, the numeral 145 is made up of the digits 1, 4, and 5. (2) Any one of the symbols in any number system. For example, A, B, C, D, E, and F are digits along with 0–9 in the base-16 notation used in some computer programming.

discount The amount by which a price of an item is reduced in a sale, usually given as a fraction or *percent* of the original price or as a percent off. For example, a \$4 item on sale for \$3 is discounted to 75% or $\frac{3}{4}$ of its original price. A \$10.00 item at 10% off costs \$9.00, or $\frac{1}{10}$ less than the usual price.

displacement method A method for estimating the *volume* of an object by submerging it in water and then measuring the volume of water it displaces. The method is especially useful for finding the volume of an irregularly shaped object. Archimedes of Syracuse (circa 287–212 B.C.) is famous for having solved a problem of finding the volume and density of a king's crown by noticing how his body displaced water in a bathtub and applying the method to the crown. He reportedly shouted "Eureka!" at the discovery, so similar insights are today sometimes called "Eureka moments."

Distributive Property A property that relates multiplication and addition or subtraction. This property gets its name because it "distributes" a factor over terms inside parentheses.

Distributive Property of Multiplication over Addition:
$$a * (b + c) = (a * b) + (b * c),$$
$$\text{so } 2 * (5 + 3) = (2 * 5) + (2 * 3)$$
$$= 10 + 6 = 16.$$

Distributive Property of Multiplication over Subtraction:
$$a * (b - c) = (a * b) - (b * c),$$
$$\text{so } 2 * (5 - 3) = (2 * 5) - (2 * 3)$$
$$= 10 - 6 = 4.$$

dividend The number in division that is being divided. For example, in $35 / 5 = 7$, the dividend is 35.

```
                divisor
   dividend        |       quotient
       ↘           ↓          ↙
          35 / 5 = 7

                divisor
   dividend        |       quotient
       ↘           ↓          ↙
          40 ÷ 8 = 5

   quotient ──→  3
   divisor ──→ 12)36 ←── dividend
```

divisibility rule A shortcut for determining whether a counting number is *divisible by* another counting number without actually doing the division. For example, a number is divisible by 5 if the *digit* in the ones place is 0 or 5. A number is divisible by 3 if the sum of its digits is divisible by 3.

divisibility test A test to see if a *divisibility rule* applies to a particular number.

divisible by If the larger of two counting numbers can be divided by the smaller with no *remainder,* then the larger is divisible by the smaller. For example, 28 is divisible by 7, because $28 / 7 = 4$ with no remainder. If a number n is divisible by a number d, then d is a *factor* of n. Every whole number except 0 is divisible by itself.

divisor   In division, the number that divides another number, the *dividend*. For example, in $35 / 7 = 5$, the divisor is 7.

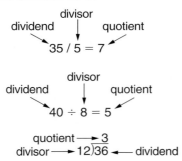

dollars-and-cents notation   The U.S. customary notation for writing amounts of money as a number of dollars and hundredths of dollars (cents). The decimal is preceded by the $ symbol, as in $8.98, meaning "eight dollars and 98 cents."

double-stem plot   A *stem-and-leaf plot* in which each stem is split into two parts. Numbers on the original stem ending in 0–4 are plotted on one half of the split, and numbers ending in 5–9 are plotted on the other half. Double-stem plots are useful if the original stem-and-leaf plot has many leaves falling on few stems. The following plot shows eruption duration in minutes of the Old Faithful Geyser. For example, the first two stems show one observation each of durations lasting 42, 44, 45, 48, and 49 minutes.

Eruption Duration of Old Faithful (minutes)

Stems (tens)	Leaves (ones)
4	2 4
4	5 8 9
5	0 1 1 1 3 3 3 4
5	5 5 6 6 7 7 8
6	0 1 1
6	6 7 7 8 8 9
7	0 0 1 1 2 2 3 3 4 4
7	5 5 6 6 6 7 7 8 8 9 9 9
8	0 0 1 1 1 2 2 3 3 4 4 4
8	5 6 6 6 6 8 8 9
9	
9	

A double-stem plot

edge   (1) Any side of a *polyhedron's faces*. (2) A line segment or curve where two *surfaces* of a *geometric solid* meet.

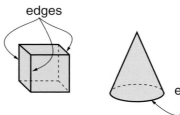

edges

edge

elapsed time   The *difference* in two times. For example, between 12:45 P.M. and 1:30 P.M., 45 minutes have elapsed.

equal   The same in value but possibly in a different form. For example, $\frac{1}{2}$, 0.5, and 50% are all equivalent.

equal parts   Equivalent parts of a *whole*. For example, dividing a pizza into 4 equal parts means each part is $\frac{1}{4}$ of the pizza and is equal in size to the other 3 parts.

4 equal parts, each $\frac{1}{4}$ of a pizza

equally likely outcomes   Outcomes of a chance experiment or situation that have the same *probability* of happening. If all the possible outcomes are equally likely, then the probability of an event is equal to:

$$\frac{\text{number of favorable outcomes}}{\text{number of possible outcomes}}$$

equation   A *number sentence* that contains an equal sign. For example, $5 + 10 = 15$ and $P = 2l + 2w$ are equations.

equilateral polygon   A *polygon* in which all sides are the same *length*.

Equilateral polygons

equilateral triangle   A triangle with all three sides equal in *length*. Each angle of an equilateral triangle measures 60°, so it is also called an equiangular triangle.

An equilateral triangle

equivalent fractions   Fractions with different *denominators* that name the same number.

estimate   (1) An answer close to, or approximating, an exact answer. (2) To make an estimate.

even number   (1) A counting number that is *divisible by* 2. (2) An integer that is divisible by 2. Compare to *odd number*.

expanded notation   A way of writing a number as the sum of the values of each *digit*. For example, 356 is 300 + 50 + 6 in expanded notation. Compare to *number-and-word notation, scientific notation,* and *standard notation*.

exponent   A small raised number used in *exponential notation* to tell how many times the *base* is used as a *factor*. For example, in 5^3, the base is 5, the exponent is 3, and $5^3 = 5 * 5 * 5 = 125$. Same as *power*.

exponential notation   A way of representing repeated multiplication by the same *factor*. For example, 2^3 is exponential notation for $2 * 2 * 2$. The *exponent* 3 tells how many times the *base* 2 is used as a factor.

expression   (1) A mathematical phrase made up of numbers, *variables, operation symbols,* and/or grouping symbols. An expression does not contain *relation symbols* such as $=, >,$ and $\leq$. (2) Either side of an *equation* or inequality.

$2 + 3$
$\sqrt{2ab}$
πr^2
$9x - 2$
Expressions

F

face   (1) In *Everyday Mathematics,* a flat *surface* on a 3-dimensional shape. Some special faces are called *bases.* (2) More generally, any 2-dimensional surface on a 3-dimensional shape.

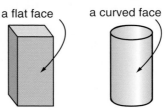

a flat face   a curved face

fact power   In *Everyday Mathematics,* the ability to automatically recall basic arithmetic facts. Knowing the facts automatically is as important to arithmetic as knowing words by sight is to reading.

factor   (1) Each of the two or more numbers in a *product*. For example, in $6 * 0.5$, 6 and 0.5 are factors. (2) To represent a number as a product of factors. For example, factor 21 by rewriting as $7 * 3$.

factor pair   Two *factors* of a counting number n whose product is n. A number may have more than one factor pair. For example, the factor pairs for 18 are 1 and 18, 2 and 9, and 3 and 6.

factor rainbow   A way to show *factor pairs* in a list of all the *factors* of a number. A factor rainbow can be used to check whether a list of factors is correct.

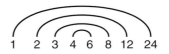

A factor rainbow for 24

factor string   A counting number written as a *product* of two or more of its counting-number *factors* other than 1. The *length of a factor string* is the number of factors in the string. For example, $2 * 3 * 4$ is a factor string for 24 with length 3. By convention, $1 * 2 * 3 * 4$ is not a factor string for 24 because it contains the number 1.

factor tree A way to get the *prime factorization* of a counting number. Write the original number as a *product* of *factors*. Then write each of these factors as a product of factors, and continue until the factors are all *prime numbers*. A factor tree looks like an upside-down tree, with the root (the original number) at the top and the leaves (the factors) beneath it. See *tree diagram*.

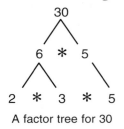

A factor tree for 30

fair game A game in which every player has the same chance of winning.

false number sentence A *number sentence* that is not true. For example, $8 = 5 + 5$ is a false number sentence. Compare to *true number sentence*.

fathom A *unit* of *length* equal to 6 feet, or 2 yards. It is used mainly by people who work with boats and ships to measure depths underwater and lengths of cables.

fathom

flat surface A *surface* contained entirely in one plane.

formula A general rule for finding the value of something. A formula is usually an *equation* with quantities represented by letter *variables*. For example, a formula for distance traveled d at a rate r over a time t is $d = r * t$. The *area* of a triangle A with base length b and height h is given below.

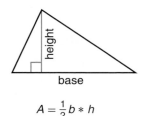

$$A = \frac{1}{2}b * h$$

fraction stick In *Fifth* and *Sixth Grade Everyday Mathematics,* a diagram used to represent simple fractions.

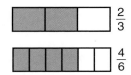

fractional part Part of a *whole.* Fractions represent fractional parts of numbers, sets, or objects.

frequency (1) The number of times a value occurs in a set of data. (2) A number of repetitions per *unit* of time. For example, the vibrations per second in a sound wave.

frequency graph A graph showing how often each value occurs in a data set.

Colors in a Bag of Gumdrops

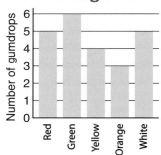

frequency table A table in which data are tallied and organized, often as a first step toward making a *frequency graph.*

Color	Number of Gumdrops
Red	⊬⊬
Green	⊬⊬ /
Yellow	////
Orange	///
White	⊬⊬

G

generate a random number To produce a random number by such methods as drawing a card without looking from a shuffled deck, rolling a fair die, and flicking a fair spinner. In *Everyday Mathematics,* random numbers are commonly generated in games.

geoboard A manipulative 2-dimensional *coordinate* system made with nails or other posts at equally-spaced intervals relative to both axes. Students loop rubber bands around the posts to make *polygons* and other shapes.

geometric solid The *surface* or surfaces that make up a 3-dimensional figure such as a *prism, pyramid, cylinder, cone,* or *sphere.* Despite its name, a geometric solid is hollow, that is, it does not include the points in its interior. Informally, and in some dictionaries, a solid is defined as both the surface and its interior.

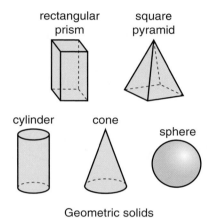

Geometric solids

Geometry Template A *Fourth* through *Sixth Grade Everyday Mathematics* tool that includes a millimeter ruler, a ruler with $\frac{1}{16}$-inch intervals, half-circle and full-circle protractors, a *Percent Circle, pattern-block* shapes, and other geometric figures. The template can also be used as a compass.

greatest common factor (GCF) The largest *factor* that two or more counting numbers have in common. For example, the common factors of 24 and 36 are 1, 2, 3, 4, 6, and 12, and their greatest common factor is 12.

great span The distance from the tip of the thumb to the tip of the little finger (pinkie), when the hand is stretched as far as possible. The great span averages about 9 inches for adults. Compare to *normal span.*

Great span

height (altitude) (1) In *Everyday Mathematics,* same as height of a figure. See *height of a parallelogram, height of a rectangle, height of a prism or cylinder, height of a pyramid or cone,* and *height of a triangle.*

Altitudes of 2-D figures are shown in red.

Altitudes of 3-D figures are shown in red.

(2) Distance above sea level.

height of a parallelogram (1) The *length* of the shortest line segment between a *base of a parallelogram* and the line containing the opposite side. The height is *perpendicular* to the base. (2) The line segment itself. See *base of a parallelogram.*

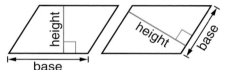

height of a prism or cylinder (1) The *length* of the shortest line segment from a *base of a prism or cylinder* to the plane containing the opposite base. The height is *perpendicular* to the bases. (2) The line segment itself.

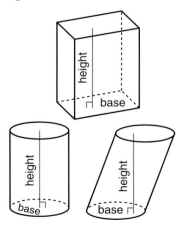

height of a pyramid or cone   (1) The *length* of the shortest line segment from the *apex* of a *pyramid* or *cone* to the plane containing the *base*. The height is *perpendicular* to the *base*. (2) The line segment itself.

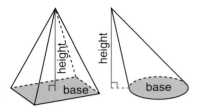

height of a rectangle   The *length* of a side *perpendicular* to a *base of a rectangle*.

height of a triangle   (1) The *length* of the shortest segment from a *vertex* of a triangle to the line containing the opposite side. The height is *perpendicular to the base*. (2) The line segment itself. *See base of a triangle*.

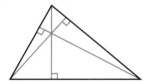

The heights of the triangle are indicated in red.

horizontal   In a left-to-right orientation. Parallel to the horizon. Compare to *vertical*.

 I

improper fraction   A fraction with a *numerator* that is greater than or equal to its *denominator*. For example, $\frac{4}{3}$, $\frac{5}{2}$, $\frac{4}{4}$, and $\frac{24}{12}$ are improper fractions. In *Everyday Mathematics,* improper fractions are sometimes called "top-heavy" fractions.

instance of a pattern   In *Everyday Mathematics,* a specific example of a general pattern. For example, $6 + 6 = 12$ is a special case of $y + y = 2y$ and $9 = 4.5 * 2$ is a special case of $A = l * w$.

interest   A charge for using someone else's money. Interest is usually a *percent* of the amount borrowed.

interpolate   To *estimate* an unknown value of a function between known values. Graphs are useful tools for interpolation.

"in the black"   Having a positive *account balance;* having more money than is owed.

"in the red"   Having a negative *account balance;* owing more money than is available.

irrational numbers   Numbers that cannot be written as fractions where both the *numerator* and *denominator* are integers and the denominator is not zero. For example, $\sqrt{2}$ and π are irrational numbers. An irrational number can be written as a nonterminating, nonrepeating decimal. For example, $\pi = 3.141592653\ldots$ continues forever without any known pattern. The number $1.10100100010000\ldots$ is irrational because its pattern does not repeat.

irregular polygon   A *polygon* with sides of different *lengths* or angles of different measures.

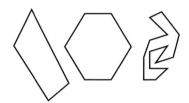

Irregular polygons

isosceles triangle   A triangle with at least two sides equal in *length*. Angles opposite the congruent sides are congruent to each other.

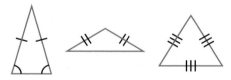

Isosceles triangles

K

kite   A quadrilateral with two distinct pairs of adjacent sides of equal *length*. In *Everyday Mathematics,* the four sides cannot all have equal length; that is, a rhombus is not a kite. The diagonals of a kite are *perpendicular*.

A kite

landmark In *Everyday Mathematics,* a notable feature of a data set. Landmarks include the *median, mode, mean, maximum, minimum,* and *range.*

latitude A degree measure locating a place on Earth north or south of the equator. A location at 0° latitude is on the equator. The North Pole is at 90° north latitude, and the South Pole is at 90° south latitude. Compare to *longitude.* See *lines of latitude.*

lattice multiplication A very old *algorithm* for multiplying multidigit numbers that requires only basic multiplication facts and addition of 1-digit numbers in a lattice diagram.

least common multiple (LCM) The smallest number that is a multiple of two or more given numbers. For example, common multiples of 6 and 8 include 24, 48, and 72. The least common multiple of 6 and 8 is 24.

length The distance between two points on a 1-dimensional figure. For example, the figure might be a line segment, *arc,* or a hiking path. Length is measured in *units* such as inches, kilometers, and miles.

length of a factor string The number of factors in a *factor string.*

line graph A graph in which data points are connected by line segments.

line plot A sketch of data in which check marks, Xs, or other symbols above a labeled line show the *frequency* of each value.

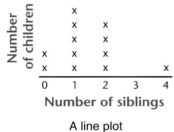

A line plot

lines of latitude Lines of constant *latitude* drawn on a 2-dimensional map or circles of constant latitude drawn on a globe. Lines of latitude are also called "parallels" because they are parallel to the equator and to each other. On a globe, latitude lines (circles) are intersections of planes parallel to the plane through the equator. Compare to *lines of longitude.*

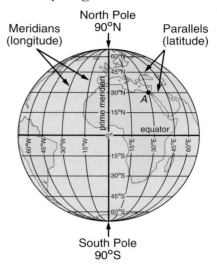

Point *A* is located at 30°N, 30°E.

lines of longitude Lines of constant *longitude* drawn on a 2-dimensional map or semicircles of constant longitude drawn on a globe connecting the North and South Poles. Lines of longitude are also called "meridians." Compare to *lines of latitude.*

liter (L) A metric *unit* of *volume* or *capacity* equal to the volume of a *cube* with 10-cm-long *edges.* 1 L = 1,000 mL = 1,000 cm³. A liter is a little larger than a *quart.*

longitude A degree measure locating a place on Earth east or west of the prime meridian. A place at 0° longitude is on the prime meridian. A place at 180° east or west longitude is on or near the international date line, which is based on the imaginary semicircle opposite the prime meridian. Compare to *latitude.* See *lines of longitude.*

M

magnitude estimate   A rough *estimate* of whether a number is in the tens, hundreds, thousands, or other *powers of 10*. For example, the U.S. national debt per person is in the tens of thousands of dollars. In *Everyday Mathematics*, children give magnitude estimates for problems such as *How many dimes are in $200?* or *How many halves are in 30?*

map direction symbol   A symbol on a map that identifies north, south, east, and west. Sometimes only north is indicated.

map legend (map key)   A diagram that explains the symbols, markings, and colors on a map.

map scale   The *ratio* of a distance on a map, globe, or drawing to an actual distance. For example, 1 inch on a map might correspond to 1 real-world mile. A map scale may be shown on a segment of a number line, given as a ratio of distances such as $\frac{1}{63,360}$ or 1:63,360 when an inch represents a mile, or by an informal use of the = symbol such as "1 inch = 1 mile."

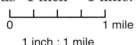

0   1 mile

1 inch : 1 mile

maximum   The largest amount; the greatest number in a set of data. Compare to *minimum*.

mean (average)   For a set of numbers, their sum divided by the number of numbers. Compare to the other data *landmarks, median* and *mode*.

median   The middle value in a set of data when the data are listed in order from smallest to largest or vice versa. If there is an *even number* of data points, the median is the *mean* of the two middle values. Compare to other data *landmarks, mean* and *mode*.

memory in a calculator   Where numbers are stored in a calculator for use in later calculations. Most calculators have both a short-term memory and a long-term memory.

milliliter (mL)   A metric *unit* of *volume* or *capacity* equal to $\frac{1}{1,000}$ of a *liter,* or 1 *cubic centimeter.*

minimum   The smallest amount; the smallest number in a set of data. Compare to *maximum.*

minuend   In subtraction, the number from which another number is subtracted. For example, in $19 - 5 = 14$, the minuend is 19. Compare to *subtrahend.*

mirror image   Same as a *reflection* image.

mixed number   A number that is written using both a whole number and a fraction. For example, $2\frac{1}{4}$ is a mixed number equal to $2 + \frac{1}{4}$.

mode   The value or values that occur most often in a set of data. Compare to other *landmarks, mean* and *median.*

multiple of a number *n*   (1) A *product* of n and a counting number. For example, the multiples of 7 are 7, 14, 21, 28, ... (2) A product of n and an integer. For example, the multiples of 7 are . . . , $-21, -14, -7, 0, 7, 14, 21, ...$

multiples of equal groups   A *multiple* of a *rate* in an equal-grouping situation. For example, *How many balloons are there altogether in 6 packages with 20 balloons per package?* is a multiple of an equal-group problem.

multiplication counting principle   A way of determining the total number of possible outcomes for two or more separate choices. For example, suppose you roll a typical die and then flip a coin. There are 6 choices for which a number on the die lands up (1, 2, 3, 4, 5, or 6) and 2 choices for which side of the coin lands up (HEADS *H* or TAILS *T*). So there are $6 * 2 = 12$ possible outcomes altogether: (1, *H*), (1, *T*), (2, *H*), (2, *T*), (3, *H*), (3, *T*), (4, *H*), (4, *T*), (5, *H*) (5, *T*), (6, *H*), (6, *T*).

N

name-collection box   In *Everyday Mathematics,* a diagram that is used for collecting equivalent names for a number.

25
37 − 12
20 + 5
twenty-five
veinticinco

negative numbers   Numbers less than 0; the opposites of the positive numbers, commonly written as a positive number preceded by a − or OPP. Negative numbers are plotted left of 0 on a *horizontal* number line or below 0 on a *vertical* number line.

nested parentheses   Parentheses within parentheses in an *expression*. Expressions are evaluated from within the innermost parentheses outward.

normal span   The distance from the end of the thumb to the end of the index (first) finger of an outstretched hand. For estimating *lengths,* many people can adjust this distance to approximately 6 inches or 15 centimeters. Same as *span.* Compare to *great span.*

number-and-word notation   A notation consisting of the significant *digits* of a number and words for the *place value.* For example, 27 billion is number-and-word notation for 27,000,000,000. Compare to *expanded notation, scientific notation,* and *standard notation.*

number model   A *number sentence, expression,* or other representation that models a number story or situation. For example, the story *Sally had $5, and then she earned $8* can be modeled as the number sentence $5 + 8 = 13$, or as the expression $5 + 8$, or by

$$\begin{array}{r} 5 \\ +\ 8 \\ \hline 13 \end{array}$$

number sentence   Two *expressions* with a *relation symbol.* For example,

$$5 + 5 = 10$$
$$2 - ? = 8$$
$$16 \le a * b$$
$$a^2 + b^2 = c^2$$

Number sentences

numerator   The dividend a in a fraction $\frac{a}{b}$ or a/b. In a part-whole fraction, in which the *whole* (the ONE or unit whole) is *divided* into a number of equal parts, the numerator is the number of equal parts being considered. Compare to *denominator.*

obtuse angle   An angle with measure between 90° and 180°.

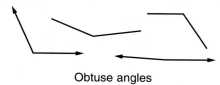

Obtuse angles

odd number   A counting number that is not *divisible by* 2. Compare to *even number.*

open proportion   A proportion with one or more *variables.* An open proportion is an *open sentence* and is neither true nor false. For example, $\frac{2}{3} = \frac{a}{5}$ and $\frac{z}{15} = \frac{y}{3}$ are open proportions.

open sentence   A *number sentence* with one or more *variables.* An open sentence is neither true nor false. For example, $9 + \underline{\ \ \ } = 15$, $? - 24 < 10$, and $7 = x + y$ are open sentences.

operation symbol   A symbol used in *expressions* and *number sentences* to stand for a particular mathematical operation. Symbols for common arithmetic operations are listed below:

addition	$+$
subtraction	$-$
multiplication	$\times, *, \cdot$
division	$\div, /$
powering	$\wedge$

opposite angles   Same as *vertical angles.*

opposite of a number n A number that is the same distance from 0 on a number line as n, but on the opposite side of 0. In symbols, the opposite of a number n is $-n$ and, in *Everyday Mathematics,* OPP(n). If n is a *negative number,* $-n$ is a positive number. For example, the opposite of -5 is 5. The sum of a number n and its opposite is zero; $n + -n = 0$.

order of operations   Rules that tell the order in which operations in an *expression* should be carried out. The conventional order of operations is as follows:

1. Do operations inside grouping symbols. Work from the innermost set of grouping symbols outward. Inside grouping symbols, follow Rules 2–4.
2. Calculate all expressions with *exponents.*
3. Multiply and divide in order from left to right.
4. Add and subtract in order from left to right.

For example:

$$5^2 + (3 * 4 - 2) / 5 = 5^2 + (12 - 2) / 5$$
$$= 5^2 + 10 / 5$$
$$= 25 + 10 / 5$$
$$= 25 + 2$$
$$= 27$$

order of rotation symmetry   The number of times a rotation image of a figure coincides with the figure before completing a 360° rotation.

A figure with order 5
rotation symmetry

ordered pair   (1) Two numbers, or *coordinates,* used to locate a point on a rectangular *coordinate grid.* The first coordinate x gives the position along the *horizontal* axis of the grid, and the second coordinate y gives the position along the *vertical* axis. The pair is written (x,y). (2) Any pair of objects or numbers in a particular order, as in letter-number spreadsheet-cell names or map coordinates.

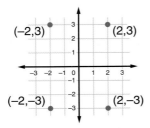

Ordered pairs

origin   The zero point in a *coordinate* system. On a number line, the origin is the point at 0. On a *coordinate grid,* the origin is the point (0,0) where the two axes intersect.

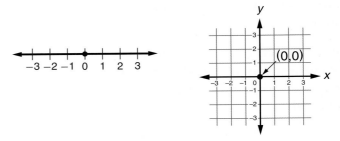

The points at 0 and (0,0) are origins.

outlier   A value far from most of the others in a data set. Commonly, outliers are much larger or smaller than other values.

pan balance   A device used to weigh objects or compare their weights.

parallel lines   Lines in a plane that never meet. Two parallel lines are always the same distance apart. Line segments or rays on parallel lines are parallel to each other.

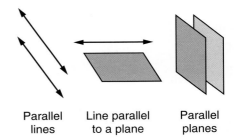

Parallel lines   Line parallel to a plane   Parallel planes

parallel planes   Planes in space that never meet. Two parallel planes are always the same distance apart. A figure in one plane is parallel to the other plane. *Polygons* in one plane are said to be parallel to polygons in the other plane. However, 1-dimensional shapes such as lines, segments, and rays in one plane are not necessarily parallel to 1-dimensional shapes in a parallel plane.

parallelogram   A quadrilateral with two pairs of parallel sides. Opposite sides of a parallelogram have the same *length,* and *opposite angles* have the same measure. All rectangles are parallelograms, but not all parallelograms are rectangles because parallelograms do not necessarily have *right angles.*

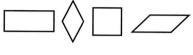

Parallelograms

partial-differences subtraction   A subtraction *algorithm* in which separate differences are computed for each *place value* of the numbers and then added to get a final difference.

partial-products multiplication   A multiplication *algorithm* in which partial products are computed by multiplying the value of each *digit* in one *factor* by the value of each digit in the other factor. The final *product* is the sum of the partial products.

partial-quotients division   A division *algorithm* in which a partial quotient is computed in each of several steps. The final *quotient* is the sum of the partial quotients.

partial-sums addition   An addition *algorithm* in which separate sums are computed for each *place value* of the numbers and then added to get a final sum.

parts-and-total diagram   In *Everyday Mathematics,* a diagram used to model problems in which two or more quantities (parts) are combined to get a total quantity.

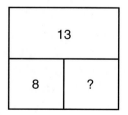

Parts-and-total diagrams for 13 = 8 + ?

parts-and-total story   A number story in which a *whole* is made up of distinct parts. For example, *There are 15 girls and 12 boys in Mrs. Dorn's class. How many students are there in all?* is a parts-and-total story. In other stories, the total and one or more parts may be known and the last part unknown.

pattern blocks   A set of *polygon*-shaped blocks of varying sizes in which smaller blocks can be placed on larger blocks to show fractional parts. The blocks are used for geometric-shape identification and fraction activities. Compare to *attribute blocks.*

pentagon   A 5-sided *polygon.*

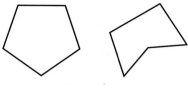

Pentagons

per   For each, as in "ten chairs per row" or "six tickets per family."

percent (%)   Per hundred, for each hundred, or out of a hundred. $1\% = \frac{1}{100} = 0.01$. For example, *48% of the students in the school are boys* means that, on average, 48 of every 100 children in the school are boys.

Percent Circle   A tool on the *Geometry Template* that is used to measure and draw figures that involve *percents,* such as *circle graphs.*

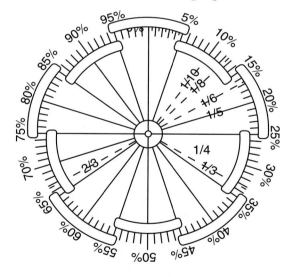

perimeter   The distance around the boundary of a 2-dimensional figure. The perimeter of a circle is called its *circumference.* A formula for the perimeter P of a rectangle with *length l* and width w is $P = 2 * (l + w)$. Perimeter comes from the Greek words for "around measure."

perpendicular (⊥)   Two lines or two planes that intersect at *right angles*. Line segments or rays that lie on perpendicular lines are perpendicular to each other. The symbol ⊥ means "is perpendicular to."

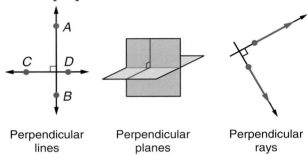

| Perpendicular lines | Perpendicular planes | Perpendicular rays |

perpendicular bisector   A line, ray, or segment that bisects a line segment at a *right angle*.

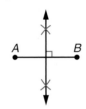

Construction of a
perpendicular bisector of $\overline{AB}$

perpetual calendar   A table that can be used to determine the correct day of the week for any date in a wide *range* of years.

personal-measurement reference   A convenient approximation for a standard *unit* of measurement. For example, many people have thumbs that are approximately one inch wide.

pi (π)   The *ratio* of the *circumference* of a circle to its *diameter*. Pi is also the ratio of the *area* of a circle to the square of its *radius*. Pi is the same for every circle and is an *irrational number* that is approximately equal to 3.14. The symbol π is the sixteenth letter of the Greek alphabet.

pie graph   Same as *circle graph*.

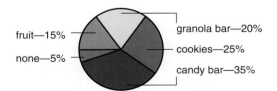

fruit—15%
none—5%
granola bar—20%
cookies—25%
candy bar—35%

place value   A system that gives a *digit* a value according to its position, or place, in a number. In our standard, base-10 (decimal) system for writing numbers, each place has a value 10 times that of the place to its right and 1 tenth the value of the place to its left.

thousands	hundreds	tens	ones	.	tenths	hundredths

A place-value chart

polygon   A 2-dimensional figure formed by three or more line segments (sides) that meet only at their endpoints (*vertices*) to make a closed path. The sides may not cross one another.

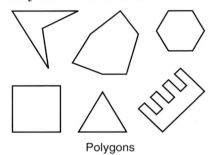

Polygons

polyhedron   A 3-dimensional figure formed by *polygons* with their interiors (*faces*) and having no holes. Plural is polyhedrons or polyhedra.

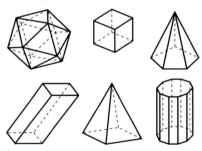

Polyhedrons

population   (1) The total number of people living within a defined geographic region. (2) In data collection, the group of people or objects that is the focus of study. Large populations are often studied by picking a representative random *sample* from the population.

power   Same as *exponent*.

power of a number   A *product* of *factors* that are all the same; the result of a^b for any numbers a and b. For example, $5^3 = 5 * 5 * 5 = 125$ is read "5 to the third *power*" or "the third power of 5" because 5 is a factor 3 times.

power of 10 (1) In *Everyday Mathematics,* a number that can be written in the form 10^a, where a is a counting number; that is, the numbers $10 = 10^1$, $100 = 10^2$, $1,000 = 10^3$, and so on, that can be written using only 10s as *factors.* Same as positive power of 10. (2) More generally, a number that can be written in the form 10^a, where a is an integer, that is, all the positive and negative powers of 10 together, along with $10^0 = 1$.

precipitation Condensed atmospheric moisture that falls to the ground, including rain, snow, and hail. In the United States, rainfall is typically measured in inches. Snow and hail are first melted and then measured like rain.

predict In mathematics, to say what will happen in the future based on experimental data or theoretical calculation.

prime factorization A counting number written as a *product* of *prime-number factors.* Every counting number greater than 1 has a unique prime factorization. For example, the prime factorization of 24 is $2 * 2 * 2 * 3$.

prime number A counting number greater than 1 that has exactly two whole-number *factors,* 1 and itself. For example, 7 is a prime number because its only factors are 1 and 7. The first five prime numbers are 2, 3, 5, 7, and 11. Also simply called "primes." Compare to *composite number.*

prism A *polyhedron* with two parallel and congruent polygonal regions for *bases* and lateral *faces* formed by all the line segments with endpoints on corresponding edges of the bases. The lateral faces are all *parallelograms.* Lateral faces intersect at lateral *edges.* In a *right prism,* the lateral faces are rectangular. Prisms get their names from the shape of their bases.

A triangular prism   A rectangular prism   A hexagonal prism

probability A number from 0 through 1 giving the likelihood of an event happening. The closer a probability is to 1, the more likely the event is to happen. The closer a probability is to 0, the less likely the event is to happen. For example, the probability that a fair coin will show HEADS is $\frac{1}{2}$.

Probability Meter In *Fifth* and *Sixth Grade Everyday Mathematics,* a tool used to show *probabilities* as fractions, decimals, and *percents.*

product The result of multiplying two numbers, called *factors.* For example, in $4 * 3 = 12$, the product is 12.

program a calculator To instruct a calculator to repeat a calculation using its *memory* instead of having the user enter a key sequence over and over. In *Everyday Mathematics,* students program their calculators to skip count using the machines' built-in constant operation feature.

pyramid A *polyhedron* made up of any polygonal region for a *base,* a point (*apex*) not in the plane of the base, and all of the line segments with one endpoint at the apex and the other on an *edge* of the base. All *faces* except the base are triangular. Pyramids get their names from the shape of their bases.

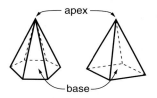

A hexagonal pyramid   A square pyramid

Q

quadrangle A polygon that has four angles.

quart (qt) A U.S. customary *unit* of *volume* or *capacity* equal to 32 fluid ounces, 2 pints, or 4 *cups.*

quick common denominator (QCD) The *product* of the *denominators* of two or more fractions. For example, the quick common denominator of $\frac{3}{4}$ and $\frac{5}{6}$ is $4 * 6 = 24$. In general, the quick common denominator of $\frac{a}{b}$ and $\frac{c}{d}$ *is* $b * d$. As the name suggests, this is a quick way to get a *common denominator* for a collection of fractions, but it does not necessarily give the least common denominator.

quotient The result of dividing one number by another number. For example, in 10 / 5 = 2, the quotient is 2.

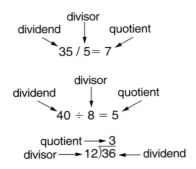

radius (1) A line segment from the *center of a circle* (or sphere) to any point on the circle (or *sphere*). (2) The *length* of this line segment. The length of a radius is half the length of a *diameter*. Plural is radiuses or radii.

random draw Taking an object from a set of objects in which each object has an *equally likely* chance of being chosen. For example, drawing a card from a deck or drawing a domino from a bag of dominos are random draws.

range The *difference* between the *maximum* and the *minimum* in a set of data. Used as a measure of the spread of the data.

rate A comparison by division of two quantities with different *units*. For example, traveling 100 miles in 2 hours is an average rate of $\frac{100 \text{ mi}}{2 \text{ hr}}$, or 50 miles *per* hour. Compare to *ratio*.

rate-multiplication story A number story in which one quantity is a *rate* times another quantity. A typical rate is speed, which multiplied by a time traveled gives distance traveled. There are many other rates such as price *per* pound or hours per person. For example, *8 people work a total of 20 hours. What is the average number of work hours per person?* is a rate-multiplication story.

ratio A comparison by division of two quantities with the same *units*. Ratios can be fractions, decimals, *percents,* or stated in words. Ratios can also be written with a colon between the two numbers being compared. For example, if a team wins 3 games out of 5 games played, the ratio of wins to total games is $\frac{3}{5}$, 3 / 5, 0.6, 60%, 3 to 5, or 3:5 (read "three to five"). Compare to *rate*.

rectangle method A strategy for finding the *area* of a *polygon* in which one or more rectangles are drawn around all or parts of the polygon through its *vertices*. The sides of the drawn rectangle(s), together with the sides of the original figure, define regions that are either rectangles or triangular halves of rectangles. Add and/or subtract the areas of these rectangular and triangular regions to get the *area* of the original polygon. For example, rectangle *RYSX* was drawn around the original triangle *XYZ*.

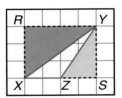

Area of △*XYZ* = area of rectangle *RYSX* −
area of △*XRY* − area of △ *YSZ*

rectangular array An arrangement of objects in rows and columns that form a rectangle. All rows have the same number of objects, and all columns have the same number of objects.

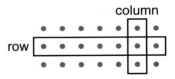

A rectangular array

rectanglar prism A *prism* with rectangular *bases*. The four *faces* that are not bases are either rectangles or *parallelograms*. For example, a shoe box models a rectangular prism in which all sides are rectangles.

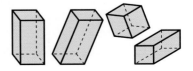

Rectangular prisms

reflection A *transformation* in which the image of a figure is a *mirror image* of the figure over a line of reflection. Each point *A* on the figure and its corresponding point *A'* on the image are the same distance from the line of reflection on a line *perpendicular* to it. Informally called a flip.

A reflection

reflex angle An angle with a measure between 180° and 360°.

A reflex angle

regular polygon A *polygon* in which all sides are the same *length* and all angles have the same measure.

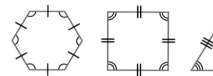

Regular polygons

regular tessellation A *tessellation* of one *regular polygon*. The only three regular tessellations are shown below.

The three regular tessellations

relation symbol A symbol used to express a relationship between two quantities.

Relation Symbol	Meaning
=	is equal to
≠	is not equal to
<	is less than
>	is greater than
≤	is less than or equal to
≥	is greater than or equal to
≈	is approximately equal to
≅	is congruent to

remainder An amount left over when one number is divided by another number. For example, in 16 / 3 → 5 R1, the *quotient* is 5 and the remainder (R) is 1.

repeating decimal A decimal in which one *digit* or a group of digits is repeated without end. For example, 0.3333. . . and 0.$\overline{147}$ are repeating decimals.

right angle A 90° angle.

Right angles

right cone A *cone* whose *base* is *perpendicular* to the line segment joining the *apex* and the center of the base.

A right circular cone

right cylinder A *cylinder* whose *bases* are *perpendicular* to the line segment joining the centers of the bases.

A right circular cylinder

right prism A *prism* whose *bases* are *perpendicular* to all of the *edges* that connect the two bases.

A right triangular prism

right triangle A triangle with a *right angle*.

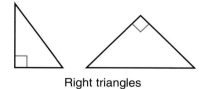

Right triangles

round To approximate a number to make it easier to work with, or to make it better reflect the precision of the data. "Rounding up" means to approximate larger than the actual value. "Rounding down" means to approximate smaller than the actual value.

round to the nearest To *round* a number up or down in a particular decimal place, depending on which approximation is closer to the actual value.

S

sample A part of a *population* intended to represent the whole population.

scalene triangle A triangle with sides of three different *lengths*. The three angles of a scalene triangle have different measures.

scientific notation A system for representing numbers in which a number is written as the product of a *power of 10* and a number that is at least 1 and less than 10. Scientific notation allows you to write large and small numbers with only a few symbols. For example, in scientific notation, 4,300,000 is $4.3 * 10^6$, and 0.00001 is $1 * 10^{-5}$. Scientific calculators display numbers in scientific notation. Compare to *expanded notation* and *standard notation*.

sector A region bounded by, and including, an *arc* and two *radii* of a circle. A sector resembles a slice of pizza. *Circle graphs* are made with sectors corresponding to parts of a data set. Also called a wedge.

sector

simplest form of a fraction A fraction that cannot be renamed in simpler form. A *mixed number* is in simplest form if its fractional part is in simplest form. Simplest form is not emphasized in *Everyday Mathematics* because other equivalent forms are often equally or more useful. For example, fractions with *common denominators* are easier to compare or add than fractions in simplest form but with different denominators.

situation diagram A diagram used to organize information in a problem situation in one of the addition/subtraction or multiplication/division use classes.

slide An informal name for a *translation*.

solution of an open sentence A value or values for the *variable(s)* in an *open sentence* that make the sentence true. For example, 7 is the solution of $5 + n = 12$. Although *equations* are not necessarily *open sentences,* the solution of an open sentence is commonly referred to as a "solution of an equation."

span Same as *normal span*.

sphere The set of all points in space that are an equal distance from a fixed point called the center of the sphere. The distance from the center to the sphere is the *radius* of the sphere. The *diameter* of a sphere is twice its radius. Points inside a sphere are not part of the sphere.

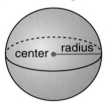
A sphere

square array A *rectangular array* with the same number of rows as columns. For example, 16 objects will form a square array with 4 objects in each row and 4 objects in each column.

A square array

square corner Same as a *right angle*.

square numbers Figurate numbers that are the *product* of a counting number and itself. For example, 25 is a square number because $25 = 5 * 5$. A square number can be represented by a *square array* and as a number squared, such as $25 = 5^2$.

square root of a number *n*   A number that multiplied by itself is *n*, commonly written as $\sqrt{n}$. For example, 4 is a square root of 16, because $4 * 4 = 16$. Normally, square root refers to the positive square root, but the *opposite* of a positive square root is also a square root. For example, -4 is also a square root of 16 because $-4 * -4 = 16$.

square unit   A *unit* to measure *area*. A model of a square unit is a square with each side a related unit of *length*. For example, a square inch is the area of a square with 1-inch sides. Square units are often labeled as the length unit squared. For example, 1 cm^2 is read "1 square centimeter" or "1 centimeter squared."

Square units

standard notation   Our most common way of representing whole numbers, integers, and decimals. Standard notation is base-10 *place-value* numeration. For example, standard notation for three hundred fifty-six is 356.

stem-and-leaf plot   A display of data values in which *digits* with larger *place values* are "stems" and digits with smaller place values are "leaves."

Data List: 24, 24, 25, 26, 27, 27, 31, 31, 32, 32, 36, 36, 41, 41, 43, 45, 48, 50, 52

Stems (tens)	Leaves (ones)
2	4 4 5 6 7 7
3	1 1 2 2 6 6
4	1 1 3 5 8
5	0 2

A stem-and-leaf plot

step graph   A 2-dimensional coordinate graph that looks like steps because the *vertical* values of points are the same over an interval of *horizontal* values and then change, or "step," for another interval. Horizontal values in a step graph often represent time.

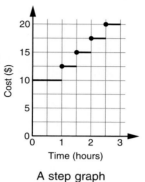

A step graph

straight angle   A 180° angle.

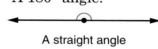

A straight angle

subtrahend   The number being taken away in a subtraction problem. For example, in $15 - 5 = 10$, the subtrahend is 5. Compare to *minuend*.

summer solstice   The longest day of the year, when the sun is farthest north of Earth's equator. The number of hours of daylight depends on the *latitude* of a location. In Colorado, the summer solstice averages a little less than 16 hours of daylight.

surface   (1) The boundary of a 3-dimensional object. The part of an object that is next to the air. Common surfaces include the top of a body of water, the outermost part of a ball, and the topmost layer of ground that covers Earth. (2) Any 2-dimensional layer, such as a plane or a *face* of a *polyhedron*.

surface area   The *area* of the *surface* of a 3-dimensional figure. The surface area of a *polyhedron* is the sum of the areas of its *faces*.

survey   A study that collects data. Surveys are commonly used to study "demographics" such as people's characteristics, behaviors, interests, and opinions.

T

tessellate To make a *tessellation;* to tile a *surface.*

tessellation A pattern of shapes that covers a *surface* completely without overlaps or gaps.

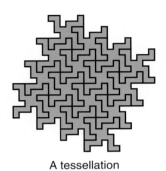

A tessellation

thermometer A tool to measure temperature in degrees according to a fixed scale. The most common scales are Celsius and Fahrenheit.

trade-first subtraction A subtraction *algorithm* in which all necessary trades between places in the numbers are done before any subtractions are carried out. Some people favor this algorithm because they can concentrate on one thing at a time.

transformation An operation on a geometric figure (the preimage) that produces a new figure (the image). The study of transformations is called transformation geometry. Transformations are often based on rules for how points behave, as in the translation below. Although the preimage does not actually move under a transformation, it is convenient to think and talk about transformations as moving a figure from one place to another and sometimes changing its size or shape. So *Everyday Mathematics* encourages using informal terms such as flip, turn, and *slide.* See *reflection* and *translation.*

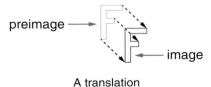

A translation

translation A *transformation* in which every point in the image of a figure is at the same distance in the same direction from its corresponding point in the figure. Informally called a *slide.*

tree diagram A network of points connected by line segments and containing no closed loops. *Factor trees* and *probability* trees are diagrams used, respectively, to *factor* numbers and to represent probability situations in which there is a series of events. The first tree diagram below shows the *prime factorization* of 30. The second tree diagram models flipping one coin two times.

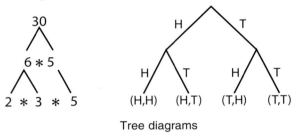

Tree diagrams

true number sentence A *number sentence* stating a correct fact. For example, $75 = 25 + 50$ is a true number sentence. Compare to *false number sentence.*

turn-around rule A rule for solving addition and multiplication problems based on the *Commutative Properties of Multiplication* and Addition. For example, if you know that $6 * 8 = 48$, then, by the turn-around rule, you also know that $8 * 6 = 48$.

U

unit A label used to put a number in context. In measuring *length,* for example, inches and centimeters are units. In a problem about 5 apples, apple is the unit. In *Everyday Mathematics,* students keep track of units in unit boxes.

unit fraction A fraction whose *numerator* is 1. For example, $\frac{1}{2}$, $\frac{1}{3}$, $\frac{1}{12}$, $\frac{1}{8}$, and $\frac{1}{20}$ are unit fractions. Unit fractions are especially useful in converting among *units* within measurement systems. For example, because 1 foot = 12 inches you can multiply a number of inches by $\frac{1}{12}$ to convert to feet.

unit percent One *percent* (1%).

unlike denominators *Denominators* that are different, as in $\frac{1}{2}$ and $\frac{1}{3}$.

unlike fractions Fractions with *unlike denominators.*

value of a variable A specific number or quantity represented by a *variable.* For example, in $y = 4x + 3$, if the value of x is 7, then the value of y that makes the *equation* true is 31.

variable A letter or other symbol that represents a number. A variable can represent a single number, as in $5 + n = 9$, because only $n = 4$ makes the sentence true. A variable may also stand for many different numbers, as in $x + 2 < 10$, because any number x less than 8 makes the sentence true. In *formulas* and properties, variables stand for all numbers. For example, $a + 3 = 3 + a$ for all numbers a.

Venn diagram A picture that uses circles or rings to show relationships between sets. In this diagram, $22 + 8 = 30$ girls are on the track team, and 8 are on both the track and the basketball teams.

Numbers of Girls on Sports Teams

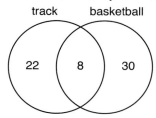

A Venn diagram

vertex The point at which the rays of an angle, the sides of a *polygon,* or the *edges* of a *polyhedron* meet. Plural is vertexes or vertices.

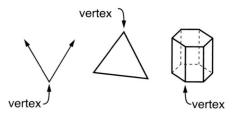

vertical Upright; *perpendicular* to the horizon. Compare to *horizontal.*

vertical angles The angles made by intersecting lines that do not share a common side. Same as *opposite angles.* Vertical angles have equal measures.

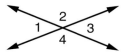

Angles 1 and 3 and angles 2 and 4
are pairs of vertical angles.

volume (1) The amount of space occupied by a 3-dimensional figure. Same as *capacity.* (2) The amount a container can hold. Volume is often measured in *cubic units,* such as cm³, cubic inches, or cubic feet.

whole (ONE, unit whole) An entire object, collection of objects, or quantity being considered in a problem situation; 100%.

Grade-Level Goals

Everyday Mathematics organizes content through Program Goals and Grade-Level Goals. The Grade-Level Goals Chart shows the units in which goal content is taught and then practiced and applied. For more information, see the *Assessment Handbook*.

The Grade-Level Goals are divided according to the content strands below.

Content Strands   Pages

How to Read the Grade-Level Goals Chart

Each section of the chart includes Grade-Level Goals organized by content strand. The three grade-level columns divided into units indicate in which units the goals are addressed.

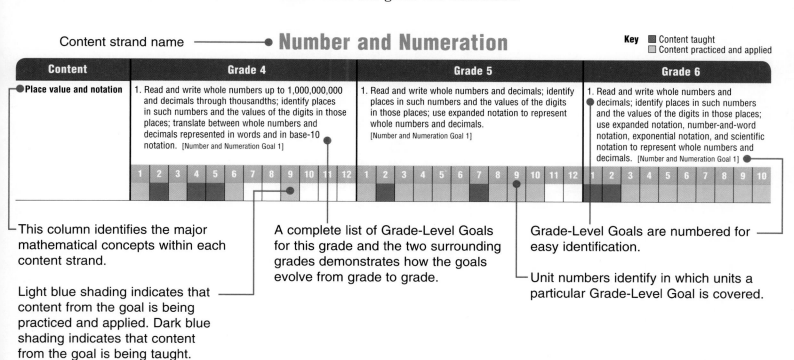

Content strand name ⟶ **Number and Numeration**   Key ▪ Content taught ▫ Content practiced and applied

This column identifies the major mathematical concepts within each content strand.

A complete list of Grade-Level Goals for this grade and the two surrounding grades demonstrates how the goals evolve from grade to grade.

Grade-Level Goals are numbered for easy identification.

Light blue shading indicates that content from the goal is being practiced and applied. Dark blue shading indicates that content from the goal is being taught.

Unit numbers identify in which units a particular Grade-Level Goal is covered.

Number and Numeration

■ Content taught
□ Content practiced and applied

Content	Grade 4	Grade 5	Grade 6
Place value and notation	1. Read and write whole numbers up to 1,000,000,000 and decimals through thousandths; identify places in such numbers and the values of the digits in those places; translate between whole numbers and decimals represented in words and in base-10 notation. [Number and Numeration Goal 1] (grades 1–12)	1. Read and write whole numbers and decimals; identify places in such numbers and the values of the digits in those places; use expanded notation to represent whole numbers and decimals. [Number and Numeration Goal 1] (grades 1–12)	1. Read and write whole numbers and decimals; identify places in such numbers and the values of the digits in those places; use expanded notation, number-and-word notation, exponential notation, and scientific notation to represent whole numbers and decimals. [Number and Numeration Goal 1] (grades 1–10)
Meanings and uses of fractions	2. Read, write, and model fractions; solve problems involving fractional parts of a region or a collection; describe and explain strategies used; given a fractional part of a region or a collection, identify the unit whole. [Number and Numeration Goal 2] (grades 1–12)	2. Solve problems involving percents and discounts; describe and explain strategies used; identify the unit whole in situations involving fractions. [Number and Numeration Goal 2] (grades 1–12)	2. Solve problems involving percents and discounts; explain strategies used; identify the unit whole in situations involving fractions, decimals, and percents. [Number and Numeration Goal 2] (grades 1–10)
Number theory	3. Find multiples of whole numbers less than 10; identify prime and composite numbers; find whole-number factors of numbers. [Number and Numeration Goal 3] (grades 1–12)	3. Identify prime and composite numbers; factor numbers; find prime factorizations. [Number and Numeration Goal 3] (grades 1–12)	3. Use GCFs, LCMs, and divisibility rules to manipulate fractions. [Number and Numeration Goal 3] (grades 1–10)

Content

Equivalent names for whole numbers

Grade 4	Grade 5	Grade 6
4. Use numerical expressions involving one or more of the basic four arithmetic operations and grouping symbols to give equivalent names for whole numbers. [Number and Numeration Goal 4]	4. Use numerical expressions involving one or more of the basic four arithmetic operations, grouping symbols, and exponents to give equivalent names for whole numbers; convert between base-10, exponential, and repeated-factor notations. [Number and Numeration Goal 4]	4. Apply the order of operations to numerical expressions to give equivalent names for rational numbers. [Number and Numeration Goal 4]

1	2	3	4	5	6	7	8	9	10	11	12

1	2	3	4	5	6	7	8	9	10	11	12

1	2	3	4	5	6	7	8	9	10

Equivalent names for fractions, decimals, and percents

Grade 4	Grade 5	Grade 6
5. Use numerical expressions to find and represent equivalent names for fractions and decimals; use and explain a multiplication rule to find equivalent fractions; rename fourths, fifths, tenths, and hundredths as decimals and percents. [Number and Numeration Goal 5]	5. Use numerical expressions to find and represent equivalent names for fractions, decimals, and percents; use and explain multiplication and division rules to find equivalent fractions and fractions in simplest form; convert between fractions and mixed numbers; convert between fractions, decimals, and percents. [Number and Numeration Goal 5]	5. Find equivalent fractions and fractions in simplest form by applying multiplication and division rules and concepts from number theory; convert between fractions, mixed numbers, decimals, and percents. [Number and Numeration Goal 5]

Comparing and ordering numbers

Grade 4	Grade 5	Grade 6
6. Compare and order whole numbers up to 1,000,000,000 and decimals through thousandths; compare and order integers between −100 and 0; use area models, benchmark fractions, and analyses of numerators and denominators to compare and order fractions. [Number and Numeration Goal 6]	6. Compare and order rational numbers; use area models, benchmark fractions, and analyses of numerators and denominators to compare and order fractions and mixed numbers; describe strategies used to compare fractions and mixed numbers. [Number and Numeration Goal 6]	6. Choose and apply strategies for comparing and ordering rational numbers; explain those choices and strategies. [Number and Numeration Goal 6]

Operations and Computation

Content

Addition and subtraction facts

Grade 4	Grade 5	Grade 6
1. Demonstrate automaticity with addition and subtraction fact extensions. [Operations and Computation Goal 1]		

1	2	3	4	5	6	7	8	9	10	11	12

Key
- ■ Content taught
- ▨ Content practiced and applied

Operations and Computation (cont.)

Content	Grade 4	Grade 5	Grade 6
Addition and subtraction procedures	2. Use manipulatives, mental arithmetic, paper-and-pencil algorithms and models, and calculators to solve problems involving the addition and subtraction of whole numbers and decimals through hundredths; describe the strategies used and explain how they work. [Operations and Computation Goal 2] *(months 1–12)*	1. Use manipulatives, mental arithmetic, paper-and-pencil algorithms and models, and calculators to solve problems involving the addition and subtraction of whole numbers, decimals, and signed numbers; describe the strategies used and explain how they work. [Operations and Computation Goal 1] *(months 1–12)*	1. Use mental arithmetic, paper-and-pencil algorithms and models, and calculators to solve problems involving the addition and subtraction of whole numbers, decimals, and signed numbers; describe the strategies used and explain how they work. [Operations and Computation Goal 1] *(months 1–10)*
Multiplication and division facts	3. Demonstrate automaticity with multiplication facts through 10 * 10 and proficiency with related division facts; use basic facts to compute fact extensions such as 30 * 60. [Operations and Computation Goal 3] *(months 1–12)*	2. Demonstrate automaticity with multiplication and division fact extensions. [Operations and Computation Goal 2] *(months 1–12)*	
Multiplication and division procedures	4. Use manipulatives, mental arithmetic, paper-and-pencil algorithms and models, and calculators to solve problems involving the multiplication of multidigit whole numbers by 2-digit whole numbers and the division of multidigit whole numbers by 1-digit whole numbers; describe the strategies used and explain how they work. [Operations and Computation Goal 4] *(months 1–12)*	3. Use manipulatives, mental arithmetic, paper-and-pencil algorithms and models, and calculators to solve problems involving the multiplication of multidigit whole numbers and decimals and the division of multidigit whole numbers and decimals by whole numbers; express remainders as whole numbers or fractions as appropriate; describe the strategies used and explain how they work. [Operations and Computation Goal 3] *(months 1–12)*	2. Use mental arithmetic, paper-and-pencil algorithms and models, and calculators to solve problems involving the multiplication and division of whole numbers, decimals, and signed numbers; describe the strategies used and explain how they work. [Operations and Computation Goal 2] *(months 1–10)*
Procedures for addition and subtraction of fractions	5. Use manipulatives, mental arithmetic, and calculators to solve problems involving the addition and subtraction of fractions and mixed numbers; describe the strategies used. [Operations and Computation Goal 5] *(months 1–12)*	4. Use mental arithmetic, paper-and-pencil algorithms and models, and calculators to solve problems involving the addition and subtraction of fractions and mixed numbers; describe the strategies used and explain how they work. [Operations and Computation Goal 4] *(months 1–12)*	3. Use mental arithmetic, paper-and-pencil algorithms and models, and calculators to solve problems involving the addition and subtraction of fractions and mixed numbers; describe the strategies used and explain how they work. [Operations and Computation Goal 3] *(months 1–10)*

Content	Grade 4	Grade 5	Grade 6
Procedures for multiplication and division of fractions		5. Use area models, mental arithmetic, paper-and-pencil algorithms and models, and calculators to solve problems involving the multiplication of fractions and mixed numbers; use visual models, paper-and-pencil methods, and calculators to solve problems involving the division of fractions; describe the strategies used. [Operations and Computation Goal 5]	4. Use mental arithmetic, paper-and-pencil algorithms and models, and calculators to solve problems involving the multiplication and division of fractions and mixed numbers; describe the strategies used and explain how they work. [Operations and Computation Goal 4]
Computational estimation	6. Make reasonable estimates for whole number and decimal addition and subtraction problems, and whole number multiplication and division problems; explain how the estimates were obtained. [Operations and Computation Goal 6]	6. Make reasonable estimates for whole number and decimal addition, subtraction, multiplication, and division problems and fraction and mixed number addition and subtraction problems; explain how the estimates were obtained. [Operations and Computation Goal 6]	5. Make reasonable estimates for whole number, decimal, fraction, and mixed number addition, subtraction, multiplication, and division problems; explain how the estimates were obtained. [Operations and Computation Goal 5]
Models for the operations	7. Use repeated addition, skip counting, arrays, area, and scaling to model multiplication and division. [Operations and Computation Goal 7]	7. Use repeated addition, arrays, area, and scaling to model multiplication and division; use ratios expressed as words, fractions, percents, and with colons; solve problems involving ratios of parts of a set to the whole set. [Operations and Computation Goal 7]	6. Use ratios and scaling to model size changes and to solve size-change problems; represent ratios as fractions, percents, and decimals, and using a colon; model and solve problems involving part-to-whole and part-to-part ratios; model rate and ratio number stories with proportions; use and explain cross multiplication and other strategies to solve proportions. [Operations and Computation Goal 6]

Data and Chance

Content	Grade 4	Grade 5	Grade 6
Data collection and representation	1. Collect and organize data or use given data to create charts, tables, graphs, and line plots. [Data and Chance Goal 1]	1. Collect and organize data or use given data to create graphic displays with reasonable titles, labels, keys, and intervals. [Data and Chance Goal 1]	1. Collect and organize data or use given data to create graphic displays with reasonable titles, labels, keys, and intervals. [Data and Chance Goal 1]
	Grades 1 2 3 4 5 6 7 8 9 10 11 12	*Grades 1 2 3 4 5 6 7 8 9 10 11 12*	*Grades 1 2 3 4 5 6 7 8 9 10*
Data analysis	2. Use the maximum, minimum, range, median, mode, and mean and graphs to ask and answer questions, draw conclusions, and make predictions. [Data and Chance Goal 2]	2. Use the maximum, minimum, range, median, mode, and mean and graphs to ask and answer questions, draw conclusions, and make predictions. [Data and Chance Goal 2]	2. Use data landmarks, measures of spread, and graphs to ask and answer questions, draw conclusions, and make predictions; compare and contrast the median and mean of a data set. [Data and Chance Goal 2]
	Grades 1 2 3 4 5 6 7 8 9 10 11 12	*Grades 1 2 3 4 5 6 7 8 9 10 11 12*	*Grades 1 2 3 4 5 6 7 8 9 10*
Qualitative probability	3. Describe events using *certain, very likely, likely, unlikely, very unlikely, impossible,* and other basic probability terms; use *more likely, equally likely, same chance, 50-50, less likely,* and other basic probability terms to compare events; explain the choice of language. [Data and Chance Goal 3]	3. Describe events using *certain, very likely, likely, unlikely, very unlikely, impossible,* and other basic probability terms; use *more likely, equally likely, same chance, 50-50, less likely,* and other basic probability terms to compare events; explain the choice of language. [Data and Chance Goal 3]	
	Grades 1 2 3 4 5 6 7 8 9 10 11 12	*Grades 1 2 3 4 5 6 7 8 9 10 11 12*	
Quantitative probability	4. Predict the outcomes of experiments and test the predictions using manipulatives; summarize the results and use them to predict future events; express the probability of an event as a fraction. [Data and Chance Goal 4]	4. Predict the outcomes of experiments, test the predictions using manipulatives, and summarize the results; compare predictions based on theoretical probability with experimental results; use summaries and comparisons to predict future events; express the probability of an event as a fraction, decimal, or percent. [Data and Chance Goal 4]	3. Use the Multiplication Counting Principle, tree diagrams, and other counting strategies to identify all possible outcomes for a situation; predict results of experiments, test the predictions using manipulatives, and summarize the findings; compare predictions based on theoretical probability with experimental results; calculate probabilities and express them as fractions, decimals, and percents; explain how sample size affects results; use the results to predict future events. [Data and Chance Goal 3]
	Grades 1 2 3 4 5 6 7 8 9 10 11 12	*Grades 1 2 3 4 5 6 7 8 9 10 11 12*	*Grades 1 2 3 4 5 6 7 8 9 10*

Measurement and Reference Frames

Content	Grade 4	Grade 5	Grade 6
Length, weight, and angles	1. Estimate length with and without tools; measure length to the nearest $\frac{1}{4}$ inch and $\frac{1}{2}$ centimeter; use tools to measure and draw angles; estimate the size of angles without tools. [Measurement and Reference Frames Goal 1]	1. Estimate length with and without tools; measure length with tools to the nearest $\frac{1}{8}$ inch and millimeter; estimate the measure of angles with and without tools; use tools to draw angles with given measures. [Measurement and Reference Frames Goal 1]	1. Estimate length with and without tools; measure length with tools to the nearest $\frac{1}{16}$ inch and millimeter; estimate the measure of angles with and without tools; use tools to draw angles with given measures. [Measurement and Reference Frames Goal 1]
Area, perimeter, volume, and capacity	2. Describe and use strategies to measure the perimeter and area of polygons, to estimate the area of irregular shapes, and to find the volume of rectangular prisms. [Measurement and Reference Frames Goal 2]	2. Describe and use strategies to find the perimeter of polygons and the area of circles; choose and use appropriate methods, including formulas, to find the areas of rectangles, parallelograms, and triangles, and the volume of a prism; define *pi* as the ratio of a circle's circumference to its diameter. [Measurement and Reference Frames Goal 2]	2. Choose and use appropriate formulas to calculate the circumference of circles and to solve area, perimeter, and volume problems. [Measurement and Reference Frames Goal 2]
Units and systems of measurement	3. Describe relationships among U.S. customary units of measure and among metric units of measure. [Measurement and Reference Frames Goal 3]	3. Describe relationships among U.S. customary units of measure and among metric units of measure. [Measurement and Reference Frames Goal 3]	
Coordinate systems	4. Use ordered pairs of numbers to name, locate, and plot points in the first quadrant of a coordinate grid. [Measurement and Reference Frames Goal 4]	4. Use ordered pairs of numbers to name, locate, and plot points in all four quadrants of a coordinate grid. [Measurement and Reference Frames Goal 4]	3. Use ordered pairs of numbers to name, locate, and plot points in all four quadrants of a coordinate grid. [Measurement and Reference Frames Goal 3]

Key
- Content taught
- Content practiced and applied

Content	Grade 4	Grade 5	Grade 6
Lines and angles	1. Identify, draw, and describe points, intersecting and parallel line segments and lines, rays, and right, acute, and obtuse angles. [Geometry Goal 1]	1. Identify, describe, compare, name, and draw right, acute, obtuse, straight, and reflex angles; determine angle measures in vertical and supplementary angles and by applying properties of sums of angle measures in triangles and quadrangles. [Geometry Goal 1]	1. Identify, describe, classify, name, and draw angles; determine angle measures by applying properties of orientations of angles and of sums of angle measures in triangles and quadrangles. [Geometry Goal 1]
Plane and solid figures	2. Describe, compare, and classify plane and solid figures, including polygons, circles, spheres, cylinders, rectangular prisms, cones, cubes, and pyramids, using appropriate geometric terms including *vertex, base, face, edge,* and *congruent.* [Geometry Goal 2]	2. Describe, compare, and classify plane and solid figures using appropriate geometric terms; identify congruent figures and describe their properties. [Geometry Goal 2]	2. Identify and describe similar and congruent figures and describe their properties; construct a figure that is congruent to another figure using a compass and straightedge. [Geometry Goal 2]
Transformations and symmetry	3. Identify, describe, and sketch examples of reflections; identify and describe examples of translations and rotations. [Geometry Goal 3]	3. Identify, describe, and sketch examples of reflections, translations, and rotations. [Geometry Goal 3]	3. Identify, describe, and sketch (including plotting on the coordinate plane) instances of reflections, translations, and rotations. [Geometry Goal 3]

Grade 4 goals are charted across grade levels 1–12. Grade 5 goals are charted across grade levels 1–12. Grade 6 goals are charted across grade levels 1–10.

Patterns, Functions, and Algebra

Key
- ■ Content taught
- ▨ Content practiced and applied

Content	Grade 4	Grade 5	Grade 6
Patterns and functions	1. Extend, describe, and create numeric patterns; describe rules for patterns and use them to solve problems; use words and symbols to describe and write rules for functions that involve the four basic arithmetic operations and use those rules to solve problems. [Patterns, Functions, and Algebra Goal 1]	1. Extend, describe, and create numeric patterns; describe rules for patterns and use them to solve problems; write rules for functions involving the four basic arithmetic operations; represent functions using words, symbols, tables, and graphs and use those representations to solve problems. [Patterns, Functions, and Algebra Goal 1]	1. Extend, describe, and create numeric patterns; describe rules for patterns and use them to solve problems; represent patterns and rules using algebraic notation; represent functions using words, algebraic notation, tables, and graphs; translate from one representation to another and use representations to solve problems involving functions. [Patterns, Functions, and Algebra Goal 1]
Algebraic notation and solving number sentences	2. Use conventional notation to write expressions and number sentences using the four basic arithmetic operations; determine whether number sentences are true or false; solve open sentences and explain the solutions; write expressions and number sentences to model number stories. [Patterns, Functions, and Algebra Goal 2]	2. Determine whether number sentences are true or false; solve open number sentences and explain the solutions; use a letter variable to write an open sentence to model a number story; use a pan-balance model to solve linear equations in one unknown. [Patterns, Functions, and Algebra Goal 2]	2. Determine whether equalities and inequalities are true or false; solve open number sentences and explain the solutions; use a pan-balance model to solve linear equations in one or two unknowns; use trial-and-error and equivalent equations strategies to solve linear equations in one unknown. [Patterns, Functions, and Algebra Goal 2]
Order of operations	3. Evaluate numeric expressions containing grouping symbols; insert grouping symbols to make number sentences true. [Patterns, Functions, and Algebra Goal 3]	3. Evaluate numeric expressions containing grouping symbols and nested grouping symbols; insert grouping symbols and nested grouping symbols to make number sentences true; describe and use the precedence of multiplication and division over addition and subtraction. [Patterns, Functions, and Algebra Goal 3]	3. Describe and apply the conventional order of operations. [Patterns, Functions, and Algebra Goal 3]
Properties of the arithmetic operations	4. Describe and apply the Distributive Property of Multiplication over Addition. [Patterns, Functions, and Algebra Goal 4]	4. Describe and apply properties of arithmetic. [Patterns, Functions, and Algebra Goal 4]	4. Describe and apply properties of arithmetic and multiplicative and additive inverses. [Patterns, Functions, and Algebra Goal 4]

Scope and Sequence Chart

Throughout *Everyday Mathematics*, students repeatedly encounter skills in each of the content strands. Each exposure builds on and extends students' understanding. They study important concepts over consecutive years through a variety of formats. The Scope and Sequence Chart shows the units in which these exposures occur. The symbol ● indicates that the skill is introduced or taught. The symbol ■ indicates that the skill is revisited, practiced, or extended. These levels refer to unit content within the *K–6 Everyday Mathematics* curriculum.

The skills are divided according to the content strands below.

Content Strands

How to Read the Scope and Sequence Chart

Each section of the chart includes a content strand title, three grade-level columns divided by units or sections, and a list of specific skills grouped by major concepts.

Number and Numeration ●——Content Strand

Key ● Content taught ■ Content practiced

	Grade 4 Units												Grade 5 Units												Grade 6 Units									
Rote Counting	1	2	3	4	5	6	7	8	9	10	11	12	1	2	3	4	5	6	7	8	9	10	11	12	1	2	3	4	5	6	7	8	9	10
Count by tenths and hundredths				●																														
Place Value and Notation	1	2	3	4	5	6	7	8	9	10	11	12	1	2	3	4	5	6	7	8	9	10	11	12	1	2	3	4	5	6	7	8	9	10
Read and write numbers to hundred millions		●	■	■	■		■							■	■	●	■			■						●	■		■					
Read and write numbers to billions		●			●										■	■										●	■		■					

This row identifies the major mathematical concepts within each content strand. A list of related concepts and skills appear below this head.

Find specific skills in this list and then follow across the row to find where they appear at each grade level.

The colored circle indicates where the skill is introduced or taught.

The colored square indicates where the skill is primarily revisited, practiced, or extended.

Number and Numeration

Key ● Content taught ■ Content practiced

	Grade 4 Units												Grade 5 Units												Grade 6 Units									
	1	2	3	4	5	6	7	8	9	10	11	12	1	2	3	4	5	6	7	8	9	10	11	12	1	2	3	4	5	6	7	8	9	10
Rote Counting																																		
Count by tenths and hundredths				●																														
Place Value and Notation																																		
Read and write numbers to hundred millions	●		■		■		■						■		●	■			■								■		■			■	●	●
Read and write numbers to billions	●				●										■										●		■		■		■			●
Explore numbers to trillions					●										●										●						■		●	
Investigate or identify place value in numbers to hundred millions	●			■			■						■		●	■			■						●	●	■	■			■		●	●
Identify place value in numbers to billions	●				●								■		●								■		●								●	
Name the values of digits in numbers to billions	●				●									●	■										●								●	
Make exchanges among place values	●			■									■		■		■		■						■						■			
Investigate and apply powers of 10					■				●				●		■			■	●						●			■	■	●				●
Investigate and apply expanded notation					●				●			■		●	■			■	●						●		■							
Read and write numbers to trillions in standard and expanded notation	●			●	●				●						●	■			■						●		●							●
Investigate, use, or apply exponential notation					●		■						●		■			■	●						●							■		●
Investigate and apply scientific notation																			●						●									●
Use dollar-and-cents notation			●	●	■	■	●	■	●	■		●	■												●		●	●						●
Explore uses of decimals				■							■																■							
Model decimals with base-10 materials				●																														
Read and write decimals to ten-thousandths in standard and expanded notation				●	■	■	■	■	●				●						■						■				■					
Identify place value in decimals through ten-thousandths; compare decimals				●	●								■	●	■	■			●		●				■	●	■	●					●	
Investigate and apply expanded notation of decimals				■											●					■					●									
Translate words into numerical expressions																	■							■						●				
Meanings and Uses of Fractions																																		
Explore uses of fractions		■				●											●					■												

Meanings and Uses of Fractions (cont.)

	1 2 3 4 5 6 7 8 9 10 11 12	1 2 3 4 5 6 7 8 9 10 11 12	1 2 3 4 5 6 7 8 9 10 11 12	1 2 3 4 5 6 7 8 9 10
Identify fractional parts of regions				
Identify fractional parts of a set				
Decompose a fraction				
Identify the whole for fractions				
Identify fractions on a number line				
Identify/find fractional parts of units of money				
Find a fraction of a number				
Use percents to describe real-life situations				
Find a percent of a number				
Find the whole, given a percent of the whole				
Solve percent problems				
Estimate and calculate percent				
Find the unit fraction or unit percent to calculate unit prices				
Determine the better buy				

Number Theory

	1 2 3 4 5 6 7 8 9 10 11 12	1 2 3 4 5 6 7 8 9 10 11 12	1 2 3 4 5 6 7 8 9 10 11 12	1 2 3 4 5 6 7 8 9 10
Identify even and odd numbers				
Find the factors of numbers				
Investigate, identify, or apply the concepts of prime and composite numbers				
Find the prime factorization of numbers				
Find multiples of a number or the least common multiple of two numbers				
Find the greatest common factor of two numbers				
Investigate or identify square numbers, square roots, and absolute value				
Understand properties of rational numbers				

Key ● Content taught   ■ Content practiced

	Grade 4 Units												Grade 5 Units												Grade 6 Units									
---	1	2	3	4	5	6	7	8	9	10	11	12	1	2	3	4	5	6	7	8	9	10	11	12	1	2	3	4	5	6	7	8	9	10
Equivalent Names for Whole Numbers																																		
Find equivalent names for numbers	■	●		■	●											●		■			■	■			●	●				■		■	●	
Rename numbers written in exponential notation					●	■							●						●						●	●				■		■		
Equivalent Names for Fractions, Decimals, and Percents																																		
Find equivalent fractions							●	●	■	■						●	●	●		●				●				●		●	●	●	●	
Rename fractions as decimals				●		■	●	■	●	■				■			●	■									■	●	●	●		■	■	
Relate fractions and decimals				●			●	■	●	■		■					●		●							●		●		■				
Convert between fractions and decimals							●	■	●	●							●			■						●		●		■				
Estimate equivalent percents for fractions									■								●	●										●		●			●	
Rename fractions and mixed numbers in simplest forms								■	●			■		■			■			●				■				●		●	■	●	●	
Convert between fractions, mixed numbers, decimals, and/or percents		●		●					●					■			●			●				■				●		●		●	●	
Use a calculator to rename any fraction as a decimal or percent									●								●									●				●		●		
Comparing and Ordering Numbers																																		
Compare numbers using <, >, and = symbols	■			■	■	■	●	■	■			■				■	■	●	●	■	■				●	●		●		●			■	
Compare larger numbers					●	■						■		●												■								
Compare and order decimals				●		■		■	■			■						●	●	●								●		●	●	■		
Compare and order integers			●							●	■	■												■		●		●	■	●				
Compare and order fractions with or without benchmarks							●				●																		●					
Plot and compare decimals on a number line										●															●		■			■				
Explore uses for positive and negative numbers										●	●									●		●						●		●	■			
Use properties of positive and negative numbers										●	●									●		●								●	■			
Explore reference points for zero										●													●	●						■				

Operations and Computation

Skill	G4-1	G4-2	G4-3	G4-4	G4-5	G4-6	G4-7	G4-8	G4-9	G4-10	G4-11	G4-12	G5-1	G5-2	G5-3	G5-4	G5-5	G5-6	G5-7	G5-8	G5-9	G5-10	G5-11	G5-12	G6-1	G6-2	G6-3	G6-4	G6-5	G6-6	G6-7	G6-8	G6-9	G6-10
Addition and Subtraction Facts																																		
Practice basic facts and extended facts	■									■				■			■				■											■		
Practice extensions of basic facts			■												■															■				
Add/subtract multiples of 10 or 100		●																																
Addition and Subtraction Procedures																																		
Use addition/subtraction algorithms	●			■									●													■	■	■	●	●	■	■		
Add/subtract using a calculator	●		●																							●								
Add/subtract multidigit numbers	●			■	●								●		■										●	●	■	■						
Solve addition/subtraction number stories	●				●			■					●			●											■							
Add/subtract multidigit whole numbers and decimals	●				■	■		■		■			●		■	●						■			■	●	●	●						
Use estimation or algorithms to add/subtract money amounts/decimals; make change				●								●	●			●			●						■	●	●	●				●		
Solve decimal addition/subtraction number stories			●																															
Add/subtract positive and negative numbers; model addition and subtraction on a number line										●		●							●							■	●	●	●	●		■		
Compute with positive and negative integers												■							●							■				●				
Multiplication and Division Facts																																		
Use a Multiplication/Division Facts Table		●																																
Practice multiplication/division facts		●	●	●				■						■	■	●			■				■		●	●	■	■	■			●		■
Practice extended multiplication/division facts			●		●									■	■	●		●							●	●	■	■						
Solve multiplication/division problems involving multiples of 10, 100, and 1,000					●					●		●				●								■	●	●								
Understand the relationship between multiplication and division							●							●																				
Multiplication and Division Procedures																																		
Model multiplication with arrays			■		■										■									■	●	●		■				■		
Use mental arithmetic to multiply/divide					●				■							●				■				■	●	●						■		
Use multiplication/division algorithms					●		■		●															■		●						●		●

Operations and Computation (cont.)

Skill	G4-1	G4-2	G4-3	G4-4	G4-5	G4-6	G4-7	G4-8	G4-9	G4-10	G4-11	G4-12	G5-1	G5-2	G5-3	G5-4	G5-5	G5-6	G5-7	G5-8	G5-9	G5-10	G5-11	G5-12	G6-1	G6-2	G6-3	G6-4	G6-5	G6-6	G6-7	G6-8	G6-9	G6-10
Multiplication and Division Procedures (cont.)																																		
Relate fractions and division			■																●								■	●	■	■		■		
Divide by 1-digit numbers						●			■						■			■								●	■	●	■	■		■		
Divide by 2-digit numbers						●			■								■									●						■		
Use a calculator to multiply/divide					■				●			●	●			●			■					●	●	●	■	●	■	■		●	●	●
Identify or investigate square numbers			●										●												●	●								●
Solve multiplication/division number stories			■			●			■			●		●		●	■	■							●	●	■	●	■	■		●		●
Solve multidigit multiplication/division problems							■								■	●					●	●		●	●	●	■				■			
Multiply/divide decimals by powers of 10									●		■			●											●	●	■	●				●		●
Multiply decimals by whole numbers									●		■			●		●		■	■		■				●	●	■	●				●		
Divide decimals by whole numbers									●		■					●				●	■	●			●	●	■				■			
Multiply/divide money amounts							■			●		●		●		●						●		●	●	●	■	●				●		●
Solve multiplication/division decimal number stories					■				●							●							■		●	■		●				●		●
Interpret a remainder in division problems						●										●									●	●	■	●				●		
Express remainders as fractions or decimals						●										●		■							●	●	■	●		■		●		●
Express quotients as mixed numbers or decimals						●																			●	●	■	●				●		
Locate the decimal point in a product or quotient									●														■		●	●	■	●	■			●		
Round a decimal quotient to a specified place														●				●			●				●	●	■	●				●		
Multiply decimals by decimals																										●	■					●		
Multiply by positive and negative powers of 10												●								●				●		●		●		●		■		
Multiply/divide positive and negative numbers												●												■		●	■	●			■	■		
Use divisibility tests to determine if a number is divisible by another number													●													●	■	●						
Procedures for Addition and Subtraction of Fractions																																		
Use benchmarks to add and subtract fractions																	■	●		■	●									●				
Use models to add/subtract fractions and mixed numbers							●												■	●								■				●		

1032 Scope and Sequence Chart

Procedures for Addition and Subtraction of Fractions (cont.)

	1	2	3	4	5	6	7	8	9	10		1	2	3	4	5	6	7	8	9	10	11	12		1	2	3	4	5	6	7	8	9	10	11	12
Add/subtract fractions with like denominators			■	●	■	■	●	■	●									●	●	■	■	■									●	■			
Add/subtract fractions with unlike denominators			■	●	■	■	●	■	●									●	●	■	■	■									●	■			
Solve fraction addition/subtraction number stories; model addition and subtraction with pictures or words				●	■			■								●		■	■			■													
Use an algorithm to add/subtract mixed numbers with like denominators				●	■			■										●	■																
Use an algorithm to add/subtract mixed numbers with unlike denominators				●	■			■								■		●	■			■													

Procedures for Multiplication and Division of Fractions

	1	2	3	4	5	6	7	8	9	10		1	2	3	4	5	6	7	8	9	10	11	12		1	2	3	4	5	6	7	8	9	10	11	12
Find common denominators				●	■	●	●	●									●		●	■											●	■			
Use an algorithm to multiply fractions by whole numbers								■	■	■						●		●	●	■		■													
Use an algorithm to multiply fractions				●	■	●	●	●	■	●								●	●	■	●	■													
Use an algorithm to multiply mixed numbers				●	●	●	●	●	■	●								●	●			●									●				
Solve multiplication/division fraction number stories						●	●	●		●								●	●																
Solve "fraction-of-a-fraction" problems								●											●																
Use a common denominator to divide fractions						●	●	●	■									●	●																
Use an algorithm to multiply/divide fractions and mixed numbers; use area models to demonstrate								●										●	●																
Understand the effect of multiplying fractions by a number less than 1, equal to 1, or greater than 1								●											●																

Computational Estimation

	1	2	3	4	5	6	7	8	9	10	11	12		1	2	3	4	5	6	7	8	9	10	11	12		1	2	3	4	5	6	7	8	9	10
Round whole numbers to a given place		●		■	●	●								■	■	■	●		■	●										■	■	●	●	■		●
Use estimation to add/subtract				●	●			■	■						●	●				●										●		●	●	■		●
Use estimation to multiply/divide			■		●			■	■						●	●				●	●											■	●			■
Make magnitude estimates to solve *, ÷ problems					●				■						●	●				●										●			●			●
Estimate sums/differences of fractions							●									■																●	●			●
Round decimals to a given place																●																	■			●

Operations and Computation (cont.)

	Grade 4 Units												Grade 5 Units												Grade 6 Units									
---	1	2	3	4	5	6	7	8	9	10	11	12	1	2	3	4	5	6	7	8	9	10	11	12	1	2	3	4	5	6	7	8	9	10
Computational Estimation (cont.)																																		
Estimate costs				■		■			■								■								■									
Estimate products and multiply decimals		●							■	■	■			●											●									■
Estimate the quotient and divide a decimal by a whole number				●					●	■	■					●	■											●		■				
Models for the Operations																																		
Understand multiplicative comparisons		■	●	●	●	■		●					■		■	■	■			■														
Understand additive comparisons				●	●																													
Find unit rates																					●	●				■						●	■	
Collect and compare rate data; evaluate reasonableness of rate data											●											●		●		●					■	●		
Use rate tables to solve problems												●									●	●		●		●					●	●		
Represent rates with formulas, tables, and graphs												●									●	●	●	●		●					●	●		
Solve rate and ratio number stories; find equivalent ratios												●									●	●		●		●					●	●	●	
Explore uses of ratios and ways of expressing ratios; differentiate between rate and ratio												●								■	●	●		●		●					●	●	●	
Find opposites and reciprocals of numbers																					■									●		■		
Solve problems involving a size-change factor																															●	●	●	
Write open proportions to solve model problems																							●								■	●	●	
Use cross-multiplication to solve open proportions																															■	●	■	

Data and Chance

	Grade 4 Units												Grade 5 Units												Grade 6 Units									
---	1	2	3	4	5	6	7	8	9	10	11	12	1	2	3	4	5	6	7	8	9	10	11	12	1	2	3	4	5	6	7	8	9	10
Data Collection and Representation																																		
Collect data by counting/interviewing	●		●						●			●					●	●						●	●									
Collect data from print sources	●		■	■	■	■	■	■	■	■	■	■			■				■				■	■		■								
Collect data from a map	●	●	■	●														●										●						

Key ● Content taught ■ Content practiced

Data Collection and Representation (cont.)	1	2	3	4	5	6	7	8	9	10	11	12	1	2	3	4	5	6	7	8	9	10	11	12	1	2	3	4	5	6	7	8	9	10
Find locations on a map or globe		●	●		●	●	■		■		■										●													
Collect and compare rate data												●										●		●			●					●		
Conduct a survey									●									●		●					●	■								
Organize and tabulate survey data									●									●							●									
Make a tally chart		●																●													■			
Record data in a table/chart		●	●						●	■		●						●		■		●	●	●	●		●			■	■	■	●	
Record data on a map									●																									
Record/compare numerical data		●					●	■	●			●		●				●						●	●		●	●				■		
Create/interpret bar graphs		●		■	■	■			■	■	■	■		■			●	●							●	■		■			■			
Create/interpret box plots																									●	■	■							
Create/interpret broken-line graphs and line plots		■	●				■				■	■		●				●	●	■	■	●	■	●	●	■	●			■	■			
Create/interpret circle graphs with or without a Percent Circle			■	■	■	■										■	●	●		■		■	■		●	■		●	●	■		■		
Create/interpret step graphs																									●									
Create/interpret Venn diagrams	■		■		■						■						■		●				●	■					■		●	■		
Create/interpret number-line plots		●					●				●			●				●							●	■								
Create/interpret stem-and-leaf plots		■																●	■			●			●	■		■					■	
Interpret mystery graphs																						●				■	■			■			■	
Use technology to create graphs																									■									
Use a spreadsheet																											●	■				■	●	
Explore misleading ways of presenting data																									●	■								
Data Analysis	**1**	**2**	**3**	**4**	**5**	**6**	**7**	**8**	**9**	**10**	**11**	**12**	**1**	**2**	**3**	**4**	**5**	**6**	**7**	**8**	**9**	**10**	**11**	**12**	**1**	**2**	**3**	**4**	**5**	**6**	**7**	**8**	**9**	**10**
Interpret tables, graphs, and maps	■		●	■	■	■			●					●	■	■	●	●	●	●	■	●	■	●	●	■	●	■				●	■	
Use a map scale			●	■	■	●	■	●	■					●		●																●	●	
Use a mileage map					●									●		●																●		
Make and interpret scale drawings								●													■											●	●	
Identify locations for given latitudes and longitudes						●															●													

Data and Chance (cont.)

Data Analysis (cont.)	Grade 4 Units												Grade 5 Units												Grade 6 Units									
	1	2	3	4	5	6	7	8	9	10	11	12	1	2	3	4	5	6	7	8	9	10	11	12	1	2	3	4	5	6	7	8	9	10
Find latitude and longitude for given locations						●															●													
Summarize and interpret data				■				■	■					●				●		●		●		●		■	●	■				■		■
Compare two sets of data; compare graphical representations of the same data			●						■					●				●						■		■	■							
Make predictions about data							●		●									●						■				●			●			
Find/use the minimum/maximum	●	●	■					●	■				■	●						●		●		●	●	●	●				■			
Find/use the range	●	●	●	■				●		■			■	●		■		●		●	■		■	●	●	●	●	■					■	
Find/use the median	●		●	■				●		■			■	●		■		●		●		●		●	●	●	●	■					■	
Find/use the mode	●		●	■				●		■			■	●				●		●				●	●	●	●				●			
Find/use the mean	■	●										●		●				●	■	■	■	●			●	■	●	■		●		■		■
Find/use the lower quartile, upper quartile, and the interquartile range																		●										■						
Understand how sample size or outliers affect results							■											●						■				■						
Determine whether the mean, median, or mode provides the most useful information in a given situation	■	●																●						■										
Use data in problem solving	■							■										●				●		●	●	●	●					■		■

Qualitative Probability	Grade 4 Units												Grade 5 Units												Grade 6 Units									
	1	2	3	4	5	6	7	8	9	10	11	12	1	2	3	4	5	6	7	8	9	10	11	12	1	2	3	4	5	6	7	8	9	10
Explore likelihood of events						■	●		●			■		●							●			●						●	●			
Explore fair and unfair games							●										■	●												●	●			

Quantitative Probability	Grade 4 Units												Grade 5 Units												Grade 6 Units									
	1	2	3	4	5	6	7	8	9	10	11	12	1	2	3	4	5	6	7	8	9	10	11	12	1	2	3	4	5	6	7	8	9	10
Predict outcomes; solve problems involving chance outcomes							●	■	■					●				■						●							●	■		
Conduct experiments							●					■		●				■						●							●	■		
Record outcomes							●	■						●				■						●							●	■		
Use fractions to record probabilities of events							●		■									■						●							●	■		
Compute the probability of equally-likely outcomes							●																	●							●	●	■	
Calculate and express the probability of simple events					■	■						■					■	■		■	●			●						■	●			

Quantitative Probability (cont.)

	1	2	3	4	5	6	7	8	9	10	11	12	1	2	3	4	5	6	7	8	9	10	11	12	1	2	3	4	5	6	7	8	9	10
Understand and apply the concept of random numbers to probability situations							●											●												●	●			
Understand how increasing the number of trials affects experimental results								■				■	●												●									
Investigate/apply the Multiplication Counting Principle, tree diagrams, lists, and other counting strategies to identify all possible outcomes for a situation			■				■	■				●						●													●			
Explore random sampling									●																						●			

Measurement and Reference Frames

Length, Weight, and Angles	Grade 4 Units												Grade 5 Units												Grade 6 Units									
	1	2	3	4	5	6	7	8	9	10	11	12	1	2	3	4	5	6	7	8	9	10	11	12	1	2	3	4	5	6	7	8	9	10
Add and subtract units of length, weight, and capacity		●			■		■		■		■												■										●	●
Estimate and compare lengths/heights of objects			●		■		■		■							●	■							●									●	
Measure to the nearest foot								●																●										
Measure to the nearest inch			●				■																										●	●
Measure to the nearest $\frac{1}{2}$ inch						■											■			■					■					●		●		
Measure to the nearest $\frac{1}{4}$ inch				●				●						■		■									■					●		●		
Measure to the nearest $\frac{1}{8}$ inch																●													■					
Draw or measure line segments to the nearest centimeter	●		■	●												■		●							■				■				●	●
Measure to the nearest $\frac{1}{2}$ centimeter				■																					■									
Draw or measure line segments to the nearest millimeter	●		●					●										●							■				■					
Investigate the meter																●			●					●					●					●
Express metric measures with decimals																																		
Estimate and compare distances				●	●	●		●						●		●						■												●
Solve length/height/distance number stories				●					●	●	■										●							●				●		
Estimate and compare weights			●	●			■				●																					■		
Estimate/weigh objects in ounces or grams											●																■							

Measurement and Reference Frames (cont.)

	Grade 4 Units												Grade 5 Units												Grade 6 Units									
---	1	2	3	4	5	6	7	8	9	10	11	12	1	2	3	4	5	6	7	8	9	10	11	12	1	2	3	4	5	6	7	8	9	10
Length, Weight, and Angles (cont.)																																		
Use a pan balance/spring scale										●	●											●												
Solve weight number stories										●	●											●	●											
Estimate the measure of an angle			■						■							■										■		■						■
Use full-circle and half-circle protractors to measure and draw angles						●	■		■						●		■	●	●									■	●					
Measure angles with degree units to within 2°						●	■		■					■	●	■			●										■					
Area, Perimeter, Volume, and Capacity																																		
Investigate area and perimeter							■		●									●			●				●	●	●						●	
Find the areas of regular shapes								●	■								■		■	●	●	■			●	●	●	●		●			●	
Find the perimeters of regular shapes			■					●		■					■		■				●	■			■	■	●					■	●	
Find the areas of irregular shapes								●										■			●		■					■					■	●
Find the perimeters of irregular shapes								●	■									●					●										●	
Estimate area								●													●		■					■					●	
Compare perimeter and area												■																					●	
Find the area of a figure by counting unit squares and fractions of unit squares inside the figure							■														●	■	●		■									
Use formulas to find areas of rectangles, parallelograms, and triangles; understand the relationship between these formulas								●													●	●			■						■	■	●	■
Find the surface areas of prisms, cylinders, and pyramids																					●							●						
Investigate/understand the concept of volume of a figure											●										●	■	●		■								■	
Understand the relationships between the volumes of pyramids and prisms, and the volumes of cones and cylinders																					■												■	
Estimate volume or surface area								●			●										●		●										●	
Find and use an approximate value for π (pi)																					●	●											■	●
Use a formula to find the circumference of a circle																							■	■			●						●	●
Use a formula to find the area of a circle																							■	■							■		■	●
Distinguish between circumference and area of a circle																								■										●

Area, Perimeter, Volume, and Capacity (cont.)

Skill	1	2	3	4	5	6	7	8	9	10	11	12
Solve cube-stacking volume problems with unit cubes and fractions of unit cubes									●	■		
Use formulas to calculate volumes of 3-dimensional shapes		■			■				●	●	■	
Investigate/understand the concept of capacity									●	●		
Estimate and calculate capacity					■				●	●	■	
Solve capacity number stories						■			●	●	●	

Units and Systems of Measurement

Skill	1	2	3	4	5	6	7	8	9	10	11	12
Identify equivalent customary units of length	■		■		■			●		■	●	
Identify equivalent metric units of length	■			●		■		■	●	■		
Convert between metric/customary measures	●		■		■			■		■	●	
Use personal references for metric/customary units of length			■		●	●			●			
Identify equivalent customary units of weight				●						■	■	
Identify equivalent metric units of weight				●					●	■	●	
Identify metric units of capacity				●					●		●	
Identify equivalent metric units of capacity										■	●	■
Examine the relationships among the liter, milliliter, and cubic centimeter	■			■					●			
Use personal references for common units of area												

Money

Skill	1	2	3	4	5	6	7	8	9	10	11	12
Compare money amounts	■		■	■					■			●

Temperature

Skill	1	2	3	4	5	6	7	8	9	10	11	12
Read, record, and convert units of temperature			●						■	●		■

Time

Skill	1	2	3	4	5	6	7	8	9	10	11	12
Investigate 1-minute intervals						●						
Calculate elapsed time			●		■	●				●		
Convert units of time		■			●		●	■				

Measurement and Reference Frames (cont.)

	Grade 4 Units												Grade 5 Units												Grade 6 Units									
	1	2	3	4	5	6	7	8	9	10	11	12	1	2	3	4	5	6	7	8	9	10	11	12	1	2	3	4	5	6	7	8	9	10
Time (cont.)																																		
Solve time number stories			●		●								■																					
Coordinate Systems																																		
Plot ordered number pairs on a one or four-quadrant coordinate grid						●		■		■		●								■	●	■		●		■	■	●	●		■	■	■	■
Use ordered number pairs to name points in four quadrants								■												■	●	■			■	■	■		■		■	■		■
Find distances between ordered number pairs along lines								■																					●	●				■

Geometry

Lines and Angles	Grade 4 Units												Grade 5 Units												Grade 6 Units									
	1	2	3	4	5	6	7	8	9	10	11	12	1	2	3	4	5	6	7	8	9	10	11	12	1	2	3	4	5	6	7	8	9	10
Identify and name points	●																												■					
Identify and name line segments	●		■											■	■											■		■	●			■	■	
Draw line segments to a specified length		●													●													●	●					
Identify parallel and nonparallel line segments	●				■									■	■													■	●				■	
Identify and name lines	●													■	■														●	■		■	■	
Identify and name intersecting lines	●				■									■	■													■	●	■		■	■	
Identify and name rays				■																														
Name, draw, and label line segments, lines, and rays	●													■											■			■	●	■				■
Identify and name acute, obtuse, right, straight, and reflex angles	●				■				■						●		■			■				■				■	●	●				
Identify and describe right angles, parallel lines, skew lines, and line segments	●				■		■		■					■	■													■	●		■	■	■	
Use full-circle and half-circle protractors to measure and draw angles						●			■						●		■	●							■			■	●		■	■	■	■
Use a compass and a protractor to draw and measure angles formed by intersecting lines															●														●					■

Key
- ● Content taught
- ■ Content practiced

Lines and Angles (cont.)

Skill	Grades
Determine angle measures based on relationships among common angles	
Find angle sums for geometric shapes	
Apply properties of adjacent, supplementary, complementary, and vertical angles; recognize properties in real-world settings	
Apply properties of sums of angle measures of triangles and quadrilaterals	
Apply properties of angles of parallelograms	
Apply properties of angles formed by two parallel lines and a transversal	
Explore the relationship between endpoints and midpoints	
Make turns and fractions of turns; relate turns to angles	
Solve construction problems	

Plane and Solid Figures

Skill	Grades
Explore shape relationships	
Identify characteristics of 2-dimensional shapes; use symbolic notation to denote these characteristics	
Identify 2-dimensional shapes	
Construct/draw 2-dimensional shapes; create designs with 2-dimensional shapes	
Use a compass and a straightedge to construct geometric figures	
Identify the bases and heights of triangles and parallelograms	
Use a compass to draw a circle with a given radius or diameter, and angles formed by intersecting lines	
Investigate the relationship between circumference and diameter	
Form shapes by combining polygons	
Identify properties and characteristics of polygons	
Classify and name polygons	
Classify triangles and quadrilaterals according to side and angle properties	

Geometry (cont.)

Plane and Solid Figures (cont.)	G4-1	G4-2	G4-3	G4-4	G4-5	G4-6	G4-7	G4-8	G4-9	G4-10	G4-11	G4-12	G5-1	G5-2	G5-3	G5-4	G5-5	G5-6	G5-7	G5-8	G5-9	G5-10	G5-11	G5-12	G6-1	G6-2	G6-3	G6-4	G6-5	G6-6	G6-7	G6-8	G6-9	G6-10
Name, draw, and label angles, triangles, and quadrilaterals	●																			■					●	■			●					■
Identify types of triangles		■													●	■																	●	
Verify and apply the Pythagorean Theorem																																	●	
Solve problems involving 2-dimensional shapes				■			●	●							●						●							●						
Identify and classify 3-dimensional shapes																					●		●						■				●	
Identify characteristics of 3-dimensional shapes; compare them with their 2-D faces																					●	■	●						■				●	
Construct 3-dimensional shapes																					●		●										●	
Describe properties of geometric solids											●										●		●						■				●	
Identify faces, edges, vertices, and bases of prisms and pyramids												■											●										●	
Perform and identify topological transformations																				■									●					
Identify congruent figures										●					●					■								●	●					■
Draw or form a figure congruent to a given figure										●					●						■											●		■
Identify and draw similar figures								■							●																	■		
Describe relationships among angles, side lengths, perimeter, and area of similar polygons								■												■							■				■			

Transformations and Symmetry	G4-1	G4-2	G4-3	G4-4	G4-5	G4-6	G4-7	G4-8	G4-9	G4-10	G4-11	G4-12	G5-1	G5-2	G5-3	G5-4	G5-5	G5-6	G5-7	G5-8	G5-9	G5-10	G5-11	G5-12	G6-1	G6-2	G6-3	G6-4	G6-5	G6-6	G6-7	G6-8	G6-9	G6-10
Identify lines of reflection, reflected figures, and figures with line symmetry										●											●				■									
Use a transparent mirror to draw the reflection of a figure							●													■					■									
Identify symmetrical figures								●													■				■									
Identify lines of symmetry								●	■												■							●	■					
Translate figures on a coordinate grid										■											●				●									
Rotate figures										■	■										■				●									
Model clockwise/counterclockwise turns/rotations						●																		■										
Explore transformations of geometric figures in a plane; identify preimage and image											■										●								●				●	
Explore rotation and point symmetry										■					●																			●

Patterns, Functions, and Algebra

Grade 4 Units (columns 1–12) · **Grade 5 Units** (columns 1–12) · **Grade 6 Units** (columns 1–10)

Patterns and Functions

Skill	G4 1–12	G5 1–12	G6 1–10
Explore and extend visual patterns	■ (1), ■ (2)	● (2), ■ (10)	● (2), ■ (3), ● (5), ● (8), ● (9), ● (10)
Create patterns with 2-dimensional shapes	● (6), ● (8)	● (8), ● (9)	■ (9), ● (10)
Define and create tessellations/frieze patterns	● (9)	● (3)	● (8)
Identify and use notation for semiregular tessellations	● (9)	● (3)	● (9)
Identify regular tessellations			■ (9)
Find and extend numerical patterns	■ (3), ■ (10)	● (9), ■ (10), ● (12)	● (2), ● (3), ● (4), ● (5), ● (8), ● (9)
Make/complete a sequence with a number line	● (3), ● (4), ● (6)	● (1), ● (4)	■ (9)
Solve "What's My Rule?" (function machine) problems; find a rule for a set of problems	● (2), ■ (3), ■ (5)	● (1), ■ (5), ● (6), ■ (9), ■ (11)	● (2), ■ (6), ■ (7), ■ (9)
Solve pan-balance problems			■ (7), ● (9)
Describe a pattern with a number sentence that has one to three variables	■ (5), ● (7)	● (3), ● (5), ● (9)	● (2), ● (3), ● (6), ● (8), ● (9), ● (10)
Find patterns in addition, subtraction, multiplication, and division facts	■ (3)	■ (10)	
Find number patterns in data; complete a table of values	● (8)	● (8)	● (10)
Solve and graph solutions for inequalities		● (9)	
Combine like terms to simplify expressions and equations		■ (5)	● (5), ● (6), ● (7)
Write and identify equivalent expressions and equivalent equations	● (3)	● (4)	● (4), ● (5), ● (6), ● (9)
Write and solve equations that represent problem situations	● (3), ● (5), ● (6), ■ (7), ■ (9)	● (4)	■ (2), ■ (3), ● (6)

Algebraic Notation and Solving Number Sentences

Skill	G4 1–12	G5 1–12	G6 1–10
Compare numbers using <, >, and = symbols	■ (2), ■ (4), ■ (6), ● (7), ■ (8), ■ (9), ■ (11), ■ (12)	■ (1), ■ (3), ■ (4), ■ (6), ● (7), ■ (9)	■ (1), ● (2), ● (3), ● (4), ● (5), ● (6), ● (7), ● (8), ● (9), ● (10)
Evaluate expressions using <, >, =, and ≈ symbols	■ (3), ■ (5), ■ (6), ■ (9)	■ (2), ■ (3), ● (4), ● (6), ● (7), ● (8)	● (1), ● (2), ■ (3), ● (4), ■ (5), ● (6), ● (7), ■ (10)
Translate number stories into expressions	● (3)	● (2), ● (4)	● (4), ● (5), ● (6), ● (7), ● (8), ● (9)
Write/solve addition and subtraction number sentences	● (2)	■ (2), ● (3)	■ (3), ● (4), ● (5), ● (6), ● (7), ● (9)
Write/solve multiplication/division number sentences	■ (3), ● (4)	● (2), ● (4)	● (5), ● (6), ● (7), ■ (9)
Use variables to describe general patterns		● (4)	● (4), ● (6), ● (7), ● (9)

Patterns, Functions, and Algebra (cont.)

Skill	Grade 4 Units												Grade 5 Units												Grade 6 Units									
	1	2	3	4	5	6	7	8	9	10	11	12	1	2	3	4	5	6	7	8	9	10	11	12	1	2	3	4	5	6	7	8	9	10
Algebraic Notation and Solving Number Sentences (cont.)																																		
Determine the value of a variable		■		■									■		■				■	■	●	●	■	●			●	●	●	●	●	●	●	■
Write and solve open sentences or number sentences with variables			●		■	●	■	■	■			■	●	●	■		■		●	●	●	●	■	●		■	●	●		●	■	■	●	■
Determine if number sentences are true or false			●		■			■									■		●	■							■			●	■	■		
Write or evaluate algebraic expressions and formulas to describe situations			●		■	●			■													●		■			●	■	■	●		■	●	■
Use variables and formulas in spreadsheets																												■	■			■	■	
Evaluate formulas																					●		●				●			●			●	■
Use formulas to solve problems																					●		●				●	●		●		■	●	
Identify dependent and independent variables			●																															
Order of Operations																																		
Apply the use of parentheses in number sentences			●		■	■	■	■	■		■		●					■	●	■	■	●	●	●	■		●		■		●	■	■	■
Understand and apply the order of operations to evaluate expressions and solve number sentences					■	■	■	■	■		■			■				■	●	■	■	●	■		■	●		■			■		●	■
Simplify expressions and equations that have parentheses					●	■	■	■	■										●										■					
Properties of Arithmetic Operations																																		
Investigate properties of multiplication/division			●			■							●	■		●										■				●	■			
Understand and apply the Commutative Property for addition and multiplication																				■								●		●	●	●		
Apply the Distributive Property					●														●				■					●		●			●	■
Understand and apply the Identity Property for multiplication																														●		●		
Understand and apply the Associative Property for addition and multiplication																	●						●					●		●	●		●	

Index

Notes

Notes

Notes

Notes

Notes